05-30

05-30

SCIENCE Perspectives 1

Authors

Maurice Di Giuseppe

Toronto Catholic District School Board and York University

Barry LeDrew

Formerly of Newfoundland Department of Education

Jill Roberts

Formerly of Ottawa-Carleton District School Board

Kimberley Walther

Durham Catholic District School Board

James Young

Limestone District School Board

Program Consultant

Barry LeDrew

Formerly of Newfoundland Department of Education

THOMSON

NELSON

Australia   Canada   Mexico   Singapore   Spain   United Kingdom   United States

Science Perspectives 1

Authors
Maurice Di Giuseppe
Barry LeDrew
Jill Roberts
Kimberley Walther
James Young

Associate Vice President of Publishing
David Steele

Acquisitions Editor, Science
John Yip-Chuck

Executive Managing Editor, Development and Testing
Cheryl Turner

Program Manager
Lee Geller

Developmental Editors
Lee Geller
Julia Lee
Louise MacKenzie
Lisa McManus
Lina Mockus
Betty Robinson

Editorial Assistant
Alisa Yampolsky

Executive Managing Editor, Production
Nicola Balfour

Production Editor
Lisa McManus

Copy Editor
Paula Pettitt-Townsend

Proofreader
Laura Peetoom

Senior Production Coordinator
Sharon Latta Paterson

Creative Director
Angela Cluer

Art Director
Ken Phipps

Art Management
ArtPlus Design & Communications

Illustrators
ArtPlus Design & Communications
Joelle Cottle, Donna Guilfoyle,
Sarah Orr, Corey Slone

Roy Condy
Sacha Warunkiw
Jane Whitney

Design and Composition Team
ArtPlus Design & Communications
Dave Murphy
Heather Brunton
Ruth Nicholson

Cover Design
Peter Papayanakis

Cover Image
NASA/Science Photo Library

Photo Research and Permissions
Robyn Craig

Printer
Transcontinental Printing Inc.

National Library of Canada Cataloguing in Publication Data

Nelson science perspectives 1 / written by Barry LeDrew ... [et al.] ; edited by Lee Geller ... [et al.].

Includes index.

ISBN 0-17-626808-1

1. Science—Textbooks.
I. LeDrew, Barry
II. Geller, Lee
III. Title: Nelson science perspectives one.

Q161.2.N48 2004   500   C2004-904727-2

Reviewers

Tom Card
Peel District School Board, ON

Wayne Cole
London District Catholic School Board, ON

Karen Dodds
Renfrew County District School Board, ON

Naomi Epstein
Jewish Board of Education, ON

Arlene Higgins Wright
York Region District School Board, ON

Andrea Lundy
York Region District School Board, ON

Iori Miller
Toronto District School Board, ON

Kerry Odlum
York Region District School Board, ON

Dermot O'Hara
Toronto Catholic District School Board, ON

Rasa Pruden
Halton District School Board, ON

Ron Ricci
Greater Essex District School Board, ON

Richard Towler
Peel District School Board, ON

Patrick Wells
Avalon East District School Board, NL

STSE Reviewer

Erminia Pedretti
OISE/University of Toronto
Department of Curriculum, Teaching, and Learning

Safety Reviewer

Stella Heenan
STAO Safety Committee

Contents

UNIT
D Body Input and
BODY FUNCTION

UNIT
E Science and
SPACE

Appendices

Being Scientifically Literate

The Apollo Moon Hoax: It's Not Rocket Science!

On July 16, 1969, *Apollo 11* lifted off from the Kennedy Space Center in Florida, headed for the Moon. Four days later, on July 20 at 4:17 P.M., the lunar module *Eagle* landed on the surface of the Moon in an area called the Sea of Tranquility. Two astronauts, Neil Armstrong and Edwin Aldrin, became the first humans to set foot on the Moon. This was a historic event for space exploration and for science.

From the outset there were some people who refused to believe that humans had actually travelled to and walked on the Moon. Today, more than 30 years later, the non-believers have what they consider evidence that the Moon landing never occurred. In 2001 the Fox TV Network aired a program entitled "Conspiracy Theory: Did We Land on the Moon?" which claimed that NASA faked the Moon landings of the 1960s and 1970s. Much of the evidence to support this claim is from photographs. For example, those who believe in the hoax ask "Where are the stars in the photographs taken on the Moon?" In all of the Moon photographs where the sky is shown, no stars are visible (**Figure 1**). When we look at the night sky from Earth we see stars. Why should we not see them from the Moon?

This piece of evidence is relatively easy to refute. Imagine for a moment that you are on the Moon and about to take a photo of a friend. Because you are on the light side of the Moon, you set your camera to take a photo of a well-lit subject. (The Apollo astronauts were never on the dark side of the Moon.) The shutter opens and shuts very quickly—in a fraction of a second. Because there is no atmosphere surrounding the Moon, the sky is black, even during the day, and stars are visible. However, the amount of light from the visible stars is so small that it does not show up on the photo. The effect is similar to that seen in **Figure 2**. The exposure time for the brightly lit stadium is not sufficient to permit the stars to show up. Of course, it is possible to take a photo of a starry sky. The small amount of light coming from the stars simply requires you to use a long exposure time—many minutes or even hours—in order to capture the image of the stars (**Figure 3**). So it really is no surprise that stars were not present

Figure 2 No stars are visible in this nighttime photograph even though they would likely be visible to the unaided eye.

Figure 3 An exposure time of approximately 2.5 h was required to capture the image of the stars in this photograph. Each streak of light represents a star during that period of time. The rotation of Earth makes the stars appear to be moving across the sky.

Figure 1 No stars were visible in the sky in the Apollo Moon photographs.

in the photos taken by the Apollo astronauts on the surface of the Moon. In fact, it would have been very surprising to see the stars.

Another piece of photographic evidence that was presented by the non-believers deals with the shadows created by people and objects on the Moon's surface. The shadows made by the astronauts in **Figure 4** are obviously of significantly different lengths even though the astronauts are approximately the same height. It has been suggested that the shadows were made by different light sources, further "evidence" that the photograph is a fake. Again, this evidence is easy to refute. If there were two light sources (as in a staged setup on Earth), each astronaut would cast two shadows. However, before you accept that explanation, try **0.1 Activity: Light and Shadows** and decide for yourself whether it is possible to have shadows of two different lengths from one light source.

Figure 4 There was only one source of light on the Moon—the Sun. Yet the different lengths of the shadows seem to suggest that there was a second light source.

0.1 Activity | LIGHT AND SHADOWS

In this activity you will use simple materials to demonstrate how shadows are created and to determine how certain factors affect the characteristics of a shadow.

Materials
2 pieces of wooden dowel (or pencils) of equal length
sheet of lightweight cardboard or Bristol board
flashlight or other light source

Procedure
1. In your group, use the materials to create shadows. Experiment to vary the characteristics of the shadows.

2. Use a second light source to demonstrate that two light sources from slightly different angles will produce two shadows for a single object.

3. Design and carry out a procedure to determine how the following factors affect the length of the shadow created:
   – the length of the object casting the shadow
   – the position of the light source in relation to the object

   – the distance of the light source from the object
   – the shape of the surface on which the shadow falls

Analysis
(a) Explain how each factor affects the length and other characteristics of a shadow.

(b) Based on your evidence, is it possible to use one light source and two objects of the same length to create shadows of different lengths? Explain.

(c) What conclusion can you draw about the shadow evidence presented by the non-believers? How does this affect your view of their claim?

Evaluation
(d) Do you believe that the Apollo Moon landings were a hoax? Explain why or why not.

Obvious questions arise that are related to the claims of the non-believers. Is it possible that we have all been fooled by some trick photography? How likely is this? How credible is the evidence that has been presented to show that the Moon landings were a hoax? Which evidence is more credible—that presented by the non-believers or that presented by NASA? How do we find the answers to these questions?

The purpose of this introduction is not to answer such questions but to explore the processes by which we can arrive at acceptable answers and respond rationally to claims that are proposed, intentionally or unintentionally, as being scientific. It is intended to help you think about how and why it is important to be scientifically literate.

(a) What are your expectations for this course, or how do you expect this course to help you?

What Is Science?

The main goal of science is to understand the natural world. There are many other ways to interpret the natural world but the best way to understand it is through scientific investigation. The National Science Teacher's Association describes science as "the systematic gathering of information through various forms of direct and indirect observations and the testing of this information by methods including, but not limited to, experimentation." It continues to say "The principal product of science is knowledge in the form of ... concepts and the laws and theories related to those concepts."

Science is the process of gathering knowledge about the natural world and organizing that knowledge into testable laws and theories. Scientists describe nature using evidence gained by the five senses—touch, smell, taste, vision, and hearing—and by special tools and equipment (such as microscopes, telescopes, radars, and sensors) that expand the range or capabilities of the senses. Knowledge that is obtained in this way is generally referred to as *empirical evidence*.

(b) How has technology such as the microscope contributed to the advancement of science? Think about what we would not know if technology was not available. Use specific examples to illustrate your answer.

Scientists cannot always make direct observations from which conclusions can be drawn. Instead, they make indirect observations and measurements that provide the basis for inferences. An *inference* is a tentative conclusion that is based on logical reasoning. For example, if you observe that flowers planted in soil with added compost grow better than the same type of flowers planted in regular soil with no compost, you can infer that the compost has caused the flowers to grow better.

> "Science is built up of facts, as a house is built of stones; but an accumulation of facts is no more a science than a heap of stones is a house."
>
> –Henri Poincaré, *Science and Hypothesis*, 1905

Scientists analyze their observations to look for patterns or regularities. If a pattern is discovered, a law may be formulated. A *law* is a generalization about what has happened, based on observational data. From a law, scientists can predict what they expect to happen. The law of gravity is a good example. There is a common story that Isaac Newton discovered the law of gravity while he was sitting under an apple tree and an apple fell on his head. Since laws are not discovered so easily, this is unlikely. However, observing a falling apple may have started Newton thinking that a falling object must experience some sort of force that causes it to speed up, or accelerate, as it falls. Through extensive and repeated observations Newton concluded that all objects in the universe exert a gravitational force on each other and that the strength of the force depends on two factors: the masses of the objects and the distance between the objects. Thus, the attractive force between two objects is directly proportional to their masses (it increases as their masses increase) and inversely proportional to the distance between them (it decreases as the distance between them increases). This Universal Law of Gravitation can also be expressed mathematically.

A law cannot be proven true because it is impossible to test every possible situation in which the law might apply. We accept a law on the basis of a vast number of observations that support the generalization. However, a law can be falsified by observations that contradict it. For example, suppose a location is found in a remote part of our solar system where objects fall upward. This contradicts the law of gravity as we know it and the law may have to be thrown

Your teacher will give you a sealed opaque box containing an unknown object(s). In Part 1, you need to find out everything you can about the object(s) in the box without opening the box. You may use your senses and any tools and equipment that extend your senses without actually looking inside. In Part 2, you will open one side of the box, collect additional evidence, and once again try to determine the identity of the object(s).

Procedure

Part 1

1. Obtain a closed box.

(a) Describe the process that you will follow to investigate the object(s) in the closed box.

(b) Collect and record all empirical evidence regarding the object(s) in the box.

(c) Make inferences regarding the identity of the object(s) in the box.

Part 2

2. Open the side of the box marked "Open Here" when you are instructed to do so by your teacher.

(d) Observe the contents of the box through the opening in the box. Record all additional empirical evidence regarding the object(s) in the box.

(e) Make inferences regarding the identity of the object(s) in the box.

Analysis

(f) Create a model of the object in the box (e.g., a written description, sketch, clay sculpture, or physical model).

(g) Compare your model with those of your class-mates. Try to arrive at a consensus regarding the identity of the object(s) in the box.

(h) How does the work you carried out in this activity compare with the work of scientists who develop scientific models?

---

out or modified to account for the new observations. However, the likelihood of observing such phenomena is very remote, so it is reasonable to have confidence in scientific laws.

Unlike a law, which is determined by careful analysis of observations, a theory is a product of a scientist's creativity and inventiveness. A *theory* is an explanation of observations (or of a law). In attempting to develop a theory, a scientist first suggests a tentative answer or an untested explanation called a *hypothesis*. The most important characteristic of a hypothesis is its testability or its ability to predict. Here, the ability to predict does not refer to the ability to say that something is going to happen in the future, but rather it suggests a test. Such a test can either refute or support a hypothesis, but can never prove it.

A scientific theory is a *tentative* explanation; this means that it is always subject to change. Even though scientific knowledge is very reliable, it is also tentative, one of the characteristics that distinguishes scientific knowledge from other types of knowledge. A theory is accepted by the scientific community when all available empirical evidence supports it. However, a theory can change when new scientific evidence suggests that a change is warranted. This does not make the original theory any less valuable. Just because a theory is not 100% correct does not automatically make it 100% wrong. Even a theory that is not quite right provides a basis for further scientific investigation and results in an improved theory. For example, in the early 1600s, Galileo believed that the force of gravity depended only on the mass of an object. His theory did not properly explain the arrangement and movements of the planets in the solar system. So Newton and other scientists used Galileo's work as the basis for further investigations, which eventually led to modifications to account for new observations. Even today, scientists are continuing to investigate gravity in an attempt to refine the current understanding.

Another example of the tentative nature of science comes from the early days of microscopy in the 17th and 18th centuries. While it was becoming apparent that living things were made of cells, the basics of cell structure and function were yet to be unraveled. Anton van Leeuwenhoek and other scientists of his time claimed that they saw miniature, fully-formed babies inside sperm cells. The miniature human was known as a *homunculus*, from the Latin meaning "little man" (**Figure 5**). The theory of preformation suggested that an individual developed from the homunculus simply by growing larger. This theory was influenced by the belief at the time that the female's only role in reproduction was to provide the womb as an incubator for the development of the baby. Over time, this theory was modified. Scientists who accepted the theory of preformation separated into "spermists" and "ovists" depending on whether they believed that the sperm or the egg controlled the development of the baby.

Figure 5 Natural scientists of the 17th and 18th centuries believed that the sperm contained a homunculus—a completely formed but miniature individual that would be deposited in the female body to develop in the womb.

In 1828, Karl Ernst von Baer published what was probably the first formal work dealing with embryology called *On the Development of Animals*. He demonstrated that animal embryos develop in layers of cells that differentiate into the various organs and systems. This publication was the beginning of the end of the theory of preformation. The end finally came in 1875 when Oscar Hertwig confirmed that hereditary material was passed on through the two sex cells in sexual reproduction. As scientific knowledge of animal anatomy and physiology grew, the theory of preformation was replaced by a revised theory of heredity in which both the male and female contribute sex cells that unite to form a new individual of the species.

Science is progressive and can advance because scientists build on existing knowledge. Michael Shermer, in his book *Why People Believe Weird Things*, defines scientific progress as "the cumulative growth of a system of knowledge over time, in which useful features are retained and nonuseful features are abandoned, based on the rejection or confirmation of testable knowledge."

"The whole of science is nothing more than a refinement of everyday thinking."
–Albert Einstein

The Importance of Peer Review in Scientific Research

Scientists must be willing to submit their ideas and results to independent testing and replication by other scientists. This exchange of data, procedures, and materials provides a mechanism for self-correction—the foundation of the credibility of science.

One of the main characteristics of good science is that it is *replicable*—it can be repeated, again and again if necessary, to verify and validate results. Scientists tend to be critical of their own work and their colleagues' work. Faulty thinking and reasoning are discovered very quickly provided the opportunity exists for scientists to review each other's research. This process of generating knowledge, reviewing research results, and correcting faulty information leads to the continual growth of the database of valid and reliable scientific knowledge.

One of the purposes of peer review is to ensure that scientific research is *objective*. This can only be attained by subjecting scientific research to high-quality, unbiased review. Peer review enables scientists to maintain a high degree of scientific rigour, integrity, and credibility. It does not guarantee that the research will be without faults, but it does increase the likelihood that the research will be of high quality.

The peer review process is aimed not only at maintaining or improving the quality of the scientific research but also at eliminating scientific misconduct. Being human, some scientists occasionally cheat. Cheating can occur in a number of ways, for example, by using but not crediting the work of others, fudging results, disclosing privileged information, engaging in unethical practices (such as illegal animal research), not acknowledging conflicts of interest, or not keeping proper records. The motives for cheating include money, fame, and pressure.

The peer review process is the best mechanism available for ensuring consistent quality in scientific research and ensuring that published research represents "good science."

(c) Identify and summarize the important characteristics that define science as a way of understanding the natural world. Which of these characteristics do you consider to be the most important? Explain.

Cold Fusion: The Miracle Discovery that Never Happened!

An announcement on March 23, 1989 by two scientists at the University of Utah, Stanley Pons and Martin Fleischmann (**Figure 6**), caused quite a stir in the scientific community, and among the media and general public. Pons and Fleischmann announced that they had a solution to the world's energy problems. They had discovered a way to initiate nuclear fusion, which produces large quantities of energy, at near room temperature—a process referred to as cold fusion. Nuclear fusion happens when the nuclei of hydrogen atoms are forced together or fused. It occurs naturally only in the interior of stars like our Sun and requires very high temperatures (millions of degrees Celsius) and intense pressures. Nuclear fusion also happens when a hydrogen bomb explodes. Up to this point there had been no cheap and easy way to bring about nuclear fusion.

What was amazing about Pons' and Fleischmann's claim was that it was relatively simple, used readily available materials,

Figure 6 Pons and Fleischmann did not follow the normal protocol in announcing the preliminary findings of their research. They did not subject their work to peer review in the scientific community.

and resulted in a net gain of energy—literally getting something for nothing. The possibility of unlimited energy at very little cost could change the world! The positive implications for energy production prompted scientists around the world to attempt to replicate the process. However, Pons' and Fleischmann's results could not be duplicated. Shortly after the announcement, the Energy Research Advisory Board in the United States set up a panel of scientists to investigate cold fusion. They examined the evidence but were not convinced that cold fusion was possible.

What went wrong? Why did two accomplished scientists announce a discovery that no one else was able to replicate? Both Pons and Fleischmann had been opposed to making the announcement. Because of competition with another university and some circumstances beyond their control, they had been forced to make the announcement several months before they had planned to present their findings for review. This was the major problem. Had they presented their findings for review, the scientific community would have reviewed their work, attempted to replicate it, and made their judgment about the validity of the research. If the research could not be replicated it would not have been accepted for publication and there would have been no major announcement. The two scientists would probably have gone back to the drawing board, and have been spared

the embarrassment brought about by their premature announcement.

In the end, however, Pons and Fleischmann were ridiculed by the mainstream scientific community and dismissed as frauds. Supporters of Pons and Fleischmann claim that the two scientists were victims of a political decision to avoid a conflict and continue funding the established "hot fusion" research. There are a few scientists around the world who have not given up on the possibility of cold fusion and continue to conduct research, hoping for a major breakthrough and the vindication of the two discredited scientists. On March 23, 2004, 15 years after Pons' and Fieischmann's announcement, the *New York Times* reported that the U.S. Department of Energy had agreed to have a second look at the research into cold fusion.

(a) In a couple of sentences, summarize the discovery that was announced by Pons and Fleischmann.

(b) Why was the announcement big news in the scientific community and among the media and general public?

(c) Using the characteristics of science, describe what went wrong in this case.

(d) What did Pons and Fleischmann do that scientists do not normally do?

(e) Why do you think the research is being revisited?

CS

Misconceptions about Science

Science attempts to be objective and rational, basing its conclusions on logic and evidence. But science is often portrayed and perceived as being much more than it really is; it is not always perfectly objective or free of bias, but can be influenced by personal, social, and cultural biases; it cannot provide an answer to every question, because some questions are unanswerable; and it cannot answer some questions even though they may be answerable. There are many misconceptions about what science is and what science can do. Some of the most commonly held misconceptions are briefly described here.

Misconception 1: There is one "scientific method"

Many textbooks talk about using "the scientific method" as if there were only one method. The scientific method is generally described as a series of steps that scientists carry out in their research. The steps include asking a testable question, developing a hypothesis or possible answer to the question, designing and carrying out a controlled experiment, collecting and analyzing data, drawing a conclusion based on the data, and comparing the conclusion with the hypothesis to determine whether the evidence supports the hypothesis. While variations of this method are very common in science, different scientists approach problems differently. If you asked 10 scientists to describe their method for carrying out an investigation, you would likely get 10 different descriptions. However, there would likely be some elements that were common to all 10 methods.

There is no doubt that science is methodical; it follows procedures and protocols that generally lead to a logical conclusion. Nevertheless, there is no one scientific method that all scientists follow. No scientist consciously goes through a series of "steps" that lead to an answer to the question that initiated the investigation. The scientific process is a continuous interaction of hypotheses, predictions, observations, and conclusions.

So "the scientific method" refers to the general pattern and the types of mental and physical activities that are used to create, refine, extend, and apply knowledge in all scientific fields.

Misconception 2: Science always involves experimentation

It is commonly believed that experimentation is the process that leads to the generation of scientific knowledge, laws, and theories. However, experimentation is not the only approach to conducting scientific investigations. Valid and valuable scientific investigations can be conducted without carrying out controlled experiments. Some science disciplines, such as astronomy and environmental science, do not lend themselves to experimental procedures because the variables are impossible to control. There are other types of scientific investigation, such as observational studies, that are equally valid in producing valuable evidence which may lead to new knowledge. Many of the basic discoveries in astronomy have been based on extensive observations rather than on experimentation.

Misconception 3: Scientific inquiry provides absolute proof

While scientific inquiry can result in a body of evidence that supports a position, it cannot provide absolute proof. Empirical evidence can support or validate a law or theory but can never prove a law or theory to be true. The only real proof that can be provided by science occurs when an idea is falsified. Consider the earlier example of the law of gravity. All of the evidence that has been collected worldwide leads scientists to conclude that "all objects fall downward or toward Earth." The discovery of a situation in which objects fall upward would falsify the law, or prove that it is not true. However, scientific laws are very durable and, once a law is formulated, it is highly unlikely that conflicting evidence will be found. Scientific laws are seldom falsified. The law of gravity and other scientific laws are probably as close to the scientific "truth" as we will ever come.

Misconception 4: Science is unreliable

Critics of science point to some of the obvious everyday things that science has not done—for example, finding a cure for cancer or the common cold, or predicting the weather accurately. However, considering the outstanding achievements of science in a relatively short period of time in history, science has provided a very reliable way of learning about the structure of the physical world and how it functions. For example, we now know with near certainty that matter is made up of invisible atoms, living things are made up of cells that pass on their genetic information in the form of molecules of DNA, and the continents are slowly moving across the surface of Earth. Such knowledge has allowed us to land on the Moon, communicate at the speed of light, and perform routine open-heart surgery. Recent advances in the diagnosis and treatment of cancer are possible because scientists are learning more and more about what causes cancer and how different types of cancer behave. A cure has not yet been found but the database of knowledge that is being built should one day provide this cure. Science is not perfect, but it is the best way we have to explore and learn about the natural world. Albert Einstein, one of the most famous scientists of all time, said "All our science, measured against reality is primitive and childlike—yet it is the most precious thing we have."

Misconception 5: Science can answer all questions
While science is the best way we have to learn about the structure and function of the natural world, it cannot, and should not, address moral, ethical, aesthetic, and social questions. Is abortion appropriate? Should euthanasia be used? Should we allow mining in environmentally sensitive areas? Which of 10 potential recipients should receive a donor kidney? Questions such as these cannot be answered by science. Science can, however, inform the decision-making process. A scientist who provides answers to such questions is speaking as an individual and not as a scientist. Scientists, after all, are entitled to personal opinions just like everyone else, but they cannot use their authority as scientists to justify their opinions on these questions.

(d) Before reading these misconceptions about science, did you hold any of these misconceptions? Has your understanding of the nature of science changed? Why or why not?

What Isn't Science?

Now that you have a reasonable understanding of the nature of science, you may find it a little easier to identify what isn't science, or what science is not. What is presented intentionally or unintentionally as science, but really is not science, comes in a variety of forms: *non-science*, subject matter that is not in the domain of science at all; *bad science*, investiga-

tions that are scientific in nature but not rigorous in procedure; *pseudoscience*, information that is presented as scientific without the scientific evidence to support it; *hoaxes* or *frauds*, supposedly scientific information presented with the intention of misleading the scientific or general community; and *urban legends*, interesting or fascinating stories that may have been based on real events but have been told and retold so many times and are so widely spread that they are accepted as fact.

Non-Science

There are some areas of study that are presented as scientific when, in fact, they represent disciplines such as religion or history. For example, what is commonly referred to as "creation science" is really a belief system that uses scientific jargon and language to create the illusion of valid, credible science. A belief system does not rely on evidence, verification, and replication of experiments; it relies on belief and faith. Creationism is not science and cannot be studied using scientific methods.

Bad Science

Bad science results when scientists do not follow the established standards of objectivity. Even if you accept the fact that scientists are human and have personal biases that could influence their work, the goal of science is to be as objective as possible. One practice that is often associated with bad science is the funding of medical studies by large pharmaceutical companies whose products are being used in the research. This casts doubt on many of the claims made in the biomedical research area, because the scientific procedures may have been compromised by conflicts of interest and bias. Most readers of medical research reports are unaware that the data presented may have been collected and analyzed by the company that made the product being tested.

Similarly, university and medical researchers who are funded by pharmaceutical companies are often at the mercy of their corporate sponsor. Researchers who attempt to be objective in reporting their research results may lose their funding. For example, Dr. Nancy Olivieri, a researcher at Toronto's Hospital for Sick Children and the University of Toronto, received funding from a company called Apotex Incorporated to test the drug deferiprone, which is used to treat a blood disorder. The hospital rules state that researchers must report adverse findings to the Research Ethics Board. After a lengthy dispute over Olivieri's interpretation of the results of the study, the funding was terminated. Both parties offer different explanations for the termination.

Pseudoscience

In his book called *Why People Believe Weird Things*, Michael Shermer defines pseudoscience (*pseudo* means "false") as "claims presented so that they appear scientific even though they lack supporting evidence and plausibility." In contrast, he defines science as "a set of methods designed to describe and interpret observed and inferred phenomena, past or present, and aimed at building a testable body of knowledge open to rejection or confirmation."

One alternative medicinal practice, magnetic healing (**Figure 7**), relies on the scientific concept of magnetic fields to lend credibility to its main idea. The advocates of magnetic therapy claim that magnetic fields promote the healing of bones and help blood circulation. There has been very little scientific testing of magnetic healing and most of the evidence used by those who practice or support it is in the form of personal testimonials or anecdotes. When magnetic healing has been scientifically investigated there has been no evidence to suggest that the magnet therapy had any healing effect whatsoever. In one double-blind investigation, people with heel pain wore special inserts in their shoes; one group had magnetic inserts and the other group had inserts without magnets. None of the participants knew which group they were in. In both groups 60% of the patients reported some improvement in their condition.

Ironically, in an age of science and technology, there are numerous non-scientific and pseudoscientific beliefs. For example, 57% of Canadians believe in angels and in life after death. Nearly a third of Canadians believe that ghosts and aliens exist. As an intelligent species, humans tend to believe in many phenomena that have no scientific basis and are not supported by objective, empirical evidence. In recent years the percentage of people who believe in such phenomena appears to be increasing. **Table 1** shows some of the results of two Gallup polls conducted in 1990 and 2001 regarding belief in paranormal ideas.

Table 1 Belief in Paranormal Ideas

Paranormal idea	Percent of polled people who believe	
	1990	2001
psychic or spiritual healing (the power of the human mind to heal the body)	46	54
extrasensory perception (ESP)	49	50
haunted houses	29	42
ghosts (or spirits of dead people) can come back in certain places and situations	25	38
telepathy (communication between minds without using the traditional five senses)	36	36
extraterrestrial beings have visited Earth at some time in the past	27	33
clairvoyance (the power of the mind to know the past and predict the future)	26	32
people can hear from or communicate mentally with someone who has died	18	28
astrology (the position of the stars and planets can affect people's lives)	25	28
witches	14	26
channeling (allowing a "spirit-being" to temporarily assume control of a human body during a trance)	11	15

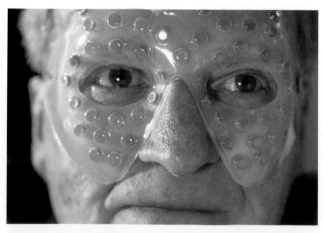

Figure 7 The strength of the magnetic field in most magnetic therapy pads isn't strong enough to penetrate the skin.

Hoaxes or Frauds

Hoaxes are misguided jokes or malicious attempts to gain revenge for a perceived wrong-doing by embarrassing another person. Hoaxes may also be carried out because of greed, fame, or pressure to achieve a significant scientific discovery.

A well-known joke that illustrates intent to trick or mislead using scientific terminology involves dihydrogen monoxide. As an April Fool's joke a newspaper correspondent wrote an article about dihydrogen monoxide, describing it as a chemical that is found in many toxic substances and often used as a solvent. The article included a list of true statements about the chemical, but in a very misleading way. Many people who read the article did not recognize that dihydrogen monoxide is simply a scientific name for water, or H_2O. A city council introduced a resolution to ban the use of Styrofoam cups because dihydrogen monoxide was used in their production. The resolution was with-drawn and the council was spared further embarrassment when one of its members recalled from her high-school chemistry that dihydrogen monoxide is simply water.

Urban Legends

There are many interesting stories or claims that have been circulated so widely, and for so long that they are generally accepted as true. Such stories, referred to as urban legends, are often presented as being scientific and many people never question their truth. They become a part of our cultural land-scape and no one knows where or why they began.

0.3 Activity   URBAN LEGEND OR SCIENTIFIC FACT?

There are literally thousands of urban legends, many of which have a science connection. The problem with urban legends is that they are gen-erally accepted as true so it is important to ques-tion all claims until a satisfactory "scientific" explanation is available. The ultimate test, of course, is verification through replication. However, some of the claims are not easily verified and we have to rely on reliable experts to help us make our judgment.

(a) In a small group, discuss each of the follow-ing urban legends. Using your science knowl-edge, decide if it is totally false (F), totally true (T), partially true (PT), or if its truth is undetermined (U). Explain your answer.

- A special chemical added to the water in swim-ming pools will reveal the presence of urine.
- Pouring salt water into the coin slots of vend-ing machines will cause them to dispense free products.
- Water boiled in a microwave oven can sud-denly explode.
- Because of the leftover charges from the skin of electric eels, credit cards placed in an eelskin wallet will become demagnetized.
- If you tap the side of a shaken can of pop you will prevent the contents from foaming over when you open it.
- The only human-made object visible from the Moon is the Great Wall of China.

- More people are killed annually in bicycle accidents than in commercial airline crashes.
- The average person swallows eight spiders per year.
- Hair and fingernails continue to grow for a period after a person dies.
- Your loved one's cremated remains can be turned into diamonds.
- A penny placed on the tracks will derail a train.
- Because of the Coriolis Effect, toilets flush clockwise in the northern hemisphere and counterclockwise in the southern.
- It takes more muscles to frown than it does to smile.
- A person who weighs 150 pounds at the equator would weigh about 1 pound heavier if he/she stood at the North Pole.
- Lemmings commit suicide by jumping off cliffs.
- Spontaneous human combustion is real: people can suddenly burst into flame.
- Fire walking is an example of the power of the mind over matter.
- Turtles never die of old age.
- Cockroaches can survive for up to a month with their heads cut off.
- Sharks do not get cancer so eating shark cartilage can prevent cancer in humans.

(b) Using the Internet and other resources, research to determine the "scientific" explanation of these claims.

 www.science.nelson.com

Being Scientifically Literate **xv**

The Role of the Media

The media, intentionally or unintentionally, probably contribute as much to the spread of nonsense and pseudoscience as the people who make the claims. In particular, the Internet and the World Wide Web have made mass communication available to just about anyone who has an idea or a message to share. This has contributed to a proliferation of claims that are presented as scientific when in fact they are pseudoscientific or simple hoaxes.

Figure 8 shows a picture that was circulated on the Internet as a satellite image of North America during the blackout of August 14, 2003. There is convincing evidence to show that this image is a fake. For example, there is no imaging satellite called GeoStar, the timestamp on satellite images is usually marked UT (universal time) rather than EST (Eastern Standard Time), and the blackout area in the image extends too far south and not far enough west. **Figure 9** shows actual satellite images from NOAA (National Oceanic and Atmospheric Administration) taken on August 13 and 15.

Figure 9 Actual NOAA satellite images of North America on **(a)** August 13 and **(b)** August 15, 2003.

Figure 8 A convincing, but fake, image of North America during the August 2003 blackout.

(e) Why is distinguishing fake science from real science so difficult? Describe an example of a fake science phenomenon that you believed when you encountered it only to find out later that it was not authentic. How did you find out that it was not real science?

Scientific Literacy

We live in a time when growing scientific knowledge and rapid technological innovations are playing an increasingly significant role in everyday life. Carl Sagan, a renowned astronomer and author, recognized the role of science and technology and the importance of being scientifically literate when he said in his book *The Demon-Haunted World* in 1995 "We've arranged a global civilization in which the most crucial elements profoundly depend on science and technology. We have also arranged things so that almost no one understands science and technology. This is a prescription for disaster. We might get away with it for a while, but sooner or later this combustible mixture of ignorance and power will blow up in our faces."

To make wise personal decisions and to fulfill the responsibilities of citizenship, it is critical for you to be scientifically literate. Scientific literacy has been defined as "an evolving combination of the science-related attitudes, skills, and knowledge needed to develop inquiry, problem-solving, and decision-making abilities, to become lifelong learners, and to maintain a sense of wonder about the world around us." One of the key words in this definition is "evolving." Scientific literacy is continuously developing so you can never claim to have achieved it. It is not a stage that can be reached, like graduation from high school. It evolves as you gain new knowledge, develop and refine new skills, and adopt appropriate attitudes.

The Importance of Skepticism

So what does it mean to be scientifically literate? It does not mean that you will be able to quickly and easily distinguish authentic science from pseudo-science, hoaxes, and other sorts of flimflam artistry. It does mean that you will be skeptical, that you will question all claims including your own beliefs and conclusions. Being skeptical does not mean being close-minded, dismissing all claims that you encounter, but rather accepting claims and holding beliefs tentatively and examining them objectively. As a skeptical person you must be open-minded, and willing to change your opinion when faced with sound scientific evidence and logical arguments.

T. H. Huxley (1825–1895), a self-educated but renowned scientist and author, wrote about the importance of skepticism in 1871: "The improver of natural science absolutely refuses to acknowledge authority, as such. For him, skepticism is the highest of duties: blind faith the one unpardonable sin." Carl Sagan is quoted as saying "Skeptical scrutiny is the means, in both science and religion, by which deep thoughts can be winnowed from deep nonsense."

Every day you face bizarre and outrageous claims about matters related to science. You need a way to decide what is true and what is a pseudoscientific or a paranormal claim. The methods of science combined with ordinary critical thinking will help you make such decisions. You may not be able to verify every claim yourself, but you should be able to determine if verification has taken place and feel confident that it was done in a scientific manner. If you cannot verify a claim yourself you should ask yourself a few simple questions, such as these: Does the person making the claim have appropriate credentials? Is any evidence presented to support the claim, and, if so, is the evidence of sound scientific quality? Does the phenomenon work as claimed?

As you address the topics and issues in this text, analyze the available information to determine what is and what is not scientific. Think critically about the claims made by those representing different perspectives. Above all, use empirical evidence, ordinary common sense, and your personal values to help you make and defend a position on an issue.

✔ Check Your Understanding

1. Summarize the characteristics of scientific knowledge that make it different from other types of knowledge.

2. What are the benefits to science of the process of peer review?

3. Write a one-sentence summary of each of the common misconceptions about science. Describe what you believe to be one other misconception about science.

4. What is pseudoscience? Why is "pseudoscience" an appropriate name?

5. The media can play a critical role in the development of a scientifically literate population. Explain how the media can be both a positive and negative influence in helping people distinguish between real science and fake science.

6. Conduct a survey in your school to determine what percentages of students believe in paranormal ideas.

7. Why is it important to be skeptical when faced with new ideas and claims?

8. Suppose that you read a magazine about the discovery of a new miracle cure for cancer. Explain your reaction and describe what you might do before you accepted such a claim.

9. Write a paragraph describing why being scientifically literate is important to you.

Technologies in EVERYDAY LIFE

On August 14, 2003, Megan and Jaimee are sitting in a crowded train, moving through a dark tunnel of Toronto's subway system. Megan is working on her laptop computer, and Jaimee is listening to music on her MP3 player. Glancing at her digital watch, Megan notes that it is 4:11 P.M. Suddenly, the train screeches to a halt and people brace themselves so they do not topple over. The cabin lights flicker on and off. People look around for a moment and then go back to reading their books and newspapers. Most of them figure that it's just another rush-hour traffic jam. Then they begin to wonder why the delay is taking so long.

A subway conductor holding a walkie-talkie and a flashlight pushes through the cabin doors. He yells, "Don't panic! We're doing everything we can to correct the problem. Things will be back to normal shortly!" Another 15 min pass. People are starting to look worried. The conductor returns and explains that the city is experiencing a blackout that extends over most of Ontario and the eastern United States. There's no power anywhere!

After about 2 h of waiting in sweltering heat, a subway official announces that the train will be evacuated car by car. Megan and Jaimee gather their belongings and follow other passengers through the dimly lit tunnel, up several flights of stairs, and out onto the road. As they look around, they notice that the road is full of people walking in every direction. Traffic lights are out, and ordinary citizens are in the middle of intersections conducting traffic.

The Great Blackout of 2003 left over 50 million people in Ontario, Ohio, Connecticut, and New York State without electric power. It was caused by the sudden collapse of the massive power generation and distribution systems that serve these areas (**Figure 1**). The next day, most businesses were closed, public transportation was not working, and flights were cancelled. In some places, it took over one week for power to be restored to full capacity. **Table 1** lists some interesting facts about the Great Blackout of 2003.

Figure 1   A typical electricity-generating plant

Table 1   Facts about the Great Blackout of 2003

Time of blackout	4:11 P.M. (ET)
Time to collapse the grid	9 s
Total area affected	24 086 km^2
Number of people affected	50 million
Number of flights cancelled in North America on Friday, August 15	400
Age of North American power grid	60 years
Cost of modernizing the power grid	$50 to $100 billion
Number of power plants shut down	100
Number of nuclear power plants shut down	22
Average time to restart a nuclear power plant	36 h
Average daytime temperature in Ontario on Friday, August 15	31°C
Number of elevator rescues in Toronto on Friday, August 15	110
Number of elevator rescues in New York City on Friday, August 15	800

(a) List four devices you rely on that require current electricity for their operation. How would you cope if the loss of electric power prevented you from using these devices?

(b) Do you think that North Americans have become overly dependent on electricity? Explain your reasoning.

Technology

Humans have many needs and wants including food, air, water, shelter, education, communication, recreation (**Figure 2**), transportation, protection, sanitation, and health care. Over the course of history, humans have fashioned many tools and developed many processes to help them meet their needs and attain their wants. Today, toilets, T-shirts, traffic lights, screwdrivers, stethoscopes, computers, and cell phones are just a few of the technological products that help us accomplish useful tasks and solve everyday problems. *Technology* is the process by which humans develop ways to help them satisfy some of their needs and desires.

Figure 2 Recreation is just one of the many wants that humans have.

(c) List the following items as needs or wants: dinner every day, telephone, weekly garbage pickup, running water, daily newspaper, electricity, car, soap, television, X-ray machine, swimming pool, Coca-Cola, personal deodorant, home, high-school education, online computer, flush toilet, hair dryer, and shoes. Rank these items from most important to least important to you.

Technologies: Today and Yesterday

In the past, food was obtained by hunting and farming. It was preserved in cold cellars (**Figure 3**) for relatively short periods of time, and then it was cooked in a wood-burning fireplace, stove, or oven. Clean water was obtained directly from rivers, lakes, and wells. Fresh air was available everywhere. Buildings were primarily constructed from wood, masonry, and glass. Clothing was made from natural materials, such as cotton, wool, silk, and leather. People travelled on foot or in horse-drawn carriages, and children played games like hopscotch, cards, and tag. The usual treatment for illness was isolation, bed rest, and tonics. People communicated in face-to-face meetings or by sending post cards and letters by mail.

Today, however, you may wake up in the morning to the sound of rock music coming from your digital alarm clock. You may put on stretchy Lycra pants, a polyester shirt, and form-fitting running shoes made of synthetic rubber, foam, and plastic. You may brush your teeth with an electric toothbrush, and weigh yourself on a computerized electronic scale that also measures your body mass index. For breakfast, you may cook bacon in a microwave oven and make

coffee in an automatic electric coffeemaker using deionized water, freeze-dried coffee, low-calorie sweetener, and ultra-high-temperature sterilized table cream. To make sure that your body gets the nutrients it needs, you may take a multivitamin pill. When we say that times have changed, we often mean that technologies have changed.

(d) Describe four technological products or processes in your home, school, workplace, or neighbourhood that were not in widespread use 10 years ago.

(e) Briefly explain how one of the products or processes you described in **(d)** has changed your lifestyle. Is this product or process a need or a want?

Technologies Abound

There are many different types of technologies, but they are often grouped into four general categories: Information and Communication Technology, Transportation Technology, Biotechnology, and Construction Technology. In this unit, you will focus on the first three categories.

Figure 3 In the past, food was preserved in cold cellars.

Information and Communication Technology

We live in the Information Age. Books, magazines, newspapers, posters, signs, billboards, radios, televisions (**Figure 4**), VCRs, CDs, DVDs, MP3 players, telephones, e-mail, and the Internet are only some of the contemporary tools we use to communicate information.

Figure 4 Humans have produced many different technological devices to help them satisfy their need for communication.

Information and communication technology includes the knowledge, processes, tools, and skills that people use to communicate information. Communication usually involves the production, transmission, reception, and storage of information. Could you imagine a world without information and communication technology?

(f) What do you consider to be the most important information and communication technology? Describe and explain your choice.

Transportation Technology

Moving people and goods from place to place is a vital part of everyday life. People rely on transportation to get to and from work or school. Goods are manufactured in one country and transported to another country to be sold. Tourists travel to destinations all over the world. Bicycles, cars, trucks, buses, airplanes, trains, and boats are common modes of transportation, and new modes are continually being researched and developed (**Figure 5**).

Transportation technology includes the knowledge, processes, tools, and skills that are used to move people and goods from place to place. Transportation requires energy. People use the energy in food when they ride a bicycle, walk, or run from place to place. Vehicles that transport people and goods use various sources of energy, including fossil fuels (such as gasoline and diesel fuel), electricity, and wind. Some vehicles, such as submarines, may use nuclear fuel as a source of energy. Burning fossil fuels and using nuclear fuels create environmental pollution. Scientists, engineers, and technicians dedicate much time and effort to design and build less polluting and more energy-efficient vehicles.

(g) In general, Europeans drive smaller cars than North Americans. Why do you think this is so? Is it better to drive smaller cars? Explain.

Biotechnology

Adequate supplies of nutritious foods, contaminant-free water, and effective health-care services are high on the list of priorities for most people in contemporary societies. Recent advances in the biological sciences, especially genetics and biochemistry, have allowed researchers to develop and produce drought-resistant and disease-resistant crops and more effective medicines and vaccines.

Figure 5 One modern mode of transportation is the Segway. This is a personal transportation device, marketed as an alternative method for commuting to work, running errands, or travelling short distances.

Who invented the World Wide Web? When was the automatic banking machine (ATM) developed? Where was the first snowboard produced? Many exciting technological changes have occurred in your lifetime. In this activity, you will create a personal time line of technological changes.

1. Look around your home, school, or neighbourhood, and identify technologies that you believe may have been developed within your lifetime.

2. Conduct library and/or Internet research to verify when these technologies were developed.

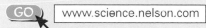 GO   www.science.nelson.com

3. Use your findings to create a time line of technological changes that have occurred in your lifetime. Include inventions, inventors, dates, and places, and arrange these on the time line along with significant events that have occurred in your own life.

Biotechnology includes the knowledge, processes, tools, and skills that people use to affect the activities of living organisms. Biotechnology includes medical technologies, such as magnetic resonance imaging (MRI), heart pacemakers, contact lenses, artificial limbs, artificial insemination, and drug therapies (**Figure 6**). Biotechnology also includes agricultural technologies, such as machines for ploughing fields, sowing seeds, and harvesting crops, and processes for preserving foods.

Figure 6   Biotechnology includes the development, production, and use of drugs.

Some modern biotechnology, such as the cloning of animals and the production of food from genetically engineered organisms, have raised safety and ethical concerns. Many people feel that government regulations have not kept up with the pace of scientific and technological advances, and that more controls and accountability are necessary.

(h) A local grocery store sells two types of tomatoes. One type is labelled "organically grown," and the other type is labelled "genetically engineered." The genetically engineered tomatoes are rounder, redder, firmer, and cheaper than the organically grown variety. If you had to choose between them, which type of tomatoes would you buy? Provide reasons for your decision.

The Great Blackout of 2003 reminded us of how dependent we have become on the conveniences of modern technologies. When the provision of basic goods (such as food, fuel, and medicine) or basic services (such as telephone and electricity) is interrupted, it becomes difficult to find adequate substitutes. Many of the current technologies of everyday life seem to have become basic needs, even though people were able to cope without these technologies not too long ago.

Questions to Think About ...

As you explore the topics in this unit, keep the following questions in mind:

- What is the difference between science and technology, and how are they related?
- Is it important for the government to fund research that does not immediately produce an end product?

- How was the Internet developed?
- What is being done to make cars and trucks more environmentally friendly?
- Are genetically modified foods safe to consume?

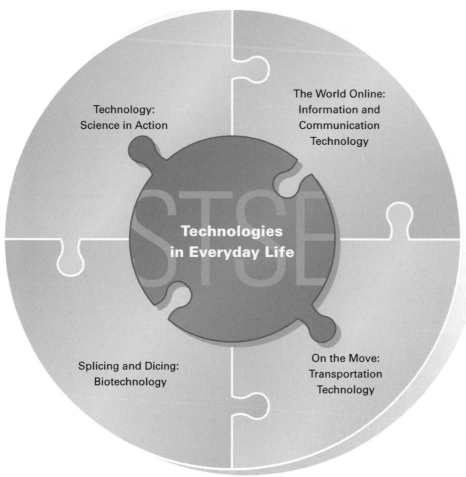

Technology: Science in Action

The World Online: Information and Communication Technology

Technologies in Everyday Life

Splicing and Dicing: Biotechnology

On the Move: Transportation Technology

Unit Task Introduction

We all use technological devices to help us accomplish the tasks of everyday life. Some people use technologies more than others and seem to have a gadget for every purpose. Other people use only the most essential technologies, preferring to do most things "naturally." The number of technologies we use depends on many factors, including personal preference, ability, availability, usefulness, and affordability.

In this Unit Task, you will develop a technology index to assess overall use of technologies. An index is like a grading system: points are awarded and deducted. In your technology index, you will award

and deduct points based on the number of technologies used and the costs and benefits of these technologies to society and the environment. You will use your technology index to assess your classmates, and then you will analyze and compare your results.

In order to develop a useful technology index, you must note the advantages and disadvantages of the technologies that you will learn about in the four topics of this unit. Read the description and requirements on pages 68 to 69 before you start the unit topics, so that you can prepare for the Unit Task as you progress through the unit.

Technology: SCIENCE *in* ACTION

Arthur Fry, a new-product-development researcher at 3M Company, became very excited one day in the early 1970s when 3M chemist Dr. Spence Silver presented his latest discovery—a repositionable adhesive. Unlike the many other sticky substances developed by 3M (such as Scotch Tape), this adhesive was composed of molecules that made only intermittent contact with a surface. Thus, it did not stick very strongly when used as a coating on the back of tape, allowing the tape to be moved from place to place, or repositioned. Silver knew that he had discovered a very unusual adhesive, but he could not think of a practical use for it. He and the other chemists were always in search of stronger adhesives, not weaker ones.

Fry was an avid singer in his church choir, and he always marked pages in his hymn book with pieces of scrap paper. Using scrap paper frustrated Fry because the pieces fell out as he flipped the pages. When he heard of Silver's discovery, he immediately realized that the repositionable adhesive could be used to make sticky bookmarks that would stay in place, but could also be lifted and moved to other pages as required. The broader concept of Post-it Notes (**Figure 1**) soon followed, along with paper tapes and labels.

(a) Why is it important for scientists to share their new discoveries with others, including non-scientists?

All people—including scientists, engineers, and technologists—tend to be skeptical of new developments. Although Post-it Notes sounded like a good idea, there were many at 3M who had their doubts. For example, the engineering and production departments told Fry that Post-it Notes would create considerable production difficulties and would produce enormous quantities of waste. The company's marketing department doubted if people would pay for a product when they could use cost-free scrap paper. Fry was convinced, however, that the invention would be successful. He challenged 3M to find solutions to the problems, and they did. By 1981, one year after their introduction, Post-it Notes were named the company's Outstanding New Product, and they have since become one of the best-known 3M products.

What are some of the relationships between science and technology? Who are the scientists in your community? What do they do? What is the role of science in modern society?

Figure 1 Post-it Notes are available in a large assortment of colours, sizes, and shapes.

Discovery, Invention, and Innovation

Science and technology are different, yet highly interrelated, activities. **Science** is the study of the natural world, and those who practise science are called scientists. Scientists are curious and watchful people. They describe nature using **empirical knowledge**: knowledge gained by the five senses (touch, smell, taste, vision, and hearing). An observation of nature that no one has made before, or that no one has made in the same way before, is called a **discovery**. Scientists make discoveries by looking for patterns and regularities in nature (natural phenomena). These regularities are sometimes called laws of nature and, in some cases, laws are described mathematically. For example, Isaac Newton discovered a mathematical relationship between the force, F, and acceleration, a, of an object whose mass is m. In general, if the force used to push or pull an object increases, its acceleration increases. This law is commonly called Newton's second law of motion, and it can be expressed mathematically as

$$F = ma$$

The scientific community accepted Newton's second law of motion because it was simple, understandable, and supported by believable empirical evidence.

Unlike a scientific law, which is determined by careful observation, a **scientific theory**, or scientific explanation, is the product of creativity and inventiveness. Scientists use scientific theories to try to explain natural phenomena whose root cause is not easily noticeable. To develop a theory, a scientist may first suggest an untested explanation called a **hypothesis**. For example, many years ago people noticed that certain diseases are contagious (they can be spread by person-to-person contact), but there was no satisfactory explanation for this observation. With the invention of the compound microscope in the 17th century, scientists discovered microorganisms and hypothesized that the spread of certain microorganisms (called germs) could be the root cause of infectious diseases. After conducting many experiments and gathering evidence to support this hypothesis, the transfer of germs was accepted as an explanation for the spread of infections. With the support of confirming evidence, the germ hypothesis of infectious diseases became the germ theory of infectious diseases.

Scientific theories, such as the germ theory, are tentative explanations, which means that they are subject to change. Theories are changed when new scientific evidence indicates that a change is required. For example, the germ theory was changed when viruses were discovered. Viruses are non-living entities that are much smaller than bacteria and other microorganisms, so they cannot be seen under a typical light microscope. When viruses were discovered, many scientists hypothesized that they too could cause infectious diseases. After obtaining experimental evidence to support this hypothesis, the germ theory was revised to include viruses as potential causes of infections.

Invention

Technology is the application of science to help people satisfy some of their needs and desires. People use skills and resources to develop processes and equipment that help them solve problems in everyday life. Professionals such as technologists, technicians, and engineers develop technologies through invention and innovation.

Invention is the creative development of a novel device or process that helps people meet their needs or satisfy their desires. For example, people have invented beds to satisfy their need for comfortable rest. They have invented microwave ovens, refrigerators, freezers, and the canning process to meet their needs for cooking and preserving food. They have invented radios, televisions, telephones, computers, and the Internet to help them satisfy their desire for efficient communication. In general, inventions are newly found solutions to problems in everyday life.

The great Greek philosopher Plato once wrote, "Necessity is the mother of invention." This was certainly the case in 1891, when American inventor Whitcomb Judson saw a need for a device to fasten boots quickly. After much trial and error, Judson invented the world's first zip fastener, or zipper (**Figure 2**).

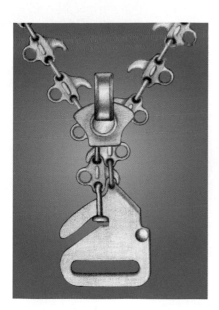

Figure 2 Whitcomb Judson's invention of the zipper was originally called a clasp locker and unlocker.

Innovation

Some technological devices combine existing inventions in new ways to solve new problems. Modifying an existing technology to serve a new purpose is called **innovation**. You have probably innovated many times in your everyday life. If you have ever used a piece of chewing gum to stick a note on a wall, or used a butter knife as a screwdriver, you've innovated! The wheel is a good example of an invention that has been used innovatively. The wheel was invented long ago in prehistoric times. It is now used in gears and pulleys; on trains, bicycles, carts, and automobiles; and as the rotating base of dials on a radio and the rollers in a computer mouse.

In 1959, Canadian inventor Joseph-Armand Bombardier combined a number of existing technologies to produce the world's first recreational snowmobile, called the Ski-Doo (**Figure 3**).

While unique in its overall design, the snowmobile uses a number of existing technologies in innovative ways. For example, a pair of modified skis allows the front end of the machine to slide over the snow. Handlebars, like those on a motorcycle, are used for steering. A rubber track, like that used for farm and military equipment, grips the snow and allows the vehicle to move forward. Notice the features of modern snowmobiles, shown in **Figure 4**.

Figure 4 Modern snowmobiles

Science–Technology Relationships

Science and technology are closely related fields. Scientists use the products of technology in their research; engineers and technologists use the principles, laws, and theories of science when planning and developing new technologies.

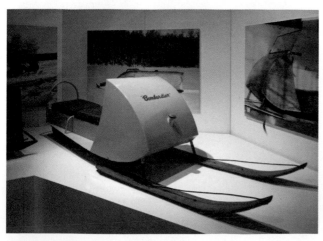

Figure 3 A Ski-Doo from 1960

In some cases, scientific discoveries follow technological inventions and innovations. For example, Alessandro Volta invented the battery in 1800, well before theories about current electricity were developed. Other inventions—such as the thermometer, microscope, telescope, and computer—have helped in the advancement of science. In many cases, technological inventions and innovations follow scientific discoveries (**Table 1**). For example, the television was invented in 1927 by Philo T. Farnsworth (**Figure 5**), after he learned about electrons, current electricity, and electromagnetism.

Thus, science and technology work together in the development of devices and processes that help us satisfy our needs and desires. A good example of the science–technology relationship is the development of the heart (cardiac) pacemaker. When the heart works properly, it pumps oxygen-rich blood to all the cells in the body. Unfortunately, some people have a defect in the natural system that controls the heartbeat rate. This defect can decrease the amount

Figure 5 Philo T. Farnsworth (1906–1971) tunes one of his early televisions as he views an image on the small circular picture tube.

of oxygen that reaches the cells. Canadian heart researchers Dr. W.G. Bigelow and Dr. J.C. Callaghan worked with Dr. J. Hopps, an engineer, at the National Research Council in Ottawa to develop the first cardiac pacemaker in 1950. They used scientific knowl-

Table 1 Science–Technology Connections

Science	Technology	Example
Chemists learn about the structure of materials and their chemical reactions.	Engineers and technologists design useful products, using materials with suitable properties (e.g., HEAT TREAT Hand Warmers).	
Physicists explain how forces act on an object under a load.	Structural engineers and technologists design buildings, bridges, roads, and tunnels that can support specific loads.	
Physiologists discover the biochemical reactions that keep organisms alive and healthy.	Technologists design life-support systems for astronauts and space stations.	
Plant biologists learn how roots absorb nutrients from water and soil.	Engineers and technologists design hydroponic systems for efficient crop production in areas with poor soil.	

edge regarding the normal function of the heart and the problems associated with an irregular heartbeat to develop a device that could correct the problem. The cardiac pacemaker controls heartbeat rate by sending tiny electric shocks to the heart on a periodic basis. Today, over one million North Americans a year are fitted with cardiac pacemakers. Unlike the large pacemaker that was developed by Bigelow and his associates, today's pacemakers are small machines that can be placed under the skin (**Figure 6**).

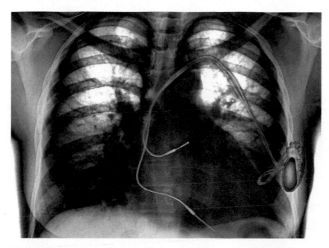

Figure 6 A coloured chest X-ray that shows a surgically-implanted heart pacemaker (blue/orange)

Often, one technological invention leads to another. For example, the compound light microscope (**Figure 7**) could not be developed before glass lenses were invented, because glass lenses focus and magnify the image of the specimen being observed.

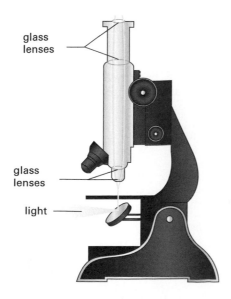

glass lenses

glass lenses

light

Figure 7 Glass lenses focus and magnify the image in a compound light microscope.

"Chance Favours the Prepared Mind"

Many scientific discoveries and technological inventions occur by chance, or serendipity. **Serendipity** is the act of discovering or inventing something useful by accident. A famous example of serendipity in science is the discovery of background radiation.

While tuning a powerful antenna used for astronomy experiments, American physicists Arno Penzias and Robert Wilson (**Figure 8**) noticed a constant, low-level noise coming from the antenna. The noise was being formed by an invisible type of light energy (radiation), which was detected no matter what direction the antenna was facing. Soon Penzias and Wilson realized that the radiation was present everywhere. They also discovered that they had stumbled on the best evidence to date supporting the big bang theory—a theory that explains how the entire universe was created in a huge explosion of matter and energy.

Figure 8 Both Arno Penzias and Robert Wilson received a Nobel Prize in Physics in 1978 for their discovery of background radiation. The radiation is called cosmic microwave background and is now thought to be radiation left over from the big bang.

DID **YOU** KNOW?

A Home-Grown Business
Liquid Paper was invented by Bette Nesmith-Graham in 1951, while working as a typist to support herself and her son. Using her kitchen and garage as a laboratory, she developed a paint–turpentine mixture she called "Mistakes Out" to hide her typing mistakes at the office. She later changed the name of her product to Liquid Paper and sold it out of her home for 17 years. In 1979, the Gillette Company purchased Liquid Paper for $47.5 million U.S. Her son, Michael Nesmith, was a member of the 1970s rock group called The Monkees.

Serendipity can also occur in technology, as shown by the invention of Velcro. In 1948, George de Mestral, a Swiss engineer, returned from a walk in the woods and noticed that some burs were stuck to his cloth jacket and pants. He examined a bur under his microscope and noticed that it contained little green hooks that clung to fabric and fur. De Mestral immediately recognized the potential for a practical new fastener. After eight years of experimentation and development he created Velcro (**Figure 9**), the first synthetic hook-and-loop fastener.

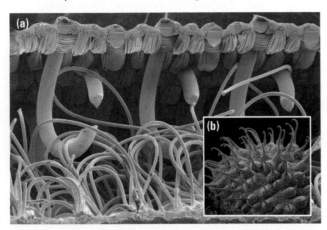

Figure 9 **(a)** A magnified view of Velcro, which is composed of two nylon strips, one with small hooks and the other with small plastic loops. When the two strips are pressed together, the hooks get caught in the loops and form a strong bond.
(b) Magnified view of the hooks on a bur

Technological Systems

Every technology can be described as a **system**, which is a group of components that work together to achieve a common goal. There are four main components of a system: input, process, output, and feedback.

Input

Input (also referred to as system resources) is everything that is put into a system. Input can include people, information, materials, tools and machines, energy, finances (money and land), and time. People are, by far, the most important input. People have needs and wants. They decide which problems need technological solutions, and they provide the necessary knowledge, creativity, and problem-solving skills. When faced with a technological problem, people gather information and decide if tools and equipment are required to solve the problem.

Often several different forms of input are required to create the finished product. **Table 2** lists some of the inputs of a system for making cellular telephones.

Table 2 Inputs of a Cell-Phone Manufacturing System

Input	Examples
people	Scientists, engineers, and technicians design the cell phone's functional components and overall structure. Workers construct the phone. Salespeople sell the phone.
information	Science provides information about the energy transformations that make a phone work. Science provides information about the materials from which a phone is constructed.
materials	Plastics, metals, and rubber are needed to make the case for the phone. Metals are needed for wires. Silicon is needed to form the integrated circuits.
tools and machines	Saws, drills, soldering equipment, robots, plastic moulding equipment, computers, printers, and conveyor belts are needed to build the phone.
energy	Human energy is needed to design, build, and sell the phone. Electricity is needed to power the lights in the buildings, and the motors in the production equipment such as conveyor belts. Fossil fuels are needed to heat the buildings, and to run the engines in delivery trucks.
finances (money and land)	Land is needed to build a manufacturing plant. Money is needed to pay for land, materials, tools and equipment, energy, and workers' salaries.
time	Time is required to design, build, deliver, and sell the phone.

Procc33

A **process** is all the activities of a system that produce an expected result. In cell-phone manufacturing, the process includes the work done by the machines and people to build the cell phones (**Figure 10**).

Figure 10 Many cell-phone parts are assembled manually, although some factories are exploring the use of robots.

Output

The **output** is the end result of the input and process components of a system. Like all systems, technological systems produce both intended and unintended outputs. The **intended output** of a system is the result that is planned for and desired. In cell-phone manufacturing, the intended output is a functioning cell phone. The **unintended output** is the result that is not planned for or desired and would rather be avoided. Unintended outputs include solid, liquid, and gaseous wastes that are created in the manufacturing process, as well as the cell phone when it is eventually discarded.

Both the intended and unintended outputs of a technological system have effects, or impacts, on society and the environment. Impacts may be beneficial or detrimental. Beneficial impacts are called **positive impacts,** and they are normally produced by the intended outputs of a system. For cell phones, positive impacts include the personal freedom that comes when people can efficiently communicate with each other from almost anywhere at any time, as well as the many jobs that are produced by the cell-phone manufacturing system.

Negative impacts are the negative effects of unintended system outputs on society and the environment. For example, the invention of cell phones may eventually cause a decrease in the sale and use of conventional telephones, causing unemployment in this industry. The use of cell phones while driving has been linked to an increase in automobile accidents, and environmental pollution is produced during the cell-phone manufacturing process.

The impacts of a technology on society and the environment can be assessed by conducting a cost-benefit analysis. As its name implies, a **cost-benefit analysis** involves measuring the costs (costs or disadvantages) and benefits (advantages), associated with the development, distribution, and use of a technology, and relating these to one another. See **Appendix A1** for more information about cost-benefit analysis and an example.

Feedback

Feedback is information about the quality of a system's processes and outcomes. Feedback is generally used to improve a system, and it can take many forms. In cell-phone manufacturing, for example, technicians in the factory test the phones to make sure that they are functioning properly before they are packaged for sale. Cell-phone users provide feedback to the manufacturer by communicating complaints about phone malfunctions and the benefits of the features of a phone. Magazines such as *Consumer Reports,* and certain Web sites rate cell phones on the basis of their function, style, and price. Feedback often leads to changes in the system. For example, feedback may cause a cell phone or cell-phone service to be redesigned. The new design will change the input, process, and output. When the new product or process is tested, additional feedback may result in still more changes. Systems undergo continuous change throughout the input, process, output, and feedback components (**Figure 11**).

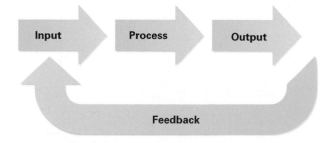

Figure 11 System components include input, process, output, and feedback.

A1: Technology: Science in Action **15**

When the first cell phones were consumer-tested in 1977, people complained that they were too large and too heavy to carry (**Figure 12**). Cell phones went through many system changes over the years, resulting in the compact, portable devices that they are today.

Figure 12 Early cell phones were large, heavy, and inconvenient for users who often carried them in briefcases and purses.

A1.1 *Activity* | THE MOUSETRAP EXTINGUISHER CHALLENGE >

People solve technological problems in many different ways. A step-by-step process is helpful, however, for keeping your work organized and efficient. In this activity, you will use the problem-solving process described in **Appendix A3**.

With a partner or small group, you will design, build, test, and evaluate a device that uses the energy from the spring of a standard mousetrap (**Figure 13**) to extinguish the flame of a candle placed 1 m away (**Figure 14**).

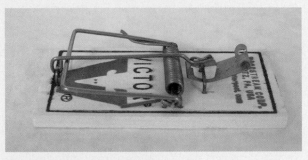

Figure 13 A standard mousetrap

Your goal is to build an efficient device. This means that your device should extinguish the flame as quickly as possible. You may use any materials that are approved by your teacher to build your device. Make sure that you record all your ideas and plans for your design as labelled diagrams and written descriptions, and that you always take safety into account. Once your design is complete, have your teacher approve it before you implement and evaluate it as your best solution to the problem.

Materials

standard mousetrap
duct tape or other adhesive tape
small clamps
aluminum foil pie plate
sand to fill bottom of pie plate
tealight
lighter
metre stick
pencil or pen
stopwatch
other materials, depending on design

Procedure

(a) Together with your partner(s), design a device that, when placed between the mousetrap and the candle, will extinguish the flame of the candle when the mousetrap is released.

1. Fill the pie plate with sand to a depth of about 1 cm. Set the tealight in the sand so that it will not easily move.

2. On the floor or on a large, sturdy table, build your device according to your design. Make sure that the mousetrap and the tealight are exactly 1 m apart, as shown in **Figure 14**. Also make sure that you tape the mousetrap to the floor or clamp it to the table, in order to minimize recoil when it is released.

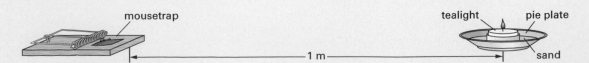

Figure 14 Mousetrap activity setup

3. Carefully set the mousetrap according to your teacher's instructions.

🛑 Mousetraps can be painful if released on your fingers. Follow your teacher's instructions for setting and releasing the mousetrap.

Do not leave a lit tealight unattended. Keep flammable materials well away from the flame.

4. Using the lighter, light your tealight. Activate the system by snapping the mousetrap with a pencil or pen, according to your teacher's instructions. Using a stopwatch, determine the time it takes for your device to extinguish the flame. If your device does not extinguish the flame, do not record a time.

5. Evaluate your results, taking note of the actions of the system.

6. If you wish to make improvements to your device, go back to step 3 of the problem-solving process.

7. Set up your system, and perform three trials to extinguish the flame. Record your results.

Analysis

(b) List the materials you chose for building your device. Justify your choice of each material.

(c) How is your device, the mousetrap, and the tealight a system?

(d) Analyze your solution to the problem in terms of input, process, output, and feedback.

Evaluation

(e) Evaluate the design of your device. What improvements did you make (or could you have made) to your device to make the system more efficient?

(f) Compare your final device with a device created by another pair or group. Consider overall design (Did the other device have more parts? Did it have more moving parts?), overall success (Did it extinguish the flame?), efficiency of action (Did it extinguish the flame more quickly?), and aesthetics (Was the design more elegant or more appealing?).

Synthesis

(g) Describe at least one scientific law, theory, or principle that was operating in your device or the system.

✔ Check Your Understanding

1. What is the difference between a scientific law and a scientific theory?

2. Describe one or two innovations that you have developed in your everyday life. (Think of innovations that are not mentioned in this text.)

3. The historical development of sports equipment (such as running shoes, hockey sticks, fishing rods, golf clubs, and safety helmets) illustrates the relationship between science (especially the science of materials) and technology.
   (a) Choose a piece of sports equipment, and describe how advances in science have influenced its technological development.

   (b) Describe how the changes in technology you described in (a) have affected the performance of the athlete who uses the equipment and the sports event in which the equipment is used.

4. In a four-column table with the headings Input, Process, Output, and Feedback, analyze a mass transit system, such as a bus system, a subway system, or a system with both buses and subway trains (such as the Toronto transit system).

Society & the Environment

The Importance of Research

Scientists, engineers, and technologists conduct research to further our understanding of the natural world and to develop better solutions to the practical problems of life. There are two types of research: basic research (also called fundamental research or pure research) and applied research (also called product research).

Basic research is research that helps people learn more about how the natural world works. It is focused on the discovery and development of principles, laws, and theories of nature. Basic research is carried out by scientists and mainly occurs in university and government laboratories around the world. **Applied research** is research that is primarily focused on developing new and better solutions to practical problems. Both types of research can be thought of as complex systems, which can be analyzed in terms of input, process, output, and feedback. One of the key inputs of basic and applied research is money.

Modern research is very expensive. Research facilities employ highly paid, highly skilled professionals. They consume large amounts of energy and require expensive and sophisticated tools and equipment. Product research and development (R&D)—such as the research and development of new cosmetics, telephones, automobiles, computer software, and sports equipment—is usually carried out in privately owned companies that have research facilities (**Figure 15**).

Figure 15 Many private companies conduct product research and development.

Scientists who work in basic research may receive funding from government agencies, such as the Natural Sciences and Engineering Research Council of Canada (NSERC) and the Social Sciences and Humanities Research Council of Canada (SSHRC). In 2003, NSERC and SSHRC invested a total of almost $1 billion in basic research. With such a large investment of tax dollars, many people question the value of basic research in comparison to applied (product) research. The general public more readily appreciates the results of applied research, such as effective drugs, safer cars, healthier foods, and Post-it Notes. Many people have difficulty seeing the value in the detection of a new planet, the development of atomic theory, or the discovery of a new compound, such as Silver's repositionable glue.

Basic research often produces knowledge that is used by engineers and technologists to develop practical solutions to everyday problems. Unfortunately, it is often difficult to predict whether a given research project has the potential to produce technological products and processes. Useful products are often developed long after the basic research is completed, if at all. How could Ernest Rutherford have known in 1911 that his discovery of the atom's nucleus would one day be used to develop nuclear power plants? Few scientists have the foresight of British scientist and inventor Michael Faraday who, in the early 1800s, discovered many of the basic principles of electricity and magnetism.

People often asked Faraday about the significance of his discoveries. One recorded incident occurred at a demonstration of one of Faraday's electrical experiments. William Gladstone, a high-ranking British government official, remarked "It is very interesting, Mr. Faraday, but what practical worth is it?" Faraday replied, "One day, sir, you may tax it." Although Faraday could never have imagined how dependent on electricity society would eventually become, he was able to foresee the future usefulness of his work.

Today, scientists do their best to predict the practical usefulness of their research when they apply for government grants. Many feel, however, that basic research should be funded for its own sake. They try to convince the public that basic research is valuable simply to extend human knowledge and understanding. Robert R. Wilson, a scientist and the first director of Fermilab, a large physics laboratory located near Chicago, was once asked by a U.S. government official, "What will your lab contribute to the defence of the United States?" Wilson replied, "It has nothing to do directly with defending our country, sir, except to make it worth defending."

Explore *an* Issue

Funding Basic Research

Modern scientific research is very expensive. Sometimes scientists and engineers can show how their research may produce useful products. Often, however, research projects show no promise of technological development. Funding agencies must decide whether or not scarce funds should be used for basic research.

Statement: Governments should only fund basic research that clearly demonstrates a potential for practical application.

1. With a partner or in a small group, prepare to debate the issue by either defending or opposing the statement.

2. Research arguments to support your position. If possible, collect evidence directly from government agencies and other organizations that fund research, as well as from library and Internet resources.

GO www.science.nelson.com

Decision-Making Skills

- ○ Define the Issue
- ● Research
- ● Defend a Decision
- ○ Identify Alternatives
- ● Analyze the Issue
- ● Evaluate

3. Prepare arguments that focus on real issues in science and technology. Consider issues related to industries such as forestry, agriculture, manufacturing, medicine, and transportation. Points and counterpoints may include, but are not limited to, those in **Table 3**.

4. Once you have prepared your arguments, defend your position in a formal debate (see **Appendix A7**).

5. Discuss the outcome of the debate with your partner or small group. Determine the value of debating as a way of resolving controversial issues in science.

Table 3 Points and Counterpoints for Limiting the Funding Used for Basic Research

Point	Counterpoint
Modern basic research is expensive and does not always yield useful results.	Governments sometimes spend money on frivolous things, such as unnecessary trips, expensive gifts, and lavish receptions. This money should, instead, be used to fund basic research.
Some basic research projects produce completely useless scientific facts, such as the shape of snowflakes and the twitching rate of a grasshopper's hind legs.	History shows that many technological inventions and innovations start with a new scientific principle or theory.
Scarce government money should be used to care for the needy, not to fund new research that may or may not produce useful results.	Serendipity may result in useful discoveries, even when basic research projects appear to be useless.

SUMMARY

- Science is the study of the natural world. Scientists explain natural phenomena by conducting experiments and developing scientific theories based on their experimental evidence.
- A discovery is an observation of nature that no one has made before.
- An invention is a device or process that helps people meet their needs. Innovation is the process of modifying an already existing technology to serve a new purpose.
- Science and technology are closely related fields. Scientists use the products of technology in their research. Engineers and technologists use the principles of science to develop new technologies.
- A system is a group of components that work together to achieve a common goal. Every technology can be described as a system.
- Technological systems can be analyzed in terms of input, process, output, and feedback.
- There are two types of research: basic research and applied research. Basic research is the systematic investigation of the natural world. Applied research is primarily focused on developing new and better solutions to practical problems.

- Scientists who work in basic research apply to government agencies and other organizations for funding.
- The general public more readily appreciates the practicality and usefulness of applied research. However, many people see much value in basic research, and understand the connections between basic research and applied research.

Key Terms

science	process
empirical knowledge	output
discovery	intended output
scientific theory	unintended output
hypothesis	positive impact
technology	negative impact
invention	cost-benefit analysis
innovation	feedback
serendipity	basic research
system	applied research
input	

ASSESSMENT

Understanding Concepts

1. How does the development of 3M's Post-it Notes illustrate the relationship between science and technology?

2. (a) Use a specific example to illustrate the difference between a hypothesis and a scientific theory.
   (b) Do scientific theories stay forever unchanged? Explain.

3. Read each statement. Does it describe a scientific law or a scientific theory?
   (a) Unbalanced forces make objects accelerate.
   (b) Solids expand when heated because their particles vibrate more vigorously and thus take up more space.

4. Determine whether each statement is true or false. Explain your answer using an example.

   (a) A technology satisfies a basic need or desire.
   (b) Scientific laws and principles must be known before technological development can occur.

5. (a) Distinguish between the inputs and outputs of a system.
   (b) List two inputs, processes, outputs, and feedback related to a city's traffic control system.
   (c) Describe two positive impacts and two negative impacts of a city's traffic control system.

6. Radar is a radio device that may be used to determine the distance of faraway objects. It was developed by Sir Alexander Watson-Watt in 1935. The radar gun (**Figure 16**) is a device that detects the speed of an oncoming vehicle. It was first used in the 1950s. Which of these two devices is an invention, and which is an innovation? Explain.

Figure 16   A modern radar gun

7. **(a)** What role do governments play in basic and applied research?

   (b) What role do private companies play in basic and applied research?

8. Using the Key Terms, create a concept map for this topic. Indicate connections among related terms.

Making Connections

9. **(a)** Choose a simple but useful gadget (such as a paper clip, staple, or can opener), and conduct library or Internet research to determine its history and development. Summarize your findings in a brief report. Include people, places, and dates, and describe the circumstances in which the gadget was invented.

   GO | www.science.nelson.com

   (b) What impact has the gadget had on the way people live or on society in general?

10. Why are basic research and applied research so expensive today?

11. Write a brief essay (three or four paragraphs long), explaining why you agree or disagree with the following statement: "Some basic scientific research is useless."

12. Ernest Rutherford discovered the atomic nucleus in his famous gold foil experiment. He once said, "Anyone who expects a source of power from the transformation of atoms is talking moonshine."

(a) What did Rutherford mean by this statement?

(b) Explain how Rutherford's statement turned out to be wrong.

13. In 1993, the U.S. government cancelled the construction of the world's largest and most powerful particle accelerator (**Figure 17**), the Superconducting Supercollider, because government officials decided that the $11 billion U.S. price was too high. The Superconducting Supercollider is a machine that would help scientists better understand the structure of the atom.

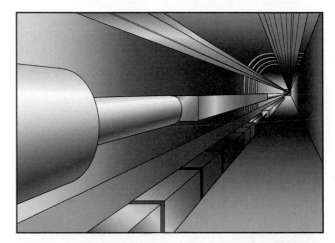

Figure 17   Artist's conception of the Superconducting Supercollider

(a) List reasons why cancelling the construction was a good decision.

(b) List reasons why cancelling the construction was a bad decision.

14. Conduct library or Internet research to answer the following questions about the Human Genome Project.

   GO | www.science.nelson.com

(a) What is the Human Genome Project?

(b) Is the Human Genome Project considered to be basic research or applied research? Explain.

(c) How can the results of the Human Genome Project be put to practical use?

The World Online: Information and COMMUNICATION TECHNOLOGY

In the mid-1990s, a new type of Internet-based network called a peer-to-peer (p2p) network was developed. This network allowed computer users to swap files, such as music files, free of charge. In the summer of 1999, Shawn Fanning (**Figure 1**) created a unique program that allowed Internet users to share their favourite music files. Fanning named his program Napster and by December 2000, Napster had over 20 million users worldwide. At one point, with over one billion music files available to its users, Napster became the largest storehouse of music or art in history!

Figure 1
Shawn Fanning, inventor of Napster

A key feature of the Napster program was that music files were not stored on a central computer owned by the company. Instead, users stored music files on their own computers. They sent (or uploaded) files directly to, and received (or downloaded) files directly from, other users' computers. The Napster program simply allowed the transfers to occur.

(a) List three reasons why you think Napster became so popular so quickly.

(b) Why do you think Napster developed a system that allowed the transfer of files from person to person, but not the storage of files on its own computers?

Soon after Napster was created, artists and music companies began to complain that the network was allowing people to "steal" copyrighted music. The first band to complain was Metallica.

(c) Do you think that downloading and listening to music files on Napster was the same as stealing? Explain.

Metallica accused Napster of breaking the law since the band was not getting paid for any of their songs that were being traded on Napster. Napster challenged Metallica to identify users that were doing this. The band hired a computer monitoring company, called NetPD, to identify Napster users who traded Metallica files. Using state-of-the-art Internet monitoring equipment, NetPD discovered that 335 435 Metallica files were exchanged on Napster in just three days. The band delivered the evidence to Napster and as a result, Napster disconnected over 300 000 users.

Unlike Metallica, some artists, such as Limp Bizkit, welcomed Napster and used it to boost their popularity. Nevertheless, on May 5, 2000, a U.S. district judge ruled that swapping music files on Napster was illegal. Napster appealed the ruling, and offered record companies over $1 billion U.S. to drop the lawsuit. The companies refused the offer. Finally, after being ordered by a U.S. federal court to stop trading all copyrighted material on its network, Napster shut down completely on February 12, 2001.

Immediately after Napster's demise, dozens of other file-swapping programs appeared on the Internet. Virtually all of them are p2p networks similar to Napster, but so far none have become as popular or notorious as Napster.

New information and communication technologies are being developed at rapid speeds. How have they allowed us to communicate more effectively? What are some of the negative aspects of new technologies? For example, what is SPAM? How could it be controlled or regulated? How do modern communication technologies, such as the Internet and cell phones, threaten individual privacy?

Science & Technology

The Evolution of the Computer

Humans have invented devices and processes that help them manipulate, store, and exchange information. The knowledge, processes, tools, and skills that people use to communicate information make up **information and communication technology**. Imagine a world without telephones, televisions, pagers, printers, computers, cameras, photocopiers, radios, and books. What would everyday life be like? What would you *not* be able to do? How would you adjust? Certainly you would not have magazines or books to read. As well, you would not be able to talk to a faraway friend, watch a hockey game at home, or listen to your favourite rock band in a car. Instead, you would communicate by word of mouth with the people around you, or you would send handwritten letters by mail. The amount of information you could send and receive would be greatly diminished. A power blackout like the Great Blackout of 2003 reminds us what a world without modern information and communication technologies would be like. It also reminds us that virtually all of our communication systems run on electricity.

The Amazing Microchip

At the heart of almost every modern electronic communication and information-processing system is an amazing little device called a microchip. A **microchip**, or **integrated circuit (IC) chip** (**Figure 2**), is a thin

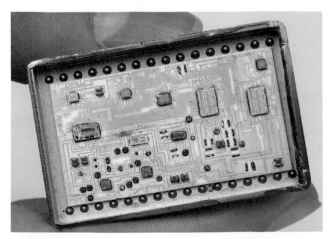

Figure 2 A microchip or integrated circuit chip contains thousands of tiny interconnected electric circuits.

wafer of silicon that contains thousands of tiny interconnected electric circuits. The electric circuits work together to receive, process, and send information. The invention of the microchip stimulated the development of the personal computer and other modern electronic devices. Before the microchip, electronic devices (such as radios, televisions, and telephones) contained conventional circuits composed of insulated metal wires, and electronic components such as diodes, resistors, capacitors, and transistors (**Figure 3**).

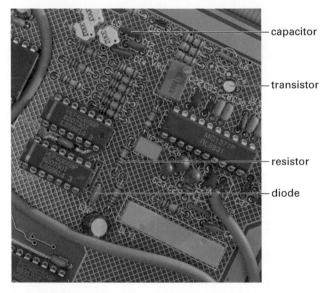

capacitor
transistor
resistor
diode

Figure 3 Electronic components, such as transistors, capacitors, resistors, and diodes, are used in radios, televisions, computers, and other electronic devices.

The wires in the circuits carry the electric current, and the diodes, resistors, capacitors, and transistors control the strength and direction of the current. In early electronics the diodes and transistors were relatively large vacuum tubes, making the circuits bulky and heavy (**Figure 4**).

DID **YOU** KNOW?

Want to Open a Microchip Factory?
A microchip fabrication facility, commonly known as a *fab*, costs over $1 billion U.S. to construct, because most of the work is done by high-precision robots.

A2: The World Online: Information and Communication Technology

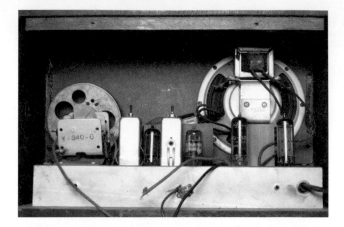

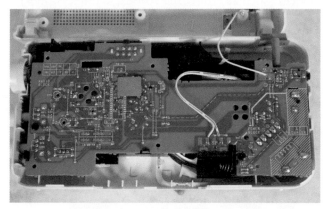

Figure 4   (a) In the past, radios were bulky and heavy, and contained many vacuum tubes. (b) Newer radios are more portable, and contain electric circuit boards.

Dawn of the Computer Age

Computers have come a long way in size and sophistication since 1945, when scientists and engineers built one of the first electronic computers, the Electrical Numerical Integrator And Calculator I (ENIAC I) (**Figure 5**). The ENIAC 1 contained thou-

Figure 5   The ENIAC 1 was one of the first computers.

sands of vacuum tubes and other electronic components, and occupied 167 m² — about the size of a small house. Unlike today's computers, which perform millions of calculations per second using very little electricity, the ENIAC I could perform only 5000 additions and 357 multiplications or divisions per second. It used so much electricity that it caused the city of Philadelphia to experience brownouts when it was turned on!

Continued research and development in electronics resulted in smaller, lighter circuit components. A significant breakthrough in the development of electronic circuitry occurred in 1959, when two American engineers, Jack Kilby of Texas Instruments and Robert Noyce of Fairchild Semiconductor Corporation, simultaneously invented the IC chip (**Figure 6**). A typical IC chip, or microchip, contains all the components in a conventional circuit, but in miniature form.

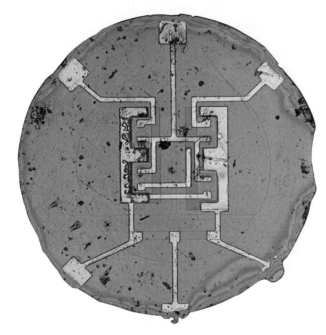

Figure 6   The first integrated circuit chip was invented by Jack Kilby and Robert Noyce in 1959.

Conductors, Insulators, and Semiconductors

Electronic devices require electric current to operate. Electric current can be obtained by using batteries or by plugging an electric cord into a wall outlet. Have you noticed that the electric cords attached to electronic devices are made of plastic? In fact, the cords are not plastic all the way through. They are composed of metal wires (usually copper) surrounded by a thin covering of plastic (**Figure 7**).

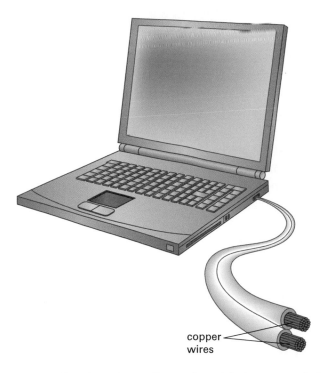

copper wires

Figure 7 Electric cords usually contain metal wires surrounded by a plastic covering. Electric charges move easily through the metal wires but not through the plastic covering.

The moving electric charges of an electric current pass easily through the inner metal wires, but not so easily through the plastic covering. Thus, the plastic covering prevents the electric charges from escaping into the surroundings, including the people who may be handling the cords. (The plastic covering is what prevents you from getting a shock!) The metals in electric cords are called conductors, because they allow electric charges to pass through with relative ease. The plastic covering is called an insulator, because electric charges do not move through it easily. Using insulated copper wires as conductors and relatively large circuit components, the designers of ENIAC 1 produced a relatively large computer with limited computing power.

Kilby and Noyce took advantage of the unique properties of elements called semiconductors in the development of their miniature integrated circuits. Unlike good conductors of electricity (such as copper and aluminum) and insulators (such as plastic and glass), **semiconductors** are intermediate conductors of electricity. Their ability to conduct depends on environmental conditions, such as temperature.

A2.1 *Activity* CONTROLLING ELECTRONIC CIRCUITS: THE DIODE

A diode is a semiconductor-based circuit component that is used to control the flow of electric current. A diode has a positive terminal and a negative terminal. The electronic symbol for a diode is $\xrightarrow{+}\!\!\blacktriangleright\!\!|\xrightarrow{-}$. The negative and positive signs in the symbol identify the negative and positive terminals of the diode. A white, black, or red band on the diode body identifies the negative terminal. In this activity, you will explore the action of a diode in a simple circuit to better understand how a semiconductor works.

Materials
diode
switch
connecting wires
60-V 60-mA lamp
12-V battery

1. Construct the circuit as shown in **Figure 8**.

2. Close the switch.

(a) Describe what happens to the lamp.

3. Open the switch, and remove the diode from the circuit.

4. Reconnect the diode to the circuit in the opposite direction.

5. Close the switch.

(b) Describe what happens to the lamp.

6. Disconnect all the circuit components.

(c) Describe the action of a diode in an electric circuit.

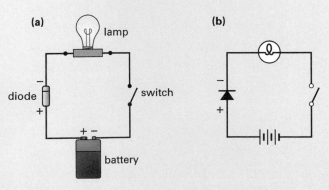

Figure 8 **(a)** A diagram of a simple circuit using pictures **(b)** A diagram of a simple circuit using symbols

A2: The World Online: Information and Communication Technology

Semiconductors, such as silicon and germanium, can be used to control the flow of electricity in a circuit. Today, virtually all of the electronic components of an IC chip are made of a semiconductor, usually silicon.

The first IC chip contained one transistor, three resistors, and one capacitor, and it was the size of your small finger (recall **Figure 6** on p. 24). Today, the most complex IC chip may contain over 200 million transistors in a few square millimetres of space. Working alone, a technician would take years to construct a single IC chip. Robots, however, can produce several million IC chips per second.

The integrated circuit is one of the most important inventions of the 20th century. Modern computing, communications (including the Internet), manufacturing, and transportation systems all depend on integrated circuits.

The Computer Chip

In 1961, the Fairchild Semiconductor Corporation began mass-producing integrated circuits, resulting in the rapid development of the personal computer and other modern electronic devices. Further development of the integrated circuit resulted in the production of the microprocessor, also known as a central processing unit (CPU) or computer chip. A **microprocessor** contains all the electronic components that are needed to perform calculations on a single IC chip. The world's first microprocessor was the Intel 4004 chip (I-4004), built in 1971 (**Figure 9(a)**). The I-4004 had roughly the same calculating power of the original ENIAC 1, but it occupied an area of only a few square millimetres. Over time, more sophisticated microprocessors were developed. Recent models include the Intel Pentium 4 (**Figure 9(b)**) and Advanced Micro Devices (AMD) Athlon microprocessors.

Table 1 summarizes the development of Intel microprocessors. In general, the greater the number of transistors on a chip, the more powerful it is.

Table 1 Development of the Intel Microprocessor

Name of microprocessor	Date of introduction	Approximate number of transistors
8080	1974	6 000
8088	1979	29 000
80286	1982	134 000
80386	1985	275 000
80486	1989	1 200 000
Pentium	1993	3 100 000
Pentium II	1997	7 500 000
Pentium III	1999	9 500 000
Pentium 4	2000	42 000 000

(a)

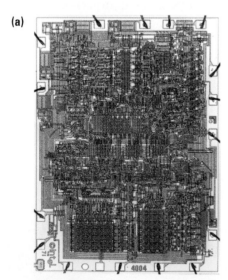

(b)

Figure 9 **(a)** The Intel 4004 was the first microprocessor. It contained just over 2300 transistors on a space occupying approximately 12 mm². **(b)** The Intel Pentium 4 is one of the latest microprocessors. The microchip is located under the protective black square. Even though the microchip is slightly larger than the I-4004 (it occupies a space of approximately 146 mm²) it contains about 42 000 000 transistors!

The Personal Computer

The invention of the microprocessor made possible the development of the **personal computer** (**PC**), or microcomputer. PCs were the first computers that were small enough and cheap enough for everyday use. Many scientists, engineers, technicians, and inventors have contributed to the development of the personal computer over the years. However, Steve Wozniak and Steve Jobs, cofounders of Apple Computer Corporation, and Bill Gates (**Figure 10**), founder of Microsoft Corporation, have made exceptionally significant contributions.

Figure 10 Bill Gates, founder of Microsoft Corporation

In 1976, Wozniak and Jobs constructed the first pre-assembled personal computer, the Apple I, in Jobs' parents' garage in Los Altos, California. They soon formed the Apple Computer Corporation, using $1300 they had raised by selling Jobs' car and Wozniak's calculator. Today, Apple Computer competes with a number of larger computer hardware manufacturers, including DELL Computers (the largest personal computer manufacturer in 2003), Compaq, IBM, and Hewlett-Packard.

Bill Gates became interested in computers at the age of 13. In 1973, he developed a version of the computer programming language BASIC for one of the world's first computers, the Altair. The Altair 8800 (**Figure 11**) was the first popular personal computer. It was marketed as a do-it-yourself kit in an issue of *Popular Electronics* magazine in 1975.

Figure 11 The Altair 8800 was the first popular personal computer.

Convinced that the computer would one day become a useful tool for businesses and the general public, Gates formed Microsoft Corporation, a company dedicated to the development and production of computer programming software. Today, Microsoft is the largest software company in the world. It is responsible for the development of the popular MS-DOS and MS-Windows computer operating programs.

Computer Components

The many inventions and innovations in computer technology over the past 20 years have resulted in the development of various types of personal computers, including desktops, laptops, palmtops, and hand-held computers (**Figure 12**).

Figure 12 Small laptop and palmtop computers are becoming very popular.

(a)  **(b)**  **(c)**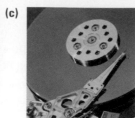

Figure 13
(a) A floppy disk
(b) A CD-ROM
(c) A hard disk

In addition to the CPU, personal computers contain other IC chips. Memory chips allow computers to store information, and graphics processing chips (graphics cards) allow computers to display photos and other images, including moving pictures. The components of a computer system are commonly divided into computer hardware and computer software. **Computer hardware** includes the physical components of a computer, such as the CPU, memory chips, keyboard, and display monitor. These components may be further classified as internal devices and external, or peripheral, devices. **Internal devices** are basic components, such as the CPU and memory chips. These are the components that essentially make the computer work. **Peripheral devices** are components that allow the computer to perform optional functions, such as print documents, communicate with other computers, take photos, and reproduce music and other sounds. Peripheral devices include printers, joysticks, and scanners.

In order to perform its functions, a computer requires information in the form of a **computer program**, which is a list of instructions that tells a computer what to do. Computer programmers have devised several different computer languages (such as BASIC, Fortran, C++, and Java) that they use to write computer programs. A computer program may be recorded onto circular pieces of metal or plastic called floppy disks, hard disks, and CD-ROMs (**Figure 13**).

Floppy disks and CD-ROMs can be moved from computer to computer. Hard disks are connected to a computer's internal circuitry. Each type of storage has a corresponding device, called a disk drive, that can be used to transfer program instructions to the computer's CPU. A disk drive can also be used to record programs onto a floppy disk, hard disk, or CD-ROM. These programs are known as **computer software**.

The Computer as an Information Processing System

You can think of a computer as an information processing system. Information enters a computer through input devices such as a keyboard or a mouse. Instructions for processing the information first enter the computer through a keyboard, a mouse, or prepackaged computer software. The computer's CPU then processes the information and displays the results, or output, on an output device such as a monitor, printer, or speaker (**Figure 14**).

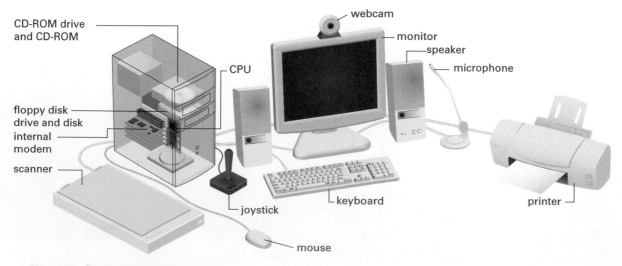

Figure 14 Parts of a personal computer

Table 2 describes the basic functions of the various parts of a PC.

Computers have become very common, useful instruments. However, they emit various amounts of potentially dangerous **electromagnetic radiation** (EMR), which is an invisible form of energy that is emitted by devices with strong electric currents. Some health experts believe that excessive exposure to EMR may cause medical conditions such as leukemia and fatigue.

Table 2 Personal Computer Parts

Part	Basic function	Description
keyboard	input	enters information into the computer
mouse	input	interacts with the computer
monitor	output	displays information in graphic form
CPU	processing	changes information entered into the computer according to instructions contained in a computer program
floppy disk	storage	stores computer programs (software) or data
floppy disk drive	input/output	transfers computer programs or data from a floppy disk to the computer memory for storage or to the CPU for processing; transfers computer programs from the computer memory or CPU to a floppy disk for storage
CD-ROM	storage	stores computer programs (software) or data
CD-ROM drive	input/output	transfers computer programs or data from a CD-ROM to the computer memory for storage or to the CPU for processing; transfers computer programs from the computer memory or CPU to a CD-ROM for storage
printer	output	prints documents produced with computer software
speakers	output	reproduces music and other sounds
microphone	input	transfers sound to the computer
modem	input/output	allows computers to communicate with each other through phone lines, network lines, or radio waves
webcam (camera)	input	attaches to a computer and captures still and moving images
joystick	input	allows a computer user to control computer game activities effectively
scanner	input	captures images of printed documents and transfers the information to the computer

A2.2 Activity MEASURING EMR

Various components of a computer system, such as the monitor, release electromagnetic radiation. In this activity, you will use an electromagnetic radiation detector to assess the release of electromagnetic radiation from computer components.

Materials
digital electromagnetic radiation detector
personal computer with monitor
metre stick or tape measure

1. Read the directions for the use of a radiation detector.

2. Design a procedure for determining the amount of radiation that is emitted from different sides of a personal computer system, and at different distances from the computer system.

(a) Create a table to record your measurements. Display your measurements in the form of graphs.

(b) Analyze your results, and draw conclusions.

(c) Write a report in which you make recommendations for the safe use of the computer you studied.

The Information Superhighway

By the early 1980s, millions of personal computers were being used by individuals and businesses all over the world. As the number of computers increased, many people wondered if computers, like telephones, could help us communicate with each other. Little did most people realize that a branch of the U.S. military, called the Advanced Research Projects Agency (ARPA), had been developing a system called the ARPAnet since 1969. The **ARPAnet** allowed distant computers to communicate with each other over dedicated transmission lines. The original ARPAnet connected four computers at American universities: the University of California at Los Angeles (UCLA), the University of California at Santa Barbara (UCSB), Stanford University, and the University of Utah. Over the years, the ARPAnet evolved into today's **Internet**: an enormous computer network that allows over 170 million computers all over the world to exchange information. The Internet, or information superhighway, is one of the most significant technological developments in history.

The ARPAnet was originally developed to allow the U.S. military to continue communicating if a nuclear bomb destroyed parts of the system. The system was used mostly by military personnel, computer experts, and university professors. It was not user friendly (users had to learn a complex computer language), and connections often failed. In 1972, Ray Tomlinson of BBN Technologies introduced e-mail to the ARPAnet, allowing written messages to be exchanged. (Tomlinson is responsible for using the @ sign to link an e-mail username to its address.) By 1974, there were 62 computers connected to the ARPAnet, and engineers, scientists, and librarians began exchanging useful information online. Over time, a number of other computer networks developed in North America, Europe, and

Asia. These networks were eventually linked to the ARPAnet. By the late 1980s, with over 100 000 computers linked to the system, it became more commonly called the Internet or the "net."

At this time, the Internet was entirely text-based and relatively difficult to operate. In 1989, however, two major developments made the Internet easier to use. Peter Deutsch of McGill University in Montreal helped to develop Archie, the Internet's first search engine. A **search engine** is a program that allows users to search for information on the Internet. In the same year, Tim Berners Lee, a Swiss computer expert, introduced hypertext and the World Wide Web to the Internet.

Hypertext is a system in which certain words or phrases in a document are electronically linked to related information (such as other words, phrases, images, or sounds) elsewhere in the same document or other documents (**Figure 15**). When a user selects hypertext using a computer keystroke or a mouse, the linked information is retrieved and displayed on the computer's monitor. Hypertext allowed Berners Lee to develop the **World Wide Web** (**WWW**); a collection of information that is generally written in a computer language called **HyperText Mark-up Language** (**HTML**). HTML documents can include text, sound, and images, and may be viewed on a computer using a type of computer program called a Web browser.

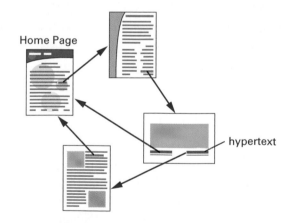

Figure 15 Hypertext (shown in blue) electronically links words, phrases, images, or sounds to other information.

A **Web browser**, such as Netscape Navigator or Microsoft Internet Explorer, allows a computer to find, retrieve, and display HTML documents that are stored in other computers connected to the Internet's WWW. A collection of HTML documents stored at a particular location, or address, in the WWW is known as a **Web site**. Today, there are over 50 million Web sites in the WWW offering information in the form of online magazines, dictionaries, and games; and services such as online banking, courses, shopping, and music transfer. Although the WWW does not include all of the information that is available on the Internet, it is the largest, most popular, and fastest growing component.

Cell Phones: Digital or Analog?

Today, many people use cell phones, which were first introduced in Japan in December 1979 and made their way to North America in 1983. There are two types of cell phones: analog and digital. The first cell phones were analog. Digital cell phones became available in the early 1990s.

Analog cell phones transmit sound in a continuous signal that must bounce off an analog tower (**Figure 16**). An analog signal is a radio wave that is produced by a voltage or current proportional to the sound. A digital signal, in comparison, uses binary code to represent the sound. The binary code is gathered by a digital tower, transmitted to the receiver, and then translated back to sound by the receiver.

Each type of signal has advantages and disadvantages. Because a digital signal needs to be decoded, there is less chance of eavesdropping and number stealing. Thus, digital cell phones are more secure than analog cell phones.

As well, the voice transmission is clearer (there is less "static," or unwanted noise), so the number of digital calls that can be relayed by a tower is hugely increased. This, in turn, improves the chance of a cell phone working when close to a tower. However, digital towers are not yet widely available, whereas analog towers are available in most populated areas in North America. Analog service costs more because analog towers can handle fewer calls than digital towers can at any given time. Sometimes the analog towers are overwhelmed by calls, so a connection fails. One solution is to build more analog towers.

So, is it better to have an analog cell phone or a digital cell phone? The current trend is toward dual-mode phones. These phones use digital mode wherever possible (for clarity and security), but switch to analog mode when digital signal towers are not accessible, for improved geographic coverage in rural areas.

In many countries, people are accustomed to paying for each phone call, whether a conventional telephone is used or not. In these countries, the transition to cell phone use has been very quick. If you have to pay per call, you may as well have a phone that you can take with you. This is particularly true in areas with high population density, where many phone towers provide excellent coverage. Even in North America, where cell phone adoption has been slower, many of us cannot imagine life without our cell phones.

(a) Give two advantages of an analog cell phone over a digital cell phone.

(b) Give two advantages of a digital cell phone over an analog cell phone.

(c) Why might cell phone companies allow analog phones to be phased out?

(d) Why are dual-mode cell phones popular?

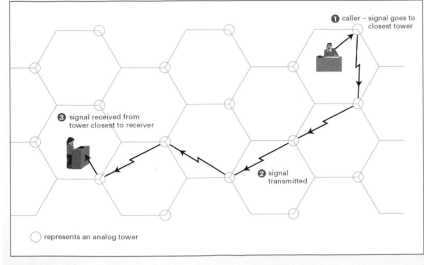

❶ caller – signal goes to closest tower

❸ signal received from tower closest to receiver

❷ signal transmitted

◯ represents an analog tower

Figure 16

A2: The World Online: Information and Communication Technology　**31**

✓ Check Your Understanding

1. Perform a cost–benefit analysis of Napster from the perspectives of a Napster user, the Napster company, and an artist or group whose files are exchanged on Napster (see **Appendix A1**).

2. **(a)** What is a microchip?
   (b) How did the invention of the microchip affect the size and portability of electronic devices?

3. **(a)** Distinguish between a conductor and a semiconductor. Provide an example of each.
   (b) What types of electronic components are composed of semiconductors?

4. **(a)** Draw a line graph to represent the information in **Table 1** (on p. 26). Put "Approximate Number of Transistors" along the *y*-axis, and "Year" along the *x*-axis.
   (b) Describe the change in the number of transistors in Intel microprocessors between 1971 and 2000.

5. What is a microprocessor, and what is it used for?

6. Describe three main differences between early computers, such as ENIAC 1, and modern PCs.

7. Why do computers require computer programs?

8. Apple Computers and Microsoft Corporation developed simultaneously over 30 years. Why did these two companies grow in step with one another?

9. **(a)** Why is the ARPAnet significant in the development of information–communication technologies?
   (b) Who were the first groups to use the ARPAnet? What did the ARPAnet allow people to do that they could not do before its invention?

10. **(a)** What is an Internet search engine?
    (b) Why is a search engine useful?

11. Complete **Table 3** by placing a checkmark in the appropriate column for each computer part. Write a brief description of the part in the last column. The first row has been completed for you.

Table 3

Part	Type of Device		Basic Function					Description
	Internal	Peripheral	Input	Output	Input/Output	Storage	Processing	
monitor		✔		✔				displays information in graphic form
printer								
modem								
CD-ROM								
CD-ROM drive								
scanner								
CPU								
mouse								
keyboard								
microphone								

Society & the Environment

Why Do Humans Communicate?

The computer has made it possible to develop many useful and affordable computer-based devices. For example, sophisticated word-processing programs and printers allow computer users to compose and print high-quality documents that in the past could only be produced by professionals using very expensive commercial equipment. Advanced graphics software allows amateurs and professionals alike to produce high-quality animations and presentations. With the development of digital cameras and photo-quality colour printers, many people are now able to take and print their own high-quality photographs. The computer has revolutionized human communication.

Information affects every aspect of our lives. It has social, cultural, economic, and political impacts. We exchange messages for many purposes. We dress according to weather forecasts, buy name-brand products we see on television, stop at a red light at an intersection, and vote in elections based on our reactions to poster campaigns and televised debates. In general, we communicate to inform, educate, persuade, entertain, or control.

We demand a large amount of high-quality information and we want to receive it quickly. We have created communication and information technologies to improve our ability to send and receive information. Computers, the Internet, telephones, and televisions allow us to communicate faster and better. While these "high-tech" electronic devices provide fast and exciting ways to communicate information, many people still find "low-tech" methods extremely useful. **Table 4** lists the purposes of communication, and some of the high-tech and low-tech devices that help us communicate.

The Impacts of Information and Communication Technology

Like all technology, information and communication technology has positive and negative impacts on people, the workplace, society, and the environment. Thanks to radios, televisions, telephones, and the Internet, we now have quick and affordable access to vast amounts of information. Satellite communication systems allow us to know what is happening on the other side of the world as it happens, and they help in the navigation of ships and airplanes. Computers have revolutionized the world of business, politics, education, and health care. Bar-code scanners at grocery store checkout counters, ATMs, library catalogues, and computerized medical imaging machines, such as CAT scanners, have had enormous benefits for society.

While information and communication technology has many positive impacts, it is also responsible for many problems. Although electronic mail (e-mail) has become a very popular method of communication, some businesses and unscrupulous pranksters use it to spread commercial and nonsense messages to thousands of unsuspecting recipients. These unwelcome broadcasts of e-mail messages, called **SPAM**, are a significant nuisance on the Internet.

Another problem is the vast amount of personal information (including medical and financial) that is stored in computer systems all over the world. Some of this information is available to a variety of individuals and institutions, including telemarketing companies that sell products over telephones and fax machines. Such practices have raised questions about

Table 4 Why People Communicate

Purpose	Technologies
information	books, newspapers, radio and television newscasts, telephones, the Internet, videos, and computer software
education	textbooks, the Internet, videos, computer software, newspapers, magazines, and television
persuasion	posters, radio and television commercials, and the Internet
entertainment	movies, MP3 players, computer software, and the Internet
control	automobile cruise control, traffic signals, railway crossing signals, smoke alarms, and computer virus protection programs

the right to privacy and have prompted governments to enact laws to protect personal information.

In January 2004, the Canadian federal government enacted the Personal Information Protection and Electronic Documents Act (PIPEDA) to ensure the protection of the personal information of Canadians. Under PIPEDA, personal information must be

- collected with consent and for a reasonable purpose
- used only for the purpose it was collected
- accurate
- accessible for inspection and correction by the person the information applies to
- stored securely

PIPEDA defines personal information as "information about an identifiable individual," including address, telephone number, gender, income, medical history, racial or ethnic origin, religious beliefs, trade union membership, credit records, loan records, and sexual preferences. Under PIPEDA, personal information does not include the name, business title, business address, or business telephone number of an employee (that is, the information on a business card).

Communication technologies are also responsible for many environmental problems. Every year, thousands of hectares of trees are cut down to make paper for newspapers, magazines, books, computer printouts, and photocopies. As well, the pulp and paper mills that produce the paper release significant quantities of pollutants into the environment (**Figure 17**).

In addition, the use of communication and information technology has been associated with a number of serious medical conditions. Some people fear that the use of headphones and loudspeakers may cause hearing loss, and that prolonged viewing of television and computer screens may cause vision problems such as blurred vision, eyestrain, and headaches. A painful condition of the hands and forearms, called carpal tunnel syndrome, has been associated with the repetitive motion of the hands while operating a computer keyboard or mouse.

Figure 17 Pulp and paper mills release significant amounts of pollution into the environment.

A2.3 Activity   ERGONOMICS: REDESIGNING THE COMPUTER KEYBOARD   >

Ergonomics is the study of the design of tools, machines, systems, tasks, jobs, and environments for productive, safe, comfortable, and effective human use. The computer keyboard is quickly becoming one of the most commonly used tools in the world. The standard English computer keyboard is called the QWERTY keyboard (**Figure 18**). This name comes from the first six characters on the top letter row of the keyboard. Christopher Sholes, the inventor of the typewriter, designed the arrangement of the characters on a QWERTY keyboard in 1868.

Figure 18   Typical QWERTY computer keyboard

According to popular myth, Sholes separated the commonly used letter combinations to prevent typists from typing too fast and jamming the keys on the mechanical typewriter (**Figure 19**).

Figure 19 A mechanical typewriter

Today, computers are used so jamming the keys is not an issue. Keyboards are now designed for speed typing. Speed typing for long periods of time, however, can lead to painful disorders of the nervous and musculoskeletal systems. These disorders are called repetitive motion injuries or repetitive strain injuries. As mentioned earlier, a common repetitive motion injury is carpal tunnel syndrome (CTS).

The carpal tunnel receives its name from the eight bones in the wrist, called the carpals, which form a tunnel-like structure. The carpal tunnel provides a pathway for nerves to reach cells in the hand. It is filled with tendons, which control finger movement. Repetitive motion of the wrist may cause a thickening of the protective coverings that surround the tendons. The swollen tendon coverings apply pressure on the nerve and produce the pain associated with CTS.

In this activity, you will determine the frequencies of the letters of the alphabet in a passage of English prose. Based on these frequencies, you will redesign the typical QWERTY keyboard to produce an arrangement of the keys that you believe will be more ergonomic (efficient and comfortable). The following basic principles of ergonomics will help you establish specific criteria for comfortable key positions:

- Fingers should travel minimal distances to reach more commonly used characters.

- Ring fingers and little fingers should be used for least commonly used characters.

- Repetitive strikes by any one finger, or the fingers of one hand, should be minimized.

- Ideally, the fingers of both hands should share the load equally.

Question

(a) What problem do you need to solve in this activity?

Prediction

(b) Observe **Figure 19** and, using the criteria for ergonomic design, predict whether or not a more ergonomic arrangement of the characters is possible.

Materials

passage of English prose, containing approximately 200 words
calculator
computer with word processor and QWERTY keyboard
sticky notes
pen

Procedure

1. Prepare a table with all the characters of the English alphabet listed in alphabetical order down the left column.

2. Count the number of times (the frequency) that each character of the alphabet appears in the passage of English prose. Use your table to record each frequency.

3. Convert the frequencies to percents by dividing each frequency by the total number of characters in the passage.

4. List the ten most common characters in the prose passage, from most frequent to least frequent.

5. Use your percents, the normal position of the hands on a computer keyboard, and the four basic principles of ergonomics to rearrange the characters on the QWERTY keyboard.

Analysis

(c) Answer the Question.

(d) Justify the arrangement of the characters in your redesigned keyboard, based on the four basic principles of ergonomics. Why would your design reduce the incidence of repetitive motion injury?

(e) Compare your keyboard design with the keyboard designs created by other students in your class. Identify similarities and differences.

(f) Conduct research to learn about the Dvorak keyboard—a keyboard that was designed to be more ergonomic than the QWERTY keyboard. Compare your keyboard design with the Dvorak keyboard. Identify similarities and differences.

 www.science.nelson.com

Evaluation

(g) Describe some of the weaknesses and limitations of the Procedure you used to design your keyboard.

Explore *an* Issue

Regulating the Use of Electronic Resources in Your School

In addition to the enormous amount of useful and legal information that is available on the Internet, there are many illegal and fraudulent materials that are easily accessible. Illegal pornographic sites are available, and the Napster experience illustrates the uncertain legal status of some popular Internet services. The Internet also provides resources that, while legal, may promote dishonesty or fraud. For example, there are Web sites that give away or sell prepared assignments, essays, and other academic materials. Most of these Web sites provide prepared papers, but some will write papers according to student specifications.

Imagine that you and the other members of your group belong to your school's Electronic Resources Policy Committee. You have been asked to review the school's plagiarism policy and determine if it needs to be updated. The committee includes the vice-principal of your school, the librarian, and the student council president. Assign a role to each member of your group, and complete the following tasks.

1. Conduct Internet research to determine the nature and availability of academic materials on the Internet.

 www.science.nelson.com

Decision-Making Skills

- ● Define the Issue
- ● Research
- ● Defend a Decision
- ● Identify Alternatives
- ● Analyze the Issue
- ○ Evaluate

2. Conduct a survey of students in your school to determine
   - if they are aware that prepared academic materials are available on the Internet
   - if they have obtained and made use of prepared academic materials from Web sites
   - if they think that using prepared materials from these Web sites is plagiarism

3. Review your school's current policy on plagiarism, including Internet plagiarism.

4. Review the plagiarism policy of at least one other school.

5. Determine whether your school's plagiarism policy needs updating.

6. Write a report to your principal outlining your group's findings and describing a course of action. In your report, include possible changes to the school's existing policies on plagiarism. Also include a list of strategies that the school could use to help students avoid Internet-based plagiarism.

SUMMARY

- A microchip, or IC chip, is at the heart of almost every modern electronic communication and information-processing system.
- An IC chip is a thin wafer of silicon that contains thousands of tiny interconnected electric circuits. These circuits work together to receive, process, and send information.
- Components such as diodes, resistors, capacitors, and transistors are used to control the strength and direction of electric current in electronic circuitry.
- Integrated circuits are made of semiconductors, such as silicon and germanium.
- Semiconductors are intermediate conductors of electricity. Their ability to conduct electricity depends on environmental conditions such as temperature. Semiconductors can be used to control the flow of electricity in a circuit.
- A computer's microprocessor, also known as a CPU or computer chip, is an integrated circuit that contains all the components needed to perform the computer's calculations.
- Computer hardware includes the physical components of the computer, such as the CPU, memory chips, keyboard, and display monitor. Computer software refers to computer programs stored on floppy disks, CD-ROMs, or the hard drive.

- EMR that is emitted by electronic devices may cause medical conditions such as leukemia and fatigue.
- In 1969, the U.S. military developed the ARPAnet, which allowed distant computers to communicate with each other over dedicated transmission lines. This was the beginning of the Internet.
- People communicate to inform, educate, persuade, entertain, or control.

Key Terms

information and communication technology	electromagnetic radiation (EMR)
microchip	ARPAnet
integrated circuit (IC) chip	Internet
semiconductor	search engine
microprocessor	hypertext
personal computer (PC)	World Wide Web (WWW)
computer hardware	Hypertext Markup Language (HTML)
internal device	Web browser
peripheral device	Web site
computer program	SPAM
computer software	

ASSESSMENT

Understanding Concepts

1. **(a)** Describe five different ways that you use information and communication technology in everyday life.
   (b) Which technology described in **(a)** do you consider to be the most valuable? Why?

2. **(a)** Why is the current period of time being called the Information Age? Why is it also being called the Computer Age?
   (b) Suggest another name for this period.

3. **(a)** How did the widespread use of semiconductors affect the use of vacuum tubes in electronic circuits?

   (b) What effect did the change in **(a)** have on the design of electronic devices, such as computers?

4. **(a)** Why are semiconductors useful in the construction of microchips?
   (b) Name the semiconductor that is most commonly used in microchips.

5. **(a)** Why is the microprocessor sometimes called the "brains" of a computer?
   (b) What has happened to the "brains" of a computer over time?

6. **(a)** Describe four major developments in chronological order that led to the invention of the Internet.

(b) Figures **20** and **21** illustrate two components of the World Wide Web. Identify each component and describe its major function.

Figure 20

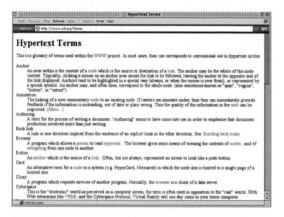

Figure 21

7. (a) Identify the purpose of each communication situation (to entertain, to inform, to persuade, to educate, or to control).

  (i) You see a street sign indicating that there is a student crosswalk ahead.

  (ii) You hear an ambulance siren in the distance.

  (iii) You receive a pamphlet that describes the causes of AIDS.

  (iv) You watch a video about building your own canoe.

  (v) You watch a television commercial describing a new broom that picks up dust like a magnet.

  (vi) You play a game on the Internet.

  (b) Compare your answers with those of a classmate and evaluate similarities and differences.

Applying Inquiry Skills

8. Modern electronics have given us many interesting and useful devices including computers, cell phones, video cameras, CD-ROMs, CD-ROM players, and MP3 players. All of these devices have special features that accomplish specific actions. For example, a computer word processor allows the user to "cut and paste" text and images from one location to another. A video camera allows the user to place words, dates, and times directly on the images. An MP3 player allows the user to select a particular song.

  (a) Choose an electronic device and describe a feature of the device that you find particularly convenient.

  (b) Why is the feature you chose in **(a)** so convenient for you?

  (c) Evaluate the design and function of the device by listing other convenient features and some inconvenient features.

Making Connections

9. (a) Describe two ways in which the Internet has benefited people, and two ways in which it has caused problems.

  (b) Provide a suggestion for solving each problem you identified in **(a)**.

10. The term "SPAM" is used to describe repeat junk e-mail. Conduct research to find out where this term came from.

GO www.science.nelson.com

11. Choose a technological device that has undergone major changes, such as a computer, cell phone, or portable music player. Compare and contrast an early model with a current model using criteria such as cost, environmental impact, and appearance.

12. If you were unable to leave your home for one week, what everyday tasks could the Internet help you complete? Which of these tasks would you not be able to complete without the Internet?

On the Move: TRANSPORTATION TECHNOLOGY

People have invented many different ways of moving people and goods, including elevators, escalators, automobiles, trains, boats, airplanes, submarines, and space shuttles. **Transportation technology** includes the knowledge, processes, tools, and skills that are used to move people and goods from place to place. Transportation technology has facilitated the development of cities, economies, sports and recreation, space exploration, and the military.

(a) What is your favourite mode of transportation? Why?

(b) Which mode(s) of transportation do you consider indispensable? Why?

The motor vehicle is probably the most important mode of transportation ever developed. Cars, motorcycles, and buses move people from place to place, and trucks, vans, and tractor-trailers deliver goods and services (**Figure 1**).

Figure 1 Cars move people and trucks move goods on a busy highway.

(c) Do you believe that the motor vehicle is the most important mode of transportation ever developed? If so, why? If not, why not?

In North America, the motor vehicle has become an integral part of everyday life. It has greatly increased personal freedom, convenience, and mobility. Until Henry Ford mass-produced the Model T in 1908,

however, cars were recreational vehicles that only the rich and famous could afford.

By developing the first moving assembly line, Ford was able to realize his dream of producing "a car for every family at a price they can afford." Today, there are approximately 600 million motor vehicles in the world, and about 75% are personal vehicles. According to estimates, there will be over one billion vehicles within the next 20 years. Traffic jams on city roads are becoming a daily occurrence, motor vehicle accidents now account for over 300 000 deaths worldwide per year, and pollution caused by motor-vehicle exhaust (**Figure 2**) threatens the welfare of natural and built environments. Should there be better alternatives to personal vehicles, such as high-speed trains, in Canada? Why can we not simply build more freeways and expand existing ones to accommodate the growing number of automobiles on the road?

Figure 2 Motor-vehicle exhaust is a major source of air pollution.

(d) Describe two additional environmental problems that are caused by motor vehicles.

(e) Some European cities ban motor vehicles from city centres on European Car Free Day. Describe some advantages and disadvantages of restricting car and truck traffic from city centres during business hours.

DID **YOU** KNOW?

Dangerous Driving
Over 17 million people have been killed worldwide in motor vehicle accidents since 1910.

A Close Look at the Engine

Modern vehicular transportation would not be possible without the use of a powerful engine such as the **internal combustion engine (ICE)** shown in **Figure 3**. The ICE converts the chemical energy of non-renewable fossil fuels into mechanical forces that make a vehicle move. The ICE is presently the driving force behind the entire North American transportation system. Internal combustion engines are dependable, powerful, affordable, and convenient, and they may be very difficult to replace.

Figure 3   A typical internal combustion engine

The Internal Combustion Engine

An internal combustion engine produces mechanical energy by burning (combusting) a fuel (usually a fossil fuel such as gasoline or diesel) in a combustion chamber. Two of the most common types of internal combustion engines are the Otto-cycle engine and the diesel engine. The Otto-cycle engine is named after Nikolaus Otto, the German engineer who invented it in 1876. This engine is the familiar gasoline-powered engine that is used in most of today's cars. The diesel engine is named after another German engineer, Rudolf Diesel, who invented it in 1892. The diesel engine uses less costly diesel fuel, and is generally used in electricity-generating power plants, large trucks, buses, locomotives, and some cars.

DID **YOU** KNOW?

A Primitive Motorcycle
Gotfried Daimler, an employee of Nikolaus Otto, invented the motorcycle in 1885 by attaching a small Otto-cycle engine to a wooden bicycle.

Basic Components of ICEs

Otto-cycle and diesel engines have the same basic parts (**Figure 4**). The heart of both engines is the combustion chamber, which consists of a cylinder that is closed at one end and a close-fitting piston that slides into the cylinder. As the piston moves, the volume of the space between the head of the piston and the closed end of the cylinder changes. One end of the piston is connected to a crankshaft by a connecting rod. The in-and-out motion of the piston turns the crankshaft, which eventually causes the vehicle's wheels to turn. Engines may have from 1 to 28 cylinders, but most car and truck engines have 4, 6, or 8 cylinders.

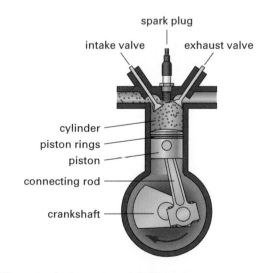

Figure 4   An internal combustion engine

The fuel supply system of a modern internal combustion engine consists of a fuel storage tank, a fuel pump, and an electronic fuel injection system that delivers the proper mix of air and fuel to the cylinder when required. In addition, the ICE has a mechanism for igniting the fuel–air mixture that enters the cylinder.

There are a few differences between an Otto-cycle engine and a diesel engine. In an Otto-cycle engine, an electric spark from a spark plug ignites the fuel–air mixture (**Figure 5(a)**). A diesel engine does not have spark plugs; instead, heat that is generated by compressing the fuel–air mixture ignites the mixture (**Figure 5(b)**). Another difference between the two engines is the type of fuel used. While both engines use a complex mixture of hydrocarbons as fuel, diesel fuel contains larger hydrocarbon molecules than gasoline. Diesel fuel is therefore denser and more "oily," and it boils at a higher temperature than gasoline.

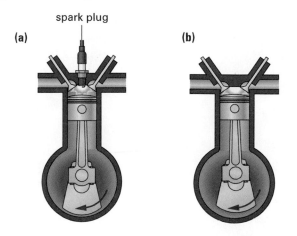

Figure 5 **(a)** The spark from a spark plug ignites the gasoline–air mixture in the cylinder of an Otto-cycle engine. **(b)** High pressure ignites the diesel–air mixture in a diesel engine.

The Basic Operation of an Otto-Cycle Engine

Each motion of the piston in an engine is called a **stroke**. Almost all modern North American cars have a four-stroke Otto-cycle engine (**Figure 6**). The four strokes are

1. the intake stroke
2. the compression stroke
3. the combustion stroke (also called the power stroke)
4. the exhaust stroke

Motor-Vehicle Pollution

Enormous quantities of carbon dioxide are produced by the operation of internal combustion engines around the world. The carbon dioxide gas adds to the global warming caused by the greenhouse effect. As well, high concentrations of carbon monoxide, solid carbon (soot), and toxic hydrocarbons harm humans and other organisms in the environment.

In addition to hydrocarbons, the combustion of gasoline or diesel fuel also produces sulfur-containing compounds. During combustion, sulfur reacts with oxygen to form sulfur dioxide, $SO_{2(g)}$, which is released into the environment in the engine exhaust fumes. Eventually, sulfur dioxide reacts with water in the environment to produce sulfuric acid, $H_2SO_{4(aq)}$, which is a major cause of acid precipitation such as acid rain and acid snow. In addition to sulfur dioxide, the combustion process also produces nitrogen

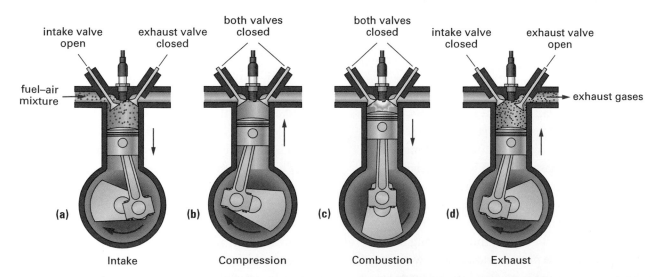

Figure 6 **(a)** On the intake stroke, the piston moves downward, reducing the pressure in the cylinder. The intake valve opens, allowing fuel and air to enter the cylinder. **(b)** On the compression stroke, both valves are closed and the piston moves upward, compressing the fuel–air mixture. **(c)** On the power stroke, an electric spark is created in the spark plug. The fuel–air mixture explodes, forcing the piston downward. **(d)** During the exhaust stroke, the exhaust valve opens and the piston rises, pushing the exhaust gases out of the cylinder.

monoxide, $NO_{(g)}$, and nitrogen dioxide, $NO_{2(g)}$ by the reaction of nitrogen, $N_{2(g)}$, and oxygen, $O_{2(g)}$. Nitrogen is a major component of air (air contains approximately 21% oxygen gas, 78% nitrogen gas and 1% other gases). The nitrogen oxides react with water in the environment to produce nitric acid, $HNO_{3(aq)}$, which is another major cause of acid precipitation.

The Catalytic Converter

To reduce pollution, all motor vehicles that are produced in or imported to Canada must be equipped with a device called a catalytic converter. A **catalytic converter** (**Figure 7**) is attached to a vehicle's exhaust system. It contains special metals, such as platinum and palladium, which are called catalysts. **Catalysts** aid in the conversion of waste products (such as carbon monoxide and nitrogen oxides) into less polluting substances (such as carbon dioxide, oxygen, and nitrogen).

Figure 7   Catalytic converters help reduce air pollution.

Engines and Vehicles

Larger, more powerful internal combustion engines are needed to move larger and heavier vehicles. This is primarily due to increased inertia and increased friction. **Inertia** is an object's resistance to a change in motion caused by mass. **Friction** is a force that acts in the direction opposite to the motion of a vehicle and its moving parts. Friction is caused by contact between the vehicle's wheels and the road or track, between the vehicle's body and the air it moves through, and between parts such as pistons and cylinder walls, gears, and bearings. Reducing inertia and friction reduces the size of engine that a vehicle requires, the quantity of fuel that the engine uses, and the quantity of pollutants that are released into the atmosphere.

Reducing Inertia

Vehicles with smaller masses require smaller engines. Therefore, they are more fuel-efficient, less costly to operate, and less polluting. Mass can be reduced by building a smaller vehicle or by using more lightweight materials. In general, cars and trucks are much smaller today than they were in the past and contain a greater proportion of lighter materials (such as aluminum and plastics (**Figure 8**)) instead of steel.

Figure 8   Most of an automobile's interior is made of lightweight plastic.

Reducing Friction

Friction can be reduced by decreasing the amount of surface area contact between the moving parts of a vehicle and by lubricating the moving parts with motor oil. Friction between the wheels and the road or track can only be reduced to a limited extent because this type of friction helps the vehicle grip the road and maintain control. Friction between the vehicle's body and the surrounding air can be reduced by shaping the vehicle's body in a way that reduces **aerodynamic drag**: the friction that is produced when a body moves through air.

Engineers use **aerodynamics** (the science that deals with the interaction of air and moving bodies) to design streamlined vehicles, as shown in **Figure 9**.

These vehicles are more aerodynamically efficient because air can glide more smoothly over, under, and around the vehicle's body. Much progress has been made in reducing aerodynamic drag in cars, trucks, and trains. Aerodynamic vehicles are quieter and more

Figure 9 **(a)** The streamlined shape of this car reduces aerodynamic drag. **(b)** Nose cones on the front of tractor-trailers reduce aerodynamic drag and increase fuel efficiency.

fuel efficient, and they are safer and easier to handle. For example, aerodynamic design can make vehicles more stable when hit by crosswinds.

Maglev Train Technology

The principles of aerodynamics and friction reduction are used in the design of maglev train systems. **Maglev trains** are *mag*netically *lev*itated trains (**Figure 10**). This means that the trains are suspended

Figure 10 This Japanese maglev train system can reach a speed of 411 km/h. Current diesel-powered trains in Ontario allow you to travel from Toronto to Ottawa in just under 4 h. A maglev train system would allow you to travel the same distance in only 1 h!

in air as they move along modified rails called guideways. Maglev trains work on the law of magnetism. This law states that like poles of a magnet repel and unlike poles of a magnet attract (**Figure 11**).

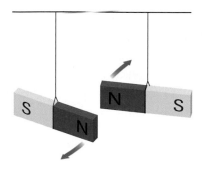

Figure 11 A magnet possesses a north pole and a south pole. Opposite poles attract (north pole/south pole), and like poles repel (north pole/north pole and south pole/south pole).

A maglev train is able to levitate because strong electromagnets on the sides and/or bottom of the guideway exert forces on magnets located on the sides and/or bottom of the train's cars. There are basically two designs for maglev systems:

1. electromagnetic suspension (EMS), which is presently used in Transrapid systems in Germany and China
2. electrodynamic suspension (EDS), which is presently used in Japan's MLX01 system

In the German-designed Transrapid system (**Figure 12**), the guideway is the track on which the train runs. The electromagnet on the undercarriage of the train faces the guideway and creates a magnetic force that levitates (raises) the train approximately 1 cm above the guideway. Therefore, the train remains

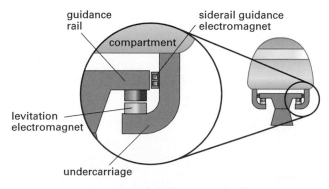

Figure 12 The Transrapid maglev train uses undercarriage levitation magnets to raise the train above the ground and siderail magnets to give horizontal stabilization and allow safe acceleration and deceleration

aloft even when it is at rest. Other guidance magnets on the side rails ensure stability as the train moves.

Unlike the German Transrapid maglev system, the Japanese MLX01 system does not use undercarriage levitating magnets. Instead, it uses the principle of electromagnetic induction to levitate the train and move it forward. Electromagnetic induction refers to the process of generating an electric current (and therefore a magnetic field) in a conductor (such as a coil of metal wire) by allowing a magnet to pass near or through the conductor (**Figure 13**).

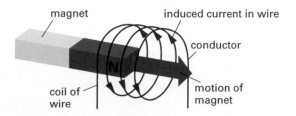

Figure 13 When a magnet passes by a conductor such as a coil of metal wire, an electric current and a magnetic field are induced in the wire.

An electrodynamic suspension system has a series of coils (each shaped like the number 8) attached to each siderail and strong superconducting magnets attached to each side of the train (**Figure 14**). When the train moves, the superconducting magnets on the train induce a current and a magnetic field in the coils on the siderails. The magnetic field keeps the train moving and levitated. For the levitation system to work, the superconducting magnets on the sides of the train must pass just below the centres of the coils on the siderails. This arrangement creates an upward force on the train's superconducting magnets, which levitates the train.

Since the coils on the siderails generate magnetism only when the superconducting magnets on the train are moving, the train cannot be levitated when it is at rest. Therefore, this type of maglev train begins its journey on wheels, using an electric motor for energy. Eventually, as the train picks up speed, the magnetic forces levitate the train and the wheels retract into undercarriage compartments like those on an airplane. The motor is then turned off and the magnetic forces between the siderails and onboard magnets move the train forward. Changing the strength and polarity of the electromagnets on the siderails can either speed up the train or slow it down (**Figure 15**).

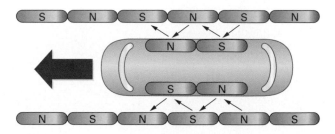

Figure 15 A wave of electric current sweeping down the figure-8-coils on the siderails generates the forces that propel the maglev train forward.

An almost frictionless riding surface and aerodynamic design allow some maglev trains to reach speeds over 500 km/h. These trains move swiftly and quietly along their guideways using relatively little energy. Because maglev trains do not have internal combustion engines, they create no polluting exhaust fumes like conventional diesel-powered and gasoline-powered trains do. Nevertheless, maglev systems require a source of current electricity to produce the magenetic field that propels a train. Fully functional maglev systems are presently operating in Germany, Japan, and China. Plans for building a maglev system in the United States are presently being developed.

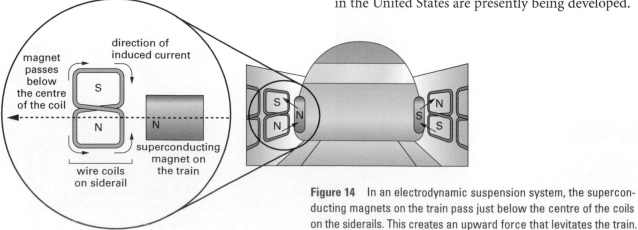

Figure 14 In an electrodynamic suspension system, the superconducting magnets on the train pass just below the centre of the coils on the siderails. This creates an upward force that levitates the train.

The development of efficient mass transit systems may help to solve many of today's transportation problems. However, most conventional trains and buses use inefficient wheel and road (or wheel and rail) technologies. As well, they are powered by internal combustion engines, which cause pollution. Train systems that apply the principles of magnetism (maglev systems) avoid the friction associated with wheel-based vehicles and do not require ICEs for power. The magnetic energy that maglev trains "float" on is created by the attractive and repulsive forces between magnets.

In this activity, your group will use the problem-solving process outlined in **Appendix A3** to design, build, test, and evaluate a model maglev train system.

Materials

Guideway
magnetic strips (self-adhesive)
6-mm thick hardboard, stiff cardboard, or foamcore (as base)
angled aluminum or angled plastic strips

Base of vehicle
4-mm thick hardboard, stiff cardboard, or foamcore
circular magnets (self-adhesive)

Body of vehicle
pliable cardboard
cardboard tubes
Styrofoam
paper
masking tape or duct tape

Other materials
stopwatch
metre stick
glue gun
glue sticks
markers
paints
coins (pennies or dimes)
other materials according to design

Procedure

Part 1: Guideway Construction

1. Construct a 60-cm guideway based on **Figure 16**.

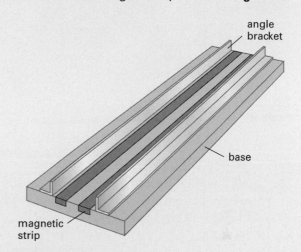

Figure 16   Model maglev guideway

Part 2: Vehicle Construction

2. Use aerodynamic principles to design a maglev vehicle that is approximately 4.5 cm wide and 6 cm to 9 cm long (**Figure 17**). The vehicle should fit between the siderails of the guideway, with a few millimetres of space between the vehicle and the siderails. Ensure that the base of the vehicle is flat.

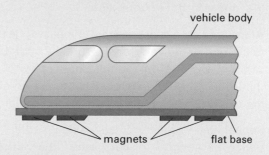

Figure 17   Model maglev vehicle

3. Construct your vehicle.

4. Attach magnets to the base of the vehicle so that the vehicle magnetically levitates and moves freely when placed in an inclined guideway. Begin by using as few magnets as possible on the underside of the vehicle to obtain stable levitation. **Figure 18** shows one example of a model maglev system.

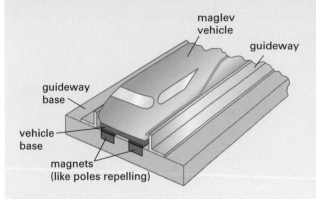

Figure 18 Model maglev system

Part 3: System Efficiency Test

5. Create a table to record values for distance travelled (*d*), time elapsed (*t*), average speed (*v*), number of passengers, and number of magnets.

6. Using a metre stick, measure the length of the guideway and the length of the vehicle. Calculate the distance that the vehicle travels (*d*). Record this distance in your table.

7. Incline the guideway so that the vehicle travels the entire length in 4 s to 5 s. Use the stopwatch to precisely measure the time (*t*) the vehicle takes to travel the full length of the guideway. Record this time in your table.

8. Calculate the average speed of the vehicle (*v*), and record it in your table.

9. Attach one coin representing one passenger to the roof of the vehicle. Measure the time the vehicle takes to travel the full length of the guideway. Calculate the average speed (*v*) of the vehicle. Record this speed in your table.

10. Repeat step 9 several times, using an additional "passenger" for each trial. If the vehicle loses levitation due to increased mass, add more magnets to the base. Add only as many magnets as required to keep the vehicle running smoothly down the guideway. Record these values in your table. Make sure that the total distance travelled by the train remains the same for each trial. Calculate the average speed (*v*) of the vehicle for each trial.

Analysis

(a) What scientific principles, if any, are operating in your model maglev system?

(b) In what significant ways does your model maglev system differ from a real maglev system? Is your system more like an electromagnetic suspension system or an electrodynamic suspension system? Explain.

(c) You can estimate the efficiency (eff) of your model maglev system by relating the following efficiency factors: vehicle speed (*v*), number of passengers, and number of magnets used to carry the passengers. The efficiency is directly proportional to the speed and to the number of passengers per trip. The efficiency is inversely proportional to the number of magnets, because increasing the number of magnets increases the cost to the system. You can relate these three efficiency factors to the overall efficiency of the system by using the following equation:

$$\text{eff} = \frac{v \times \text{number of passengers}}{\text{number of magnets}} \times 100\%$$

Use this efficiency equation to calculate the efficiency of your maglev vehicle for different values of each factor. Determine the most efficient combination of factors.

(d) What assumptions are made when assessing the efficiency of your model maglev system using the efficiency equation?

(e) Describe two other factors that also affect the efficiency of your model maglev system.

Evaluation

(f) Compare your best value for the efficiency calculation with the best values of other groups. Evaluate the efficiency of your model maglev system.

(g) What changes could you make to your model maglev system to increase its efficiency?

Combustion Reactions and the Environment

The combustion (oxidation) reactions that occur in the cylinders of Otto-cycle and diesel engines can be represented by the following equations for the combustion of octane, $C_8H_{18(l)}$, a major component of gasoline:

complete combustion:

$$2\ C_8H_{18(l)} + 25\ O_{2(g)} \rightarrow 16\ CO_{2(g)} + 18\ H_2O_{(g)}$$

incomplete combustion:

$$2\ C_8H_{18(l)} + 17\ O_{2(g)} \rightarrow 16\ CO_{(g)} + 18\ H_2O_{(g)}$$

incomplete combustion:

$$2\ C_8H_{18(l)} + 9\ O_{2(g)} \rightarrow 16\ C_{(s)} + 18\ H_2O_{(g)}$$

Notice that the complete combustion reaction produces carbon dioxide, $CO_{2(g)}$, and water vapour as the only products. The two incomplete combustion reactions produce poisonous carbon monoxide gas, $CO_{(g)}$, solid carbon, $C_{(s)}$, and water vapour as products. Also notice that complete combustion occurs when the oxygen to fuel ratio is relatively high (2 molecules C_8H_{18}: 25 molecules O_2) and incomplete combustion occurs when the ratio is lower (2 molecules C_8H_{18}: 17 molecules O_2 in the carbon monoxide-producing reaction, and 2 molecules C_8H_{18}: 9 molecules O_2 in the carbon-producing reaction). These ratios are shown in **Figure 19**.

All three reactions occur during the combustion process. The incomplete combustion reactions occur more frequently, however, in poorly tuned cars because the fuel–air mixture being delivered to the cylinder is less than ideal. Nevertheless, all the products of combustion, except for water, are polluting when released into the environment in large quantities.

The Race to Replace the ICE

The search for a suitable alternative to the internal combustion engine has been a major preoccupation of scientists, engineers, and the general public for a long time. In fact, the development of a pollution-free engine that uses a renewable source of energy was predicted by Jules Verne in 1870. Verne claimed that "Water will one day be employed as a fuel." Little did he know that about 30 years earlier, in 1839, British physicist Sir William Grove had already built a device called a **fuel cell** that could produce electric energy by a reaction between hydrogen gas and oxygen gas (**Figure 20**) with water as the only waste product.

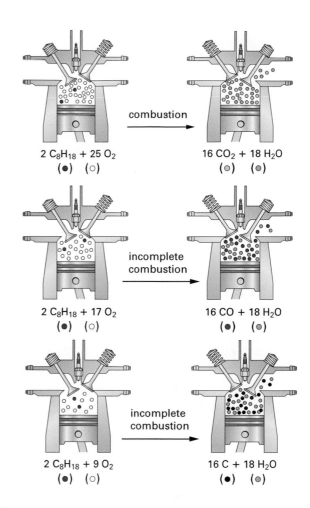

Figure 19 Complete combustion requires a higher oxygen to fuel ratio than incomplete combustion.

Figure 20 A typical automotive fuel cell

The Invention of the Fuel Cell

In 1800, two British scientists, Anthony Carlisle and William Nicholson, discovered electrolysis (**Figure 21**). **Electrolysis** is the process of using electrical energy to split water molecules into hydrogen molecules and oxygen molecules:

$$2\ H_2O_{(l)} + \text{electrical energy} \rightarrow 2\ H_{2(g)} + O_{2(g)}$$

A3.2 Activity | BURNING DIRTY VERSUS BURNING CLEAN

In this activity, you will test a Bunsen burner flame for complete and incomplete combustion. Most school science labs use natural gas as a fuel for Bunsen burners. Natural gas contains mainly methane gas, $CH_{4(g)}$. Some school labs use propane, $C_3H_{8(g)}$. Both methane and propane are fossil fuels. Your teacher will identify the fuel that is used in your lab.

Materials
Bunsen burner
Bunsen burner igniter
gas supply
2 glass microscope slides
tongs

1. Light the Bunsen burner. Adjust the nozzle until a strong blue flame is produced.

2. Using tongs, hold a glass microscope slide approximately 6 cm above the flame. Remove the slide after a few seconds. Describe the appearance of the glass slide.

 Be careful when using a Bunsen burner and handling a hot apparatus. Use tongs to transfer the hot slide. See **Appendix B2** for more information.

3. Cover half of the holes in the Bunsen burner base with your fingers. While doing this, use tongs to hold a clean microscope slide approximately 6 cm above the Bunsen burner flame. Remove the slide after a few seconds. Describe the appearance of the glass slide.

(a) If a material formed on the slide in step 3, what is the material likely to be? Why was it produced?

(b) Describe the combustion reactions in steps 2 and 3 as complete combustion or incomplete combustion.

(c) Which type of combustion reaction is most suitable for everyday use in vehicle engines? Why?

Figure 21 In electrolysis, electricity decomposes water into hydrogen gas and oxygen gas.

Knowing about electrolysis, William Grove reasoned that it should be possible to reverse the electrolysis reaction and generate electrical energy from the reaction of oxygen and hydrogen. This reaction, called **reverse electrolysis**, can be written as follows:

$$2 H_{2(g)} + O_{2(g)} \rightarrow 2 H_2O_{(l)} + \text{electrical energy}$$

To test his prediction, Grove enclosed two strips of platinum in separate sealed bottles. One bottle contained hydrogen gas, and the other bottle contained oxygen gas. When the gas bottles were immersed in dilute sulfuric acid, an electric current began to flow between the two electrodes and water formed in the bottles. Reverse electrolysis had been achieved.

To increase the electrical energy produced, Grove linked several of these devices (each called a "cell") in series and created what he called a "gas battery" (**Figure 22**).

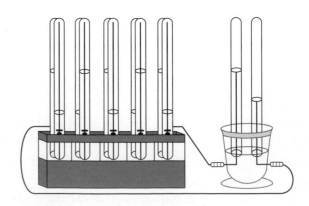

Figure 22 William Grove's gas battery

Grove used the name "gas battery" because, like a conventional battery, his device converted the chemical energy of the reactants (hydrogen gas and oxygen gas) directly into electrical energy. Unlike a conventional battery that eventually runs out of chemical energy and "dies," however, Grove's gas battery continued to produce electrical energy as long as hydrogen gas and oxygen gas were supplied. With further experimentation, other chemists discovered that different substances, or fuels, could be used to make gas batteries. Soon chemists started using the term "fuel cell" to describe each cell in a gas battery. Since Grove's device used hydrogen as a fuel, it became known as a hydrogen fuel cell. **Figure 23** illustrates the basic operation of a hydrogen fuel cell.

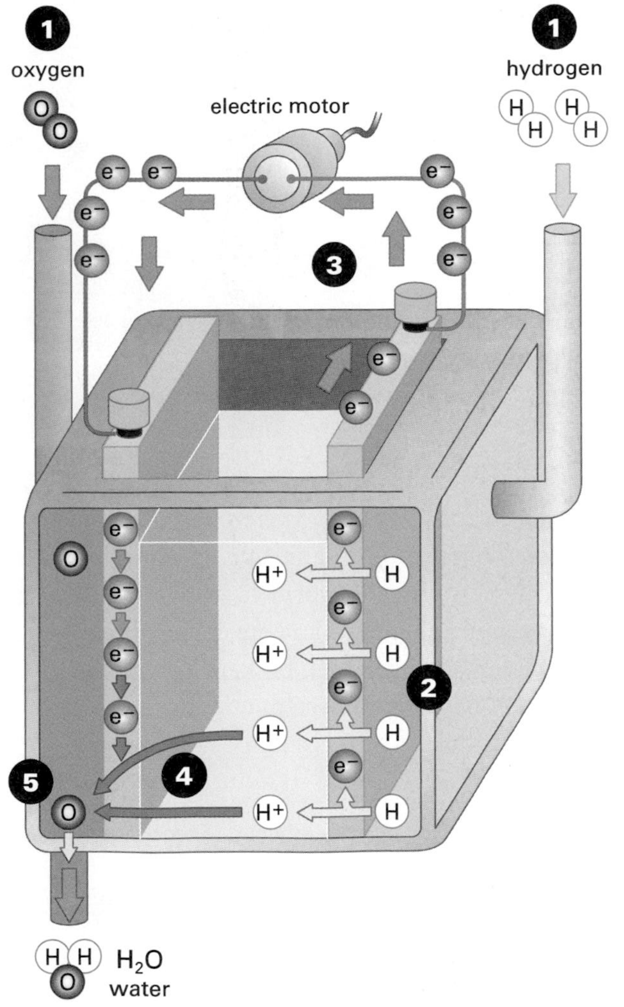

Figure 23 1. Hydrogen and oxygen enter the fuel cell.
2. Hydrogen atoms are separated into protons, H^+, and electrons.
3. The electrons move through the external conductor, providing electric current to power external electrical devices.
4. The protons move through the electrolyte to the other side.
5. The protons combine with electrons and oxygen to form water.

Although the fuel cell is not the water-powered engine envisioned by Verne, it has no moving parts, uses lightweight hydrogen gas and oxygen gas as fuels, and produces clean water as the only waste product. Unfortunately, scientists lost interest in the fuel cell after the discovery of large deposits of fossil fuels near the end of the 19th century and the resulting development of the internal combustion engine. As well, scientists soon realized that while oxygen is relatively safe and readily available (in air), hydrogen gas is rare and difficult to produce. Hydrogen is also potentially explosive, as witnessed in the *Hindenberg* disaster (**Figure 24**).

Figure 24 In 1937, the airship *Hindenberg* exploded when a spark ignited the hydrogen gas that kept it afloat.

It was not until the 1960s that NASA rediscovered fuel cells, developed them into a safe source of electrical energy, and used them to generate both power and water (for drinking and cooling) in their Gemini and Apollo space missions. Since then, fuel cells have undergone much research and development and, along with a few other innovative technologies, have become real contenders in the race to replace the internal combustion engine.

The Future of Fuel Cell Technology

The fuel cell has come a long way since William Grove invented the gas battery. Today, two Canadian companies, Ballard Power Systems of Vancouver, British Columbia and Stuart Energy Systems of Mississauga, Ontario, are at the forefront of fuel cell research and development. These two companies believe that the hydrogen fuel cell can make a significant contribution in the search to replace internal combustion engines in cars, buses, trucks, and other vehicles. Ballard is building fuel cells for automotive and power generation applications, and Stuart Energy wants to build the necessary hydrogen fueling stations. Since 1993, Ballard has demonstrated 110 vehicles, including 45 transit buses, and Stuart Energy has installed nine hydrogen fuelling stations in North America.

The fuel cell is becoming increasingly popular as an alternative to the internal combustion engine. In 1993, Ballard amazed politicians, business people, and the media when it displayed the world's first fuel cell-powered bus in Vancouver, British Columbia. Since then, many fuel cell-powered vehicles have been demonstrated and hydrogen fuelling stations have been built around the world. (**Figure 25**).

Figure 25   This zero-emission bus is powered by a Ballard fuel cell engine. Three such buses will be in service in Santa Clara, California, beginning in 2004, in a project aimed at reducing air and noise pollution. Between 2003 and 2006, 39 additional buses will operate in 13 cities in the United States, Europe, Australia, and China.

Today, Ballard supplies six of the top ten automakers with fuel cells, including DaimlerChrysler and Ford who are part owners of Ballard. By mid-2004, there will be approximately 75 vehicles on the road powered by Ballard fuel cells. This includes 30 hydrogen fuel cell buses in ten European cities, as part of the European Fuel Cell Bus Project, and four Ford Focus FCVs (Fuel Cell Vehicles) in Vancouver, British Columbia as part of the Vancouver Fuel Cell Vehicle Project.

Despite hydrogen's promise as a clean-burning fuel, environmentalists have concerns about the processes that are used to produce hydrogen. Although hydrogen is the most abundant element in the universe, most of the hydrogen on Earth's surface is locked up in molecules such as water, H_2O, natural gas, CH_4, and gasoline, C_8H_{18}. Thus, to use

hydrogen for fuel it must be separated from other elements. Almost all commercially produced hydrogen is extracted by applying heat and steam to natural gas and gasoline. This process, called steam reforming, also releases the greenhouse gas carbon dioxide, CO_2, as a waste product.

Hybrid Vehicles

In the search to replace the internal combustion engine, some automobile companies have produced hybrid cars as a compromise. A **hybrid vehicle** is a vehicle that combines two or more sources of power. Hybrid vehicles are not new. Mopeds (motorized peddle bikes) are hybrid vehicles because they can be powered by a gasoline motor and peddles (**Figure 26**). Many train locomotives are diesel–electric hybrid vehicles.

Figure 26   A small gasoline motor is attached to the front of this moped. The peddles are used to start the moped's motion, as well as to "help" the motor for initial acceleration or on steep inclines.

More recently, car manufacturers have developed hybrid cars that are powered by rechargeable batteries, electric motors, and small gasoline engines (**Figure 27**). In general, hybrid cars have smaller, lighter gasoline engines than conventional cars and therefore consume less fuel. Electric hybrid cars use less fuel because the system converts to electric power when the car stands still. Because hybrid cars use less fuel, they help to reduce air pollution.

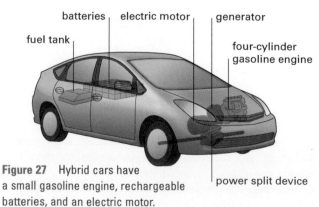

batteries   electric motor   generator

fuel tank

four-cylinder gasoline engine

power split device

Figure 27   Hybrid cars have a small gasoline engine, rechargeable batteries, and an electric motor.

1. (a) List four modes of transportation. For each mode, describe the primary source of energy, the primary purpose, a major benefit, and a major risk.
    (b) Select the mode that you think is the most beneficial to society. Provide at least three reasons for your selection.

2. How did Henry Ford manage to produce large numbers of affordable vehicles?

3. Why is the combustion stroke in an internal combustion engine also called the power stroke?

4. (a) List all the reactants and products in the complete combustion of octane.
    (b) List the names and chemical formulas of the compounds you would expect to detect in the exhaust gases of a typical car engine. Assume that all three combustion reactions occur.
    (c) What engine conditions increase the amount of incomplete combustion products that are produced in a car engine?

5. Why are internal combustion engines partially responsible for the production of sulfuric acid in the environment?

6. (a) What do catalytic converters do?
    (b) In which system of a car is the catalytic converter located? Why is it located there?

7. (a) Define inertia.
    (b) Describe two design features of an automobile that affect its inertia. How can these features be changed to reduce inertia?

8. (a) Describe the scientific principle that is responsible for the basic function of a maglev vehicle.
    (b) What is the primary source of energy for a maglev vehicle?
    (c) Why do some maglev trains have wheels?

(d) Does **Figure 28** illustrate the structure of an EMS maglev train or an EDS maglev train? Explain.

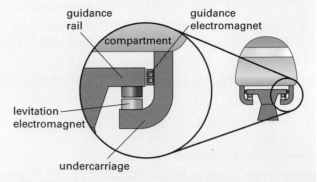

Figure 28

9. (a) What are two substances that react in a hydrogen fuel cell?
    (b) What is the only product of the reaction?
    (c) Give two reasons for the use of internal combustion engines rather than hydrogen fuel cells in most of today's motor vehicles.
    (d) Name two Canadian companies that are leaders in fuel cell technology. Briefly describe the expertise of each company in fuel cell technology.

10. (a) What is a hybrid vehicle? Give two examples.
    (b) What features of hybrid vehicles help to reduce environmental pollution?

11. (a) Identify two inputs of a transportation system that are renewable and two inputs that are non-renewable.
    (b) Choose one of the non-renewable inputs you listed in (a). Describe what you think would happen to the transportation system if this non-renewable input ran out?
    (c) Are highway maintenance workers part of the transportation system? If not, why not? If so, where do they fit into the system?

Society & the Environment

Fuel Cell Development

The internal combustion engine continues to be the primary source of power for the transportation systems in all developed countries. **Table 1** lists some of the inputs, processes, outputs, and feedback that are characteristic of a transportation system based on the internal combustion engine.

A transportation system is a complex and highly integrated system that plays a vital role in modern everyday life. Changes to any one component of a transportation system has significant effects on other components of the system. For example, if a major company such as the Ford Motor Company decided to convert all its vehicles to fuel cell-powered vehicles, many components of the system would have to change. Vehicle mechanics, technicians, designers, and engineers would have to learn about the new fuel cell system, and less gasoline and diesel fuel would be purchased by car owners. As well, a lot of time and money would be required to change manufacturing systems to produce fuel cell-powered vehicles and to build hydrogen fuelling stations.

Table 1 Components of a Modern Transportation System

Inputs	Examples
people	• truck, bus, and car drivers • vehicle designers and engineers • mechanics and technicians • gas bar attendants • sales agents
information	• road signs and maps • traffic lights • traffic reports • vehicle operating instructions
materials	• water, coolant, or antifreeze to cool engines and clean vehicles • fuel and lubricants • steel, plastics, and rubber to build vehicles • asphalt and concrete to build roads • salt for icy roads
tools and machines	• wrenches, hoists, steel presses to shape vehicle bodies • paint applicators • assembly lines, robots, and computers
energy	• fossil fuels and other fuels to power vehicle engines • batteries • electricity for traffic lights and engines
capital	• money to purchase materials, tools, and energy for building and operating vehicle manufacturing companies, roads and highways, service stations, and oil refineries
time	• time to manufacture components of the system (cars, trucks, buses) • time to use components of the system (travel time, shipping time)

Processes	Examples
management	• development of a new vehicle model • operation of a car dealership or car manufacturing plant
production	• operation, maintenance, and repair of vehicles • construction and maintenance of highways

Outputs	Examples
positive (benefits)	• employment for many people in transportation industries • freedom to travel, which allows people to visit, study, explore, live, and carry out business all over the world • goods and services available to more people at affordable prices • national and international trade • emergency vehicles, such as ambulances and fire trucks, which save lives
negative (costs)	• traffic jams and environmental pollution • farmland used for roads • traffic accidents that injure and kill people and wildlife • discarded vehicles, which add to the garbage problem

Feedback	Examples
	• consumer complaints about potholes in roads • increased traffic congestion indicating an inadequate road system • drop in sales of a particular vehicle because of poor operation or safety reports in newspapers and magazines

Leading the Way to a Low-Carbon World

At the 2003 Hydrogen and Fuel Cells Conference and Trade Show, held in Vancouver, British Columbia, participants from around the world discussed Canada's role in the development of a low-carbon world: a world in which clean transportation technologies such as hydrogen fuel cells predominate. They tackled questions like these:

- Should Canada lead the way in the global transformation to a cleaner, healthier, low-carbon world?
- Could a Canadian hydrogen and fuel cell industry become an important source of future jobs and wealth creation?

In attempting to answer these questions, participants emphasized that the changeover from a high-carbon to a low-carbon world is already underway, although a complete changeover is still more than a decade away. Conference participants also emphasized Canada's ability to take an important role in the conversion. The participants recognized a significant problem, however. Currently, Canada has no definite plans or strategies to do this.

Although the Canadian government has funded individual hydrogen fuel cell research projects, it has not committed government funds for the development of a hydrogen fuel cell industry in Canada, as governments in Europe, Japan, and the United States have already done. Fuel cell development in Canada would require government involvement in the creation of national systems for producing, distributing, and storing hydrogen. It would also require the government to provide tax incentives for fuel cell developers and users to help them lower the costs of fuel cells. As well, the government would need to raise public awareness of fuel cell technology by, for example, converting the engines in government-owned vehicles, such as Canada Post vans, to hydrogen fuel cells.

How much money does the Canadian government spend on fuel cell development? What will happen to fuel cell companies if Canada fails to become involved in the changeover?

Decision-Making Skills

- ● Define the Issue
- ● Research
- ● Defend a Decision
- ● Identify Alternatives
- ● Analyze the Issue
- ○ Evaluate

1. Imagine that you are a Transport Canada official. You have been sent on a fact-finding mission to the 2003 Hydrogen and Fuel Cells Conference and Trade Show.

2. In addition to learning the information on this page, you meet with many fuel cell experts and government officials from around the world. In particular, you have high-level meetings with representatives from France, Britain, the United States, and Japan. Conduct research on their governments' programs, plans, and priorities for the development of fuel cell technology in their countries.

 www.science.nelson.com

3. Present your findings to the Federal Select Committee on Canada's Energy Future using a series of overhead slides or a PowerPoint presentation. Include the following information:
   - background information about government involvement in fuel cell research around the world
   - current government funding
   - social, economic, and political considerations
   - an analysis of the effects of an engine-to-fuel cell changeover, using input, process, output, and feedback
   - a description of the positive and negative impacts of a quick changeover
   - arguments from different lobby groups
   - a position statement describing your views on the issue

SUMMARY

- There are two types of ICEs, the Otto-cycle engine and the diesel engine.
- Both the Otto-cycle engine and the diesel engine contain a combustion chamber. The combustion chamber consists of a cylinder that is closed at one end, and a close-fitting piston.
- In an Otto-cycle engine, a spark from a spark plug ignites the fuel–air mixture in the engine. In a diesel engine, high pressure that is produced in the cylinder ignites the fuel–air mixture.
- Complete combustion of a fossil fuel produces carbon dioxide and water. Incomplete combustion produces carbon monoxide, pure carbon, and water.
- The combustion reactions also produce nitrogen oxides and sulfur oxides that dissolve in environmental water to produce acid precipitation. Some cars have a catalytic converter, which transforms nitrogen oxides and sulfur oxides in car exhaust into less harmful substances.
- Inertia can be reduced by decreasing the mass of a vehicle. Friction with air (aerodynamic drag) can be reduced by streamlining the shape of the vehicle.
- Maglev trains operate on the principle that there are attractive and repulsive forces between magnets.
- Maglev trains reach very high speeds because they are suspended in air and experience no friction with the ground.

- Hydrogen fuel cells operate on the principle of reverse hydrolysis, in which oxygen and hydrogen combine to produce electricity and water as the only products.
- Hybrid cars combine power from a small internal combustion engine with power from an electric battery/motor combination.
- While the Canadian government has funded individual hydrogen cell research projects, it has not committed government funds for the development of a hydrogen fuel cell industry in Canada, as governments in Europe, Japan, and the United States have already done.
- The Canadian government needs to provide tax incentives for fuel cell developers and users to help them lower the costs of fuel cells. The government also needs to raise public awareness of fuel cell technology.

Key Terms

transportation technology	friction
internal combustion engine (ICE)	aerodynamic drag
	aerodynamics
stroke	maglev train
catalytic converter	fuel cell
catalyst	electrolysis
inertia	reverse electrolysis
	hybrid vehicle

ASSESSMENT

Understanding Concepts

1. (a) What is transportation?
   (b) What is a transportation system?

2. (a) Describe the gasoline-powered internal combustion engine in terms of input, process, output, and feedback. Include two positive and two negative impacts in your description.
   (b) Name and describe the two most common types of internal combustion engines. What are the main differences between these two types of engines?

(c) Describe the types of vehicles that use the engines you described in (b).

3. (a) How is the fuel–air ratio for the complete combustion reaction of a hydrocarbon, such as octane, different from the fuel–air ratio for the incomplete combustion reaction of the same hydrocarbon?
   (b) What should be done to a car on a regular basis to keep the reactions in the cylinders predominantly complete combustion?
   (c) Why is complete combustion favoured over incomplete combustion?

4. **(a)** **Figures 29** and **30** show two strokes in the operation of an Otto-cycle engine. Name each stroke, and describe what is happening.
   (b) Does either stroke provide the automobile with the power it needs to move? Explain.

Figure 29 spark plug   **Figure 30** spark plug

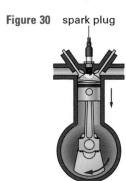

5. **(a)** Why is the production of nitrogen oxides by internal combustion engines harmful to the environment?
   (b) Why do the combustion reactions that occur in ICEs produce nitrogen oxides?
   (c) What technological device helps reduce the quantities of nitrogen oxides that are released by ICEs? Briefly describe how this device works.

6. **(a)** Define aerodynamic drag.
   (b) How do automobile designers help reduce aerodynamic drag?
   (c) Why is it impossible to eliminate aerodynamic drag in automobiles that are operated under normal conditions?

7. What design features allow maglev trains to reach speeds that exceed 400 km/h with little or no noise?

8. **(a)** How was William Grove's original hydrogen fuel cell (his so-called "gas battery") different from a conventional electric battery?
   (b) How did the *Hindenburg* disaster affect the early development of hydrogen fuel cell technology?
   (c) Determine the validity of the following statement: "Hydrogen fuel cells are pollution-free sources of energy."

9. **(a)** Is a bicycle a hybrid vehicle? Explain.
   (b) What design features do hybrid cars possess that make them more fuel-efficient than conventional gasoline-powered cars?
   (c) Why are hybrid cars not ideal replacements for ICE-powered cars?

Applying Inquiry Skills

10. **(a)** Before the invention of the wheel, people used to drag objects over the ground. Using household materials, design an experiment to determine the advantage of using the rolling action of a wheel to move an object, instead of dragging the object over the ground.
    (b) What force is overcome or reduced by using the rolling action of a wheel to move an object, instead of dragging the object over the ground?

Making Connections

11. **(a)** List two positive and two negative impacts of motor-vehicle transportation.
    (b) Suggest possible remedies for the negative impacts you listed in **(a)**.

12. Some cars (especially racecars) have devices called spoilers. What are spoilers, and what do they do?

 www.science.nelson.com

13. There are many career opportunities in the field of transportation.
    (a) List as many careers as you can under the following headings: Input, Process, Output.
    (b) Conduct library or Internet research on one of the careers you listed in **(a)**. Describe the basic requirements of the career, the minimum educational requirements, the fundamental skills required, and the average annual salary.

 www.science.nelson.com

14. **(a)** Conduct Internet research, or contact car dealerships, to identify a hybrid vehicle that the company currently sells.

 www.science.nelson.com

    (b) What are the specific features that make the vehicle a "hybrid"?
    (c) What environmental protection claims, if any, does the manufacturer make regarding the hybrid vehicle? Evaluate the claims.
    (d) Prepare a cost–benefit analysis on buying the hybrid vehicle.

SPLICING *and* DICING: BIOTECHNOLOGY

n August 1998, world-renowned food safety expert Dr. Arpad Pusztai (**Figure 1**) was fired from his job as senior researcher at Britain's leading food safety research lab, the Rowette Institute. He was fired because he stated publicly that he would not eat genetically engineered foods.

Pusztai made his controversial comments while being interviewed on the British television program *World in Action*. He said, "We are assured [by others] that this [genetically modified food] is absolutely safe, and that no conceivable harm could come to us from eating it. But if you gave me the choice now, I would not eat it." He also said, "We need to be far more careful in devising testing programs. It is expensive, it is long, but nevertheless it is the only way that you will be able to pick up differences. We are asking for less haste and more testing."

Figure 1   The firing of Dr. Arpad Pusztai from the Rowette Institute caused major controversy.

During the interview, Pusztai revealed the results of recent experiments he had performed at the Rowette Institute: rats that were fed certain genetically engineered potatoes developed stunted growth and damaged immune systems. In response to Pusztai's comments, the Rowette Institute conducted a review of his research and determined that his conclusions were not justified by the experimental evidence. In a report, the Rowette Institute stated that the comments Pusztai made in the television program were "improper and misleading." As a result, he was fired from the Institute.

After Pusztai's firing, an independent panel of 23 scientists from 13 countries reviewed both his experimental findings and the Rowette Institute report. They concluded that Pusztai's research claims were justified. While admitting that he had acted prematurely in speaking out on television, Pusztai said that he would do the same thing again. In a speech he gave to the British government's Science and Technology Committee, he explained the benefits of speaking out on important issues. He said, "What I found gave me concern, and what I achieved by speaking out is that we are all sitting here and talking about it."

(a) Why do you think Pusztai was fired from the Rowette Institute: because of his personal views regarding the safety of genetically engineered foods, because he voiced his views on television, or both? Explain.

The development, production, and distribution of genetically engineered foods continues to be one of the most hotly debated topics in biotechnology today. Many people, including scientists, government officials, and even food safety specialists like Pusztai, are calling for more safety testing and better labelling of foods. How are genetically engineered foods created? What role does DNA play in genetic engineering? Why are some people against the production and sale of genetically engineered foods?

DNA and Genetic Engineering

Biotechnology includes the knowledge, processes, tools, and skills that people use to affect the activities of living organisms. Biotechnology includes both medical technologies and agricultural technologies. Some of the most dramatic and controversial biotechnologies, such as genetic engineering, have been developed since James Watson and Francis Crick worked out the structure of deoxyribonucleic acid (DNA) in 1953 (**Figure 2**).

(a)

(b)

Figure 2 **(a)** James Watson and Francis Crick standing beside their model of DNA. **(b)** A modern model of DNA

Watson and Crick figured out the structure of DNA without performing a single experiment. To do this, they used critical laboratory information provided by their colleague, Dr. Rosalind Franklin, to piece together a cardboard model of a DNA molecule. When they saw that their model worked, they quickly submitted a one-page report to the journal *Nature*, announcing their discovery to the world.

Watson and Crick predicted that a DNA molecule could make copies of itself, thereby passing the genetic information from parent to offspring through reproduction. Watson and Crick shared the 1962 Nobel Prize with their boss, Dr. Maurice Wilkins. Franklin, who had died four years earlier of cancer, could not share the prize because Nobel Prizes are not awarded posthumously.

DNA: The Molecule of Life

DNA is sometimes called the "molecule of life" because it stores information for the production of the structural and functional components of living organisms. This information, called genetic information, determines the traits, or characteristics, of an organism. It is inheritable, meaning that it can be passed on from one generation to the next through reproduction. The colour of a flower's petals, the shape of a human's ear, and the length of a dog's tail are all traits controlled by the genetic information that is stored in DNA.

In plants and animals, DNA is found in structures called chromosomes in the nucleus of a cell (**Figure 3**). A chromosome is composed of a highly coiled molecule of DNA surrounded by many large protein molecules.

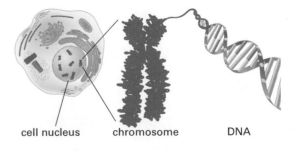

cell nucleus   chromosome   DNA

Figure 3 DNA is found in chromosomes in the nucleus of plant and animal cells.

A4.1 Activity | EXTRACTING DNA

DNA is found in the nuclei of all plant and animal cells. In this activity, you will separate, purify, and extract DNA from onion cells. In the last step of this activity, you will add phenol red indicator. Phenol red indicator is red in basic or neutral solutions and yellow in acidic solutions.

Materials

small chunk of onion
detergent–table salt solution
mortar and pestle
glass stirring rod
cheesecloth or strainer
2 test tubes
meat tenderizer solution
ethanol
glass rod
5% table salt solution
phenol red indicator

1. Place the small chunk of onion in a mortar and add 10 mL of the detergent–table salt solution. Record your observations.

2. Using a pestle, mash the onion on the bottom of the mortar. Use a glass stirring rod to gently stir the mixture.

3. Using cheesecloth or a strainer, strain the mixture into a clean test tube.

4. Add 4 to 5 drops of meat tenderizer solution to the strained mixture and swirl the test tube. Record your observations.

5. Carefully pour 10 mL of ice-cold ethanol into the test tube so that it forms a layer on top of the mixture. Record your observations.

6. Allow the mixture to stand undisturbed for 3 min to 4 min. Record your observations.

7. Lower a glass rod into the alcohol–water mixture where the two layers meet. Twirl the rod slowly to collect the stringy DNA.

8. Place the DNA in a test tube that contains about 15 mL of 5% table salt solution.

9. Add 5 drops of phenol red indicator to this test tube. Record your observations.

(a) Why did you mash the onion in step 2?

(b) Where did the DNA form in the mixture?

(c) What colour was the solution in step 9 after you added the phenol red indicator?

(d) What does the colour tell you about DNA?

Cells use the genetic information in DNA to produce proteins. Proteins give rise to an organism's inheritable (genetic) characteristics. A single DNA molecule (in a single chromosome) contains enough information to produce many different protein molecules. In many cases, several protein molecules work together to create a particular genetic characteristic. For example, your body's ability to form blood clots when you cut your skin requires the combined effort of the proteins thrombin, fibrinogen, and fibrin, among others. The portion of a DNA molecule that controls the production of a particular protein is called a **gene**. Thus, a single molecule of DNA contains many genes (**Figure 4**).

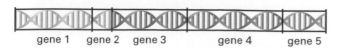

gene 1   gene 2   gene 3   gene 4   gene 5

Figure 4 A DNA molecule contains many genes.

Genetic Engineering

Genetic engineering refers to a set of technologies that are used to change the genetic information in a cell's DNA, and thus its inheritable characteristics. Genetic engineers create organisms with different genetic traits by artificially transferring genes from one species to another.

In nature, organisms with new gene combinations are produced through sexual reproduction. For many years, humans have bred different individuals of a species to produce offspring with more favourable characteristics. For example, less desirable species of corn have been selectively bred over many generations to produce today's more desirable species (**Figure 5**). The process of producing organisms with specific traits by natural means (sexual reproduction) is called **selective breeding**.

Figure 5 Prehistoric corn (a) was selectively bred over many generations to produce today's common varieties (b).

While selective breeding produces organisms with more desirable traits, the rules of sexual reproduction and the lack of certain genes limit the variety of traits possible. For example, if a white rabbit with black spots is bred with a brown rabbit, their offspring may include a brown rabbit with black spots. However, the number of possible colours is limited by the variety of colours that exist in the entire rabbit population. For example, a breeder would not be able to produce a green rabbit because the genes for a green coat are not present in the rabbit gene pool at this time. A **gene pool** is the total of all the genes that are possessed by the organisms of a species at a given time. Although frogs possess genes for green colour, a rabbit breeder could not introduce green colour from a frog because rabbits and frogs do not normally mate in nature. It may be possible, though, to transfer the genes for green colour from frogs to rabbits by means of genetic engineering. **Figure 6** shows one of the unlikely combinations that resulted from the transfer of genes by genetic engineering.

Figure 6 This creature contains genes from both a sheep and a goat. The thin white fur is produced from the goat gene, and the thick grey wool is produced from the sheep gene.

Genetic Engineering History

The development of genetic engineering began in 1973, when University of California scientists Herbert Boyer and Stanley Cohen discovered that EcoR1 (an enzyme that can cut a DNA molecule into pieces) and DNA ligase (an enzyme that can join pieces of DNA together) could be used to splice pieces of DNA from different organisms into a single molecule. DNA-cutting enzymes, such as EcoR1, are called **restriction enzymes**. Boyer and Cohen used EcoR1 and DNA ligase to splice a piece of DNA from a frog into DNA from bacteria called *E. coli*. The resulting *E. coli* bacterial cells were able to produce some protein molecules that before could only be produced by frog cells. DNA that is composed of pieces from different organisms (such as the frog–*E. coli* mix) is called **recombinant DNA**, or rDNA. When an entire gene from one organism is spliced into the DNA of another organism, the transplanted gene is called a **transgene** (**Figure 7**).

The organism that receives the transplanted gene is called a **transgenic organism**. The first transgenic animal and the first transgenic plant were both produced in 1982. The animal was a mouse that contained the gene for growth hormone from a rat (**Figure 8**). The plant was a tobacco plant that contained a transgene from a bacterial cell. The transgene in the tobacco plant produced an antibiotic in the plant's cells that protected the plant from bacterial infection. Since then, many transgenic animals and plants have been produced.

A4: Splicing and Dicing: Biotechnology

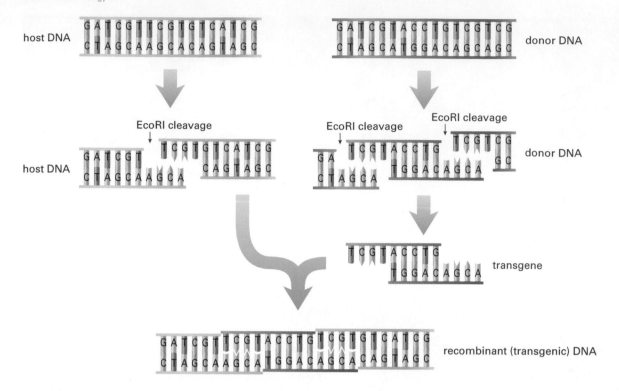

host DNA `GATCGTTCGTGTCATCG` / `CTAGCAAGCACAGTAGC`

donor DNA `GATCGTACCTGTCGTCG` / `CTAGCATGGACAGCAGC`

EcoRI cleavage

EcoRI cleavage   EcoRI cleavage

host DNA `GATCGT` / `CTAGCAAGCA`   `TCGTGTCATCG` / `CAGTAGC`

donor DNA `GA` / `CTAGCA`   `TCGTACCTG` / `TGGACAGCA`   `TCGTCG` / `GC`

transgene `TCGTACCTG` / `TGGACAGCA`

recombinant (transgenic) DNA `GATCGTTCGTACCTGTCGTGTCATCG` / `CTAGCAAGCATGGACAGCACAGTAGC`

Figure 7   EcoR1 is used to produce recombinant DNA.

Figure 8   In 1982, Ralph Brinster and Richard Palmiter created transgenic animals by inserting a rat gene for growth hormone into mouse embryos. The mice that carried the new gene, like the one shown on the left, produced growth hormone and grew twice as big as their normal siblings.

Producing Transgenic Organisms

All genetic engineering methods involve the insertion of a transgene into a host cell's DNA. Three methods can be used to transfer a transgene into a host (plant or animal): bacterial, viral, and mechanical.

Bacterial Methods

Bacterial methods are mainly used to produce transgenic plants, and they usually involve a bacterium called *Agrobacterium tumefasciens* (*A. tumefasciens*) (**Figure 9**).

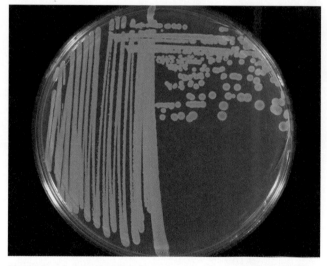

Figure 9   *A. tumefasciens* (growing in yellow colonies on this culture) is used to transfer genes from one organism to another in genetic engineering.

There are two basic stages (each with a number of steps) in the genetic engineering process (**Figure 10**):

Stage 1: The transgene is spliced into *A. tumefasciens* DNA using recombinant DNA methods (using restriction enzymes and DNA ligase).

Stage 2: Recipient cells (plant cells) are exposed to *A. tumefasciens*. *A. tumefasciens* inserts its DNA (now containing the transgene) into the plant's DNA, thus producing a transgenic plant cell.

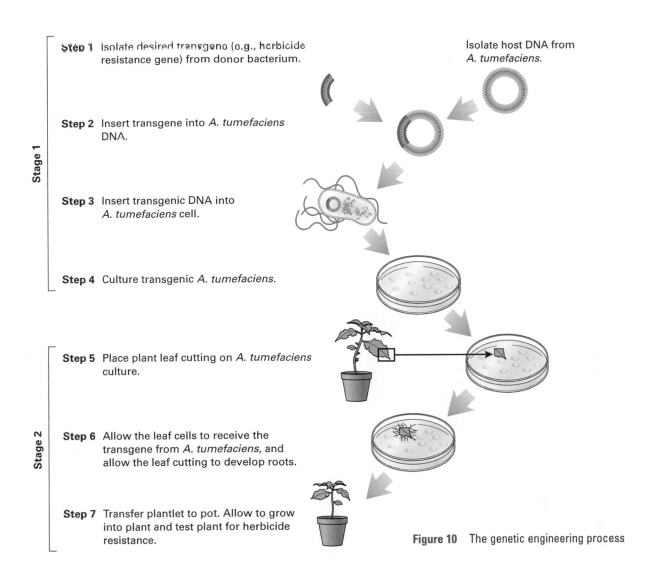

Step 1 Isolate desired transgene (e.g., herbicide resistance gene) from donor bacterium.

Isolate host DNA from *A. tumefaciens*.

Step 2 Insert transgene into *A. tumefaciens* DNA.

Stage 1

Step 3 Insert transgenic DNA into *A. tumefaciens* cell.

Step 4 Culture transgenic *A. tumefaciens*.

Step 5 Place plant leaf cutting on *A. tumefaciens* culture.

Stage 2

Step 6 Allow the leaf cells to receive the transgene from *A. tumefaciens*, and allow the leaf cutting to develop roots.

Step 7 Transfer plantlet to pot. Allow to grow into plant and test plant for herbicide resistance.

Figure 10 The genetic engineering process

During stage 2, only a small percentage of the plant cells successfully incorporate the transgene into their DNA. In order to identify the successfully infected cells, scientists link genes called **marker genes** to the transgene in steps 1 and 2. The marker genes produce characteristics that the scientists can recognize in the recipient cells. Genes that make plant cells resistant to antibiotics or herbicides are the marker genes of choice. After inserting the transgene into *A. tumefasciens* (step 3), scientists add antibiotics or herbicides that kill all the bacterial cells except those that contain the marker gene, and thus the desired transgene. These cells are used in the rest of the genetic engineering process.

Viral Methods

Viral methods are mainly used to produce transgenic animals. Most viruses are composed of a DNA molecule surrounded by a protein shell (**Figure 11**).

When a virus infects an animal cell, it inserts its DNA into the host cell's DNA, much like *A. tumefasciens* does in plants. Once the viral DNA is inserted, the animal cell is forced to copy it many times over to reproduce the virus. Viruses that are used in genetic engineering are modified so that their DNA is inserted into the animal cell's DNA, but not copied.

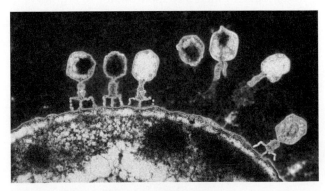

Figure 11 Viruses (blue objects) like these may be used to transfer genes in genetic engineering.

In the process, the desired transgene is first spliced into a virus' DNA. Then the virus that contains the recombinant DNA is allowed to infect the recipient animal cells, producing a transgenic animal cell. Viral methods have been used to produce a variety of transgenic animals, such as chickens that are able to make human proteins in the whites of their eggs.

Mechanical Methods

The Gene Gun

The gene gun (**Figure 12**) uses very small gold beads as bullets. The desired gene is "glued" to the surface of the gold bullet and shot into the recipient cell's nucleus.

Figure 12 A gene gun shoots a transgene directly into a recipient cell's nucleus

Microinjection

In microinjection, a solution that contains the desired gene is injected directly into the recipient cell's nucleus using an ultrafine needle (**Figure 13**).

Genetically Engineered Foods

Genetically engineered foods (GEFs) are foods that are obtained from genetically engineered organisms. **Genetically engineered organisms (GEOs)** are life forms that are normally used as food (plants, animals, fungi, and bacteria), but whose genetic makeup has been altered by recombinant DNA technologies. Genetically engineered organisms are also known as transgenic organisms or genetically modified organisms (GMOs).

On May 18, 1994, the American Food and Drug Administration (FDA) announced the release of FlavrSavr tomatoes, the first transgenic food to be sold to the public. FlavrSavr tomatoes had undergone a decade of testing at a cost of $525 million, before being approved as safe by the FDA. Engineered to remain firm as they ripen, the tomatoes cost twice as much as regular tomatoes, did not

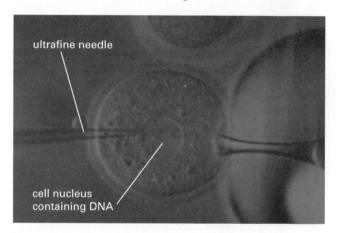

ultrafine needle

cell nucleus containing DNA

Figure 13 In microinjection, an ultrafine needle is used to inject a transgene directly into an animal cell's nucleus.

A4.2 Activity | SIMULATED GENETIC ENGINEERING

In genetic engineering, the transfer of a gene is carried out using a biochemical "cut and paste" process. In this activity, you will simulate the process. You will select suitable materials to represent or identify cell nuclei, nuclear membranes, host and donor DNA molecules, host genes, a transgene, a marker gene, and restriction enzymes. Keep in mind that you are not creating a static model of the genetic engineering process, but an active simulation that you will carry out.

1. Select appropriate materials to demonstrate your simulation.

2. Write a procedure, including relevant safety cautions, and have it approved by your teacher.

3. If your teacher does not approve your procedure, revise it so that it better represents the process described in the text.

4. Once you have your teacher's approval, perform your procedure.

5. Write a brief report. Include a statement of purpose, a list of materials used, a step-by-step procedure, and a labelled diagram that describes your procedure.

taste as good, and bruised easily. As a result, they were shunned by consumers and boycotted by chefs. This, along with production and transportation problems (the delicate tomatoes were easily damaged during transport), resulted in FlavrSavr tomatoes being pulled off the shelves in 1997.

Today, about 80% of biotechnology research is directed at food plants and 20% is directed at non-food plants, such as cotton, ornamental plants, and medicinal plants. All economically important plants, such as cotton, canola, potatoes, soybeans, corn, and rice, have genetically engineered varieties (**Figure 14**).

Common transgenes used in economically important crops are the Bt genes. These genes are obtained from the soil bacterium *Bacillus thuringiensis*. They code for Bt toxins, which are proteins that kill certain insect pests but not larger animals, such as mammals and fish. Three Bt plants are now commercially available: Bt corn, Bt cotton, and Bt potatoes. So far, cotton is the most popular of the Bt plants.

A more recent genetically engineered plant is Roundup-Ready canola. Canola is commonly used to make canola oil. Roundup-Ready canola contains a transgene that makes the plant resistant to a popular herbicide called Roundup. Roundup is toxic to many broad-leafed weeds, and it would also be toxic to broad-leafed canola plants if not for the transgene. Roundup-Ready canola allows farmers to use Roundup herbicide without fear of harming the canola plants. Roundup-Ready canola and other genetically engineered plants have been produced by a company named Monsanto, a multi-national agricultural biotechnology company.

(a)

(b)

Figure 14   Many genetically modified foods, including soybeans **(a)**, and rice **(b)**, have been produced.

✔ Check Your Understanding

1. **(a)** How is genetic engineering similar to selective breeding?
   (b) How is genetic engineering different from selective breeding?

2. **(a)** What is recombinant DNA? How is it produced?
   (b) What is the relationship between recombinant DNA and a transgenic organism?

3. **(a)** What role does *A. tumefasciens* play in the process of genetic engineering?
   (b) What is a marker gene?
   (c) Why do genetic engineers attach marker genes to a transgene before inserting the transgene into a recipient organism?

4. Describe two methods that genetic engineers can use to insert a transgene into a host cell's DNA.

5. **(a)** What are Bt plants? Why are they considered to be more useful than the same plants without the Bt gene?
   (b) What advantage do Roundup-Ready plants have over their natural counterparts?

Impacts of Genetic Engineering

The development of genetic engineering techniques has resulted in the production, distribution, and sale of many genetically engineered foods. Consumers, scientists, and politicians have all expressed concern that the foods may pose a danger to the health and well-being of humans, animals, and the environment.

The case of Dr. Pusztai and the Rowette Institute highlights some of the concerns about the widespread production and distribution of genetically engineered organisms and the consumption of genetically engineered foods.

Canadian laws regarding GEOs were passed before the development of genetic engineering technologies. These laws regulate the approval of "novel crops," which include genetically engineered crops. Biotechnology companies work with university and government researchers to test novel organisms for efficacy (value), and health and environmental safety. The test results are evaluated by two agencies, the Canadian Food Inspection Agency (CFIA) and Health Canada (HC). CFIA, HC, and other agencies around the world use the principle of substantial equivalence to assess the safety of a GEF. The **principle of substantial equivalence** requires a GEF to have the same appearance and general chemical properties as its natural counterpart. The concern with the substantial equivalence principle is that a GEF may be similar or almost identical to its natural counterpart and yet still contain unexpected and undiscovered harmful substances. Many concerned citizens and scientists reject the substantial equivalence standard as a non-scientific way of assessing food safety. Instead, they propose the precautionary principle as the only effective way to test foods for safety. The **precautionary principle** assumes that a product is unsafe until controlled scientific investigations prove otherwise.

The Case Against Genetically Engineered Foods

Many citizens are genuinely concerned about the safety and security of the laboratory practices used by genetic engineers. Like all scientific laboratory work, genetic engineering is subject to error. Although the splicing of a transgene into a virus or bacterium, such as *A. tumefasciens*, can be performed with precision, the insertion of transgenes by infection, microinjection, or a gene gun cannot. In fact, scientists cannot determine the exact location on the host cell's DNA that the transgene attaches to. The attachment is completely random. Many believe that the random insertion of foreign genes into the DNA of another organism can create unexpected and unintended effects, including cancer in animals.

It is well-known that bacteria develop resistance to antibiotics when exposed to high concentrations over a long period of time. This, together with the widespread use of marker genes that produce antibiotic resistance in genetic engineering, may result in a decrease in the effectiveness of antibiotics for treating human diseases. As well, genetic engineering may transfer new and unidentified proteins from one food into another, triggering allergic reactions.

Another concern is the spread of herbicide resistant transgenes and marker genes to weed plants in the wild by cross-pollination. The resulting superweeds would require the application of increasingly powerful herbicides to be controlled. The uncontrolled spread of transgenes and marker genes from genetically engineered organisms to unmodified organisms in the environment has been called **genetic pollution**.

In addition to the scientific and environmental concerns, many people worry about the effects of genetic engineering on society and the economy. For example, if companies that develop GEOs end up owning the organisms, the production and distribution of food plants and other useful plants will be controlled by a very small number of companies. This could affect the variety of products available, the price of the products, and the ability of some people, especially people in developing countries, to pay for basic needs such as food and clothing.

The Case in Favour of Genetically Engineered Foods

One of the most common claims in support of GEFs is the great potential of these foods to "feed the world." For example, if scientists can produce genetically engineered plants that will grow in marginal conditions, they could help many countries that struggle to produce enough food for their citizens. In fact, people all over the world would benefit from plants that are more nutritious and more pest resistant than their unmodified counterparts. Some plants that are particularly susceptible to pests, such as bananas, are expected to be completely wiped out unless scientists find a way to prevent the damage. Genetic engineering has produced grains that can tolerate early frosts, acidic soil, and drought.

Scientists have also produced plants that absorb toxic metals, such as mercury and lead, from the soil, allowing contaminated land to be used again for agriculture. There is even research underway to develop GEFs that produce vaccines.

Proponents of GEFs point out that we can never be completely sure of a new innovation's safety. They claim that if we applied the precautionary principle to every scientific breakthrough before it was used, many life-saving technologies would take forever to be approved, if ever. They also point out that 70% of the processed foods North Americans eat are bio-engineered, and that no public-health incident attributable to GEFs has yet occurred.

Explore *an* Issue

Genetically Engineered Foods: Friend or Foe?

The debate over the production, distribution, and sale of GEFs has been raging for some time now, with no resolution in sight. Individuals and organizations all over the world have expressed their views on both sides of the issue, and have produced evidence to support their views. Governments are scrambling to update food inspection and safety laws to keep up with developments in genetic engineering technology. Ultimately, however, everyone must make a personal decision either to support or oppose the development, production, and use of GEFs.

Statement: The development, production, and use of genetically modified foods must be stopped.

1. Using the Internet and other resources, research both sides of the issue.

 www.science.nelson.com

Decision-Making Skills

○ Define the Issue
● Research
● Defend a Decision
○ Identify Alternatives
● Analyze the Issue
○ Evaluate

2. Take a position for or against the statement.

3. Discuss your views with various classmates.

4. Form a group with two or three classmates who have the same views, to promote your views. Give your group a suitable name.

5. Design an information campaign, in which you produce and display posters and/or pamphlets that effectively communicate your group's views.

SUMMARY

- DNA stores genetic information that codes for the production of virtually all the structural and functional components of living organisms.
- Genetic engineering is a set of technologies that are used to change the genetic information in a cell's DNA.
- Restriction enzymes can cut a DNA molecule into pieces, and an enzyme called DNA ligase can join pieces of DNA together.
- Consumers, scientists, and politicians have expressed concerns that GEFs may pose a danger to the health and well-being of humans, animals, and the environment.
- Bacteria develop resistance to antibiotics when exposed to high concentrations over a long period of time. This may decrease the effectiveness of antibiotics for treating human diseases.
- The principle of substantial equivalence requires a GEF to have the same appearance and general

chemical properties as its natural counterpart. The precautionary principle assumes that a product is unsafe until controlled scientific investigations prove otherwise.

- Scientists have produced genetically engineered plants that resist drought, early frost, and acidic soils. They have also produced plants that absorb toxic metals from soil.

Key Terms

biotechnology	marker gene
gene	genetically engineered
genetic engineering	food (GEF)
selective breeding	genetically engineered
gene pool	organism (GEO)
restriction enzyme	principle of substantial
recombinant DNA	equivalence
transgene	precautionary principle
transgenic organism	genetic pollution

ASSESSMENT

Understanding Concepts

1. **(a)** What is the name of the molecule illustrated in **Figure 1**?

Figure 1

(b) Describe two contributions made by James Watson and Francis Crick to our knowledge of the molecule in **Figure 1**.

(c) What relationships are there between the molecule in **Figure 1**, proteins, and an organism's inheritable characteristics?

2. Explain what the following statement means: "DNA contains genetic information."

3. Using examples, distinguish between selective breeding and genetic engineering.

4. How does genetic engineering allow a species to increase the number of different genes in its gene pool?

5. Rearrange the following steps into a reasonable sequence for producing a transgenic tulip that smells like a rose.

(a) Insert a rose fragrance transgene into *A. tumefaciens* DNA.

(b) Obtain and isolate a rose fragrance gene from a rose plant.

(c) Place a tulip plant leaf cutting on a transgenic *A. tumefaciens* culture.

(d) Transfer a transgenic tulip plantlet to its own pot and allow it to grow.

(e) Allow the tulip leaf cells to receive the rose fragrance transgene.

(f) Culture transgenic *A. tumefaciens*.

6. **(a)** Name and describe two mechanical methods used to insert transgenes into host DNA.

(b) Using mechanical methods to insert a transgene into a host, can a genetic engineer determine the exact location on the host cell's DNA where the transgene will attach? Explain.

7. **(a)** What characteristics do Bt corn plants possess that common corn plants do not possess?

   (b) What process is used to produce Bt corn?

   (c) If seeds obtained from Bt corn plants are sown, will the offspring plants inherit the parent plant's characteristics? Explain.

8. Using an example, describe genetic pollution.

9. Provide an example that illustrates how genetically engineered food crops could potentially harm

   (a) a consumer of the food crop

   (b) organisms higher in the food chain of the modified organism

   (c) the environment in general

Applying Inquiry Skills

10. How does experimental error increase the potential dangers associated with genetic engineering? Describe specific methods used by genetic engineers to illustrate your answer.

Making Connections

11. **(a)** Provide three arguments in support of the development, production, and use of genetically engineered foods.

    (b) Provide three arguments against the development, production, and use of genetically engineered foods.

12. Provide an example that illustrates how genetically engineered food crops can benefit

    (a) a farmer

    (b) the economy of a developing nation

13. **(a)** Conduct Internet research to determine which countries presently require GEFs to be labelled before they are sold to the general public.

(b) What is Canada's current legal position regarding the labelling of genetically engineered foods?

(c) Write a brief position paper indicating your views on labelling genetically engineered foods that are sold to the public. In your position paper, acknowledge the benefits and costs of labelling GEFs.

(d) Would you eat a food that is labelled "genetically engineered"? Why or why not?

14. **(a)** What is the precautionary principle?

    (b) How would the precautionary principle have affected the widespread use of DDT in the 1950s?

15. How does the global population explosion and the drive to preserve natural environments, such as rain forests, affect the debate over the development and use of GEFs?

16. New technologies promise to work against, rather than for, impoverished farmers. Gene use restriction technology (GURT), commonly known as terminator technology, prevents farmers from using seeds that are harvested in one season to produce next season's crop. Conduct Internet research on GURT to answer the following questions.

(a) What is GURT?

(b) Provide one specific example of the use of GURT in GEF production.

(c) Why do biotechnology companies bother to develop or use GURT?

(d) How will GURT affect agriculture in developing countries?

17. Some supporters of genetic engineering claim that it is a minor extension of existing breeding technologies. Evaluate this claim.

TASK: My Technology Index

Technologies help with almost everything we do in everyday life. While we all use technological products and processes, we use them to varying degrees. "Techies" is a term that is used to describe people who embrace technology and enthusiastically support technological advancement. Techies like to keep up to date with new technologies and purchase the latest gizmos. At the other extreme, "Luddites" are people who reject technology and oppose technological progress. They believe that technology is detrimental to society, and that its use and development should be restricted. So, are you a techie, a Luddite, or something in between? In this activity you will assess technological tendencies by creating and using a technology index.

An index is a number that represents a person's judgment about the usefulness, worth, or importance of an object, process, or issue. Indexes are used to measure many different things. For example, the air quality index measures the overall quantity of pollutants in the air we breathe. The body mass index measures a person's overall body fat content.

Another common index is the final grade you get in some courses you take, such as a driver's certification course. The final grade is a measure, or index, of your overall achievement of the course's expectations. To determine your final grade, your instructor judges your performance in a number of categories, such as take-home assignments, in-class quizzes, and a practice road test. Your instructor may feel, however, that the assignments and quizzes are less indicative of your overall driving skills than the practice road test. To address this, your instructor may weight the mark you receive on your practice road test higher than the marks you get on your assignments and quizzes: your instructor multiples the mark you get on your practice road test by a percentage that is greater than the percentage that your mark on an assignment or quiz is multiplied by. **Table 1** outlines how an index may be calculated.

Table 1 Calculating an Index

Method	Example
1. Identify categories.	1 assignment 1 quiz 1 practice road test
2. Rate each category on a scale from 1 to 10. In this example, the rating corresponds to the mark you achieve in each evaluation task.	assignment: 6 quiz: 7 practice road test: 9
3. Multiply each category rating by a weighting factor (percentage). The sum of the weighting factors must equal 1.0 (100%). In this example, the weighting factors are 0.2, 0.2, and 0.6. Weighting factors magnify the effect of a category on the value of the overall mark. The product of category rating and category weighting results in an index for each category.	category: rating × weighting = index assignment: $6 \times 0.2 = 1.2$ quiz: $7 \times 0.2 = 1.4$ practice road test: $9 \times 0.6 = 5.4$
4. To obtain the overall index, you may choose to add some indexes and subtract others, depending on the meanings of the statements and/or questions you use. In this example, the individual indexes are all added to produce the overall index.	$1.2 + 1.4 + 5.4 = 8.0$

In this example, the overall index (overall grade) is 8.0 out of 10.0. The instructor may compare the overall index to a scale that expresses the meaning of the overall index. Here, the overall index is "excellent."

Your task is to develop an index and scale to measure a person's overall technological tendencies.

Index	Scale
1.0 – 2.9	poor
3.0 – 4.9	good
5.0 – 7.9	very good
8.0 – 10.0	excellent

Procedure

1. For each of the four topics in this unit, create one or two categories that you believe best exemplify a person's technological preferences, understanding, and activity. Create six to eight categories in total.

2. Weight each category with a percentage that, in your opinion, reflects the relative importance of the category in determining a person's overall technology index.

3. Create another scale that includes "Luddite" at the lower extreme and "techie" at the upper extreme. Determine intermediate values and descriptions, and place them in your scale.

4. Ask eight to ten students to rate themselves in each category. (Make sure that all your scales have the same values.)

5. Calculate an index for each category, for each person.

6. First determine how you will calculate an overall index, then do so for each person.

7. Use your scale to determine each person's technology index.

8. Write a report that summarizes your results. Your teacher will provide you with the report guidelines.

Analysis and Evaluation

(a) Explain the meaning of your overall index.

(b) Justify your category weightings (step 2).

(c) Justify the mathematical operations you used to calculate the overall index (step 6).

(d) Evaluate your categories by explaining why you created each one.

(e) Describe some weaknesses of your technology index.

(f) Describe some weaknesses of indexes in general.

Synthesis

(g) Allow two classmates who completed someone else's index to complete your index. Compare results, and assess similarities and differences.

(h) Should indexes be created by groups of people instead of individuals? If yes, why? If no, why not?

(i) Should governments develop and use indexes to help them make decisions? Explain.

SUMMARY

Throughout this unit, you have had opportunities to
- distinguish between, and show relationships among, science and technology
- design, construct, improve, and analyze technological systems according to stated criteria
- make connections among scientific principles, technological solutions, the needs of society, and environmental concerns

Copy the following graphic organizer into your notebook, and use it to help you summarize your understanding of the key concepts in each of the four major topics. Add the key concepts related to the topic that you chose for your Unit Task.

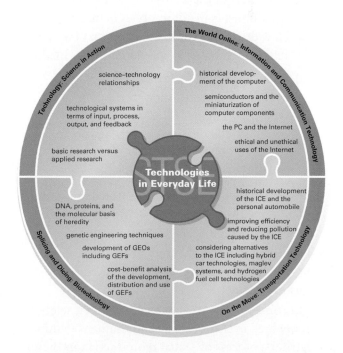

Unit A Review

Understanding Concepts

1. Describe two differences between the creative work of scientists and the creative work of engineers, technicians, and technologists. Then describe two similarities.

2. (a) A scientist is trying to develop a new scientific theory for a pattern she has discovered in nature. Describe the general steps she may take to develop this new theory.
   (b) Once a scientific theory has been accepted, should scientists continue to research the theory? Why or why not?

3. (a) Describe two differences between a scientific law and a scientific theory.
   (b) Identify each statement as a scientific law or a scientific theory.
   (i) Opposite magnetic poles attract, and like magnetic poles repel.
   (ii) Ice floats on liquid water because ice is less dense than liquid water.
   (c) Identify a technology that involves each law or theory listed in (b).

4. (a) What part of the transportation system do speedometers in automobiles belong to?
   (b) How do drivers control the output of a motor vehicle in response to speedometer information?

5. (a) How can you tell that the engine in **Figure 1** is not an Otto-cycle engine?

Figure 1

   (b) What type of engine is illustrated in **Figure 1**?
   (c) Name two vehicles that normally use this type of engine.

6. Name and describe the four strokes that make up one full cycle of a four-stroke internal combustion engine.

7. List some food organisms that have been selectively bred over time. Why have humans manipulated the process of sexual reproduction in these organisms?

8. (a) What are restriction enzymes? Where are they found in nature?
   (b) What is the purpose of restriction enzymes in genetic engineering?

9. Canadian scientists and engineers have been at the forefront of many technological inventions and innovations. Describe one Canadian technological development in biotechnology.

10. (a) Describe the steps that are involved in the production of a genetically engineered organism using bacterial methods.
    (b) Why do genetic engineers insert marker genes along with transgenes into a host cell's DNA?

Applying Inquiry Skills

11. (a) Design a quantitative investigation to test the effects of aerodynamics on the movement of a motorless toy car. In your description, state the purpose of the investigation, the question(s) to be answered, the materials, and the procedure. Make sure that you include safety precautions in your procedure.
    (b) If possible, carry out the investigation and prepare a report.

12. If you were designing the perfect transportation vehicle, what type of engine would it have? What material(s) would you use to make the body of the vehicle?

13. The metal components of an internal combustion engine, such as the pistons and the cylinder wall, rub against each other as the engine operates. This friction causes a loss of energy in the form of heat. Adding oil to the engine compartment lubricates the metal surfaces and reduces the friction and resulting loss of energy.
    (a) Design a demonstration, using simple household materials, that illustrates the effect of friction on metal objects that rub against each other. Also demonstrate the effect of a lubricant on rubbing metal parts.
    (b) If possible, perform the demonstration for a small group of your classmates.
    (c) Write a brief group report on the purpose of lubricants in internal combustion engines.

14. An internal combustion engine works on the principle that expanding gases exert a force.

(a) Design a demonstration, using a model made with a balloon and a book, to illustrate this principle. If possible, perform your demonstration for a small group of your classmates.

(b) Explain how your demonstration shows the combustion stroke of a four-stroke engine.

(c) What part of your model represents the piston of the engine?

(d) What part of your model represents the combustion of fuel in the cylinder?

(e) Is your model appropriate? Identify any short-comings of your model for demonstrating how an internal combustion engine works.

Making Connections

15. In 1945, Dr. Percy Spencer, an engineer, made a significant discovery that led him to invent a useful household appliance. Conduct research to answer the following questions.

(a) What appliance did Dr. Spencer invent?

(b) How did serendipity play a role in Dr. Spencer's discovery?

16. Conduct research to find out about Alexander Graham Bell, the Canadian inventor of the telephone.

(a) Write a brief biography of Bell, including significant dates, places, and historical events. As well, describe already developed technologies that Bell used to invent the telephone.

(b) There is a genuine competing claim for the invention of the telephone. Identify the other person, and evaluate the counterclaim.

17. **(a)** Describe some of the inventions that have led to the miniaturization of the personal computer.

(b) Choose an industry in which computers are important, such as banking, music, or retail. Create a list of the positive and negative impacts of computers on this industry.

18. **(a)** How do traffic jams add to the air pollution problem?

(b) Suggest two ways in which society could eliminate traffic jams.

19. Figure 2 shows a modern onboard motor-vehicle computer.

Figure 2

(a) Conduct Internet research to determine the functions of onboard computers.

(b) Approximately how many microprocessors does a typical late-model car contain?

(c) Describe two basic engine functions that are controlled by computers in today's motor vehicles.

(d) Discuss some costs, risks, and benefits associated with onboard motor-vehicle computer technology.

20. **(a)** Describe two advantages and two disadvantages of hybrid cars. Think about factors such as safety, cost, environmental impact, and appearance.

(b) Why may producing and using large hybrid trucks be impractical?

21. Research the efforts of concerned individuals and organizations to ensure the safety of genetically engineered foods. Read three related news articles, and write a brief essay on your findings.

22. Research the educational requirements and job prospects of a career in biotechnology. Write a brief report, outlining your findings. Identify any provincial licenses or certificates that are required to enter the field.

Waste

MANAGEMENT

At a municipal waste transfer station in Toronto, an operator guides a garbage truck back to the dumping site. Ten tonnes of garbage are dumped onto the floor, and the process of sorting the garbage begins (**Figure 1**). Thousands of bags of household trash items—such as chicken bones, food scraps, food packages, glass jars, cat litter, broken toys, newspapers (many unread), and junk mail—need to be sorted. The garbage is then compacted and squeezed into other trucks and transferred across the Canada–U.S. border to its final destination—landfill sites just outside Detroit, Michigan.

Figure 1 Garbage collection is a familiar activity in most municipalities.

Every day, up to 150 trucks from the Toronto region carry garbage to Michigan. These truckloads of garbage add up to approximately 1.6 million tonnes per year from the City of Toronto's own collection system and an additional 1.0 million tonnes from private sector garbage disposal companies, for a total of around 2.6 million tonnes annually.

(a) What happens to your garbage? How is it disposed of? How does its disposal affect you?

Similar events occur in every town and city across North America. We all create waste, either directly or indirectly, as individuals, communities, and societies. Most of us accept responsibility for the waste we produce as individuals. We often do not accept responsibility, however, for other sources of waste. Consider, for example, waste from forestry, agriculture, mining, and manufacturing industries; hospitals and medical research facilities; residential and commercial construction; public and private transportation; and electrical generation using fossil fuels and nuclear fuel. We contribute to these wastes as well. We consume agricultural and forestry products, we go to a hospital when we're sick, we paint and renovate our homes, we drive cars, and we use electricity. We all share the responsibility for the wastes that are produced, even if we are not directly involved in their production.

(b) In addition to household garbage and human waste, what types of waste do you produce?

Someone once said that to understand a civilization, studying its garbage would probably reveal more relevant information than studying other types of artifacts. Applying the principles and techniques generally used in archaeology, we can learn much about a society by studying what it throws away and how it disposes of this garbage.

In the early 1970s, Dr. William Rathje, an archaeologist at the University of Arizona, started The Garbage Project. Fresh garbage and landfills were analyzed at 11 sites in the United States, Canada, Mexico, and Australia. The results of the analyses were used to explore waste generation, waste management, dietary consumption, and recycling. Such analyses of household waste are much more common today. **Table 1** summarizes the composition of household wastes in Canada.

Table 1 Composition of Household Waste

Category	% of total (by weight)
Paper and cardboard	28
Organics (food and garden refuse)	34
Plastics	11
Glass	7
Metals	8
Textiles and other	13

Source: OECD Environmental Data Compendium 1999, p. 166

(c) What kind of information could be gathered about a family by studying its garbage?

(d) What could be learned about a society by studying its landfill sites?

(e) Based on the data in **Table 1**, do you think that the volume of waste in landfills can be reduced? Explain.

Since the beginning of time, societies have had to deal with the problem of waste. Waste is unavoidable—a fact of life. Simply eating to stay alive produces waste. All the products we consume in our work and our play use materials and processes that create waste. The nature of the waste problem, however, has changed significantly over time. The quantity of waste and the types of waste are very different now than they were even 100 years ago.

(f) How do you think garbage has changed over the past 100 years? Provide examples to illustrate your answer.

Two factors determine how much waste we produce: the size of the human population and the level of consumption of resources. Over the last few hundred years, the global population has increased dramatically. During the same period, our Western civilization has experienced an industrial and technological revolution. These changes have contributed to the increased generation of waste, much of which is harmful to humans and the environment. This, in turn, has led to a situation—perhaps a crisis—that may threaten the very existence of the human population.

DID **YOU** KNOW?

More Than a Drop in the Ocean
More than 1 billion tonnes of 30 000 different chemicals—including heavy metals, oil hydrocarbons, and radioactive materials—go into the world's oceans each year.

The time is the future, the setting is an archaeological dig in central Canada, and you are the archaeologist in charge of the dig. Your assistants have uncovered an intact domestic garbage container. Inside the container, there are two polyethylene bags that have preserved their contents extremely well. Each item of material in the two bags has been carefully documented. Your teacher will provide you with the list of materials, or you can access it on the Nelson Science Web site.

 www.science.nelson.com

Analyze the list of materials to catch a glimpse into the life of the family that produced the garbage.

(a) Make inferences about
- the year and the time of year that the garbage was created
- the number and the approximate ages of the people in the family
- the socioeconomic status of the family
- the types of activities that the family participated in
- the eating habits or the dietary characteristics of the family

Explain the evidence you used and your reasoning for each inference.

(b) Which of your inferences are you most confident about? Why?

Numerous environmental organizations warn that we are headed down a path of self-destruction. They say that managing the waste we produce should be a global political priority. While some attention has been paid to serious waste events, such as large oil spills, waste management has not become a priority. To date, there has not been the necessary global commitment to waste reduction to ensure that Earth will be a suitable place for future generations to live.

(g) Propose a possible explanation for why waste management has not become a global political priority.

The UN publishes an annual Human Development Index (HDI), which ranks countries according to quality of life. The ranking is based on a number of "quality of life" indicators, such as life expectancy, education, health standards, and income. For nearly a decade, Canada was ranked as the best country in which to live. In 2002, Canada dropped from the number one spot to third. In 2003, Canada was rated eighth overall.

Canada's high quality of life and standard of living has come with a cost. We have a very high level of material consumption. In 2001, the University of Victoria produced a report that compared Canada's environmental record with the records of other countries that belong to the Organization for Economic Cooperation and Development (OECD). Surprisingly, perhaps, Canada has one of the worst records in the industrialized world. Based on an average of 25 indicators, Canada ranks 28th out of the 29 OECD nations

surveyed (**Table 2**). Canada ranks 18th out of 29 for municipal waste production, 23rd out of 27 for the percentage of glass and paper recycled, 24th out of 27 for hazardous waste, and 28th out of 28 for the production of nuclear waste. Fortunately, Canada's performance is improving for several indicators, including reduced air pollution, reduced municipal waste, increased recycling, and improved energy efficiency.

(h) What do you think the top two countries do to earn such high rankings? What do you think Canada has to do to improve its ranking?

(i) Do you think there is a connection between Canada's high ranking on the UN quality of life scale and low ranking on the environmental record among OECD countries? Explain.

Waste comes in all three states—solids, liquids, and gases—but scientists usually categorize them according to their source or properties. While there is some variation in the names, and some overlap among the categories, the five main categories include human waste, solid nuclear waste, household waste, industrial waste, and gaseous waste. In this unit, you will examine different areas of waste production and waste management. Through investigations and activities, you will have an opportunity to develop an understanding of the science and technology associated with waste production and management. As well, you will explore some fundamental environmental, technological, economic, and political issues associated with the disposal and management of different wastes.

Table 2 Ranking of Countries on Environmental Indicators, 2001

Country	Score	Rank
Switzerland	9.20	1
Mexico	10.72	2
Turkey	10.74	3
Austria	11.18	4
Netherlands	11.24	5
Germany	11.30	6
Korea	11.62	7
Denmark	11.84	8
Hungary	12.07	9
Sweden	12.25	10
Czech Republic	12.32	11
Portugal	12.82	12
United Kingdom	13.19	13
Poland	13.25	14
Ireland	13.31	15
Greece	13.38	16
Norway	13.40	17
Italy	14.01	18
Spain	14.25	19
Finland	14.32	20
Japan	14.67	21
Luxembourg	15.45	22
France	15.56	23
New Zealand	15.80	24
Belgium	15.89	25
Iceland	16.52	26
Australia	20.58	27
Canada	21.87	28
United States	22.14	29

Questions to Think About...

As you explore the topics in this unit, keep the following questions in mind:

- Are all the wastes we produce necessary?
- How many can be avoided?
- What types of waste pose environmental problems?
- What types of waste pose risks for human health?
- Do we have a waste crisis?
- How do we best address waste problems?
- What roles do individuals, organizations, communities, and governments play in waste management?
- Who pays for the management of waste?

Unit Task Introduction

There are many other categories of waste, in addition to those you will examine in this unit. For the Unit Task, you will explore a different category of waste. You will use your understanding of the broad waste-management concepts discussed in this unit, as well as your inquiry and communication skills.

You will present your findings using the format of the topics in this unit as a model. Read the description and requirements on pages 138 to 139 before you start the unit topics, so that you can prepare for the Unit Task as you progress through the unit.

A Cost of Living: HOUSEHOLD WASTE

Phillip and Laurie Collins live in a suburb of Halifax. It is Wednesday morning, and Laurie reminds Phillip that it is "green cart" day. Last Wednesday was "regular refuse" day. Every Wednesday is "blue bag" or "recycling" day. Laurie says that she will go to the household hazardous waste depot on her way to work, and drop off the old paint cans and waste paint thinner they found in their basement.

The Halifax Regional Municipality has instituted a program aimed at reducing the amount of waste its citizens produce and the amount of waste put in landfill sites. The program consists of a four-stream system that incorporates composting, recycling, hazardous-waste management, and disposal in landfills. In 1998, the province of Nova Scotia banned putting organic waste in landfills and incinerators. Now Halifax residents are given a mini-bin and a large green cart for the collection of organic materials, such as food scraps and yard clippings. They are also given a blue plastic bag in which to put plastic recyclables for weekly pickup. Other recyclables, such as paper and paper products, are bundled separately and placed with the blue bag (**Figure 1**).

The Halifax program encourages residents to "precycle"—to prevent or reduce waste by thinking about their consumption habits, the products they buy, and the packaging of these products, and then acting accordingly. This program has helped the province have the lowest per-capita waste generation in the country—613 kg compared with the Canadian average of 1019 kg in the year 2000. In just two years, the program has reduced the percentage of waste going to landfills from 80% in 1998 to 71% in 2000.

(a) How is precycling different from recycling?

Figure 1 The Halifax waste management program includes recycling, composting, and disposal.

How often do you think about the quantity or types of garbage you produce? This activity will help you gain an appreciation for what and how much you throw away.

1. For three days (or longer), collect all the solid waste that you and your family produce. Use a table like **Table 1** to record what you collect. Indicate the number of people in your family.

2. At the end of the three days, sort the waste into the following categories: organic, plastic, paper and paper products, metal, hazardous material, and "other." Measure and record the total weight of the waste in each category.

Table 1 Garbage Record

Day 1	Day 2	Day 3
2 eggshells	1 slice toasted bread	
1 cereal box	1 bacon package (plastic and paper)	
3 paper towels		
1 newspaper		

(a) Use your data to estimate the amount of garbage that your family creates in a year.

(b) Which category of waste had the greatest weight? Which category of waste had the greatest volume?

(c) Estimate your per-capita weight of garbage per year.

(d) How does your estimate compare with the values provided by other sources?

(e) What percentage of your garbage (by weight) is recyclable?

(f) Do you think that what you collected is a representative sample of your family's garbage? Explain.

(g) How might you reduce the amount of garbage that your family produces?

(h) Compare your family's garbage production with the garbage production of classmates' families (with the same number of people).

(i) If archaeologists examined your garbage sometime in the future, what conclusions do you think they would make about your lifestyle?

Waste management was once thought of as simply picking up garbage and dumping it in a hole in the ground. Today, **waste management** is much more sophisticated. It is defined as the disposal, processing, controlling, recycling, and reusing of solid, liquid, and gaseous waste in such a way as to maintain a habitable environment. In other words, it is an attempt to manage our waste in order to ensure that we continue to have a suitable place to live.

DID **YOU** KNOW?

Trash History
The first municipal garbage dump was created in Athens, Greece, in 400 B.C.E. The first sanitation force was created by the Romans in 200 C.E. Two-person teams walked along the streets, picked up garbage, and threw it in a wagon.

(b) What are the main elements of the solid waste management program in your municipality?

The verb "waste" has several meanings, including "to consume, spend, or expend thoughtlessly or carelessly." The noun "waste" refers to "a useless or worthless byproduct; garbage or trash." Both of these definitions are appropriate when thinking about waste as a social and environmental concern. Some of our waste comes from normal, everyday, essential activities, such as eating. Other waste comes from consuming or spending thoughtlessly or carelessly. How much of our waste is avoidable, and how much is unavoidable? How many of our essential products (such as foods) do we waste? How do we best deal with the waste that we produce?

(c) List ten wastes that you consider to be unavoidable and ten wastes that you consider to be avoidable.

Municipal Solid Waste Management Methods

In his report called State of the World 1998, environmentalist Lester R. Brown says that "…we are behaving as if we have no children, as though there will not be a next generation."

The fundamental goal of solid waste management is to reduce the amount of waste that is produced. The ideal method for managing waste is not to produce it. Unfortunately, the ideal is practically impossible to achieve. The current reality is that we do produce waste and we have to find the most economical and environmentally friendly methods for managing it. There are two main components of municipal solid waste management: diversion and disposal. **Diversion** involves methods that do not result in waste going to landfills or incinerators. Diversion includes reducing, recycling, reusing, and composting. **Disposal** involves storing waste in landfill sites or incinerating (burning) it.

The collecting, recycling, and disposal of garbage has become a vast economic enterprise, operated by municipalities and private industries. In 2000, the Waste Management Industry Survey, conducted by Statistics Canada, indicated that nearly 11 million tonnes of residential waste were disposed of, at a total cost of nearly $6 billion. There were 31 000 people employed by the waste management industry (public and private), and the industry generated revenues of over $4 billion.

Diversion's Three Rs: Reducing, Recycling, Reusing

The aim of **reducing** is simply to create less garbage. The less garbage produced, the less garbage there is to manage. This may sound simple, but it is difficult to achieve because it requires a change in peoples' knowledge and attitudes and a corresponding change in their behaviour. Reducing garbage involves changes in consumption patterns: that is, buying less and buying products that produce less garbage. Unfortunately, convincing consumers to change their lifestyles cannot be done quickly. People are reluctant to give up the "good life." Furthermore, most people do not tend to think beyond their own lifetime, to consider the implications of their actions for future generations.

Recycling, the remanufacture of a material after it has been used, is the most common form of diversion. Recycling is becoming an accepted part of consumer behaviour (**Figure 2**). Remanufacturing does not mean that recycled materials are made into the original products. For example, plastic pop bottles are not recycled into new pop bottles. Instead, plastic from pop bottles is made into products such as clothing, tote bags, carpet, sewer pipes, patio furniture, and even plastic lumber.

Figure 2 Glass, paper, aluminum, and certain plastics are the most commonly recycled materials.

Recent estimates indicate that 80% of Canadian households participate in some form of recycling. A public-opinion survey would probably find few people who disagree with the principle of recycling. While there may be an economic incentive to recycle, most people claim that they do it for the environment. They claim that recycling is a convenient way for 21st-century consumers to ease their guilt for overconsumption and to avoid using more appropriate methods for dealing with the growing waste problem. Skeptics argue that recycling justifies waste. People think that throwing something away is okay if it's going to be recycled. In other words, recycling is considered a licence to consume. The success of recycling, and its popularity among the public, is viewed as undermining the efforts of municipalities to reduce the amount of waste produced.

There are limits to recycling, and these limits are at the heart of the skeptics' arguments. At some point, recycling can become impractical because it is not cost-effective or because it has hidden environmental impacts. For example, if more energy is used to collect, transport, and reprocess a material than would be used to produce a new material, then recycling may not make sense. If the cost of a product made from recycled material is too high, then people will not buy the product and recycling becomes ineffective. In addition, some products cannot be recycled indefinitely. The wood fibres that paper is made from become shorter and shorter each time they are recycled, until they eventually become unusable for paper production. At this point, the wood fibres have to be used for another purpose, such as fuel for generating heat or electricity.

Reusing is a long-term strategy that involves getting maximum use out of a product. It involves using a product for different purposes before it is discarded or recycled. Reusing reinforces both recycling and reducing strategies by eliminating the need to buy new products and by extending the lives of existing products. For example, garage sales and social service organizations give people a chance to

Figure 3 The life of any product is extended by reusing it.

reuse clothing and other items that might otherwise end up in landfills (**Figure 3**). As the saying goes, "One person's junk is another person's treasure."

Composting

Composting is a centuries-old method of dealing with waste. It is the original recycling program! In **composting**, organic matter is broken down by bacteria and other organisms into a nutrient-rich material that can be used to fertilize soil. Organic matter typically accounts for 20% to 30% of our waste. Composting provides an opportunity to divert a significant amount of this waste from landfill.

Composting has always been part of farm life and is becoming more and more common in urban areas. Many families have set up composting bins in their backyards and are composting yard clippings and food scraps (excluding meats, fats, and oils) to recycle the nutrients (**Figure 4**). They use the resulting compost to feed their lawns and gardens. Backyard composting is easy and manageable, but it requires a personal commitment to waste reduction. There are also small, indoor composters available for people living in apartments that, when managed properly, do not produce any foul odours.

Figure 4 Backyard composting is easy and clean.

Large-scale municipal composting programs relieve individuals of the responsibility for composting. All individuals have to do is separate the organic matter (including meats, fats, and oils) from household waste for curbside collection. Unfortunately, there is some resistance to the establishment of large-scale compost facilities, because of the unpleasant odour caused by rotting organic matter.

Disposal

Over the past century, the volume of household waste has increased dramatically. At the beginning of the 20th century, most garbage was organic matter, which could be burned or allowed to biodegrade in pits, backyards, and small dumpsites. Some people routinely disposed of garbage in bodies of water, such as lakes, rivers, or the oceans. As time went on, the proportion of organic waste decreased, and the proportion of paper, glass, metal, and plastics increased exponentially. Today, a typical North American generates and throws away an estimated 9.8 kg of garbage each week. Massive quantities of garbage are now dumped in enormous landfill sites or burned in incinerators. Both landfills and incinerators produce toxic chemicals, which have the potential to pollute air, ground, and water. Growing mountains of garbage are a legacy of North Americans' high rate of consumption.

Until the 1960s, garbage was routinely dumped into swamps and marshes, which were regarded as wastelands rather than biologically productive areas. Once a wetland was filled with waste, it was covered with soil and used as a building site. Today, most municipalities handle garbage with a lot more thought. They try to divert as much garbage from dumps and landfills as possible. Then they dispose of the remaining waste much more carefully, using a variety of methods.

Landfills

Most municipalities have a **landfill**: a large tract of land where garbage is stored. A landfill is specially designed so that garbage is isolated from the surrounding environment (air, land, and water), as shown in **Figure 5**.

A landfill has a liner on the bottom that separates the garbage above from the soil below. The liner also separates and protects the ground water from the contaminated water that accumulates in the landfill. The liner may be a natural material (such as clay), a synthetic material (a plastic such as polyethylene or polyvinylchloride), or a combination of the two. Most landfills include a method for releasing or collecting the methane gas that is produced as garbage decomposes. As well, most landfills include a method for collecting the **leachate**—the water and other liquids that percolate down through the garbage. The garbage is compacted by heavy machinery (**Figure 6**) into areas called cells. After one or two days, a cell is covered with soil and further compacted by heavy equipment. Compacting reduces the amount of space taken up by the garbage by eliminating the air spaces in the cells. This increases the amount of garbage that the landfill can hold, thereby extending the life of the landfill.

One of the concerns with landfills is that a liner may develop a leak and contaminated water may escape into the ground water. Landfill sites receive hundreds

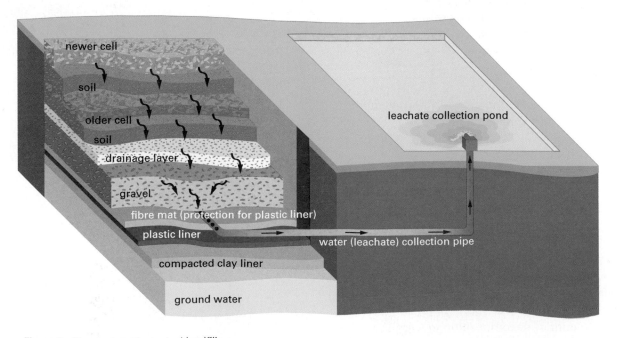

Figure 5 The design of a typical landfill.

Figure 6 To conserve space in a landfill, the volume of garbage must be reduced by eliminating air space.

of thousands of bottles that contain trace amounts of hazardous materials. These trace amounts can accumulate in the water in a landfill. Researchers have found hazardous organic chemicals leaching into ground water from landfill sites that never received industrial waste. The chemicals apparently came from residues of common household cleaners and from plastic containers, such as shampoo bottles. As household garbage has become increasingly toxic, scientists have responded by creating better landfill liners to reduce contact between the garbage and the natural environment. Many concerned citizens, environmentalists, and scientists strongly advocate a different approach: dramatically reducing the volume of garbage we generate and eliminating hazardous materials entirely from household garbage.

Although some breakdown of garbage does occur, this is not the purpose of landfills. Landfills are designed simply to bury garbage. The garbage that is dumped in a landfill is likely to stay there for a very long time. Researchers have found 50-year-old newspapers that are still readable. Even after a landfill is closed, it must be monitored and maintained for decades.

B1.2 Investigation | FACTORS AFFECTING DECOMPOSITION IN LANDFILLS >

Landfills are intended simply as a storage area for garbage. Some decomposition of organic matter does occur, but much of the garbage remains unchanged. Since reduction of volume is one of the goals of landfills, encouraging decomposition may be beneficial. In this investigation, you will determine if exposure to air or water affects the amount of decomposition that occurs in a landfill.

Question
How does exposure to air and water affect the amount of decomposition that occurs in a landfill?

Prediction
(a) Make a prediction about the relationships between air and water exposure and the amount of decomposition of household garbage in a landfill.

Experimental Design
You will expose four different landfill setups to different air and water conditions. You will observe the landfills over a period of time, and describe the amount of decomposition in each.

Inquiry Skills

○ Questioning	● Planning	● Analyzing
● Hypothesizing	● Conducting	● Evaluating
● Predicting	● Recording	● Communicating

Materials
4 clear plastic wide-mouth containers (bottles or jars)
samples of typical household waste (such as a
    newspaper, apple cores, potato peelings,
    used tea bags, plastics, light cardboard,
    and food wrappers)
soil
2 plastic sheets (can be cut from a garbage bag)
tape
2 pieces of cloth

 Do not include any human or animal products in your waste.

Procedure

1. Label the containers A, B, C, and D. Place equal types and proportions of a variety of household waste in each container. Make sure that you fill all the containers to the top. If the contents are packed down (see steps 2 to 5), add more garbage to fill the containers to the top.

2. Cover the waste in container A with a layer of soil, and pack down tightly to eliminate as much air space as possible. Use the plastic sheet to seal the top of the container. Leave as little air space as possible between the garbage and the plastic sheet.

3. Fill container B with waste, but do not pack it down. Cover the waste with a layer of soil. Cover the container loosely with a piece of cloth so that air may enter.

4. Lightly spray the contents of container C with water as you place them in the container. As in container A, cover the waste with a layer of soil and pack down tightly to eliminate air space. Dampen the soil with water. Seal the container.

5. Container D should be set up like container B. Fill it with waste, but do not pack it down. Dampen the contents with water. Cover the waste with a layer of soil, and dampen the soil. Cover the container with a piece of cloth. Gently stir and lightly water the contents at least once each week, or more often if the contents are dry.

6. Leave the containers for four to six weeks. At the end of this time, describe the amount of decomposition in each container. Record your descriptions in a table similar to **Table 2**.

Table 2 Observation Table

Container	Description of decomposition
A	
B	
C	
D	

 Use protective gloves when observing the contents of containers B and D. Observe the contents of the sealed containers without opening them. Dispose of the sealed containers without opening them.

Analysis

(b) In which container did the most decomposition occur? Describe how the contents of this container were different from the contents of the other containers.

(c) Based on your observations, which materials are resistant to decomposition, regardless of the conditions?

Evaluation

(d) Did your observations support your Prediction?

(e) How does the treatment used in container D compare with composting? How would you modify it to create a better waste management strategy?

(f) Evaluate the Experimental Design. How would you modify it to determine more accurately the effects of air and water on the decomposition of household waste?

Synthesis

(g) Create a hypothesis to explain your observations and briefly describe a procedure that could be used to test your hypothesis.

(h) Based on the results of your investigation, make a recommendation that best addresses the management of household waste.

Incineration

Incineration involves simply burning garbage. The advantage of incineration is that it reduces the volume of garbage. This, in turn, reduces the load on landfills. Large-scale incinerators burn garbage at high temperatures and reduce the mass destined for landfills very effectively (**Figure 7**). Incineration, however, releases toxic chemicals into the atmosphere and produces solid residues that contain toxic substances, such as heavy metals (mercury, lead, cadmium) and organic compounds. As a result, there is growing resistance to incineration and its use appears to be decreasing.

Biomedical waste, such as body parts and microbiological cultures, must be incinerated for health reasons. This waste represents a very small fraction of the total waste produced and is often incinerated on site.

Advanced thermal treatment (ATT) is a technology that is based on incineration. It subjects organic matter to extremely high temperatures, either in the absence of oxygen or air (pyrolysis) or in the presence of small amounts of oxygen (thermal gasification). A mixture of combustible gases (methane and other hydrocarbons, and hydrogen) and carbon monoxide are produced.

One advantage of ATT is that these gases can be used as fuels to generate heat and/or electricity. ATT has been used for more than 50 years to burn materials such as coal and wood waste. It could be used to turn the organic matter in municipal solid waste into a usable energy source. Another advantage of ATT is that it significantly reduces the leftover solid materials that have to be put in landfills. The city of Toronto is investigating an ATT system as part of its overall waste management plan.

There are also disadvantages, however. Critics claim that ATT will just reduce consumers' guilt and justify disposing of organic matter in garbage, knowing that it will be used as an energy source. Another disadvantage is that the leftover residue may still contain toxic substances that could leach into the ground water.

Biodegradation

Biodegradation is the breakdown of organic matter by living things, such as bacteria, fungi, insects, and worms. Biodegradation is nature's method of recycling. Organic matter is broken down so that its nutrients are available for other living things, especially plants. There are two types of biodegradation: anaerobic digestion and aerobic digestion.

Anaerobic digestion uses microorganisms to break down organic matter or waste biomass in the absence of oxygen. This process results in three products: biogas (typically 55% to 65% methane and 35% to 45% carbon dioxide), a solid material called a digestate, and a liquid called a leachate. Anaerobic digestion facilities are designed to produce and capture biogas, which is used as an energy source. The digestate and leachate may be composted and used as fertilizer. Anaerobic digestion is often used on cattle or hog farms. The manure is collected and fed into an anaerobic digestion facility, and the biogas produced is used to run a generator on the farm.

Aerobic digestion is similar to anaerobic digestion, but it involves two steps. First, organic matter is oxidized through exposure to air. Then, it is oxidized through the cellular respiration of bacteria and other microorganisms that require oxygen. During aerobic digestion, pollutants are broken down into carbon dioxide, water, nitrates, and sulfates. Aerobic digestion is used in composting and in wastewater treatment facilities.

Figure 7 Incinerators reduce the volume of garbage that is sent to landfills.

Waste disposal and recycling are carried out in Canada by both private and public waste disposal facilities. Your teacher will provide you with four tables (A–D) that contain data on waste disposal and recycling in Canada. Use the data to answer the following questions.

Analysis

(a) Which provinces showed an increase in the generation of waste from 1998 to 2000? Which provinces showed a decrease?

(b) Based on the most recent statistics, which province generates the most waste per capita? Which province generates the least waste per capita?

(c) In which provinces has the amount of waste decreased over the five-year period represented in Table A? In which provinces has the amount of waste increased?

(d) Which province had the greatest decrease in waste from 1996 to 2000?

(e) Which province had the greatest decrease in waste per capita from 1996 to 2000?

(f) Which province showed the greatest increase in diversion rates from 1998 to 2000? Which province showed the least increase in diversion rates?

(g) Evaluate the following statement: "The increase in the total amount of waste generated in Ontario from 1996 to 2000 is due to the increase in population during this period."

(h) In which category is the greatest amount of waste recycled?

(i) In 2000, what percentage of the total recycled materials were paper and paper products? What percentage were metals?

(j) In which province does composting make up the most significant part of the recycling program? What evidence allowed you to reach this conclusion?

(k) Of the total amount of waste produced in 2000, what percentage is prepared for recycling? (*Hint:* Use information from Tables B and C.)

(l) How did the percentage of paper and paper products recycled change from 1998 to 2000? Show your calculations.

Evaluation

(m) Do these data present an accurate picture of the status of recycling efforts in Canada? Explain why or why not.

(n) The per capita amount of waste diverted in Canada increased from 222 kg/person in 1998 to 244 kg/person in 2000. Is this increase significant? Explain.

Synthesis

(o) Propose a possible explanation for the decrease in the amount of copper and aluminum recycled from 1998 to 2000.

(p) Imagine that you are the Federal Minister of Environment Canada. You have a budget of $50 million for recycling. Based on the available data, which areas would you target? Explain your reasoning.

(q) Identify and describe any overall trends in waste generation, disposal, and diversion. As a country, are we moving in the right direction? Explain.

✓ Check Your Understanding

1. What is the main goal of all the methods of waste disposal?

2. Explain the main criticism of the recycling approach to waste management. Is this a fair criticism?

3. Describe a situation in which recycling may not be the best solution to waste management.

4. Explain the difference between incineration and ATT.

Not In My Backyard

One of the biggest problems in waste management is the NIMBY principle. **NIMBY** stands for "not in my backyard" and refers to the resistance of residents to new landfills, incinerators, recycling centres, composting facilities, and other "undesirable projects" in their neighbourhood. When people are asked if household garbage should be put in well-designed landfills, the typical reaction is "Yes, but not here." Waste disposal is deemed a necessary evil, but everyone wants it done somewhere else—not in their backyard. Many people believe that landfills and other waste management facilities will cause problems for their neighbourhood, such as increased traffic, noise, dust, and litter, ground-water contamination, pollution, and decreased property values. But if garbage cannot be put in their neighbourhood, where should it go? Waste does not just disappear—it has to go somewhere. Is it ever acceptable to dispose of our garbage in someone else's backyard? What if we pay to do this? Do all our waste disposal problems arise because of the NIMBY principle?

CASE STUDY

The Adams Mine Landfill Proposal

The proposed Adams Mine landfill site is located near Kirkland Lake in Northern Ontario. Adams Mine was an iron ore mine that was operated by Dofasco Inc. from 1964 to 1990 (**Figure 8**). When the mine closed, the site was purchased by Notre Development Corporation, part of a consortium of companies called Rail Cycle North (RCN). Notre was established to provide waste disposal services for Ontario markets. Notre developed a landfill design and, in 1996, proposed the south pit of the mine as a landfill site for non-toxic municipal waste (**Figure 9**). The south pit is about 183 m deep and can hold approximately 20 million tonnes of non-hazardous municipal waste deposited over 20 years.

The environmental assessment that is required under the current provincial Environmental Protection Act was carried out over the following three years. In 1999, the Ministry of the

Figure 8 The south pit of Adams Mine, the site of the proposed landfill

Environment approved the Adams Mine landfill site. As one of the conditions of approval, Notre also had to get approval under the Ontario Water Resources Act and permission to purchase Crown land from the Ministry of Natural Resources. In all, Notre had to get approval from three different government bodies.

During the environmental assessment, a group called the Adams Mine Intervention Coalition opposed the proposal. The Coalition represented local residents and farmers. However, five successive municipal councils in the town of Kirkland Lake had supported the development of the Adams Mine landfill site.

In 2000, the municipal government of the Greater Toronto Area issued a request for proposals for disposal of its solid non-toxic municipal waste. The proposal from RCN was one of eight proposals that were considered by the Toronto City Council. Five of these proposals involved disposal sites in the United States. Each proposal was evaluated using the same three criteria: environmental impact, cost, and economic benefit. The RCN proposal ranked first. So, on August 3, 2000, the Toronto City Council approved the proposal to ship Toronto's waste to the Adams Mine landfill site. Environmental

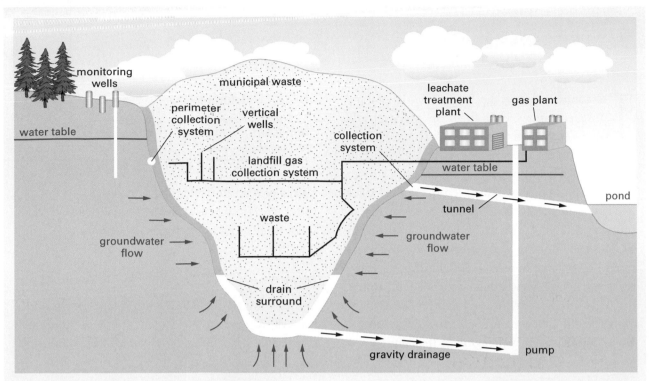

Figure 9 Proposed design of the Adams Mine landfill site

organizations targeted this decision and created a storm of protest. In addition, the Temiskaming First Nation claimed Aboriginal title to the Adams Mine area and stated its intention to initiate a land claim. In December 2001, the Toronto City Council voted to abandon its earlier decision and to investigate an alternative waste disposal solution. Since the closure of Toronto's Keele Valley landfill site in December 2002, all municipal waste from the city of Toronto have been shipped across the border to the Republic landfill site in Michigan.

The Adams Mine landfill proposal created an extremely complicated and controversial situation, which continues to be debated more than a decade after it was initially presented. The existing contract between the city of Toronto and the Republic landfill site in Michigan expires in 2005. Opponents of the Adams Mine landfill site are concerned that the original proposal will be revisited as a potential solution in the future. As the debate has dragged on, the situation has escalated from initial disagreement to complete bitterness and resentment on both sides.

(a) What approvals are required in order to use a location as a landfill site? What levels of government are involved in these approvals?

(b) Why do you think the municipal councils of the town of Kirkland Lake approved of the Adams Mine proposal when many of the local residents and organizations were against it?

(c) Why did the Toronto City Council reverse its initial decision on the Adams Mine landfill site?

(d) Suggest other criteria that the Toronto City Council might or should have included in their evaluation of the proposals.

B1: A Cost of Living: Household Waste **87**

Explore *an* Issue

>

Do We Have a Waste Management Crisis?

The controversy over the Adams Mine landfill proposal continues. Both the proponents and the opponents claim that they have common sense, sound reasoning, and scientific evidence to support their claims. The proponents claim that they are simply presenting a proposal that is economically feasible and environmentally safe. The opponents say that big business, a major supporter of the provincial government, is behind the proposal. They accuse the government of participating in a secret, backroom deal to revive the Adams Mine landfill proposal in the future.

This situation involves the city of Toronto and the Kirkland Lake area in Ontario, but the same issues could arise in any region of the country.

Decision-Making Skills

○ Define the Issue ● Identify Alternatives
● Research   ● Analyze the Issue
● Defend a Decision ○ Evaluate

You may wish to make the following questions more relevant by substituting the name of your town or city and applying the information to your own area.

Part 1

Table 3 summarizes some of the claims from both sides of the controversy. Note that not all the claims of one side are countered by claims of the other side.

Table 3 Some Opposing Claims of the Adams Mine Landfill Proposal

Proponents' claims	Opponents' claims
The proposal has undergone an environmental assessment and has received approval from the Ministry of the Environment.	The "hydraulic containment" system has not been adequately tested, and there is no history of successful implementation.
The landfill will be covered with several layers of drainage material, soil, and plant cover to ensure that very little precipitation will percolate down into the waste.	The design indicates that water will flow only into the pit. However, the surrounding rock may be fractured from blasting during the mine's operation. This would allow contaminated water to leak into the ground and surface water of the surrounding area.
The "hydraulic containment system" will ensure that contaminated water will not escape into the surrounding ground water.	
The project includes a leachate treatment plant.	The leachate treatment will not remove all the contaminants from the wastewater before it is released into the Messima River.
The gas produced by biodegradation will be collected and used as an energy source.	The drainage pipes and gravel cover may not last over the long term, and leachate could leak into the surrounding ground water.
The site is located 7 km from the nearest residential area, so the effects of irritants (such as noise, odour, and dust) will be minimized.	Areas adjacent to the Adams Mine show high mineral potential. The landfill would prevent any mining in surrounding areas because a mineshaft or pit could change the ground-water flow, allowing contaminants to escape from the landfill.
The site is a former mine, so the visual impact will not be significant—at least no worse than the former mine.	
The waste will be shipped by rail, so there will be no increase in truck traffic on the highways.	An estimated 90% to 95% of local residents oppose the proposal.
The proposal will not interfere with any potential residential or commercial developments in the area.	The proposal does not consider the Algonquin Nation's land rights in the area.
The proposal is more economical than the existing alternative (shipping waste to Michigan).	The proposal is perceived as an easy solution, which does not encourage reducing and recycling.
Jobs will be created, since people will be needed to transport the waste and operate the landfill site.	

1. Use the links at the Nelson Web site to find more claims on both sides. Analyze these claims, and determine whether they are based on factual information and scientific evidence or simply on the opinions of the proponents or opponents.

 www.science.nelson.com

2. Summarize the economic benefits of the Adams Mine landfill site for the surrounding region. How does the projected revenue for the Adams Mine landfill site compare with the revenue generated by existing landfill sites? Who stands to benefit the most?

3. Based on the evidence available, why do you think the city of Toronto reversed its decision to ship Toronto's waste to the Adams Mine landfill site? In your opinion, was reversing the decision the right thing to do? Justify your position.

4. In your group, discuss the following statement: "It is appropriate to ship garbage to another town/province/country if the recipients are willing to accept it, for the right price." In your discussion, create a definition of "willing host." As a group, reach a consensus position on the statement and provide at least three arguments to justify your position.

Part 2

Imagine that you are a member of the Toronto City Council. You are asked to participate in a debate about the city's municipal waste strategy (see **Appendix A7** on how to prepare a formal debate). In preparing for the debate, you will research and write an evaluation report. Your teacher will provide you with a copy of the report of the city's Waste Diversion Task Force 2010, a copy of the current contract with the Republic landfill site, and other relevant documents.

5. Using the information provided by your teacher, information available at the Nelson Web site, and any other available resources, evaluate the current disposal strategy for the city of Toronto (shipping waste to the landfill in Michigan).

 www.science.nelson.com

Your evaluation should be based on the following three criteria: environmental impact, cost, and economic benefits (such as employment opportunities).

(a) Summarize your evaluation in point form, under the three criteria.

(b) Rank the three criteria, based on their importance.

(c) Is the current waste management strategy appropriate for the long term? Why or why not?

6. In a small group, you will choose (or be assigned) a position on the following question: "Do we really have a landfill crisis, or are we just experiencing the NIMBY principle in action? (**Figure 10**)" You will debate this question during a special sitting of the council. Your group will present its position, using appropriate supporting evidence. At the end of the council sitting, individual members will no longer be tied to their initial group position and will be able to choose their own position on the question. A class vote will be held to determine the consensus position.

Figure 10 Most people do not want a landfill in their backyard.

SUMMARY

- The fundamental goal of any waste management strategy is to reduce the amount of waste to be managed.
- Diversion and disposal are the two main components of all waste management strategies.
- The three Rs of waste management are reducing, recycling, and reusing. Reduction is considered to be the most effective, although recycling is the most prevalent.
- Skeptics claim that recycling is a licence to consume, or a way to ease our guilt for over-consumption.
- Composting is a form of recycling that returns organic matter to the soil.
- Landfilling is a method of storing garbage underground while isolating it from the surrounding environment.
- Incineration reduces the volume of garbage by burning it. ATT (pyrolysis and thermal gasification) involves incineration at very high temperatures.
- Biodegradation relies on living organisms (e.g., bacteria, fungi, insects) to break down the

organic material in household waste. The products are biogas, a digestate, and a leachate.
- The NIMBY ("not in my backyard") principle is one of the biggest problems in waste management.
- Garbage does not just disappear—it has to go somewhere.
- The Adams Mine landfill proposal was initiated in 1996 and was accepted by the Toronto City Council in 2000. The council rescinded its decision in 2001, but the situation is still hotly debated.
- The city of Toronto ships its non-toxic municipal waste to a landfill site in Michigan, U.S.A.

Key Terms

waste management	**leachate**
diversion	**incineration**
disposal	**advanced thermal**
reducing	**treatment (ATT)**
recycling	**biodegradation**
reusing	**anaerobic digestion**
composting	**aerobic digestion**
landfill	**NIMBY**

ASSESSMENT

Understanding Concepts

1. Explain the two main components of all waste management strategies.

2. Briefly describe the two main methods of disposing of waste. Outline the advantages and disadvantages of each method.

3. Of the three Rs of waste management, which R is most effective? Explain why.

4. Why is reducing waste more difficult to achieve than recycling? Use examples to illustrate your answer.

5. Give five practical examples of how reusing products and materials can contribute to waste reduction.

6. Explain the difference between pyrolysis and thermal gasification.

Applying Inquiry Skills

7. Use the two utility bills (**Figure 11**), from two different municipalities, to answer the following questions.

UTILITY BILL 1	
1/10/2003 – 1/11/2003	
Water rate – $0.005/litre Consumption – 7648 litres	
Sewer rate – $0.002/litre Usage – 7648 litres	
Garbage flat fee – $15.00	
CHARGES	
Water	$38.24
Sewer	$15.30
Garbage	$15.00
Total Charges:	**$68.54**

UTILITY BILL 2	
1/10/2003 – 1/11/2003	
Water flat fee – $35.00	
Sewer flat fee – $20.00	
Garbage rate – $1.50/kg Usage – 10 kg	
CHARGES	
Water	$35.00
Sewer	$20.00
Garbage	$15.00
Total Charges:	**$70.00**

Figure 11 These utility bills are from two different municipalities.

(a) Which municipality encourages the three Rs of waste management? Explain your answer.

(b) Which municipality do you think has the best waste management strategy? Justify your answer.

(c) Is it more appropriate to charge for garbage collection by weight or by volume? Explain. What are the advantages and disadvantages of each approach?

(d) Propose an alternative strategy that promotes the more appropriate approach to conservation and waste management.

8. The ABC Energy Company claims that incinerating plastic bottles is more cost-effective and environmentally friendly than recycling them. Describe a procedure to evaluate and compare recycling and incineration objectively, as waste management strategies.

Making Connections

9. How do you think new technologies have affected our lifestyle and our generation of garbage? Provide several examples to illustrate your answer. Can new technologies also provide a solution to garbage problems? Explain.

10. Explain how each situation could affect the quantity and kinds of household garbage.
   (a) living in a city
   (b) living in a one-bedroom apartment in an apartment building
   (c) living in a rural area and having a vegetable garden
   (d) having two working parents and three children in a family
   (e) having three young children in a family
   (f) having four teenagers in a family
   (g) living in a climate where the average temperature is 20°C
   (h) living in a climate where the average temperature is 10°C
   (i) having a family income greater than $100 000

11. There are many old sayings that reflect the need to conserve or create products that last. Here are a few:
   • Waste not, want not.
   • An ounce of prevention is worth a pound of cure.
   • Built to last a lifetime

   Research current sayings or advertising slogans that reflect our modern lifestyle. How do these sayings or slogans reflect our attitudes to waste management? Create a saying or slogan that reflects what you consider to be an appropriate approach to waste management.

12. Research the position of the current Ontario government on the Adams Mine proposal. Evaluate this position from each of the following perspectives: political, economic, and environmental.

 GO www.science.nelson.com

13. The goal of the city of Toronto's waste management plan is to increase the diversion of solid waste from landfill from just over 30% in 2003 to over 60% by 2006, and to 100% by 2010. Assess this goal, and decide whether or not it is realistic. Explain your reasoning.

14. How should we deal with the NIMBY principle in our approach to waste management?

15. In addition to ordinary household garbage that is placed at the curb for collection, households produce toxic waste, which may have an impact on people and the environment. Select one of the following categories of toxic waste:
   • pesticides
   • paint, paint thinners, and other solvents
   • motor oils and other vehicle fluids
   • soaps, detergents, drain cleaners, and other cleaning products

   Use the Internet and other sources to investigate the potential effects on people and the environment. Present your findings in a report. In your report, include
   • the nature of the waste (chemical composition, toxicity, and so on)
   • the estimated volume of the waste in your province and in Canada (per capita and total)
   • the methods used to dispose of the waste
   • the potential impacts on human health and the environment
   • programs/strategies aimed at eliminating the problem or reducing the environmental impact

 GO www.science.nelson.com

Reflecting

16. Based on your new understanding of household waste management, how do you and your family rate? Are you part of the problem or part of the solution? What can you do to improve your contribution to the waste management solution?

Flush It *and* Forget It: HUMAN WASTE

"When you gotta go, you gotta go!" Such is the nature of all living things, including humans. We breathe, eat, drink, and produce waste. We produce waste because we breathe, eat, and drink. The body digests (breaks down) food so that it can be used in metabolic processes. All the metabolic processes produce metabolic waste. The body gets rid of digestive waste (feces) through egestion and metabolic waste (sweat and urine) through excretion. In this topic, the products of both egestion and excretion will be referred to collectively as **human waste**.

Most animals are inclined to deposit their bodily waste on the ground. Some animals, such as cats, dig a shallow hole and bury their feces and urine. In primitive times, humans were no different than other animals. Their waste are deposited whenever and wherever nature called.

As humans became less nomadic and settled in towns and cities, the management of human waste became more complex. More people produced more waste, and it was no longer appropriate to deposit the waste just anywhere. The Romans developed a system of aqueducts to bring water into residential areas. The water was used for drinking and for flushing the sewers, or open gutters, to carry human waste away from public toilets and from the first "flush" toilets in the homes of the privileged.

In rural areas, where population density was low, there were no environmental problems associated with dumping human waste in a hole in the ground. This was—and is—the basic principle of the outhouse (**Figure 1**). The outhouse was invented when privacy became important in human social evolution. People dug a hole in the ground and built a shelter over it. When the hole was nearly filled with waste, they dug another hole and moved the shelter over the new hole. The soil from the new hole was used to cover the first hole. The "privy" was usually located some distance from the home and the water supply, and it was designed with some sort of ventilation to ensure that the visit would not be unbearable. Another invention, the chamber pot (**Figure 2**), provided convenience. By having a chamber pot in the bedroom, nighttime visits to the privy could be avoided.

Figure 2 The chamber pot offered privacy and convenience, but it had to be emptied.

The development of large urban centres increased the complexity of human waste management. The outhouse and chamber pot were no longer adequate for several reasons, including the sheer volume of the waste, sanitation concerns, and the evolution of social norms that made these methods of waste management unacceptable. Today, the

Figure 1 The outhouse or privy—not luxurious, but effective when nature calls

In modern homes, the drains from kitchen and bathroom sinks, bathtubs, showers, and toilets are all connected to the same drainage system. All the wastewater ends up at the same place—the wastewater treatment facility.

1. For two days, measure the amount of water you, personally, use for drinking, cooking, personal hygiene, flushing, and other activities. Record your water-use activities and the amounts used in a table similar to **Table 1**.

Table 1 Sample Observations

Water-use activity	Amount of water used (L)
showering	40.0
flushing toilet	10.0
brushing teeth	0.50
drinking tea/coffee for breakfast	0.25
washing hands before lunch	2.0

2. Remember to record your water usage at home, at school, and at other locations. If you cannot measure the amount of water used, estimate the amount.

(a) Calculate your average daily water usage. Approximately how much do you use per year?

(b) How much water do you use daily for flushing the toilet? What proportion or percentage of the total does this represent?

(c) Do you think your water usage is about average? Explain.

(d) Identify the source of the water you use for
   (i) drinking and cooking
   (ii) flushing the toilet
   (iii) watering the lawn
   (iv) washing the car
   (v) showering

(e) Comment on your answers in (d). Is there anything unusual about your answers?

(f) What happens to the water that you use every day?

sewer system of a typical city consists of hundreds of kilometres of underground pipes, with flush toilets attached at the receiving ends. Flush toilets use millions of litres of water to move human waste from homes and other buildings to a central sewage treatment plant, more politely known as a wastewater treatment facility. Except for the toilets, the whole system and its operation are "out of sight, out of mind" for the average citizen.

(a) Does your community have a wastewater treatment facility? Where is it located? Who operates it?

Some people believe that the invention of the modern flush toilet and the treatment of wastewater are two of the greatest advancements in public health. Modern sanitation facilities have practically eliminated diseases such as typhoid and cholera in the Western world. Other people claim that the flush toilet has been an environmental disaster, overusing and polluting our water supplies and breaking the nutrient cycle. Moving human waste in a stream of clean, potable water, and then cleaning the water again, is a complex

and expensive process of questionable effectiveness. What do we need to remove from the water during the treatment? How clean is the water after treatment? What happens to the water after it is "cleaned"? What happens to the solid waste that is removed from the water? These are questions that we seldom think about when we turn on a tap or flush a toilet.

(b) Explain your understanding of the saying "the solution to pollution is dilution."

(c) Most people feel uncomfortable about discussing human waste. Describe your level of comfort or discomfort about discussing this topic.

DID **YOU** KNOW?

Pure Water for the Toilet
Less than 3% of the municipally treated water in Canada is used for drinking. About 30% of the average Canadian's daily household water use results from flushing the toilet. The average Canadian flushes 10 times per day.

Science & Technology

Wastewater Treatment

Current wastewater treatment methods are divided into two categories: private systems (used mostly in rural areas) and public or municipal systems (used in towns and cities).

Private Systems

In rural areas, houses are spaced far apart and there is no central sewer system. Homeowners are required to provide their own sewage treatment system. Most rural houses have a septic system, which consists of a septic tank and a drainage field (**Figure 3**).

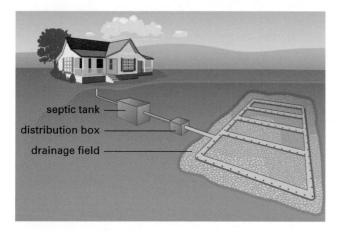

Figure 3 Rural houses require a septic system to treat human waste.

A septic tank is a large tank that is made of steel, concrete, plastic, or polyethylene. It is buried underground, near the house. Wastewater from the house flows in one end of the tank and out the other end (**Figure 4**). The wastewater that enters the septic tank, referred to as **influent**, separates into three layers once in the tank. A layer of scum and grease forms at the surface. The solid material, called **sludge**, settles to the bottom of the tank. Between these two layers is a layer of fairly clear liquid, called **effluent**, that drains from the tank as new wastewater enters. The effluent flows through a distribution box into two or more long, perforated pipes that are laid in gravel-filled trenches. The effluent seeps through the gravel and into the drainage field.

Bacteria in the septic tank begin the process of breaking down the organic matter. The most important treatment of the sewage, however, occurs in the drainage field. There, soil microbes continue the digestion process, and toxic materials get absorbed or transformed.

The whole septic system is powered by gravity, using the principle that water runs down a grade.

There are strict municipal and provincial regulations for the manufacture, installation, and operation of septic systems. These regulations specify the size of the tank, the location, the slope of the grade, and the characteristics of the drainage field. Despite these regulations, however, there are health and environmental concerns associated with septic systems:

- Clogged pipes can cause raw sewage to back up and spill into the house.
- Over time, the septic tank fills up with sludge, which has to be pumped out. How often the sludge has to be pumped out depends on the size of the tank and the amount of waste produced. The sludge has to be incinerated or sent to a landfill.
- The drainage field requires sufficient land space for proper treatment of the effluent.
- The soil must be permeable enough for proper drainage.
- Commercial additives may need to be added, to establish or supplement the natural soil microbes that digest the waste.

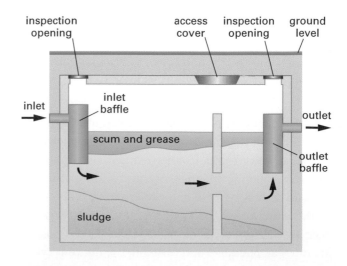

Figure 4 A two-chamber septic tank allows solids to settle and begins the decomposition of organic matter.

Public or Municipal Systems

Approximately 75% of Canadians are served by municipal sewer systems. When sewage leaves a home or business, it flows through a service line to the sewer main in the street. The service line and the sewer main follow a downhill grade, and gravity keeps the waste flowing downward. When the main line reaches a depth of 8 m to 10 m, a lift station pumps the sewage up to a higher level. From there, the sewage begins to flow again, by gravity, to a central station. Sewer pipes range in diameter from 10 cm for a service line from a house to 125 cm or larger for a main sewer line (**Figure 5**).

Figure 5 Sewer mains are buried underground, except where they cross rivers or streams.

Municipal wastewater has two components: sanitary sewage and stormwater. **Sanitary sewage** is wastewater that comes from homes, businesses, and institutions. **Stormwater** consists of rain and melting snow that run off the surface of the land. Many municipalities have separate systems for sanitary sewage and stormwater. Stormwater is normally discharged untreated, directly into the environment. Sanitary sewage is sent to a plant for treatment before the effluent is discharged into the environment. Some municipalities have a combined system, in which sanitary sewage and stormwater are collected together. In most combined systems, both sanitary sewage and stormwater are treated at the same time before being discharged. Combined systems tend to be older, but they can still be found in parts of many Canadian cities, such as Vancouver, Edmonton, Winnipeg, Toronto, Ottawa, Montreal, Quebec City, Halifax, and St. John's. The overflow of sewage into the stormwater system is the main reason for closing public beaches along the Great Lakes after heavy rainfalls.

Sewage Treatment

The first stage of sewage treatment, called **pretreatment**, involves screening out large debris, such as sticks, plastic, or rags. The wastewater is then piped into large tanks to undergo **primary treatment**. During primary treatment, heavier organic solids and other solids, such as sand and gravel, settle to the bottom of the tanks, and scum and grease form at the surface, as in a septic tank. If this is the only treatment of the sewage, the sludge is removed and incinerated or sent to a landfill. The primary effluent is discharged into the receiving environment, which may be a river, lake, or ocean (**Figure 6**).

Figure 6 Sewage effluent may be released to the environment after primary, secondary, or tertiary treatment.

B2: Flush It and Forget It: Human Waste

The sludge and effluent from primary treatment may go on to a secondary treatment. **Secondary treatment** involves anaerobic bacterial digestion of the sludge and aerobic bacterial digestion of the organic matter in the primary effluent. This process is known as **activated sludge treatment**. The effluent then goes to a secondary settling tank, where any remaining solids settle to the bottom. The secondary effluent is then released into the environment or sent for further treatment (**Figure 7**). The sludge is incinerated or sent to a landfill.

Figure 7 In secondary treatment, the primary effluent is aerated to provide oxygen to the aerobic bacteria, which use the oxygen to break down suspended or dissolved organic matter.

The third level of treatment, called **tertiary treatment** or **advanced treatment**, includes one or more physical, chemical, or biological processes. These processes remove suspended or dissolved pollutants, such as heavy metals, organic chemicals, and nutrients (phosphorus and nitrogen), from the secondary effluent. The sludge that remains after the final phase of treatment is transferred to a landfill, incinerated, composted, or used as fertilizer.

In most sewage systems, the secondary or tertiary wastewater effluent goes through a disinfection stage before being released into the environment. **Disinfection** reduces or eliminates any disease-causing microorganisms, usually by exposure to chlorine for a minimum of 30 min. Because of the potential toxic effects of chlorine on ecosystems, the effluent is required to be dechlorinated if the receiving water is ecologically sensitive or important to the fishing industry or public health. Ultraviolet radiation may also be used as a disinfectant. Only a 1-min exposure is required, and nothing is added to the effluent. Chlorine, however, is still the most commonly used method.

One way or another, the effluents from municipal wastewater treatment end up back in the environment, usually in the water but sometimes in the soil (**Figure 8**).

Most municipal sewer systems in Canada are connected to treatment plants. In 1999, 97% of the population served by municipal sewer systems had at least primary treatment. About 40% had tertiary treatment. Only 3% of the population served by municipal sewer systems deposited untreated sewage into the nearest river, lake, or ocean (**Figure 9**). While 3% may seem like a very small percentage, it translates to nearly three-quarters of a million Canadians whose waste is not treated. This is a significant improvement over 1983, however, when the waste of 28% of the Canadian population were collected by sewer systems that had no treatment.

Currently, over 4 million Canadians have access to only primary treatment. Recall that primary treatment consists of sedimentation and flotation: some

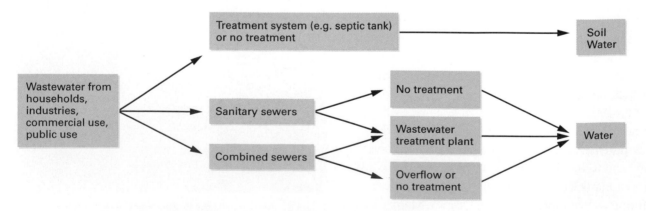

Figure 8 Water that is used to flush human waste ends up back in the environment and returns to the natural water cycle.

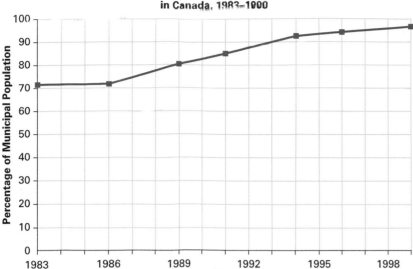

Municipal Population With at Least Primary Wastewater Treatment in Canada, 1983–1000

Figure 9 Most of Canada's population that is served by a municipal sewer system has at least primary wastewater treatment.

materials sink and some float. The materials that are suspended in the effluent, including any pathogenic organisms, are deposited into the environment without further treatment.

New Methods of Sewage Treatment

A relatively new, supplementary approach to sewage treatment is bioremediation. Bioremediation uses living organisms, such as bacteria, fungi, and plants, to degrade hazardous contaminants or transform them into less harmful compounds. **Phytoremediation**, one type of bioremediation, uses green plants to improve contaminated soil or ground water by absorbing the contaminants or by changing them into non-toxic forms.

The aquatic plants that are found in wetlands (**Figure 10**) can clean water by destroying fecal organisms (organisms found in feces), absorbing heavy metals, and breaking down organic compounds. These plants can be put to use by piping wastewater effluent to existing wetlands or by creating artificial wetlands close to wastewater treatment facilities. The advantages and disadvantages of phytoremediation are summarized in **Table 2**.

Genetic engineering may also be able to help in wastewater treatment. Plants and other organisms (such as bacteria) are being genetically engineered for their ability to absorb specific contaminants (such as heavy metals) that are found in the effluent of treated wastewater.

Figure 10 Wetlands are being used to supplement conventional wastewater treatment methods.

Table 2 Advantages and Disadvantages of Phytoremediation

Advantages	Disadvantages
Phytoremediation can be used to treat organic and inorganic contaminants.	Phytoremediation Is a slow process, appropriate for long-term treatment
It can be used by creating artificial wetlands at the site of contamination, or by piping effluent to existing wetlands.	It may be affected by climate.
It is easy to initiate and maintain. It does not require expensive equipment or specially trained personnel.	It will not work if the contamination is below the root zone.
It is very economical compared with other methods of remediation.	Plants may absorb toxic levels of contaminants.
It has low environmental impact and is acceptable to the public.	Toxic chemicals may accumulate in plant tissues.
It can reduce the volume of waste to be landfilled.	Contaminants may be moved up the food chain and may bioaccumulate.

✔ Check Your Understanding

1. Define the terms "influent" and "effluent."

2. What was the major turning point in the development of modern human waste management?

3. Briefly explain the operation of a private septic system.

4. What concerns are associated with the operation of a private septic system?

5. What risk is associated with collecting sanitary sewage and stormwater in the same system?

6. (a) What is the purpose of disinfection in sewage treatment?
   (b) What is the most common method of disinfection?

7. What is the final destination of effluent from municipal sewage treatment facilities?

8. Based on the statistics provided in the preceding pages, and assuming the 1999 population of Canada to be 30.5 million, calculate the number of people in Canada who were not served by a municipal sewer system that had at least primary treatment.

9. Why is bioremediation referred to as a "supplementary" method of sewage treatment?

10. Explain the role of gravity as a source of energy in our existing sewage systems. Include a diagram in your explanation.

11. How is human waste different from other categories of waste?

12. Your community plans to use a wetland area on the outskirts of town to implement a phytoremediation component of their sewage treatment program. In a couple of paragraphs, make an argument for OR against the plan.

Society & the Environment

Human Waste: Resource or Nuisance?

Regardless of the level of sewage treatment, the effluent and sludge that are released into the environment are not benign. The effluent is not pure water, and the sludge contains a variety of substances that are potentially toxic to humans and other organisms, and to the environment.

Environmental Impacts

The effluent and sludge from municipal wastewater treatment facilities lower the quality of both aquatic and terrestrial environments. They can have many effects:

- an increase in nutrient (nitrogen and phosphorus) levels, which can cause a dramatic increase in algae growth

- a decrease in the dissolved oxygen content in water, which may cause fish and other aquatic organisms to die
- habitat destruction from sedimentation and erosion due to increased water flow
- chemical contamination, which may kill or affect reproduction in organisms
- transfer of toxic chemicals up the food chain, and bioaccumulation in the higher levels

To determine the potential environmental effects, engineers measure selected parameters (characteristics) that indicate the quality of the effluent: biochemical oxygen demand (BOD), total suspended solids (TSS), total phosphorus (TP), total nitrogen (TN), and total coliform bacteria (**Table 3**). There is generally

Table 3 Indicators of Effluent Quality

Wastewater parameter	Description	Levels in raw human sewage	Recommendations for wastewater effluent[1]
BOD (mg/L)	The biochemical oxygen demand is an indication of the amount of organic material that is present in the effluent. It is a measure of the amount of oxygen that is required to stabilize the organic matter in five days.	220	• freshwater lakes and slow streams: 5 • rivers, streams, and estuaries: 20 • shorelines: 30
TSS (mg/L)	The total suspended solids refers to the amount of organic and inorganic material that is not dissolved in the wastewater and does not settle out as sludge. This may be removed by filtration.	700	• freshwater lakes and slow streams: 5 • rivers, streams, and estuaries: 20 • shorelines: 30
TN (mg/L)	Nitrogen is one of the main nutrients for plant growth. Nitrogen can be available as organic nitrogen or in ammonia, nitrites, and nitrates. Increased levels of available nitrogen in water bodies can cause rapid plant growth. In ground water, nitrates are a risk to human health.	40	• ammonia: 1.0 • nitrates and nitrites: 10.0
TP (mg/L)	Phosphorus is another main plant nutrient. It is available in organic or inorganic form. Increased phosphorus or phosphate levels can cause rapid plant and algae growth, which can result in oxygen depletion.	7.9	1.0
Total coliform bacteria (number/ 100 mL)	Fecal coliforms (such as *E. coli*) include several species of bacteria that live in the intestines of humans. A concentration of fecal coliform bacteria indicates the presence of sewage or other animal waste in a water body. Thus, it indicates that pathogenic (disease-causing) bacteria may be present in the water.	1.0×10^6 (1 000 000)	1000 • fecal coliforms: 100 • other coliforms: 900

[1]Recommendation for wastewater effluent discharges from Federal institutions.

B2: Flush It and Forget It: Human Waste

no monitoring of other substances, such as heavy metals or organic solvents, unless people notice health or environmental problems that may be linked to high levels of these substances.

Effluents from municipal wastewater sewer systems are the main source of the BOD, TSS, nutrients, organic chemicals, and metals that are released into Canadian streams, rivers, lakes, and oceans. Wastewater treatment reduces these contaminants. For example, conventional primary treatment removes 40% to 60% of the suspended solids and 50% of the total coliform bacteria. It reduces BOD by 25% to 40%. Even tertiary treatment, however, does not totally eliminate the contaminants. New approaches, such as phytoremediation, are crucial for supplementing the existing treatment methods.

Use of Biosolids

Biosolids are the solid residues that remain after the treatment of municipal sewage or wastewater. Biosolids were formerly known as "sewage sludge," but biosolids and sewage sludge are not quite the same. Biosolids are sludge that has been digested or treated with lime to reduce the pathogens and odour.

Biosolids from wastewater treatment can be disposed of by placing them in landfills, or by incineration, composting, or land application. All of these disposals methods have negative aspects. From a nutrient cycle perspective, composting and land application are preferable to placing biosolids in landfills and to incineration because the nutrient value of the biosolids is not lost. Safety, public acceptance, and cost are among the main concerns with the use of biosolids. In Canada, the use of biosolids is regulated by the provincial ministries of the environment. There is currently an intense debate over whether the land application of biosolids as fertilizer is a safe or sustainable practice and whether the regulations governing their use are appropriate.

So, is the use of biosolids as fertilizer safe? The answer to this question depends on how "safe" is defined and on what the acceptable level of risk is. This question is similar to asking "Is it safe to drive a car?" It all depends on the risks you are willing to accept and the measures that you take to reduce the risks to acceptable levels. Should we use biosolids as agricultural fertilizer? There are no easy answers.

DID **YOU** KNOW?

A New Word for an Old Product

The term "biosolids" was coined by public relations firms for the waste management industry. The industry wanted to change the public perception of sewage by finding a more acceptable term than "sludge."

B2.2 *Activity* | VISITING A WASTEWATER TREATMENT FACILITY

Most municipalities have at least primary wastewater treatment, and many have secondary treatment. Primary and secondary treatments are aimed at reducing the amount of organic matter and removing the potential pathogenic bacteria and viruses in the sewage. Secondary treatment involves the use of microbial organisms such as bacteria, fungi, and protozoa to break down the organic matter.

1. Plan an information-gathering visit to a wastewater treatment facility.

(a) Submit your plan to your teacher for approval, before your visit.

2. Find out the following information about the facility.

- the level of wastewater treatment
- the methods of treatment
- the quality of the effluent (based on the standards in **Table 3**, p. 99)
- where the effluent is discharged
- how and where the sludge is disposed of

3. Use the Internet and other sources to research how bacterial and other microbial organisms are used to reduce organic matter and other potentially harmful substances in wastewater effluent.

 www.science.nelson.com

(b) Write a one-page report on your research.

The Use of Human Waste as Fertilizer in China

For centuries, farmers in China and other Asian countries have used human waste as the mainstay of sustainable agricultural. Records from as early as 200 B.C.E. show that human waste was used in compost. This practice had two benefits: it provided a valuable source of nitrogen and phosphorus, two main plant nutrients, and it provided a way to use huge amounts of human waste. Thus, human waste was viewed as a resource that could be recycled.

Chinese farmers (**Figure 11**) did not simply dump human waste onto their fields, however. They had specific formulas for making compound fertilizers from a variety of organic materials (plant, animal, and human waste). The formulas varied according to the type of crop, the type of soil, and the season. All these formulas involved composting, which eliminates the human pathogens and therefore reduces the health risks associated with using human waste.

In recent years, however, the development of chemical fertilizers has significantly reduced the use of human waste as fertilizer in Asian countries. Since the 1980s, when chemical fertilizers became more widely available in China, the proportion of organic fertilizer has decreased to about 35% of the total fertilizer used.

As the populations of cities and towns have grown, increasing amounts of human waste are being produced. Approximately 70% of China's 1.3 billion citizens live in rural areas and use latrines (outhouses), which are intended for the temporary storage of waste. Around 29% of the rural population use sanitary latrines, which are protected from flies and are odourless. Another 27% have composting latrines, which reduce the risks associated with pathogens.

The knowledge of traditional composting methods is being lost, and some farmers are now applying untreated human sewage directly to the fields. This is causing an increase in sanitation-related diseases.

If the Chinese government encouraged the use of latrines that compost human waste, farmers would have a good source of organic fertilizer. In addition, the incidence of disease would be reduced.

(a) What is required for human waste to be used as fertilizer?

(b) Why has the use of human waste as fertilizer decreased in recent years?

(c) "Using human waste as fertilizer is often perceived as 'backward' and characteristic of an underdeveloped country." Discuss this statement, and write a short paragraph that summarizes your thoughts.

(d) Do you think there is any risk in importing food products from countries that use human waste as fertilizer? Explain.

Figure 11 In China, the nutrients in human waste have been used on the land for centuries.

Explore *an* Issue

Should Human Waste Be Used as Agricultural Fertilizer?

As you have learned, China and other Asian countries have a long history of using human waste as agricultural fertilizer. Western countries, on the other hand, have problems disposing of this waste. Should we or should we not use human waste as agricultural fertilizer? Some of the advantages are obvious. Their use provides a source of valuable plant nutrients, eliminates disposal problems, and is cost-effective. There are also some obvious disadvantages: the potential risk to human health and other safety concerns, public resistance to the idea, and potential negative impacts on the environment.

An average human egests 25 L to 50 L of feces per year. These feces can provide 0.55 kg of nitrogen, 0.18 kg of phosphorous, and 0.18 kg of potassium. The fibre in feces can be composted to form humus. On average, a person excretes 400 L to 500 L of urine per year. This amount contains approximately 4 kg of nitrogen, 0.4 kg of phosphorus, and 0.9 kg of potassium. Urine is not actually a biosolid. Urine is an ideal plant fertilizer, however, because it is normally sterile. Its nitrogen content converts to ammonia, which makes it more accessible to plants. As well, it has lower levels of heavy metals than feces do.

Statement: Biosolids from sewage treatment plants should be used as agricultural fertilizer.

1. Go to the Nelson Web site, and search other sources, to find information about the advantages and disadvantages of using biosolids in agriculture. Consider the issue as objectively as possible.

 www.science.nelson.com

2. Summarize your findings in a two-column table.

Decision-Making Skills

○ Define the Issue
● Research
● Defend a Decision
● Identify Alternatives
● Analyze the Issue
○ Evaluate

3. Identify and briefly describe the perspective(s) of potential stakeholders in this issue. A partial list of stakeholders includes a farmer, a consumer, a biosolids company manager, and a medical doctor.

4. In your group, you will assume the role of one stakeholder. Based on your research, prepare a position paper that reflects a possible perspective of the stakeholder.

5. Present your position in a mock public forum, organized by a municipal government to obtain public input on the development of policy guidelines for the use of biosolids.

6. Based on your research, take a personal stand on the issue. Do you agree or disagree with the statement? Explain why.

7. Did you agree with the statement conditionally? If so, explain the conditions that would have to be met in order for you to agree fully with the statement.

8. In your consideration of the issue, were you influenced by the western view of human waste as an unsanitary and disgusting nuisance? Explain.

9. Give an example of an action you might take that would demonstrate your commitment to your position on the issue.

DID **YOU** KNOW?

Plant Nutrients in Human Waste
The nutrients in the waste that is produced by an average human in one year are sufficient to grow the 230 kg of crops that an average human consumes in one year. Approximately 65% of these nutrients are found in urine.

SUMMARY

- Human waste is produced during digestion and metabolism.
- The simplest, most natural approach to human waste management is to maintain the nutrient cycle or to recycle the waste.
- Private wastewater systems consist of a septic tank and a large drainage field to filter the undesirable substances from the wastewater before it is returned to a water source.
- Public wastewater systems consist of a series of underground pipes that collect waste from homes and other buildings and move them to a central treatment facility. Wastewater goes through up to three levels of treatment (primary, secondary, and tertiary or advanced) to purify the water and eliminate the health and environmental risks associated with human waste.
- New methods, such as phytoremediation, use natural processes to remove contaminants from wastewater. Phytoremediation uses plants that absorb the contaminants, stabilize them, or transform them into non-toxic substances.
- About 97% of the population that is served by municipal sewer systems has at least primary treatment of wastewater.

- Five parameters are used to indicate the quality of the effluent from wastewater treatment: biochemical oxygen demand (BOD), total suspended solids (TSS), total phosphorus (TP), total nitrogen (TN), and total coliform bacteria. Many other substances are not routinely measured.
- Biosolids are the treated solid residues that remain after wastewater treatment.
- Human waste is still used as agricultural fertilizer in China, but the availability of chemical fertilizers has reduced their use to approximately 35% of the total fertilizers used.
- In North America, the use of human waste as agricultural fertilizer is a controversial issue.

Key Terms

human waste	secondary treatment
influent	activated sludge
sludge	treatment
effluent	tertiary treatment/
sanitary sewage	advanced treatment
stormwater	disinfection
pretreatment	phytoremediation
primary treatment	biosolids

ASSESSMENT

Understanding Concepts

1. Describe, in general terms, the historical evolution of human waste management.
2. How do the attitudes of eastern cultures toward human waste differ from the attitudes of western cultures?
3. Describe the similarities and differences between a septic system and a municipal sewer system.
4. Trace the path of wastewater from the time a toilet is flushed until the wastewater reaches its final destination. Describe what happens at various stages along the way.
5. Although phytoremediation is promising as a supplementary wastewater treatment method, it does have disadvantages. Summarize the advantages and disadvantages of phytoremediation.

Applying Inquiry Skills

6. The data in **Table 4** represent the effluent flowing from a sewage outlet pipe on a coastline in Nova Scotia.

Table 4 Effluent Analysis from Outlet Pipe in Nova Scotia

Effluent characteristic	Value
BOD	15 mg/L
TSS	45 mg/L
TN	7.0 mg/L
TP	0.75 mg/L
Fecal coliform bacteria	150/100 mL
Total coliform bacteria	675/100 mL

(a) Does this effluent meet the standards established by the federal government (**Table 3** on p. 99)? Explain why or why not.

(b) Make recommendations to ensure that the effluent meets the environmental health and safety standards.

7. You have been hired as a consultant to help a municipality decide whether or not to implement a phytoremediation project for a polluted area. One of the requirements of your contract is to recommend which plants would be most appropriate. Describe an experiment that you could carry out to determine the effectiveness of different plants in cleaning up specific pollutants. (Identify the plants being tested and the contaminants that are present in the polluted area.)

8. Use the graph in **Figure 12** to answer the questions below.

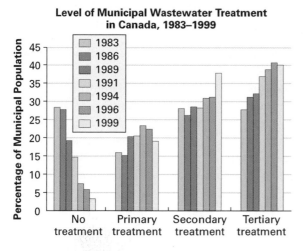

Figure 12 The percentages of different levels of wastewater treatment from 1983 to 1999, for municipal populations with sewer systems

(a) Describe the trends in the data in this graph.

(b) According to the latest data, what percentage of the municipal population has each level of treatment below?
   (i) no treatment
   (ii) primary treatment
   (iii) secondary treatment
   (iv) tertiary treatment

(c) What level of treatment has changed the most since 1983?

(d) The percentage of the population that had primary treatment decreased from 1994 to 1999. Do you consider this to be a serious problem? Why or why not?

Making Connections

9. The development and use of chemical fertilizers was part of the "green revolution" in the 1960s. Chemical fertilizers, along with new seed varieties, chemical pesticides, and other technological innovations, were promoted to increase crop production. The success of chemical fertilizers has not, however, been without a cost. Research the environmental effects associated with the decreased use of organic fertilizers and the increased use of chemical fertilizers.

 www.science.nelson.com

10. Choose one of the following environmental impacts of wastewater effluent: algal bloom, oxygen depletion, habitat destruction, toxic contamination, and bioaccumulation. Do in-depth research on how the biotic and abiotic environment is affected.

 www.science.nelson.com

11. For one week, make a list of all the substances, except human waste, that go into the sewer system from your home. Which substances might be a concern if biosolids from your local treatment plant were used as agricultural fertilizer?

12. Commercial suppliers of septic tank treatments emphasize the importance of properly maintaining a septic system. They make various claims about the effectiveness of their products in helping with this maintenance. Use the Internet to find information about a septic tank treatment. Based on the information provided, evaluate the supplier's claim and compare it with the recommendations of the government department that regulates the installation and maintenance of septic systems.

 www.science.nelson.com

13. Find out as much as you can about the operation and maintenance of composting toilets. Would you be willing to use a composting toilet in your home? Why or why not?

 www.science.nelson.com

Reflecting

14. Does it surprise you to learn that there are cities in Canada that discharge untreated wastewater into the environment? Why do you think this still happens today?

John pulls into a gas station to refuel his sport-utility vehicle, or SUV (**Figure 1**). When he first bought his SUV, he was a little shocked at the cost of the fill-ups, compared with the cost for his previous vehicle, a four-cylinder mid-sized car. Since then, gas prices have risen several times, and he is constantly reminded of his new vehicle's lower fuel economy.

Initially, John's concern was simply financial. Now he feels a little guilty about the environmental impact of his vehicle. Recent protests in the United States and Canada have drawn attention to the fact that SUVs consume more fuel and therefore produce more carbon dioxide, one of the leading contributors to global warming. In addition, SUVs do not have the same emission controls as cars, and so they produce more emissions per litre of fuel than cars do.

He justifies his decision to purchase an SUV on the basis of its safety. He lives in northern Ontario, where winter driving can be especially hazardous. He likes the idea that he and his family are safer in a large four-wheel drive vehicle. Yet, despite his satisfaction with the vehicle itself and the security it offers, he feels a little twinge of guilt every time he pulls into the gas station.

(a) What type of vehicle (or vehicles) does your family drive? Was environmental impact a factor in your family's decision to buy this vehicle? Explain why or why not.

(b) Describe your feelings toward SUVs and their impact on the environment. Are there factors that are more important than environmental impact, when deciding which type of vehicle to buy?

Figure 1 SUVs and their owners have become targets of environmental groups.

NEL

B3: Is It Warm in Here? Gaseous Waste and the Greenhouse Effect **105**

In the United States, the protests against SUVs have taken a radical turn. In the Los Angeles area, members of a group known as the Earth Liberation Front (ELF) attacked four car dealerships. They defaced or destroyed dozens of Hummers and other SUVs, and set fire to one dealership. The ELF promotes the sabotage of any business or industry that they think damages the environment. In other areas, the protests have been nonviolent. A group of artists in the Boston area, known as Earth on Empty, have been attaching tickets or bumper stickers to SUVs (**Figure 2**). The bumper stickers have slogans such as "I'm changing the climate. Ask me how." Another group, called the Detroit Project, produced television commercials that associated driving an SUV with supporting terrorism, because buying more gas and oil provides more money to countries that may support terrorism.

There are approximately 17 million passenger vehicles and light trucks on the roads in Canada. Nearly 8%, or 1.36 million, of these are SUVs. With their low fuel efficiency and their emissions, SUVs are an easy target for blame. Is a family with one 12.5 L/100 km Toyota 4Runner any less environmentally responsible than a family with two 6.1 L/100 km

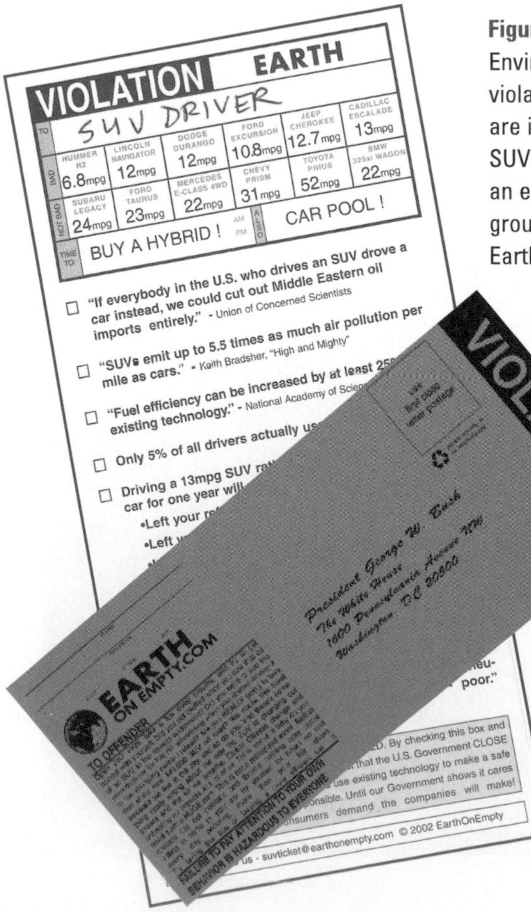

Figure 2
Environmental violation tickets are issued to SUV drivers by an environmental group called Earth on Empty.

Toyota Echos? Why do environmental groups not target two-vehicle families? Is it fair to blame an SUV owner for the vehicle's low fuel economy? Is it fair to label all SUV drivers as people who do not care about the environment?

(c) Does the claim of the Detroit Project seem logical to you? Explain why or why not.

(d) Do you think environmental groups are justified in their actions against individuals and companies who cause environmental damage? Explain your reasoning.

There is fairly wide consensus among scientists around the world that changes in global climate are linked to increasing levels of carbon dioxide and other gases (such as water vapour, methane, and nitrous oxide) in the atmosphere. There is also consensus that these increasing levels of atmospheric gases are mostly a result of human activities, such as burning fossil fuels. But although there is consensus, there is no unanimous agreement. There are some scientists who believe that the observed climate changes are due to factors other than human activities. These scientists claim, for example, that sunspot variability can account for the variations in average global temperature that have been observed during the 20th century.

What exactly do scientists know about the impact of human activities on global warming? What evidence is used to support the theories about climate change and global warming? What evidence is used to refute these theories? How confident can we be about predictions of future global climate changes? What are the consequences of global warming? What are we doing to prevent or lessen global warming? In order to answer these questions, we need to understand the science behind climate changes and global warming, as well as the strengths and limitations of science and technology. We all share the responsibility for the waste that is dumped into the atmosphere every day. It follows that we should all share the responsibility for managing this waste and preventing the potential effects on ourselves and the environment.

(e) Do you believe that human activities are affecting the atmosphere and the global climate? On what evidence do you base your belief?

(f) How do you feel about your personal contribution to the waste that goes into the atmosphere? Are there ways that you can reduce your share of this waste?

Science & Technology

The Greenhouse Effect and Global Warming

When you hear the term "greenhouse effect," you probably think of negative effects. Surprisingly, perhaps, Earth would be a very different place if there were no greenhouse effect. Life as we know it would not exist because the average global temperature would be approximately −18°C instead of the current 15°C. The greenhouse effect is, in fact, an essential temperature-regulating system. For this reason, the term "enhanced greenhouse effect" is now being used to refer to the negative effects associated with the greenhouse effect.

The Enhanced Greenhouse Effect

The trapping of heat energy by certain gases in Earth's atmosphere is known as the **greenhouse effect**. The gases involved are water vapour (H_2O), carbon dioxide (CO_2), methane (CH_4), and nitrous oxide (N_2O). In addition to these naturally occurring gases, human-made gases are also involved: halocarbons such as CFC (chlorofluorocarbon), HFC (hydrofluorocarbon), and PFC (perfluorocarbon). Together, the naturally-occurring and human-made gases are referred to as **greenhouse gases (GHGs)**, and they are all efficient absorbers of heat. They allow the wavelengths of visible light and some ultraviolet radiation from the Sun to pass through the atmosphere to Earth's surface (**Figure 3**). When the light is absorbed by Earth's surface, much of it is radiated back out as infrared radiation (heat). The infrared radiation is then absorbed by the greenhouse gases in the atmosphere. Thus, the greenhouse gases act like a thermal blanket, keeping Earth's temperature within an acceptable range.

Unfortunately, the range of temperatures can change in response to changes in greenhouse-gas concentrations. When the concentrations increase, additional global warming happens. Increases in greenhouse gases above natural levels create an **enhanced greenhouse effect**, which results in increased average global temperatures.

Sources and Sinks of Greenhouse Gases

While all the greenhouse gases, except for the halocarbons, are produced by natural processes on Earth, there are a number of human activities that directly or indirectly increase their concentrations in the atmosphere (**Table 1**).

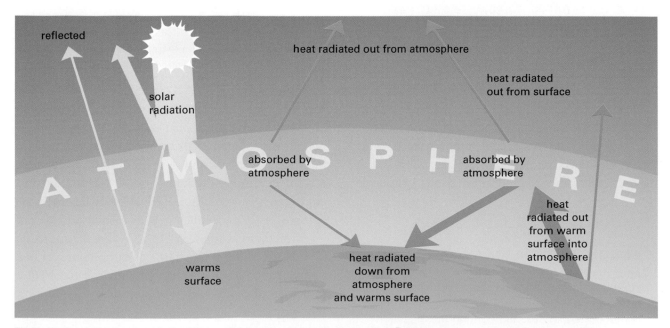

Figure 3 Greenhouse gases in Earth's atmosphere absorb heat radiating from Earth's surface, preventing it from escaping back into space. These gases have the same effect as the glass that prevents heat from leaving a greenhouse.

B3: Is It Warm in Here? Gaseous Waste and the Greenhouse Effect

Table 1 Sources of Major Greenhouse Gases

Greenhouse gas	Natural sources	Sources related to human activities
water vapour, $H_2O_{(g)}$	evaporation and transpiration processes that are part of the water cycle	combustion of fossil fuels and wood
carbon dioxide, $CO_{2(g)}$	plant and animal respiration, decay of organic matter in soil, volcanoes, forest/grass fires, and oceans	combustion of fossil fuels, deforestation, and industrial processes such as cement production
methane, $CH_{4(g)}$	decay of organic matter in wetlands and chemical reactions in soil	cattle farming, rice cultivation, biomass burning, landfills, coal mining, fuel combustion, and petroleum refining
nitrous oxide, $N_2O_{(g)}$	soil and water denitrification under anaerobic conditions	nitrogen fertilizers and the combustion of fossil fuels and wood
CFCs, HFCs, PFCs		aerosols, refrigeration units, and air conditioners

Carbon dioxide is the most significant greenhouse gas, simply because it is the most abundant in the atmosphere. As well, it accounts for approximately two-thirds of the enhanced greenhouse effect. The main sources of carbon dioxide emissions from human activities are the combustion of fossil fuels (equation 1), deforestation, and industrial processes such as cement production. The main natural sources include the respiration of plants and animals (equation 2), the decomposition of organic matter, volcanoes, forest fires, and the oceans.

$$C_8H_{18} \ + \ \frac{25}{2}\,O_2 \rightarrow \ 8\,CO_2 \ + 9\,H_2O + \text{heat}$$

hydrocarbon + oxygen → carbon dioxide + water + heat

(combustion) (1)

$$C_6H_{12}O_6 \ + \ 6\,O_2 \rightarrow \ 6\,CO_2 \ + 6\,H_2O + \text{heat}$$

sugar + oxygen → carbon dioxide + water + heat

(respiration) (2)

Methane is the next most important greenhouse gas. Cattle are a significant source of methane. The main food of cattle is grass, which contains a large amount of cellulose. Special methanogenic (methane-producing) bacteria in the guts of cattle produce an enzyme that breaks down cellulose into acetate, which is then further broken down to produce methane (equation 3).

DID **YOU** KNOW?

Stop and Smell the Methane?
Methane is an odourless gas. The odours that sometimes result from belching (eructation) or "passing gas" (flatulation) are caused by other compounds that are made during the digestion process or by bacteria in the gut.

Other methanogens in cattle consume hydrogen and carbon dioxide to produce methane (equation 4). The methane that is produced during these processes is released by the cattle into the atmosphere.

Methane is also produced by bacterial activity in rice fields and landfills (equation 5) and in commercial oil and gas fields. As well, recent studies show that up to one-fifth of the global methane emissions may come from rotting organic matter in human-made reservoirs created by hydroelectric dams.

$$CH_3COO^- \ + \ H_2O \ \rightarrow \ CH_4 \ + \ HCO_3^- \quad (3)$$

acetate + water → methane + bicarbonate

$$4\,H_2 \ + \ CO_2 \ \rightarrow \ CH_4 \ + \ 2\,H_2O \quad (4)$$

hydrogen + carbon dioxide → methane + water

$$\text{organic matter} + H_2O + O_2 \rightarrow \text{biodegraded organic matter} + CH_4 + CO_2 + \text{other gases} \quad (5)$$

organic matter + water + oxygen → biodegraded organic matter + methane + carbon dioxide + other gases

The warming potential of greenhouse gases is standardized against the warming potential of carbon dioxide. For example, the global warming potential of methane is equated to an amount of carbon dioxide that would trap an equivalent amount of heat, and is measured in tonnes (or kilotonnes) of **carbon dioxide equivalent (CO_2 eq)**. Molecule for molecule, methane absorbs 21 times as much heat as carbon dioxide, so 1 t of methane is equal to 21 t CO_2 eq. Nitrous oxide absorbs 300 times as much heat as carbon dioxide, and a single molecule of CFC has the same effect as 10 000 molecules of carbon dioxide. Since the concentrations of these gases are significantly lower than the concentration of carbon dioxide, however, their contributions to the enhanced greenhouse effect are not as significant.

Natural processes remove some greenhouse gases from the atmosphere. For example, water vapour returns to the surface of Earth as precipitation. Carbon dioxide is removed from the atmosphere during photosynthesis by trees, agricultural crops, and all other vegetation. A **sink** is any process that removes carbon dioxide, or any other greenhouse gas, from the atmosphere and stores it. Plants and soils are considered to be carbon sinks, because they store carbon from carbon dioxide for long periods of time. The carbon cycle is a sink for the carbon in methane. The nitrogen cycle is a sink for the nitrogen in nitrous oxide. When natural sources and sinks are in balance, the atmospheric concentrations of greenhouse gases are stable.

Consensus and Disagreement over Climate Change

Direct observations of global climate and climate changes are fairly recent scientific activities. For example, monitoring global temperatures started in 1860, and monitoring atmospheric carbon dioxide started in 1958 (**Figures 4** and **5**). The data from direct observations have been valuable in understanding global climate and the changes that have occurred.

If scientists only have data for the last 100 years or so, how do they know what the climate was like thousands of years ago? The study of earlier climates, called **paleoclimatology**, relies on indirect evidence. What paleoclimatologists do resembles detective work or forensic science. For example, chemical analyses of

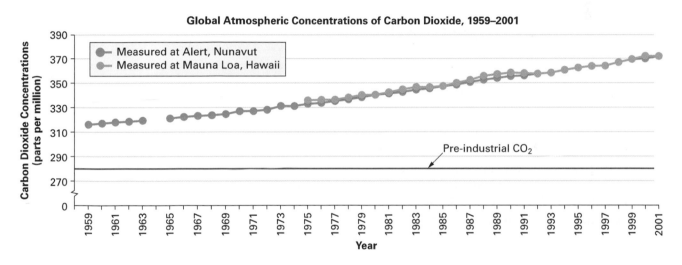

Figure 4 Since measurements of atmospheric CO_2 concentrations began in 1958, the average levels have been rising steadily.

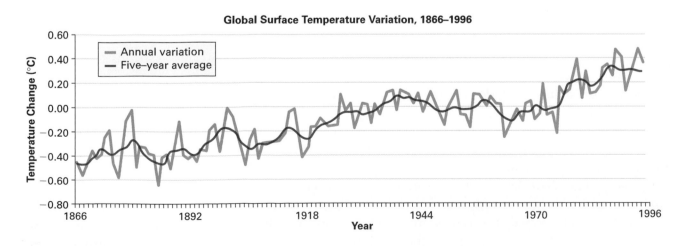

Figure 5 There is little disagreement among scientists that the average global surface temperature has increased over the last 100 years.

B3: Is It Warm in Here? Gaseous Waste and the Greenhouse Effect

B3.1 Activity | ENVIRONMENT CANADA'S GREENHOUSE GAS DIVISION DATABASE

Environment Canada has a Greenhouse Gas Division that is responsible for monitoring and reporting emissions of greenhouse gases from various sources across Canada. The Greenhouse Gas Division compiles a database using information collected from federal, provincial, and municipal organizations and from industries and businesses. As well, the Greenhouse Gas Division develops strategies for reducing greenhouse gas emissions and provides advice and technical support to organizations that are implementing these strategies.

The monitoring function is important both to understand emission trends and to measure the success of greenhouse gas reduction initiatives.

Materials

Table A: Canada's GHG Emissions by Gas and Sector
Table B: Canada's GHG Emission Trends by Sector

Your teacher will provide you with paper or electronic copies of Tables A and B. Analyze the information in these two tables, and answer the following questions.

(a) Calculate the percentages of the main greenhouse gases: carbon dioxide, methane, nitrous oxide, the halocarbons, and sulfur hexafluoride. Compare the relative global warming potential of these gases.

(b) Which major category of GHG emission sources contributes the most greenhouse gases? What percentage of the total does this represent?

(c) What percentage of the total GHG emissions comes from the generation of electricity and heat?

(d) What is the source of sulfur hexafluoride emissions?

(e) One of the subcategories of agriculture is "enteric fermentation."
   (i) Research a definition of "enteric fermentation," and describe this process.

 www.science.nelson.com

   (ii) What type of greenhouse gas is produced in this process?
   (iii) What proportion of the total methane emissions comes from enteric fermentation?
   (iv) By what percentage has the emission level from enteric fermentation increased since 1990?

(f) Explain the negative values reported in the Land Use Change and Forestry category.

(g) Identify and describe any significant trends in GHG emissions, based on the data in the tables.

---

air bubbles trapped in ice-core samples from the Antarctic ice cover can reveal the levels of carbon dioxide and other greenhouse gases in the atmosphere over the past 400 000 years. Analyses of tree growth rings can reveal temperatures and precipitation during the period represented by the rings. Analyses of ocean sediments can indicate heavy sedimentation, caused by erosion during a period of high precipitation. Evidence of changing lake levels can indicate variations in precipitation over long periods of time.

How do scientists predict what will occur in the future? While there is no foolproof way to predict anything, scientists have developed sophisticated computer models that can reconstruct past climates from indirect evidence. Scientists can use trends in the data to predict what might happen in the future. Scientists admit that indirect evidence is always

uncertain. In addition, scientists can disagree in their interpretations of the evidence. For example, scientists agree that the global climate has changed significantly over the last 100 years, but some scientists disagree over the extent of the changes.

There is consensus among scientists that global climate change is affected by human activities. The Intergovernmental Panel on Climate Change (IPCC), the leading authority on global climate change, is a network of about 2500 climate scientists from 70 countries. In 2001, the IPCC published a report in which these scientists concluded, "There is new and stronger evidence that most of the warming observed over the last 50 years is attributable to human activities." As well, they predicted, with 90% to 95% confidence, that Earth's average temperature will increase 1.4°C to 5.8°C between the years 2000 and 2100.

Materials

Climate Change Calculator software

The *Climate Change Calculator* software (**Figure 6**) was designed to raise people's awareness of the greenhouse gases they produce through their daily activities and lifestyle choices. In this activity, you will use an online or downloaded version of the calculator to determine your family's contribution to climate change through CO_2 emissions.

Figure 6 The *Climate Change Calculator* software provides an estimate of your impact on climate.

1. Access the online version of the *Climate Change Calculator* on the Nelson Web site, or obtain the downloaded version from your teacher.

 www.science.nelson.com

2. Answer the questionnaire as accurately as possible. You may have to estimate some answers.

(a) What are your estimated CO_2 emissions?

(b) How does your carbon dioxide contribution compare with the per capita average for your province or territory? How does it compare with the national per capita average?

(c) What is the largest single source of greenhouse gases in your province or territory? What percentage of the total does it represent?

(d) What recommendations are made for reducing your CO_2 emissions?

(e) Evaluate the accuracy of the *Climate Change Calculator*. Identify potential sources of error that might influence its accuracy. Do these sources of error affect its value as a tool to help people understand their personal impact on the climate?

(f) In one or two paragraphs, describe your personal beliefs about global climate change. On what evidence do you base your beliefs? Where did you get this evidence?

While there is confidence in the scientific models, however, there is some uncertainty about using these models to determine past climates, to identify the causes of climate changes, and to predict the effects of future climates and climatic changes. For example, there are discrepancies between what the models predict and what global temperature observations indicate. In a 2001 report on the science of climate change, scientists from the National Academy of Sciences, a U.S. organization, decided that the buildup of greenhouse gases in the atmosphere in the 20th century could not be definitively linked to human activities. They felt that there was too much uncertainty and variability in the climate record, and that not enough was known about the actions of halocarbons on the environment. They pointed out that the amount of global warming we are currently experiencing is actually less than the amount predicted by climate models that were created using data from the climate record.

Even the IPCC acknowledges the uncertainties that are associated with climate models. In its report entitled *Climate Change 2001: The Scientific Basis*, IPCC scientists state, "The climate system is particularly challenging since it is known that components in the system are inherently chaotic" and that "future climate changes may also involve 'surprises.'" They explain that these uncertainties may affect the ability of climate models to predict accurately.

Scientists also disagree about the interpretation of collected data. For example, the general conclusion from data collected since 1860 is that average global temperatures have risen approximately 0.6°C over the last 100 years. There are virtually no scientists who disagree with this conclusion. Skeptical scientists say, however, that average temperatures are deceiving because they do not give a complete picture of what has happened. For example, most warming occurs over land, not over water. Most warming occurs at night; and most warming is due to moderation of the lowest winter temperatures.

The role of greenhouse gases is also questioned. There is evidence that greenhouse gases are not the only cause of global warming. Recent NASA research suggests that soot is twice as effective as carbon dioxide in raising global surface air temperatures in the Northern Hemisphere. The term "soot" refers to carbon particles that are produced by the combustion of fossil fuels (such as diesel fuel and coal) and from burning vegetation. In developed countries, the greatest source of soot is the combustion of diesel fuel and coal. In underdeveloped countries, the major source is burning wood, animal dung, and other biofuels. Soot on the surface of snow and ice reduces their ability to reflect light. Clean snow normally reflects about 98% of the light that falls on it. Soot may reduce this reflection rate to between 80% and 90% (**Figure 7**). The increased absorption of radiant energy melts more ice and snow—an effect that has usually been attributed to the enhanced greenhouse effect.

Uncertainty, discrepancies, and disagreement do not mean that climate models are not valuable or that we should be unconcerned about the future. They simply point out the need to conduct further scientific studies so that climate models can be improved and predictions can be more reliable.

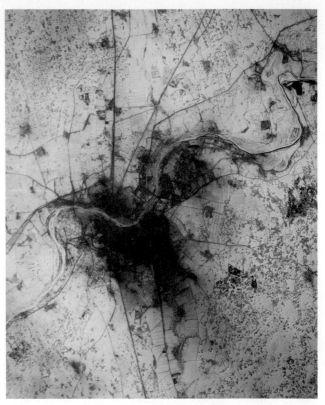

Figure 7 This satellite picture shows that the snow around an industrial city is blackened by soot, which absorbs more of the Sun's radiant energy.

✔ Check Your Understanding

1. Why is the greenhouse effect an essential phenomenon for Earth?

2. List ten human activities that contribute to increased levels of greenhouse gases in the atmosphere.

3. What is the purpose of the concept of "carbon dioxide equivalent"?

4. Using the concept of CO_2 equivalent, compare the relative effects of CO_2, methane, and CFCs in enhancing the greenhouse effect.

5. What are some of the concerns associated with using models to predict climate change or global warming?

6. List some of the evidence that paleoclimatologists use to describe past climates. Comment on the validity of this evidence.

7. What do scientists agree on regarding climate change?

8. Explain why there is both consensus and disagreement among scientists over climate change.

9. Why is the IPCC a credible organization?

10. There may be other factors, besides greenhouse gases, that contribute to global warming. Identify and describe one of these factors.

Society & the Environment

Effects of Climate Change

Emissions of carbon dioxide due to the combustion of fossil fuels are virtually certain to be the dominant influence on atmospheric CO_2 concentration in the 21st century. Even if we can be reasonably confident that future climate changes will be only half as extensive as predicted, the potential consequences for future generations are still very serious. The 2001 IPCC report describes the following effects of global warming on life support systems:

- The global average surface temperature has increased over the 20th century by about 0.6°C.
- The amount of snow cover and the extent of ice cover have decreased.
- The global average sea level has risen, and ocean heat content has increased.

- Changes have also occurred in other important areas of climate, such as precipitation, cloudiness, droughts, floods, and El Niño (**Figure 8**).

Table 2 lists many more possible effects of global warming.

Figure 8 Droughts and floods are consequences of global climate change.

Table 2 Possible Effects of Global Warming

Areas affected	Examples of possible effects
weather extremes	• prolonged heat waves and droughts • increased flooding • more intense hurricanes, typhoons, tornadoes, and violent storms
water resources	• change in water supply • decreased water quality • increased drought or flooding
biodiversity	• extinction of some plant and animal species • loss of habitat • disruption of aquatic life
forests	• change in forest composition and locations • disappearance of some forests • increased fires from drying • loss of wildlife habitat and species
sea level and coastal areas	• melting of polar ice caps and rising sea levels • flooding of low-lying islands and coastal cities • flooding of coastal estuaries, wetlands, and coral reefs • beach erosion • disruption of coastal fisheries • contamination of coastal aquifers (groundwater storage)
agriculture	• shifts in food-growing areas • changes in crop yields • increased irrigation demands • increased pests, crop diseases, and weeds in warmer areas
human populations	• increased deaths • more environmental refugees (increased migration)
human health	• increased deaths from heat and disease • disruption of food and water supplies • spread of tropical diseases to temperate areas • increased incidence of respiratory disease • increased water pollution from coastal floods

The Kyoto Protocol

In 1997, delegates from 161 nations gathered in Kyoto, Japan, to work out a new treaty aimed at reducing the atmospheric greenhouse gases that cause climate change. The **Kyoto Protocol** describes the process by which the treaty, called the Kyoto Accord, will be implemented. It commits countries to reducing greenhouse gas emissions to levels that are 5.2% below 1990 levels, by 2008 to 2012. Unfortunately, as of September 2003, the Kyoto Protocol had been ratified by only 61 of the 84 countries that had originally signed the treaty. There is some good news, however. In addition to the ratifying countries, 58 other countries have agreed to accept and follow the recommendations of the Kyoto Protocol. Some of these countries were not even involved in the conference that created the treaty. The Canadian parliament ratified the treaty on December 17, 2002, but its implementation has become a controversial political issue. The United States has stated that it will definitely not participate in the treaty, even though it is the world's leading contributor of CO_2 emissions to the atmosphere. The U.S. feels that the Kyoto Protocol is unfair and that the measures required to meet its expectations would be harmful to the U.S. economy. In addition, the president of the United States has argued that scientific knowledge about the causes of global warming, and possible solutions, is incomplete.

The Kyoto Protocol will come into effect 90 days after the date on which two criteria are met: at least 55 countries that signed the Accord ratify the Protocol or accept it in principle, and the carbon emissions of these countries totalled at least 55% of the global CO_2 emissions in 1990. In 1990, Canada's share of the global CO_2 emissions was 3.3%, which amounted to 457 441 kt. Canada's commitment extends to all greenhouse gases, however, not just carbon dioxide. In 1990, the total greenhouse gas emissions for Canada were 608 000 kt CO_2 eq. In 2001, Canada's total GHG emissions rose to 720 000 kt CO_2 eq.

Several factors contribute to Canada's high levels of GHG emissions:

- Canada is the second largest country in the world, and our population is distributed over an enormous area. This means that we consume a lot of energy to transport people and goods.
- Canada has a cold climate, which means that we consume a lot of energy for heating.
- A large part of Canada's economy is based on natural resources. Processing these natural resources (such as smelting ore) requires a large amount of energy.
- Canada has a very high standard of living. We produce and buy many goods, and we can travel to other parts of the world. Travel and the production and transportation of goods all consume energy.

Canada and the Kyoto Protocol

On December 17, 2002, nearly six years after signing the Kyoto Accord, the Canadian government ratified the Kyoto Protocol. Just before ratifying the Protocol, the federal government released The *Climate Change Plan for Canada*. This plan outlines strategies and initiatives that the federal government has undertaken, and will undertake in the future, to meet its GHG reduction targets under the Kyoto Protocol. Canada's target is to reduce CO_2 emissions by 6% below 1990 levels between 2008 and 2012. If Canada were to continue with "business as usual," we would fall far short of this target. Since emissions of greenhouse gases have risen since 1990, Canada will have to reduce emissions by approximately 20% from current levels (**Figure 9**). Canada will need innovative technological solutions to slow the trend of climate change and to adapt practices we cannot avoid, such as burning fossil fuels. Equally important is the need to change attitudes that cause us to squander energy resources.

The decision to ratify the Kyoto Protocol was met with some apprehension across the country. Opposition was primarily economic. The changes will be expensive to implement and will cost jobs. Supporters claim that implementation will save money and create new jobs, which will offset any jobs lost.

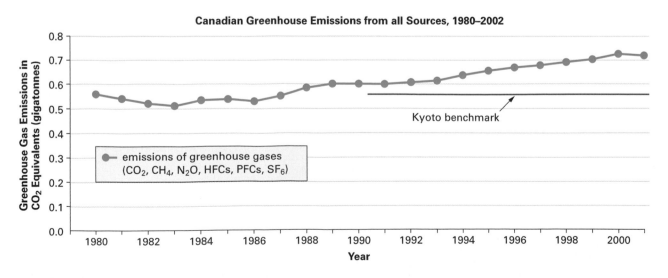

Figure 9 Canada's Greenhouse Gas Emissions

B3: Is It Warm in Here? Gaseous Waste and the Greenhouse Effect

Canada's Plans to Meet Kyoto Targets

The Climate Change Plan for Canada identifies strategies to reduce GHG emissions for each sector of the economy that produces them. These strategies are summarized in **Table 3**.

DID **YOU** KNOW?

The Ethanol Advantage
If 35% of the gasoline in Canada contained 10% ethanol, GHG emissions would be reduced by 1.8 Mt per year (1.8 million tonnes). This is equivalent to removing more than 400 000 vehicles from the road.

Table 3 Canadian Strategies to Meet Kyoto Strategies

GHG emissions target area	Strategies underway and proposed
Transportation	• 25% improvement in new vehicle fuel efficiency by 2010 • increased production of alternative fuels such as ethanol and biodiesel • development of technologies for fuel cell vehicles • strategies to reduce urban GHG emissions by improving and increasing public transit • integration of air, rail, truck, and marine transportation to improve fuel efficiency of the transport of goods
Housing and Commercial/ Institutional Buildings	• renovation of 20% of all existing buildings to energy-efficient standards by 2010 • R2000 energy-efficiency standard for all new housing by 2010 • improved energy-efficiency standards for equipment and appliances • improved National Energy Code for Buildings, requiring buildings to be 25% more energy efficient by 2010
Large Industrial Emitters	• government-industry partnership initiatives to reduce emissions • investments in development of innovative technologies aimed at reducing emissions (for example, move to dry kiln technique and use fly ash to reduce CO_2 emissions in cement production) • support of industry voluntary emission-reduction programs
Renewable Energy and Cleaner Fossil Fuels	• incentives for wind power production • reduction of barriers to interprovincial electricity trade and transmission • 10% of new electricity generation from renewable sources • development of clean coal technology • establishment of a CO_2 capture and storage pipeline • purchase of "green power" for 20% of Government of Canada electricity needs
Small and Medium-Sized Enterprises and Emissions	• Industrial Research Assistance Program (IRAP) to help reduce emissions • improvements in industrial energy efficiency • research and development to reduce fugitive emissions
Agriculture, Forestry and Landfills	• federal government funds to municipalities for the capture of methane from landfill for combustion or generation of electricity • forestry and agricultural management practices (for example, reforestation) to increase carbon sinks
International Emissions Reductions	• help for developing countries to reduce their greenhouse gas emissions • facilitation of private sector participation in international Clean Development Mechanism projects

Federal government initiatives are not the only key to success in reducing greenhouse gases. Provinces, municipalities, and companies are all voluntarily implementing strategies that reduce GHG emissions. Over 900 organizations across the country have developed, registered, and implemented voluntary plans to reduce their GHG emissions. Individual efforts will also be required if Canada is to meet its target.

One of the components of *The Climate Change Plan for Canada* challenges all individuals to reduce their GHG emissions by 1 t. This means reducing per capita emissions by approximately 20% (**Figure 10**). The plan provides practical suggestions that individuals can use to achieve this goal of a 1-t reduction (**Table 4**).

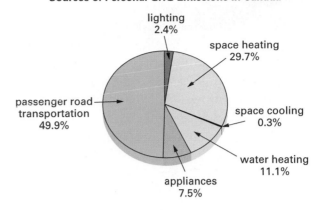

Sources of Personal GHG Emissions in Canada

lighting 2.4%
space heating 29.7%
space cooling 0.3%
water heating 11.1%
appliances 7.5%
passenger road transportation 49.9%

Figure 10 Running passenger vehicles is by far the biggest source of GHG emissions produced by individual Canadians.

Table 4 The One-Tonne Challenge of the Climate Change Plan for Canada

Location	Sample actions
at home	Retrofit older homes to make them more energy efficient. Buy an R2000 energy-efficient home. Be energy efficient at home (e.g., lower thermostats at night). Replace appliances with energy-efficient models (**Figure 11**). **Figure 11** Look for the EnerGuide label on appliances.
at work	Use computer equipment wisely (e.g., enable the monitor's energy-saving features and turn off the computer at night). Purchase more energy-efficient computers, printers, and photocopiers. Practise energy conservation (**Figure 12**). **Figure 12** Office equipment that contains the ENERGY STAR is among the most energy efficient.
on the road	Buy a fuel-efficient vehicle. Use ethanol-blend gasoline. Use the car less. Reduce idling (**Figure 13**). **Figure 13** Stop idling. You get 0 km/L when idling.

B3: Is It Warm in Here? Gaseous Waste and the Greenhouse Effect

Explore *an* Issue

Should Canada Have Ratified the Kyoto Protocol?

The debate over Canada's ratification of the Kyoto Protocol is likely to continue for some time. Whether or not the Kyoto Protocol should have been ratified is really a moot point, because this has already been done (**Figure 14**). The success of the *Climate Change Plan for Canada* depends on public support, however. It cannot be implemented without the cooperation of provinces, municipalities, businesses, and individuals.

Figure 14 On December 12, 2002, Canadian Prime Minister Jean Chretien signed the instrument for the ratification of the Kyoto Protocol surrounded by members of parliament.

You are a member of a provincial team attending a federal-provincial conference on the Kyoto Protocol. The conference has been organized to determine the support across Canada for the federal government's decision to ratify the Kyoto Protocol.

Statement: The Government of Canada was right to ratify the Kyoto Protocol, a blueprint for greenhouse gas reductions.

1. Decide which province your team would like to represent. As a provincial team, you will debate the statement either as a proponent or an opponent (see **Appendix A7**). (Your position may or may not coincide with the actual position of the province you represent.)

Decision-Making Skills

○ Define the Issue   ● Identify Alternatives
● Research   ● Analyze the Issue
● Defend a Decision   ● Evaluate

2. Research arguments for your team's position and facts to support these arguments. Collect scientific evidence from primary sources wherever possible.

 www.science.nelson.com

Your research can include, but is not limited to, the following topics:
- activities that are responsible for Canada's contribution to global greenhouse gas emissions
- the levels of greenhouse gas emissions in Canada since 1990, the baseline year for the Kyoto Protocol
- scientific evidence for or against the theory that greenhouse gases from human activities cause climate change, specifically global warming
- economic forecasts of the costs or benefits of Canada's participation in the Kyoto Protocol, in terms of direct costs of technology and infrastructure, jobs, investment in Canadian businesses and industries, and taxes
- evidence that the economic forecasts may be wrong—either overly optimistic or pessimistic
- an action plan proposed by a province, a municipality, or a business

3. Assemble the evidence to support your position, and prepare to debate.

4. After the debate, discuss how you could have improved your group's performance.

5. Based on your research for the debate, prepare a one-page report that attempts to persuade the public to support (or not support) the government's *Climate Change Plan for Canada*.

6. Did your initial opinion on climate change and the Kyoto Protocol change because of your research? If so, what evidence changed your mind? If not, what evidence confirmed your opinion?

SUMMARY

- The greenhouse effect refers to trapping heat in Earth's atmosphere by gases (water vapour, carbon dioxide, methane, nitrous oxide, and halocarbons) that absorb heat radiating from Earth's surface.
- The greenhouse effect is an essential atmospheric phenomenon because it keeps Earth's temperature within a range that can support life.
- The enhanced greenhouse effect increases the absorption of heat radiation from Earth, thereby increasing global temperatures above normal levels. Increased levels of GHGs from human activities contribute to the enhanced greenhouse effect.
- The main source of GHGs from human activities is the combustion of fossil fuels.

$$C_8H_{18} + \frac{25}{2}O_2 \rightarrow 8\,CO_2 + 9\,H_2O + \text{heat}$$
$$\text{(combustion)}$$

- The main natural source of carbon dioxide in the atmosphere is from the respiration of plants and animals.

$$C_6H_{12}O_6 + 6\,O_2 \rightarrow 6\,CO_2 + 6\,H_2O + \text{heat}$$
$$\text{(respiration)}$$

- The main sources of methane, as a GHG, are the digestive system of cattle, rice fields, landfills, oil and gas production, and the decay of organic matter in reservoirs.
- Paleoclimatologists are scientists who study earlier climates. They rely on indirect evidence (such as carbon dioxide in air bubbles trapped in glaciers, annual growth rings of trees, and ocean sediments) to determine what the global climate was like thousands of years ago.

- Water vapour and carbon dioxide are removed from the atmosphere by natural processes and stored in sinks. For example, trees and other vegetation are considered to be carbon sinks because they absorb carbon dioxide and store the carbon in their tissues.
- Possible effects of climate change due to the enhanced greenhouse effect include rising sea levels, weather extremes such as flooding and drought, plant and animal extinctions, and impacts on human health and populations.
- Some scientists disagree with the causes and extent of climate change because of the uncertainty in the measurement of climate variables. They are not confident in the ability of computer models to predict future climates accurately.
- The Kyoto Protocol is an agreement that was developed at a convention in Kyoto, Japan, in 1997. It proposes to reduce global GHG emissions to below 1990 levels.
- The Government of Canada committed Canada to reducing its GHG emissions to 6% below 1990 levels between 2008 and 2012. The government developed *The Climate Change Plan for Canada* as a blueprint for achieving this target.

Key Terms

greenhouse effect	**sink**
greenhouse gas (GHG)	**paleoclimatology**
enhanced greenhouse effect	**Kyoto Protocol**
carbon dioxide equivalent (CO$_2$ eq)	

ASSESSMENT

Understanding Concepts

1. Explain the greenhouse effect. In your description, identify the main greenhouse gases.
2. Why is the term "enhanced greenhouse effect" more appropriate for describing the influence of greenhouse gases on global climate?
3. Explain why reducing the amount of GHG emissions to the atmosphere is important.

4. Review the list of personal GHG emissions you made using the *Climate Change Calculator*. Compare your list with the sources in the pie graph in **Figure 10** on page 117. Group your personal GHG emissions using these sources. Do you have personal emissions from each source?
5. Explain Canada's target under the Kyoto Protocol. Provide both the percentage reductions and the actual reductions in carbon dioxide equivalents.

6. Summarize the arguments of scientists who disagree with the consensus that increased levels of greenhouse gases from human activities are causing global warming.

Applying Inquiry Skills

7. Analyze the data in **Figure 15**, and answer the questions that follow.

Total Greenhouse Gas Emissions Per Capita Canada (1990–2001)

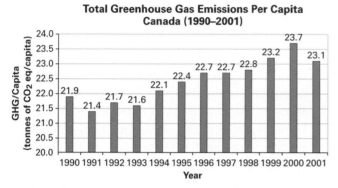

Figure 15

(a) Describe any significant trends in the total GHG emissions per capita in Canada from 1990 to 2001. Propose an explanation for each trend.
(b) What is the percentage increase from 1990 to 2001? Does this figure give an accurate representation of what happened during the period?
(c) Give two examples of additional data that would be required to provide a more complete picture of the GHG emissions in Canada.

8. Science is promoted as an objective, unbiased way of studying and understanding the world. If this is true, why is there disagreement among scientists about the causes, the extent, and the potential impacts of global warming? Give an example of another issue that scientists disagree about, and outline the nature of the disagreement.

Making Connections

9. *The Climate Change Plan for Canada* recommends a variety of new technologies that are designed to reduce the production of greenhouse gases. Some of these technologies are
   • more fuel-efficient cars
   • high-efficiency natural gas furnaces
   • fuels that produce fewer emissions (such as ethanol and biodiesel)

• improved mass transportation
• energy-saving technologies for the home (such as set-back thermostats)
(a) Select one of these technologies. Use library and Internet resources to research relevant information about it.

(b) Before people are willing to change their lifestyles or switch to new technologies, they have to be convinced that there is a benefit. Identify a target group, and prepare an advertisement (poster, video, audio, or Web ad) to promote the technology you have researched.
(c) In a separate report, identify your target group, explain why you think your advertisement will be effective, and summarize any risks and benefits of the technology that you did not include in your advertisement.

10. Research existing local, municipal, or provincial programs aimed at reducing GHG emissions. Select one program, and describe its objectives, methods, costs and benefits, and successes and failures.

11. Some people claim that scientific and technological developments have caused the problems associated with the enhanced greenhouse effect and climate change, and that science and technology will solve the problems. Others claim that science and technology cannot solve the problems because the damage to the environment is irreversible and the future effects of climate change are unknown. In a letter to the editor, express your opinion on the role of science and technology in preventing further climate change and in addressing the potential impacts of climate change on humans and the environment.

Reflecting

12. In light of what you now know about greenhouse gases and climate change, are you concerned for the future? Describe your level of concern. What are you willing to do to help prevent future climate change?

Yana timidly walks off the airplane, into the hustle and bustle of Pearson International Airport in Toronto. Yana is only 12 years old, and this is her first trip anywhere outside her country. She lives in a village just outside Mazyr, a small city in Belarus, about 150 km from Chornobyl, Ukraine. She is scared but excited to be away from home (**Figure 1**).

Figure 1 Many children from Ukraine and Belarus come to Ontario during the summer to relax and recuperate.

Yana appears to be a normal 12-year-old, but her appearance is deceiving. She was diagnosed with thyroid cancer at the age of six and has been undergoing regular medical treatment ever since. Her con-dition is stable now. Doctors expect her to live a fairly normal life, even though her immune system is weakened. Constant monitoring and treatments will continue, however, for the rest of her life.

Yana was born on April 25, 1992, almost six years to the day after an accident that changed the history of her country and the world. On April 26, 1986, the nuclear generating plant at Chornobyl exploded. Thousands of people were killed, and millions have been affected. The radioactive material that was pushed into the atmosphere drifted and settled over Yana's home town.

(a) Briefly describe your understanding of the health risks associated with radiation.

Radiation, an invisible poison, affects people in two ways: by direct exposure to the radiation and by consuming food that has been produced in the con-taminated environment. In Chornobyl, the entire food chain has been affected (**Figure 2**). One of the most dramatic health effects is the incidence of thyroid cancer, especially in children. The incidence of thy-roid cancer has increased ten-fold since the Chornobyl accident; the incidence of thyroid cancer in children is nearly 300 times the rate it was before the Chornobyl accident. An estimated 3000 children in Belarus, Ukraine, and Russia suffer from thyroid cancer.

Yana's thyroid cancer was undoubtedly the result of exposure to radiation from the Chornobyl accident. Her thyroid gland was surgically removed, which means that she will have to take medication for the rest of her life. As well, her immune system is weakened, since her body is constantly struggling to combat the direct and indirect effects of the cancer. Because Yana still lives in a contaminated area, her visit to Canada is an attempt to give her immune system a rest and help her recover her strength. Canada is one of many countries around the world where organizations have sprung up to help the children of Chornobyl. The goal of most of these organizations is to bring affected

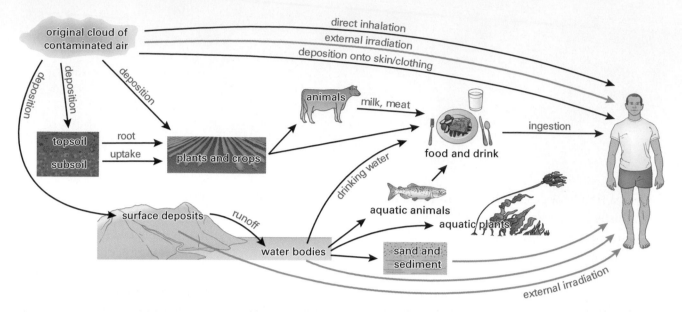

Figure 2 There are many ways humans can be exposed to radiation in the environment following an event such as the Chornobyl accident.

children to a healthier location. This break from their contaminated environment is often as valuable for emotional healing as it is for physical recuperation.

(b) Describe some of the emotions you might feel if you had to leave your home and family, for medical or other reasons, and spend time in another country with a different language and a very different culture.

The Chornobyl accident has been so significant that, in current usage, the word "Chornobyl" no longer refers to a geographic location, but rather to the events of April 26, 1986. The Chornobyl accident has forever changed the public perception of nuclear energy world wide. The nuclear industry is attempting to alleviate the fears associated with nuclear energy. For example, the proposed nuclear facility in Chalk River, Ontario—the Canadian Neutron Facility—does not contain the words "nuclear," "atomic," or "reactor" in its name. The remaining three reactors in the Chornobyl Nuclear Plant have been shut down and Germany has decided to close all of its nuclear generating facilities as of 2003. However, while there is caution in some countries, others are expanding their nuclear generating capacity. Since the Chornobyl accident, Canada has sold nuclear reactors to Korea, China, Argentina, and Romania.

The use of nuclear energy to generate electricity is very controversial. The arguments for and against nuclear energy focus mainly on its relative cost-effectiveness, its impact on the environment compared with the impact of fossil fuels, and its potential risks

to human health and safety. All of these issues are very important. In this topic, however, you will examine a related issue: solid nuclear waste management.

There are many sources of solid nuclear waste: the mining and refining of uranium, nuclear generating stations, and scientific and medical research. In this topic, you will focus on solid nuclear waste produced from electricity generation in nuclear power stations.

Proponents of nuclear energy see it as a more environmentally friendly source of energy than fossil fuels. Opponents say that nuclear energy is too expensive and poses unacceptable risks to human health and the environment.

(c) Does any of your electricity come from a nuclear generating station? If so, where is the generating station located? If not, where does your electricity come from?

(d) What assumptions are often made about the use of nuclear generating stations to produce electricity?

(e) From what you know about nuclear generating stations, how would you feel about living next door to one? Is your initial reaction positive or negative? Explain any concerns you might have.

What kinds of waste are produced by a nuclear generating station? What risks do these wastes pose to humans and the environment? How many nuclear generating stations do we have in Canada? Are there plans for future nuclear generating stations? How is the waste that is generated by these stations currently managed? What plans exist for the future management of this waste?

Chornobyl

On April 26, 1986, reactor number 4 of the Chornobyl Nuclear Plant exploded while routine tests were being conducted (**Figure 3**).

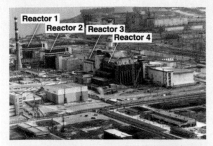

Reactor 1
Reactor 2 Reactor 3
Reactor 4

Figure 3 The explosion completely demolished reactor number 4 of the Chornobyl Nuclear Plant.

The problem was caused by operator errors and a break-down in communication between the nuclear and non-nuclear personnel. Staff misin-terpreted status indicators during the test and the meas-ures they took to correct the power fluctuations made the situation worse. The system overheated and finally exploded. The design and construction of the reactor itself may also have contributed to the explosion. To make matters worse, the Russian and Ukrainian authori-ties did not inform the rest of the world until two days later when elevated radiation levels were detected in Sweden by Swedish scientists.

The initial explosion was not a nuclear explosion but rather a thermal or heat explosion caused by a build-up of steam inside the reactor. The explosion,

and the fires that followed, evaporated tonnes of nuclear fuel and threw radioactive material as high as 10 km into the atmosphere. Most of it set-tled on the area immediately surrounding the nuclear plant. A plume of contaminated gases and dust drifted northward from Chornobyl over the nearby Belarus-Ukraine border. Belarus was affected the most because it was directly downwind of the plume. Within a month, the radioactive cloud had spread essentially around the world (**Figure 4**). Higher than normal levels of radiation have been detected as far away as the Canadian Arctic and even in northern China.

(a) Use an atlas to locate Chornobyl and Mazyr. Explain why Belarus was affected more than other countries.

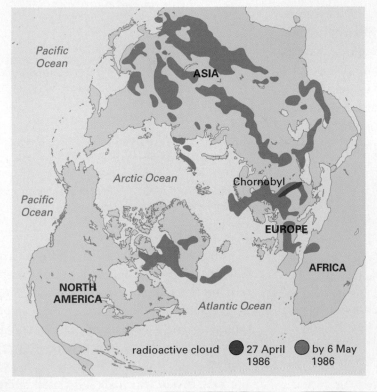

Pacific Ocean

ASIA

Arctic Ocean

Pacific Ocean

Chornobyl

EUROPE

AFRICA

NORTH AMERICA

Atlantic Ocean

radioactive cloud ● 27 April 1986 ● by 6 May 1986

Figure 4 The contaminated air and dust quickly spread thousands of kilometres beyond the site of the Chornobyl explosion.

B4: Waste from the Clean Energy Alternative: Solid Nuclear Waste

Nuclear Energy and Nuclear Waste

A nuclear generating station works in the same way as a thermal generating station. Water is heated to produce steam, which drives a turbine that generates electricity. The only difference is that uranium, rather than a fossil fuel, is the fuel that produces the heat.

In Canada, nuclear generating stations use **CANDU** reactors. CANDU stands for **Can**ada, **D**euterium, **U**ranium, which means that the reactor was designed in Canada, uses deuterium as a moderator, and requires uranium as a fuel. Uranium is not burned like a fossil fuel, however. So how does it produce heat, and why is it such a powerful fuel? If it is so powerful, producing a large amount of energy from a small amount of fuel, where does the waste come from? The answers to these questions lie in the splitting of uranium atoms.

Nuclear Chemistry

Elements such as hydrogen and uranium consist of atoms. Atoms are made up of three smaller particles. **Protons**, which are positively charged particles, are found in the nucleus of the atom along with **neutrons**, which are neutral or have no charge. **Electrons**, which are negatively charged particles, surround the nucleus. The number of protons in the nucleus of an atom is known as the **atomic number (Z)** of the atom. Uranium is the heaviest of all the natural elements, with 92 protons in its nucleus. At the other extreme, hydrogen has only one proton in its nucleus. Its atomic

number is 1. Since atoms are electrically neutral, the number of negative electrons is equal to the number of positive protons. Therefore, the atomic number also represents the number of electrons in an atom of the element. The sum of the number of nuclear particles in an atom is known as the **mass number (A)** of the atom. The number of neutrons in an atom of a given element can be calculated by subtracting the atomic number from the mass number, as follows:

$$\text{number of neutrons} = \text{mass number} - \text{atomic number}$$

This information is normally written in a short form, from which the number of protons, electrons, and neutrons in an atom can be determined (**Figure 5**). For example, an atom of sodium is written as $^{23}_{11}\text{Na}$, so it consists of 11 protons, 11 electrons, and 12 neutrons. It can also be written as Na-23 or sodium-23, where 23 is the mass number. This is acceptable and unambiguous because sodium always has 11 protons, so we understand that its atomic number is 11.

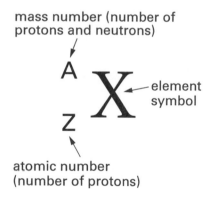

Figure 5 These symbols represent information about an individual atom of an element.

The same element can have different isotopes. The **isotopes** of an element have the same number of protons but different numbers of neutrons in their nuclei and, therefore, a different atomic mass. In other words, isotopes have the same atomic number (Z) but different neutron numbers and therefore different mass numbers (A). Uranium, for instance, has several isotopes, two of which are illustrated in **Figure 6**.

DID **YOU** KNOW?

Efficient Energy Conversion
When 1 kg (1 L) of water flows over Niagara Falls, it loses roughly 1 kJ of gravitational potential energy. A fraction of this energy can be converted into hydroelectricity. When 1 kg of gasoline burns, it releases about 4×10^4 kJ of energy. When 1 kg of uranium in a nuclear reactor undergoes fission, it releases about 1×10^{11} kJ of energy.

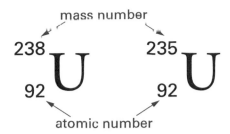

mass number

$^{238}_{92}\text{U}$ $^{235}_{92}\text{U}$

atomic number

Figure 6 Two isotopes of uranium: Notice that the atomic number is the same for both isotopes. Only the mass number is different.

Hydrogen has three different isotopes. More than 99% of all hydrogen atoms contain a single proton and no neutrons. The other 1% are the isotopes deuterium (D) and tritium (T). An atom of deuterium contains one proton and one neutron in its nucleus. An atom of tritium contains one proton and two neutrons. When an atom of deuterium combines with oxygen, the product is represented by the chemical formula D_2O and is known as heavy water. Heavy water, or deuterium oxide, is 10% heavier than regular water because of the extra neutron in each of the hydrogen atoms. Heavy water is used to control the nuclear reactions and cool the fuel in a CANDU nuclear reactor.

Many elements have one or more isotopes that are unstable. Atoms of unstable isotopes decay, emitting radiation as their nuclei change. Depending on the isotope, these nuclear changes may happen very quickly or extremely slowly. The radiation that is emitted can be fairly harmless or very dangerous to living cells. Isotopes that decay are known as **radioisotopes** and are said to be **radioactive**. Radioisotopes give off three types of radiation: alpha (α) particles, beta (β) particles, and gamma (γ) rays (**Table 1**).

Radioactive decay changes the atomic structure of an atom and, thus, results in an atom with differ-ent properties. For example, uranium-238 is a radioactive isotope that spontaneously decays to form thorium-234 and an alpha particle. An alpha particle is composed of two protons and two neutrons, which is equivalent to a ^4_2He nucleus.

$$^{238}_{92}\text{U} \rightarrow \,^{234}_{90}\text{Th} + \,^4_2\text{He}$$

Tritium is a radioisotope of hydrogen. When it decays, the number of neutrons in the tritium nucleus decreases by one and the number of protons increases. A beta particle and helium-3 are produced. Beta particles are high-energy electrons.

$$^3_1\text{H} \rightarrow \,^3_2\text{He} + \,^{0}_{-1}\text{e}$$

The emission of a gamma ray during radioactive decay does not result in any changes to the mass number or atomic number of an isotope. Gamma radiation, however, often occurs along with other types of radiation, which do result in a change in either the atomic number or mass number.

Every radioisotope has a characteristic property called its half-life. The **half-life** of a radioactive substance is the time that is required for half of the original number of radioactive atoms to decay. The half-lives of radioisotopes vary considerably, from fractions of a second to hundreds of thousands of years. For example, if left to decay naturally, uranium-238 has a half-life of 4.5×10^9 years, while polonium-216 has a half-life of only 0.16 s. What does this mean? Consider a 1000-g sample of radium-226, which has a half-life of 1600 years. After 1600 years, only 500 g of the original sample would still be radium-226. The other 500 g would have decayed to form other elements. After an additional 1600 years, 250 g of the remaining 500 g of radium-226 would have decayed, leaving only 250 g of the original radium-226.

> ### DID **YOU** KNOW?
>
> **A Canadian Discovery**
> Radioactive decay was discovered by a Canadian scientist named Harriet Brooks (1876–1933). Her investigations proved that an atom of one element can spontaneously or naturally change into another element.

Table 1 Characteristics of Radioactive Emissions

Radiation	Approximate speed	Penetration in air	Effective barrier
alpha (α)	variable, but relatively slow	a few centimetres	a sheet of paper
beta (β)	variable, but relatively fast	a few metres	1 mm–2 mm of metal
gamma (γ)	very fast (speed of light)	unlimited	1 m of lead or concrete

B4.1 Activity | HALF-LIFE MODELLING

In this activity, you will model a sample of a radioactive substance. By removing the "decayed nuclei" from the sample after each half-life, and counting the remaining nuclei, you will collect quantitative data. You will use your data to plot a graph of the half-life of the sample.

Materials

at least 30 disks that have different faces (e.g., Othello disks, coins, or cardboard cutouts with a mark on one side)
a box with a lid (e.g., a shoebox)

Procedure

1. Create a table like **Table 2** to record your observations.

Table 2 Observation Table

| Half-life | Number of disks remaining | | | |
	Trial 1	Trial 2	Trial 3	Average
0	30	30	30	30
1				
2				
3				

2. Decide which face of the disks will represent the original radioactive isotope (for example, white or heads).

3. Place all the disks in the box, "original" side up, to represent a sample that contains 100% of the radioisotope.

4. Put the lid on the box securely, and shake the box.

5. Open the box, and remove all the disks that do not have the "original" side up. In your table, record the number of disks remaining after one half-life.

6. Repeat steps 4 and 5 for at least five more half-lives.

7. Run three separate trials, and calculate the average number of disks remaining for each half-life.

(a) Create a graph with the average number of disks remaining on the *y*-axis and the number of half-lives on the *x*-axis.

(b) Draw a best-fit curve. Describe the shape of your curve.

(c) Suppose that the units on the *y*-axis were the mass of the radioactive sample (g) and each half-life represented two years. Predict the mass of radioactive material that would remain after seven years.

(d) Does the curve of your graph reach the *x*-axis? If it does not, do you think it would if you had taken the activity through another few half-lives?

(e) What do the removed disks represent? Compare this model of radioactive decay with what you know about real radioactive decay. In what ways is this a good model? In what ways is it less than perfect?

(f) What is the purpose of running three trials? Does this affect the validity of the model? Explain.

Nuclear Fission

Understanding the structure of atomic nuclei and radioactive decay has allowed scientists and technologists to initiate a **nuclear reaction** by intentionally changing the structure of nuclei. They do this by bombarding the nuclei with particles.

The CANDU reactor uses a naturally occurring radioisotope of uranium: uranium-235. Uranium oxide, which is produced from uranium ore, is formed into cylindrical ceramic pellets. About 0.7%

of the uranium in the pellets is U-235, and 99.3% is U-238. The pellets are placed in long metal rods, and the rods are clustered together into a nuclear fuel bundle (**Figure 7**).

To initiate a nuclear reaction, the fuel bundles are placed in the reactor. There the U-235 atoms are bombarded with "slow" neutrons. When a neutron collides with the nucleus of a U-235 atom, the atom splits, or undergoes **nuclear fission**. Two lighter

Figure 7 **(a)** Nuclear fuel pellets. **(b)** A nuclear fuel bundle of 43 rods is about 50 cm long and 10 cm in diameter. It has a mass of about 24 kg.

nuclei, referred to as fission fragments, are formed. The fission fragments are represented by X and Y in the following equation. U-236 is only a transition stage, which lasts for about 10^{-12} s.

"slow" neutron + $^{235}_{92}$U → $^{236}_{92}$U → X + Y + neutrons + energy

This reaction releases a considerable amount of energy and also produces two or three more neutrons (**Figure 8**). These new neutrons are travelling too quickly to cause any further fission reactions, however. To continue the nuclear reactions, the neutrons must be slowed down so that they can collide with other U-235 nuclei. The CANDU reactor uses heavy water to moderate, or slow down, these neutrons so

that more reactions can take place. The continuous sequence of splitting the atoms and releasing more neutrons, which then split more atoms, is called a nuclear **chain reaction**. A nuclear chain reaction will only happen if there is a sufficient mass of U-235 and if enough neutrons are generated to continue the sequence. An uncontrolled chain reaction could result in a nuclear explosion—a sudden release of a tremendous amount of energy—similar to a nuclear weapon exploding. In the CANDU reactor, the chain reaction is controlled by limiting the amount of uranium fuel that is available at a particular time and by using control rods, which absorb neutrons and prevent the reactions from proceeding too fast.

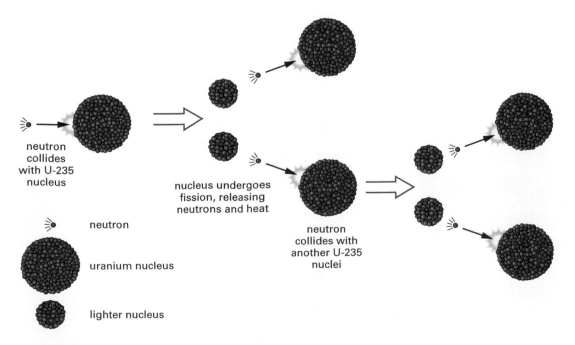

neutron collides with U-235 nucleus

nucleus undergoes fission, releasing neutrons and heat

neutron collides with another U-235 nuclei

neutron

uranium nucleus

lighter nucleus

Figure 8 Notice the chain reaction in the nuclear fission of U-235.

B4: Waste from the Clean Energy Alternative: Solid Nuclear Waste

B4.2 Activity | NUCLEAR FISSION ANIMATIONS AND SIMULATION

Computer animations and simulations can help you to visualize events that cannot be directly observed and to manipulate variables that would be impossible to manipulate in real life. To better understand how nuclear fission works, go to the Nelson Web site. Access the fission and chain reaction animations and the nuclear reaction simulation.

 www.science.nelson.oom

(a) Observe the fission animation. Describe what happens during the fission of U-235.

(b) Create a simple non-atomic model to explain the concept of a chain reaction.

(c) What two variables determine the speed and extent of a nuclear reaction?

(d) Play with the nuclear reaction simulation. Observe the effect of changing each variable. Record your observations.

(e) Describe the three things that can happen to a neutron.

(f) Quickly pause and restart the reaction. Record your observations.

(g) Change the number of neutron absorbers as the reaction progresses. Observe and record the effect.

(h) Explain how this simulation represents a CANDU nuclear reactor.

When the atoms split, or undergo fission, a large amount of energy is produced. This released energy heats the heavy water. The heat from the heavy water is used to heat ordinary water, producing the steam that is needed to turn turbines connected to electric generators (**Figure 9**).

DID **YOU** KNOW?

A Powerful Bundle
A single 24-kg nuclear fuel bundle produces enough energy to heat a home in northern Canada for about 100 years (or 100 homes for one year). This is the equivalent to the energy produced by about 400 t of coal or 2000 barrels of oil.

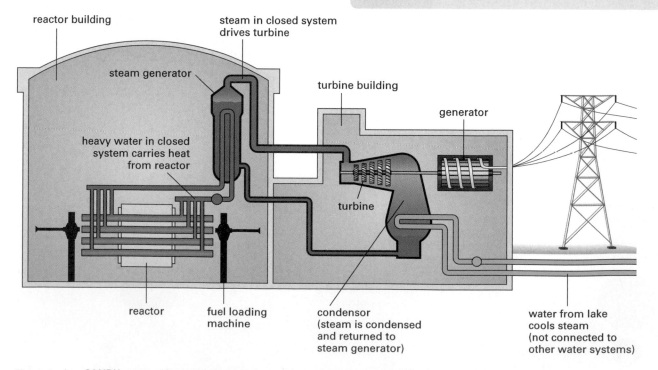

Figure 9 In a CANDU reactor, the water that produces the steam to drive the turbine and generator is completely separated from the heavy water that surrounds the nuclear fuel.

Nuclear Waste

Nuclear power plants produce two types of radioactive waste: high-level waste and low-level waste. Everything that comes in contact with radioactive materials becomes radioactive itself. For example, protective clothing, tools, and equipment all contain small amounts of radioactive materials and are considered to be low-level waste. The used fuel from a nuclear power plant is high-level waste.

Once the energy capture from the fuel bundles becomes inefficient, the fuel is considered used up, or spent. This does not mean that there is no energy left. Interestingly, the spent fuel rods have less useful energy but are much more radioactive than they were before being used. Why? Most of the original fuel (99.3%) consisted of U-238. Only the small percentage of U-235 was used up during the reactions. While the nuclei of U-235 atoms split when they are hit by neutrons, the nuclei of U-238 atoms absorb the neutrons and form atoms of U-239. Each U-239 atom naturally decays to produce an atom of plutonium-239, which can also be split to obtain more energy. The CANDU reactor is not designed to split the plutonium atoms, however. So the spent fuel contains a combination of U-238 and Pu-239. Pu-239 has a half-life of 2.41×10^4 years.

After 12 to 18 months, when the fuel rods have been spent, they are removed from the reactor. They are removed by a remote-controlled device because they are much more radioactive than they first were. They are then stored for 7 to 10 years in huge indoor pools of water at the nuclear power station. By that time, they have cooled sufficiently to be placed in large concrete containers called dry storage containers. These dry storage containers are moved to a storage building, or they are placed in lead-lined, steel casks and stored in concrete silos or vaults (**Figure 10**). Not all nuclear reactors have dry storage facilities.

Each year in Canada, approximately 85 000 used fuel bundles become high-level nuclear waste. **Table 3** summarizes the locations and amounts of nuclear fuel in Canada as of the end of 2003. According to estimates, by the end of 2033, a total of 3.6 million used fuel bundles will exist—enough to cover a soccer field to a height of nearly 3 m.

Figure 10 After the spent nuclear fuel has cooled, it can be transferred from **(a)** wet storage to **(b)** dry storage.

B4: Waste from the Clean Energy Alternative: Solid Nuclear Waste

Table 3 In-Use and Spent Fuel Bundles, 2003

Nuclear facility	Number of nuclear fuel bundles			
	In reactor(s)	In wet storage	In dry storage	Total
Point Lepreau, NB	4 560	40 970	57 240	102 770
AECL* – Gentilly 1, PQ	0	0	3 213	3 213
Gentilly 2, PQ	4 560	37 789	51 000	93 349
Bruce A, ON	12 480	354 567	3 840	370 887
Bruce B, ON	24 664	373 858	0	398 522
Pickering, ON	36 090	385 935	118 647	541 278
Darlington, ON	24 960	234 433	0	259 393
Douglas Point, ON	0	0	22 256	22 256
AECL* – Whiteshell, MB	0	0	360	360
AECL* – Chalk River, ON	0	0	4 853	4 853
Total	**107 920**	**1 427 552**	**261 409**	**1 796 881**

*These facilities are research facilities operated by AECL (Atomic Energy of Canada Limited)

✔ Check Your Understanding

1. Explain the meaning of the word CANDU in CANDU reactor.

2. In a nuclear generating plant, large amounts of water from a lake are used to cool and condense the steam that is pumped back to the steam generator. Why does the lake not become contaminated with radioactive materials?

3. Explain why D_2O is known as heavy water.

4. Describe the two roles of D_2O (heavy water) in a CANDU nuclear reactor.

5. Explain the terms "isotope" and "radioisotope."

6. Which type of radioactive emission is most dangerous? What precaution can be taken to protect organisms and/or the environment against this type of radioactivity?

7. The half-life of cesium-137 is 30 years.
   (a) What mass of cesium-137 would remain from a 12-g sample after 30 years?
   (b) What mass would remain after 60 years?

8. Briefly describe the process of nuclear fission as it occurs in a CANDU nuclear reactor.

9. What is the difference between low-level and high-level radioactive waste?

10. How many nuclear generating facilities were operating in Canada in 2002?

11. Use the data in **Table 3** to answer the following questions:
    (a) Calculate the percentage of solid nuclear fuel that is currently in reactors.
    (b) What percentage of the total number of nuclear fuel bundles is considered to be "spent"?
    (c) What is the mass of the total amount of spent nuclear fuel in Canada?

Managing Nuclear Waste

The waste that is produced from nuclear power generation are miniscule when compared with the other waste that we produce. Each year, approximately 2040 t of high-level nuclear waste are generated in Canada. Compare this with the 1.02 t of household waste that each person generates annually, for a total of 23 million tonnes in 2000. Obviously, quantity is not the primary concern with nuclear waste. Since the volume of high-level nuclear waste is relatively small, management approaches that would not be possible with larger volumes of waste can be used. The main concerns with high-level nuclear waste are their toxicity and longevity.

Health Risks of Radioactive Waste

The different types of radiation that are produced by radioisotopes can be harnessed for a wide variety of uses. For example, radiation can be used to kill bacteria in foods to prevent spoilage. Radiation is widely used in medicine, as well. Cancer patients are treated with cancer-killing radiation from cobalt-60 and radium-226.

The ability of radiation to destroy cells, however, is not always an advantage. Radiation can cause normal cells to mutate or even die (**Figure 11**). Acute exposure to radiation can cause severe skin burns. Long-term exposure can result in various forms of cancer, birth defects, and sterility in all animals. While radiation has great benefits for our standard of living, many risks are associated with it. We must constantly evaluate the balance between risks and benefits in our applications of radioisotopes.

In order to evaluate the risks that are associated with exposure to radiation, we need to understand how radiation is measured and compare the radiation we receive from various natural and created sources (**Figure 12**). When referring to the potential effects of radiation on the human body, the most common way to describe the absorption of radiation is the **equivalent dose (H)**. This is an estimate of the biological effects that radiation has on tissue. The unit of measurement of the equivalent dose is the **sievert (Sv)**. An equivalent dose of 1 Sv represents the biological damage done by the quantity of radiation that is equivalent to the effects of 1 J of energy in 1 kg of body tissue. This is a very small amount of energy, but it has the potential to do serious damage to tissue. The type of radiation affects the equivalent dose.

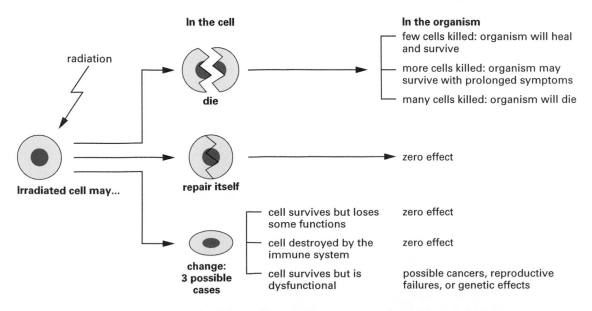

Figure 11 Exposure to radiation does not necessarily mean that a cell will die. The cell may also repair itself or mutate. Mutations in the DNA of a cell can lead to the development of cancer. Changes in the DNA of sex cells (eggs or sperm) can lead to physical defects in a developing embryo. If enough cells are killed by radiation, however, an organism will die.

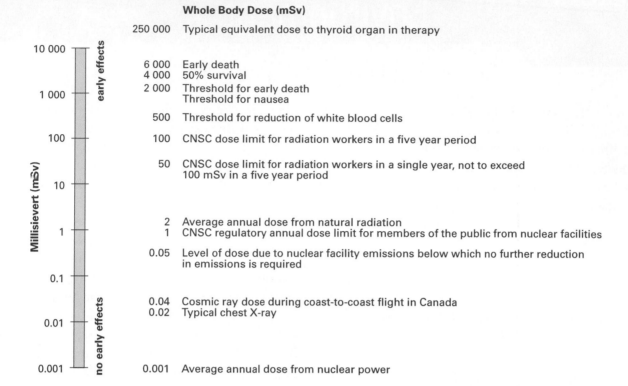

Whole Body Dose (mSv)

Millisievert (mSv)		Dose (mSv)	Effect
		250 000	Typical equivalent dose to thyroid organ in therapy
10 000	early effects		
		6 000	Early death
		4 000	50% survival
1 000		2 000	Threshold for early death / Threshold for nausea
		500	Threshold for reduction of white blood cells
100		100	CNSC dose limit for radiation workers in a five year period
		50	CNSC dose limit for radiation workers in a single year, not to exceed 100 mSv in a five year period
10			
1		2	Average annual dose from natural radiation
		1	CNSC regulatory annual dose limit for members of the public from nuclear facilities
		0.05	Level of dose due to nuclear facility emissions below which no further reduction in emissions is required
0.1			
	no early effects	0.04	Cosmic ray dose during coast-to-coast flight in Canada
		0.02	Typical chest X-ray
0.01			
0.001		0.001	Average annual dose from nuclear power

Figure 12 Potential health effects of different doses of radiation

Radiation from charged particles does more damage than an equal amount of radiation from electromagnetic energy. In practice, the measurements are often given in millisieverts (mSv) or microsieverts (μSv).

Equivalent doses of radiation are cumulative: that is, the doses from various sources of radiation are added to determine the overall biological impact on a person. So, if you had 20 X-rays in a year, the equivalent dose would be 20×0.02 mSv = 0.40 mSv. The International Commission on Radiological Protection (ICRP) and the Canadian Nuclear Safety Commission (CNSC) have set dose limits for workers who are exposed to radiation in their workplaces. The limit is an average of 20 mSv per year (over five years), with not more than 50 mSv in any one year. Health Canada sets the radiation dose limit for the public from nuclear facilities at 1 mSv per year.

The Chornobyl accident released a very large amount of radioactive materials into the environment. Plants and animals in the immediate vicinity received doses of over 2000 mSv. Within a few weeks of the accident, 31 reactor employees and firefighters had died from a combination of radiation and burns from the fire.

Exposure to radiation at any level, no matter how small, poses some health risk. How does this risk compare with other risks in our lives? **Table 4**

compares the risk associated with radiation exposure to the risks associated with a number of other common activities, in terms of estimated decrease in life expectancy. Keep in mind, however, that these are estimates. As well, there is little conclusive research that links low levels of radiation with an increased risk of cancer. Exposure to low levels of radiation is probably no more risky than some other environmental or lifestyle factors that we do not take precautions against. The difference is that we can avoid certain risks, such as smoking, but we may not be able to control whether a nuclear generating station is located in our community.

DID **YOU** KNOW?

Low Risk of Radiation from Flying

There is a risk of developing a fatal cancer as a result of absorbing increased cosmic radiation during commercial flights. This risk is approximately 1% after flying 1000 hours per year for 30 years. In other words, you would need to take about 100 one-way flights between Toronto and Vancouver in one year to get the same exposure that you get from other sources of natural background radiation in one year.

Table 4 Estimated Loss of Life Expectancy from Various Activities

Activity	Estimated loss of life expectancy (days)
living in poverty	3500 (9.59 years)
smoking 20 cigarettes a day	2370 (6.49 years)
working as a coal miner	1100 (3.01 years)
being 14 kg overweight	985 (2.70 years)
being exposed to radiation: 2.00 mSv per year (average annual dose) for 70 years	680 (1.86 years)
being 7 kg overweight	450 (1.23 years)
working in mining and refining	328
working in construction	302
working in agriculture	277
having pneumonia or influenza	130
doing office work	55
working in manufacturing	43
drinking 2.5 cups coffee per day	26

Another issue that must be considered in the management of nuclear waste is how long this waste remains hazardous. Some radioactive materials that are part of spent nuclear fuel decay fairly quickly. Others require tens of thousands of years of natural radioactive decay to reach a stable form. In essence, these materials are hazardous forever.

Because of the high-level radioactivity of nuclear waste, the general public perceives that they must be handled with special care. Toxicity and hazardous lifetime must also be considered, however, when managing non-nuclear hazardous waste. There are hundreds, or even thousands, of hazardous chemicals that cause cancer and that will remain toxic indefinitely. Municipal, industrial, and hazardous-waste landfills are supposed to be monitored for only 25 to 30 years after closure (if there are any regulations at all). Planning for nuclear waste disposal requires a long-term, permanent solution that assesses risk for up to 10 000 years into the future.

Public-opinion surveys indicate that most people consider the risk associated with nuclear waste to be much greater than the risks associated with other waste, which may be equally toxic for an equally long period of time. Chornobyl has undoubtedly contributed to this perception, even though the events of Chornobyl were not directly related to nuclear waste management. A fear of the unknown may also contribute to this perception. Most people know very little about the nature of radiation, and human senses cannot detect it. There is a possibility of being exposed to radiation without even knowing about it. A common misconception may also contribute to this perception of risk. Many people believe that a nuclear reactor could explode like a nuclear weapon. Despite some similarities between a nuclear reaction and a nuclear explosion, a nuclear reactor cannot explode like a nuclear bomb.

The public perception of the hazards of nuclear waste has influenced politicians to pay more attention to the management of nuclear waste than the management of non-nuclear waste. In 2002, the Canadian parliament legislated the creation of the Nuclear Waste Management Organization (NWMO). The mission of the NWMO is to "develop... a management approach for the long-term care of Canada's used nuclear fuel that is socially acceptable, technically sound, environmentally responsible, and economically feasible." Its mandate is to consult with all stakeholders, to propose approaches for the management of nuclear fuel waste to the federal government, and, subsequently, to implement the approach that is chosen by the federal government.

Proposed Storage and Disposal Solutions for Nuclear Waste

The NWMO faces serious challenges. The NIMBY principle will figure prominently in their consultations and in any recommendations that they make to the federal government. Is it even possible to recommend an approach to the nuclear waste issue that will satisfy a majority of citizens?

B4: Waste from the Clean Energy Alternative: Solid Nuclear Waste

There are two basic methods for managing high-level nuclear waste: storage and disposal. Storage can be defined as "keeping, unaltered, for an extended period of time." Disposal can be defined as "permanent housing without intention of retrieval." Each of these methods may have different possible approaches. The NWMO is required to consider (among others) the following three approaches for nuclear waste management:

- deep geological disposal in the Canadian Shield
- storage at nuclear reactor sites
- centralized storage, either above or below ground

Opponents of nuclear power suggest that the best solution for nuclear waste is to stop producing it. While this may be a solution for the future, it does nothing to resolve the issue of what to do with existing spent nuclear fuel. Scientists and engineers are working to devise a safe and economically feasible method of disposing of nuclear waste, but the public remains skeptical. All potential solutions must address the following criteria:

- technical feasibility
- remoteness from population centres
- economic feasibility
- very long-term protection
- public acceptability
- environmental friendliness

The five more commonly proposed approaches for dealing with nuclear waste are summarized below.

Status Quo

Keep it where it is: that is, in the pools within the nuclear facilities where it is produced, or in dry storage. This is probably the most popular suggestion at the moment, because nothing else has been done. Constant maintenance is required, however, since the facilities and their wet-storage sites are necessarily located adjacent to large bodies of water. These bodies of water are used for drinking water and could potentially become contaminated.

Deep Geological Storage

This is a longer-term disposal approach, and it has several advantages. The material is isolated from human populations and from the surface environment. The characteristics of the site (geologically stable and impermeable) ensure that the waste will not be disturbed. The risk of water damage to the containers and, thus, the risk of the waste washing away is reduced. The concern with using underground sites

for storage is that over time, even stable rock formations can shift and become unstable due to the normal slow movement of Earth's crust. This movement would probably not be significant in our lifetime, but the spent fuel will be radioactive for thousands of years, and the stability could change over geologic time. Engineers have identified some sites that they consider to be particularly stable. One underground storage site that is being developed in the United States is in Yucca Mountain, Nevada (**Figure 13**). Although potential disposal sites have been identified in the Canadian Shield, none have currently been approved.

Figure 13 The Yucca Mountain site in Nevada is being prepared for long-term storage of high-level nuclear waste. Burial in arid regions or in granite layers of old mine shafts avoids contaminating ground water.

Subductive Waste Disposal

This approach involves placing the nuclear waste at the interface of two tectonic plates of Earth's crust, in a subduction zone (**Figure 14**). In a subduction zone, one plate slides underneath another and is reabsorbed into Earth's mantle. This is obviously a very slow process (about 6 cm per year), but it would theoretically seal the radioactive materials beneath Earth's crust. The disadvantage of subductive waste disposal is that significant geological activities, such as earthquakes and volcanoes, occur within subduction zones. These activities could potentially move the nuclear waste back to the surface.

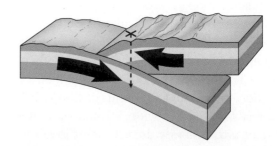

Figure 14 Nuclear waste placed in a subduction zone would be pushed deep into Earth's mantle and would, after a very long time, become part of the molten core.

Vitrification

Vitrification involves sealing the spent fuel in a glasslike compound and placing it deep underground in stable rock. Chemists have been developing suitable materials, such as lead-iron-phosphate glass, in which to encase nuclear waste to prevent its escape into the environment. This approach is promising because nuclear waste could be chemically incorporated into the stable glass and then buried in the safest possible place. The nuclear waste would become easier to dispose of once vitrified and the storage requirements would not be quite as stringent as with deep geological storage.

Space Disposal

Launching solid nuclear waste into space and sending it to the Moon, to other planets, or into distant orbits around Earth or another planet has been proposed. The main advantage is that the waste would be permanently removed from the human environment. There are some obvious disadvantages: the possibility of an accident during the launch of a space vehicle, the number of trips required, the cost, and the unlikely possibility of establishing the required international cooperation.

Explore *an* Issue

What Is the Most Appropriate Method for Dealing with Nuclear Waste?

What is the best long-term solution to the problem of spent nuclear fuel from Canada's nuclear reactors? Your group will assume the role of the NWMO. Your task is to research the various approaches for nuclear waste management and to recommend an approach to the federal government.

Decision-Making Skills

○ Define the Issue   ● Identify Alternatives
● Research   ● Analyze the Issue
● Defend a Decision   ● Evaluate

1. In your group, decide on a role for each person. Elect a chairperson, a facilitator, a recorder, a presenter, and any other role that you think is important.

2. Ensure that each member of your group represents a different perspective on the issue of nuclear waste. Consider the perspectives of the following groups:
   • Atomic Energy of Canada Limited (AECL)
   • Canadian Nuclear Safety Commission (CNSC)
   • a nuclear generating organization (such as Ontario Power Generation)
   • Environment Canada
   • Natural Resources Canada
   • a non-governmental environmental advocacy group (such as GreenPeace or Energy Probe)
   • electricity consumers

3. Research the various approaches for dealing with nuclear waste. Consider the three approaches that the NWMO is required to consider and at least two more approaches. (All members of your group should be involved in the research.)

4. Identify and evaluate your sources of information. Identify potential bias in the information from each source.

5. As a group, decide which waste management approach to recommend. Present the evidence you have researched to support your approach.

6. Conduct cost–benefit analysis of your recommended approach (see **Appendix A1**). Start by brainstorming the advantages and disadvantages of your approach, as a group.

7. Present and defend your group's recommendation. Your presentation should include an audio (oral) component and a visual component. You should illustrate how your approach meets the criteria for a feasible solution.

8. Hold a postmortem on your presentation. Could your group have presented or argued its recommendation more effectively?

9. Has your own opinion changed as a result of your research? Explain.

 www.science.nelson.com

SUMMARY

- CANDU stands for CANada, Deuterium, and Uranium.
- The mass number and the atomic number of an element are indicated in symbol format, as follows.

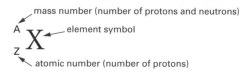

mass number (number of protons and neutrons)

element symbol

atomic number (number of protons)

- Isotopes of an element have the same number of protons but different numbers of neutrons and, therefore, a different atomic mass.

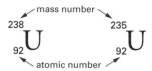

mass number

atomic number

- Unstable isotopes emit radiation (α particles, β particles, or γ rays) and are said to be radioactive. These isotopes are called radioisotopes, and the process is referred to as radioactive decay.
- The time required for half of the original number of radioactive atoms to decay is known as the half-life of a radioactive substance.
- During nuclear fission, an atom of uranium (or another radioactive element) is split when a neutron collides with the nucleus. Two lighter atoms are formed.

- During nuclear fission, additional neutrons are released. These neutrons trigger additional fissions which, in turn, release more neutrons. The process can continue in a nuclear chain reaction.
- Nuclear waste in spent nuclear fuel bundles is more radioactive than the original nuclear fuel and, therefore, are more dangerous.
- Radiation can damage or kill living cells. The effect of radiation on the human body is cumulative.
- The NWMO was created by the federal government to study the nuclear waste management problem and to recommend an appropriate approach.
- There are two basic methods for managing nuclear waste: storage and disposal. The most popular current approach is disposal in deep geological storage.

Key Terms

CANDU	**radioactive**
proton	**half-life**
neutron	**nuclear reaction**
electron	**nuclear fission**
atomic number (Z)	**chain reaction**
mass number (A)	**equivalent dose (H)**
isotope	**sievert (Sv)**
radioisotope	

ASSESSMENT

Understanding Concepts

1. What is the basic difference between a coal-fired generating station and a nuclear generating station?

2. Briefly explain what happens during radioactive decay.

3. Why is "chain reaction" an appropriate term to describe an uncontrolled nuclear reaction?

4. Why is spent nuclear fuel more radioactive that the original fuel?

5. Why are nuclear power facilities built near large bodies of water?

6. Why is it important to understand the concept of half-life when dealing with radioactive waste?

7. Radon-222 has a half-life of 4.0 days. The initial mass of a sample of this isotope is 6.8 g. Calculate the mass of radon-222 remaining in the sample
   (a) after 8 days
   (b) after 16 days
   (c) after 32 days

8. Why are radioactive materials dangerous?

9. List and briefly describe five potential approaches for nuclear waste management.

10. Using the Key Terms from the summary and any other concepts that you consider important, create a concept map that summarizes your understanding of the ideas in this topic.

Applying Inquiry Skills

11. An employee at a nuclear generating facility is exposed to the following doses of radiation within a one-year period:
    - 0.15 mSv per day at the workplace (works 225 days per year)
    - 6 chest X-rays
    - 10 flights between St. John's and Vancouver
    - natural radiation from environment
    (a) Calculate the employee's equivalent dose. Determine whether the employee has exceeded the dose limit for one year, established by the Canadian Nuclear Safety Commission (CNSC).
    (b) What do the CNSC guidelines say about an individual experiencing this amount of radiation in one year? What would you recommend for the employee?
    (c) How much energy (in joules) does the employee's equivalent dose represent?

Making Connections

12. Why is the Canadian Shield considered to be an appropriate place for disposing of solid nuclear waste?

13. It has been said that establishing the NWMO is like putting a fox in charge of a chicken coop. Explain the reasoning behind this opinion.

14. One of the myths associated with nuclear energy is that a reactor could explode like a nuclear bomb. Research and explain the difference between a nuclear explosion and a nuclear reactor meltdown.

www.science.nelson.com

15. When the nuclear facility at Chalk River was faced with cuts in government funding, the management considered storing nuclear waste from other nuclear generating facilities at the site to generate income. Use the Internet and other sources to find out what decision was made, and how the decision was made. Write a one-page report summarizing your research. Show how the same decision-making process could be applied to similar situations.

www.science.nelson.com

16. Uranium metal is obtained by mining and processing uranium ore. Uranium ore usually contains as little as 0.1% to 0.2% uranium. Research the waste that is produced during the mining and processing of uranium ore. Write a two-page report entitled "Uranium: Waste from Start to Finish." Your report should summarize the mining and milling of uranium ore, all the waste that is produced, and the management of this waste.

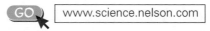
www.science.nelson.com

17. What roles can vested interests, including industries, provincial governments, and NGOs play in shaping Canada's policy on nuclear waste management?

18. Suppose you wanted to influence the federal government into taking a new position on nuclear waste management. What are three specific actions that you could take to influence decision makers? Explain your ideas.

Reflecting

19. Based on what you have learned in this topic, has your opinion of nuclear energy changed? Do you feel more or less comfortable with nuclear energy as a source of electricity generation? Do you feel confident that the nuclear waste issue will be properly addressed in the future? Explain.

TASK: Exploring Waste

A growing global population, with an increasing rate of consumption, has resulted in a significant waste management problem. In this unit, you have focused on some major categories of waste production and management. There are many more categories of waste that pose the same level of concern: toxic chemicals such as PCBs, waste from mining and mineral processing, waste from the pulp and paper industry, waste from oil and gas exploration and refining (including oil spills), hospital waste (biohazardous and infectious waste, such as cultures and stocks, human body fluids, body parts, and needles), construction and demolition waste, agrochemicals (fertilizers and pesticides), and motor vehicle waste, to name only a few (**Figure 1**). Some of these wastes are local concerns, while others are global.

Figure 1 A few more of the wastes that our society has to deal with

How are these wastes produced? Can we avoid producing them and, if so, do we want to? Can we reduce the quantities that are produced? Are these wastes dangerous to human health and the environment? How do they affect us? How do we safely manage their disposal?

Choose a category of waste that was not discussed in this unit, and prepare a report that attempts to answer the questions above. Use the format of the topics in this unit. The following guidelines will help you organize and develop your report:

1. To introduce your topic, create an interesting story that connects this category of waste to the real world.

2. Under the major heading "Science and Technology," present the facts about the waste: how and where it is produced, how much is produced, the scientific basis of the waste production (include chemical reactions if applicable), technologies that are used to prevent or lessen the impact of the waste, and current disposal methods.

3. Under the major heading "Society and the Environment," demonstrate how this waste affects society and the environment. You may use a case study to illustrate how this waste is a problem in society. Address issues such as human health risks and potential air, water, and soil pollution. Outline potential waste management solutions for this waste. Identify an issue that is related to this waste, and plan an activity to explore and resolve the issue.

4. Prepare a "Summary" that includes the key points you have addressed, as well as key terms and definitions.

SUMMARY

Throughout this unit, you have had opportunities to

- demonstrate your understanding of the nature and types of waste and waste management in industries and the community
- research and/or investigate the effectiveness of waste management approaches
- assess the impact of various wastes on the environment, and analyze and evaluate the development of waste management approaches

Copy the following graphic organizer into your notebook, and use it to help you summarize your understanding of the key concepts in each of the four major topics. Add the key concepts related to the topic that you chose for your Unit Task.

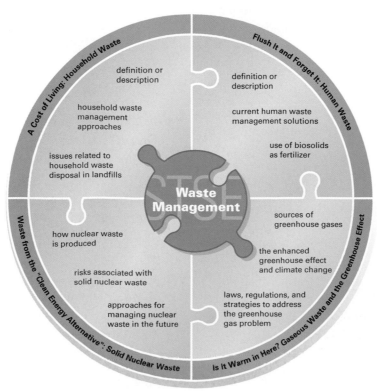

Unit B Review

Understanding Concepts

1. Ordinary household garbage is relatively harmless to the environment. Why, then, is there a need for a liner in a landfill?

2. Provide a specific example to explain the NIMBY principle.

3. Distinguish between the terms "diversion" and "disposal" as they relate to household waste.

4. How is human waste different from the other categories of waste?

5. Briefly describe the processes that are involved in sewage treatment. Use the following terms in your description, in a way that shows you understand their meanings: collection, primary treatment, settling, activated sludge, biosolids, secondary treatment, aeration, bacteria, tertiary treatment, effluent.

6. Summarize the requirements of the Kyoto Protocol, and outline Canada's commitment under the Protocol.

7. Explain the concept of a sink. What is the significance of a carbon sink in the enhanced greenhouse effect?

8. Using examples from this unit, identify and explain three technologies that have negatively affected waste management and three technologies that have positively affected waste management.

9. Explain what the following statement means: "Pu-239 has a half-life of 2.41×10^4 years."

10. Compare the risk from natural radiation with the risk from smoking, in terms of the estimated loss of life expectancy.

Applying Inquiry Skills

11. A media report has claimed there is anecdotal evidence to suggest that living near a nuclear generating plant increases the risk of human health problems, such as cancer and birth defects. You have been contracted by Health Canada to conduct a scientific study that will provide evidence to either support or refute this claim. Your contract requires you to submit a detailed plan, describing your proposed study. Prepare and present a two-page plan for your study.

12. Use the Internet and other sources to determine the differences between conventional home construction and R-2000 construction. Using information from your research, explain the data in **Figure 1**.

www.science.nelson.com

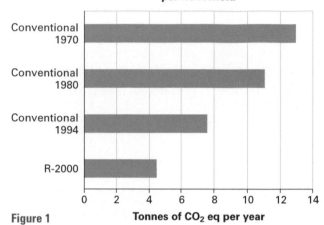

Average CO₂ eq Produced for Home Heating per Household

Figure 1   Tonnes of CO₂ eq per year

Making Connections

13. In a small group, brainstorm a list of careers related to municipal waste management. Select one career that interests you. Investigate its educational requirements and daily responsibilities and activities.

www.science.nelson.com

14. Describe your personal household waste ethic. Give at least one specific example of how your actions reflect your ethic.

15. Find a cartoon that deals with attitudes toward human waste management, or sketch one of your own.

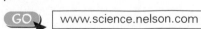
www.science.nelson.com

16. Use the Internet and other resources to find out if, where, and how biosolids are used in Canada. What are the federal government regulations regarding the use of biosolids? Summarize your findings in a one-page report.

www.science.nelson.com

17. Make up a personal action plan for reducing greenhouse gas emissions, in response to the one-tonne challenge in the federal government's *Climate Change Plan for Canada.* Set short-term and long-term goals for your action plan. Include at least three specific, realistic actions in your plan.

18. The television quiz show *Jeopardy* has sets of five increasingly difficult answers, which the contestants must supply questions for. The answers are arranged under topic headings. Make up five answers for the topic heading "Greenhouse Gas Emissions." Explain why each of your answers would be a good *Jeopardy* answer.

19. Prepare a concept web to show the social, economic, cultural, political, and environmental issues in the global warming debate. For example, one of the issues could be transportation. Identify key points related to each issue. Prepare a poster, and include quotations or pictures to illustrate the key points.

20. Research the current status of the global warming debate. Have the viewpoints converged at all? Describe any recent evidence in the debate. What new tools are being used to gather evidence?

www.science.nelson.com

21. Prepare a brief position paper that you can use to debate the following statement with others in your class: "The need to produce cheap electricity to meet our increasing energy demand justifies the environmental and human health risks associated with nuclear power generation and the management of nuclear waste."

22. Evaluate the following statement from the federal Minister of Natural Resources in 2001: "You could dig a deep geological pit, I presume, store it (nuclear waste) underneath there, and that could provide protection."

23. Update the nuclear waste management situation in Canada. Consider actions taken by governments and industries, and the roles of environmental and lobby groups. What effects have the most recent developments had on the nuclear energy industry in Canada?

24. Use specific examples to explain how the media can influence public opinions on waste-related issues. In addition to television, radio, newspapers, and magazines, include media such as Web sites, organization newsletters, art, and cultural myths or legends.

25. Is the world facing a waste management crisis due to increasing population and consumption? Explain your answer.

www.science.nelson.com

Extension

26. The water you use for flushing a toilet is the same quality as the water you use for drinking. What is your opinion about this practice? Explain your opinion, and suggest an alternative practice.

27. The Canadian Gas Association and the Government of Canada have produced a checklist that is included with the bills from most of the gas companies in Canada. The brochure is called "Canada-Wide Home Tune-Up," and it gives many practical suggestions to make your home more energy efficient. Obtain a copy of this checklist, and try to implement some of the suggestions. Do you think the suggestions are effective? What evidence do you have? How does using a high-efficiency furnace contribute to solving our waste management problem?

www.science.nelson.com

28. Environmental Defense Canada, the Canadian Environmental Law Association, and the Canadian Institute for Environmental Law and Policy have developed a project to help people use and interpret the National Pollutants Release Inventory (NPRI) data. Follow the links at the Nelson Web site to answer the following questions

www.science.nelson.com

(a) What is the function of the NPRI?
(b) Identify the ten top air-polluting facilities and the ten top water-polluting facilities in Canada.
(c) What quantity of dioxins and furans does the leading dioxin/furan polluter produce?
(d) Four of the top ten dioxin/furan polluters are from one industry. Which industry?
(e) Identify the five facilities in your province that have the highest on-site pollution releases.

Everyday Chemicals
and
SAFE PRACTICE

> **chem·i·cal:** (kem-i-kăl) *n.* a substance with a distinct molecular composition that is produced by or used in a chemical process *(Nelson Canadian Dictionary)*

Chemicals make up everything around you. Chemicals even make up you (**Table 1**)! The air you breathe and the food you eat are composed of chemicals. Your desk and chair at school, the dish soap you use at home, the plastic bags at a grocery store, the smog in the air—all are chemicals. You encounter chemicals—both natural and synthetic—in almost every aspect of your life.

Everyday Chemicals

Many of the chemicals around you and in you are *structural*: they make up the form of objects, such as a flower's stem or your bones. Other chemicals are *functional*: they are involved in chemical reactions and, in biological systems, have certain roles to perform. For example, there are specific enzymes (catalysts) in the human body that chemically break down the food you eat. Similarly, you use chemical detergents to break down dirt and clean your clothes. Whether chemicals are structural or functional, their properties are governed by the atoms and molecules that make them up, and the bonding among these atoms and molecules.

Sometimes you deliberately expose yourself to chemicals: the clothes you wear, the personal hygiene products you use, the foods you eat, and the medicines

Table 1 Chemical Composition of the Human Body

Element	Composition by weight (%)
O	65
C	18
H	10
N	3
Ca	1.5
P	1.0
K	0.35
S	0.25
Na	0.15
Mg	0.05
Cu, Zn, Se, Mo, F, Cl, I, Mn, Co, Fe	0.70
Li, Sr, Al, Si, Pb, V, As, Br	traces

you take. You also come in contact with chemicals unintentionally: contaminants in drinking water, pollution in the air, and residues on your clothes.

(a) Think of all the chemicals you are exposed to in a day. Divide them into two groups, called "Intentional contact" and "Unintentional contact." Put an asterisk beside any of the chemicals that you consider to be harmful. Why are they allowed, if they are harmful?

The variety of chemicals that we are exposed to seems to be ever increasing. In addition to natural chemicals (such as water, rice, cotton fibre, and wood), there are growing numbers of artificial or synthetic compounds being produced (such as nylon, Aspirin, chlorofluorocarbons (CFCs), and faux leather). While a few synthetic chemicals have been specifically designed for their toxic properties (such as pesticides and the nerve gas that was used in World War I), most are not intended to do any harm. In fact, many have dramatically improved our standard of living (**Figure 1**). They have not come without a cost, however.

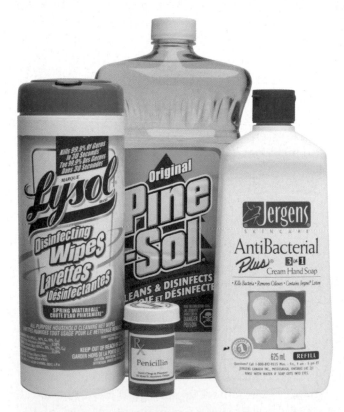

Figure 1 Many everyday chemicals are designed to kill germs.

(b) What were CFCs originally used for? What was the unintentional cost of CFCs? What has our society done to reduce this cost?

Chemicals can have both positive and negative impacts on our lives. Some chemicals are clearly either good or bad, while other chemicals fit into both categories. For these chemicals, we need to evaluate whether the good outweighs the bad, or at least how we can minimize the risks.

Nicotine

Whether or not you smoke, you have probably come in contact with tobacco smoke (**Figure 2**). This toxic smoke is a combination of over 4000 natural (from the tobacco plant) and synthetic chemicals. At least 43 of these chemicals are known carcinogens (substances that cause cancer).

Figure 2 Despite many years of controversy, it is now widely accepted that tobacco smoke contains toxic chemicals.

(c) Take a poll of the number of people in your class who smoke tobacco. Why does each person smoke?

(d) Think of as many places as you can where smoking is not permitted. How do you feel about these restrictions?

Cigarettes are one of the few legally sold products that are known to harm or kill when used as intended. Many of the most harmful chemicals in cigarettes are not naturally found in tobacco plants, but are the result of the manufacturing process. For example, benzene is a colourless compound (composed of only carbon and hydrogen), which is deposited in the tobacco from the petroleum solvent used during processing. It is a known carcinogen and is associated with increased rates of leukemia. Cigarette smoke also contains formaldehyde (a substance used in the past to preserve dead bodies), ammonia (a compound found in toilet bowl cleaners and dry-cleaning fluids), and acetone (a chemical commonly used to remove nail polish). These are not chemicals that most of us would knowingly consume.

(e) Why do you think these chemicals are in cigarettes?

Some of the natural products in cigarette smoke are also dangerous. Nicotine is one of the most addictive substances known, and one of the main reasons why smoking is such a difficult habit to break. The tar in cigarette smoke builds up in the lungs of smokers and those exposed to secondhand smoke. It eventually causes lung damage, which may lead to emphysema or lung cancer. Another dangerous product in cigarette smoke is carbon monoxide: a tasteless, odourless, colourless gas that decreases the body's ability to carry oxygen.

Antibiotics

It is easy to assume that all chemicals are inevitably harmful, but we need to be careful about making judgments. There are many chemicals that have saved millions of lives worldwide. The antibiotics that Alexander Fleming discovered are one of the best examples.

In 1928, Fleming was researching bacteria and noticed that some of his culture plates had been contaminated by mould from one of the neighbouring labs (**Figure 3**). Fortunately, he did not simply throw out his "ruined" culture plates and start over. On closer inspection, he noticed that where the mould was growing there was a surprising absence of living bacteria. Something in the mould was killing the bacteria. The contamination was caused

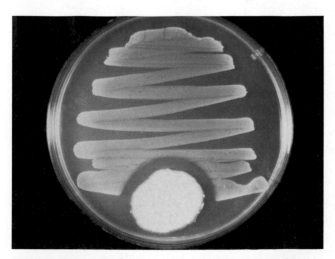

Figure 3 The accidental discovery of penicillin, followed by the development of other antibiotics, has saved hundreds of thousands of lives.

by the mould *Penicillium notratum*, so Fleming called the antibacterial agent "penicillin."

By 1940, the active ingredient in the mould was isolated and available for use as a drug. Penicillin is credited with saving thousands of soldiers' lives during World War II. The infection of wounds had been one of the main causes of death for soldiers in the past, and the introduction of penicillin virtually solved this problem. By the 1950s, penicillin was in widespread use and other antibiotics were quickly being isolated from other species of mould. These miracle drugs were effective against a range of bacterial infections, including tuberculosis, pneumonia, and scarlet fever. The medical world felt that disease had been beaten. No longer would people die from deadly infections.

Today, with millions of kilograms of antibiotics produced worldwide every year, they are still an important tool in the fight against disease. Unfortunately, however, there is a growing problem of antibiotic resistance. Medical professionals are concerned that there may be a resurgence of deadly tuberculosis and other bacterial illnesses that appeared to have been beaten. Why are antibiotics losing their effectiveness?

One reason is the overuse of antibiotics. It was, and sometimes still is, common practice for doctors to prescribe an antibiotic to any patient complaining of a runny nose or a cough. These symptoms are most often caused by either the common cold or the flu, both of which are viral infections and so are untreatable with antibiotics. Once in the body, however, the antibiotic kills any bacteria that are present. The natural process of evolution, which allows bacteria to adapt slowly, is accelerated by repeatedly killing off antibiotic-susceptible bacteria in the body. The proportion of antibiotic-resistant bacteria increases, potentially creating resistant strains that may lead to hard-to-treat infections in the future.

The improper use of appropriately prescribed antibiotics is another reason why antibiotics are losing their effectiveness. Many people stop taking an antibiotic when they start to feel better—but before all the bacteria have been killed. Those bacteria that have a slight advantage over a drug survive longer. As soon as the antibiotic leaves the patient's bloodstream, these bacteria survive and reproduce. As a result, the next infection is a little more difficult to treat with an antibiotic.

(f) Have you taken antibiotics in the past year? Did you use the entire prescription? Why or why not?

Antibacterial Soaps

A related issue is the recent proliferation of antibacterial soaps and cleaners, which now make up about 75% of the liquid soaps on the market. Antibacterial agents are used as a powerful marketing tool but, unfortunately, are helping to increase antibacterial resistance.

Are antibiotic soaps even effective? The antibacterial ingredient of hand soaps (triclosan or triclocarbon) needs to be left on the hands for about 2 min to work. Thus, most people wash off the soap before this active ingredient can take effect.

Antibacterial soaps and cleaners have little effect on viruses, so they are no more effective than regular soap for stopping the spread of viral illnesses such as colds and flus. Furthermore, antibacterial soaps kill both harmful and beneficial bacteria, so they should never be used in appliances such as composting toilets.

(g) Do you use antibacterial soaps at home? Why or why not?

Chemicals and Safety

There is no doubt that chemicals have had a dramatic impact on our standard of living. They have become so integral to our lives that we scarcely notice them. This familiarity, though, could lead to danger. Even beneficial chemicals can have a negative impact if they are handled improperly. Some chemicals, such as the propane gas used for barbecuing, are dangerous on their own, having the potential to cause poisoning, burns, or explosions. Other chemicals are hazardous because of their interactions with their surroundings, producing dangerous byproducts. For example, CFCs were tested in the 1930s and found to be safe. Only later, when CFCs were exposed to the strong ultraviolet (UV) rays in the upper atmosphere, were they shown to have a negative impact: they decompose and release chlorine atoms, which damage the ozone layer. The chlorine atoms break up the ozone, O_3, molecules, creating holes in the ozone layer that allow dangerous UV radiation to reach Earth's surface.

$$CCl_3F_{(g)} + UV \text{ energy} \rightarrow CCl_2F_{(g)} + Cl_{(g)}$$
$$Cl_{(g)} + O_{3(g)} \rightarrow ClO_{(g)} + O_{2(g)}$$
$$ClO_{(g)} + O_{(g)} \rightarrow Cl_{(g)} + O_{2(g)}$$

The chlorine atoms that are produced at the end of this series of reactions can continue to destroy more ozone molecules.

It is unlikely that the number of chemicals we create and use will decrease, but we must make sure that they are used as safely as possible.

In this unit, you are going to take an in-depth look at just a few of the thousands of chemicals that are found in the home, in the workplace, in industry, and in the environment. You will use experiments and electronic or print resources to investigate the properties, benefits, hazards, safe handling, and environmental impacts of various chemicals. Using this information, you will weigh the advantages and disadvantages of using common chemicals in everyday life and make informed, responsible decisions about their use.

Questions to Think About

As you explore the topics in this unit, keep the following questions in mind:

- How do you decide which chemicals are safe enough to use?
- Which chemicals should you avoid?

- How has the everyday use of chemicals affected our environment?
- How have chemicals improved our standard of living?
- How can the everyday use of chemicals be made as safe as possible?

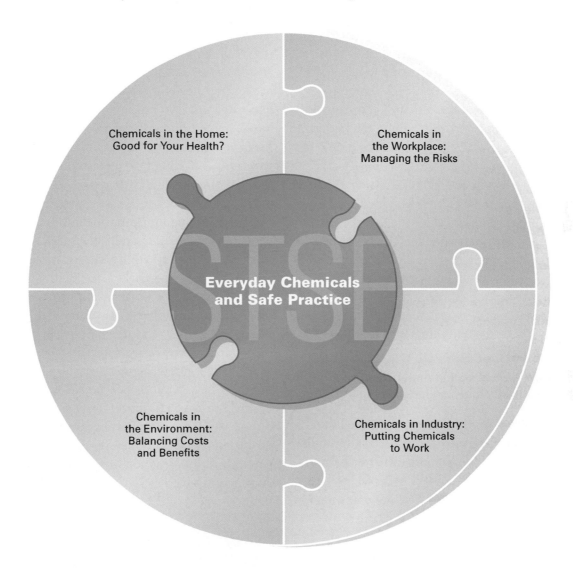

Chemicals in the Home: Good for Your Health?

Chemicals in the Workplace: Managing the Risks

Everyday Chemicals and Safe Practice

Chemicals in the Environment: Balancing Costs and Benefits

Chemicals in Industry: Putting Chemicals to Work

Unit Task Introduction

In this unit, you will find out about many different kinds of chemicals. Most of these chemicals have some impact on our environment. In the Unit Task, you will have an opportunity to explore how some chemicals affect the growth of plants. You will use your understanding of the properties, benefits, and hazards of everyday chemicals to design and carry out your investigation. Read the description and requirements on pages 212 to 213 before you start the unit topics, so that you can prepare for the Unit Task as you progress through the unit.

Chemicals *in the* Home: GOOD FOR YOUR HEALTH?

Alexandra and Sasha are expected to help with chores around their home. They have no objection to doing the laundry—it is easy to sort clothes by colours and put them in the washing machine with some washing powder. Even doing the dishes is not too bad. What they really object to is cleaning the kitchen floor and the bathroom. They know that keeping these rooms clean is particularly important, but the blue spray for the bathroom mirror makes their eyes water, and the floor cleaner dries out the skin on Sasha's already eczema-prone hands. The labels on both bottles warn users that these substances are potentially harmful. Alexandra and Sasha wonder if there are other cleaners available that do not have these unpleasant effects.

(a) When you clean your home, what cleaners do you use? Are there other materials in your home that you could use for cleaning?

It is important to remember that a clean home and good personal hygiene habits, such as thorough hand washing, do help to minimize the transfer of bacterial and viral infections. It is possible, however, that using certain products for cleaning may actually damage your health (**Figure 1**). North America's obsession with cleaning agents and antibacterial products, in our quest for an almost sterile environment, has been linked to increasing rates of allergies and asthma, and even to more serious medical conditions, such as rheumatoid arthritis and diabetes. Studies show that children growing up on farms— exposed to animal dander, pollens, moulds, and dirt—show lower incidences of allergies and asthma than children growing up in sterile environments.

(b) Do you think we would be healthier if we were less concerned about cleanliness? Under what circumstances could this be dangerous?

In the 21st century, there are more people living close together than ever before, so infections can be passed between people very easily. The 2003 outbreak of severe acute respiratory syndrome (SARS) illustrated just how important proper hygiene can be. Hospitals around the world insisted that staff, patients, and visitors wash their hands repeatedly with special cleansers to try to stop the spread of this new and potentially deadly infection. Similarly, during an outbreak of disease caused by water-borne bacteria in Walkerton, Ontario, in May 2000, townspeople were advised to add chlorine bleach to the water they used for bathing and for washing clothes and dishes. Health officials knew that the bleach would kill the *E. coli* bacteria and help to stop the disease from spreading. The strategy worked: very few people got sick after the new hygiene recommendations were put into effect.

What common chemicals are beneficial to your health? What chemicals may be harmful to your health? Are there less harmful alternatives? Where is the balance between cleanliness (which stops the spread of disease) and the overuse of cleaning products (which may lead to illness)? What information is available to help us achieve this balance?

Figure 1 Many cleaning products have warning labels such as this skull and crossbones symbol.

Science & Technology

The Quest for Cleanliness

Home cleaning generally involves water, a cloth or scrubbing pad, and a cleaning agent. How do these three simple things remove dirt, grease, and germs from our bodies, homes, and clothes?

Water has the remarkable ability to dissolve many substances. This is because water is a **polar molecule**, meaning that it has opposite charges at opposite ends (**Figure 2**). If the water is hot, soluble substances dissolve more quickly, greasy substances soften, and bacteria and viruses are less likely to survive.

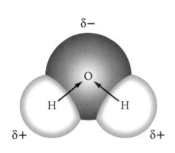

Figure 2 The oxygen atom pulls electrons away from the hydrogen atoms. This leaves the hydrogen atoms with a slight positive charge and the oxygen atom with a slight negative charge. Because the molecule is bent, this leaves one end positive and one end negative. The symbol δ (delta) means "slight charge."

Scrubbing is sometimes necessary to remove stubborn stains on a table or dried food on a stove. Scrubbing physically scrapes away most of the unwanted substance, allowing the water to penetrate through to the table or stove.

Many cleaners undergo chemical reactions with dirt. For example, a drain cleaner reacts with the grease in a blocked drain to clear the drain.

Oil and grease are particularly troublesome when cleaning, because they do not dissolve in water. Oil and water do not mix because there are only very weak forces of attraction between the water molecules and the oil molecules (**Figure 3**). Grease molecules are **non-polar molecules**, (they do not have opposite charges at opposite ends) so they do not mix with the polar water molecules (**Figure 4**). This is why you need to use detergent to wash dirty laundry. Without detergent, the water molecules and the grease molecules will not mix. The detergent molecules form a film between the grease droplets and the water, allowing the grease to dissolve in the water. The detergent-surrounded drops of grease are called micelles (**Figure 5**). The agitation of the washing machine helps to lift the grease and detergent away from the fabric, and both are then

washed away with the water. It is interesting to note that the action of soaps and detergents on grease is not a chemical reaction, but a physical interaction between molecules with different properties.

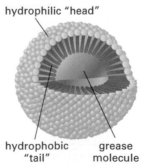

Figure 3 The oily stain on this T-shirt will not wash out in water because oil and water do not mix.

palmitin (an oil)

Figure 4 Palmitin has three long tails that are made up of mostly carbon and hydrogen molecules. All fats and oils have one or more of these non-polar tails.

hydrophilic "head"

hydrophobic "tail"   grease molecule

Figure 5 This diagram shows the structure of a micelle. The hydrophobic (water-hating) "tails" attach to the grease molecule; the hydrophilic (water-loving) "heads" surround the molecule, suspending it in water.

Canada produces and uses thousands of tonnes of cleaners every year (**Table 1**). Is Canada a nation of "clean freaks"?

Table 1 Canadian Production of Cleaners in 1995

Cleaner	Quantity produced (1000 t)
toilet bowl cleaners	20
granular detergents	19
scouring powders	15
floor polish	4
drain cleaners	4
other household cleaners	45

C1.1 Activity | MAPPING HOUSEHOLD CHEMICALS

You might be surprised at how many different hazardous chemicals there are around your home. Do you think you are storing them all correctly?

1. Draw a map of your home, including the kitchen and bathroom, and any other locations where chemicals might be stored. Indicate the possible location of a chemical with an asterisk (*).

2. Create a table with the following five column headings: Location, Chemical, Safety warnings (WHMIS symbols or the HHP symbols shown in **Table 2**), First-aid instructions, Storage situation. Fill in your table as you go around your home, searching for chemicals.

(a) Did any of the warnings surprise you?

(b) Are the first-aid instructions easy to follow?

(c) How could you improve the storage and/ or safety of the chemicals you found?

Some of the household chemicals that you identified in C1.1 Activity: Mapping Household Chemicals are probably cleaning products. While these products generally help to keep your home safe by killing germs, many have a "dark side." Some are **corrosive** (they can damage living tissue) and are concentrated enough to cause severe and even permanent injury. Swallowing some cleaners can burn and destroy the throat, vocal cords, and esophagus. Multiple surgeries would likely be required to repair the damage, and even then the victim may never talk or swallow solid food again. Toilet bowl cleaners, oven cleaners, drain openers, lye, mildew removers, and lime or rust stain removers contain strong chemicals that can cause a lot of damage.

Product Labelling

Under the federal Consumer Chemicals and Containers Regulations and the Pest Control Product Act, hazardous household products that are sold in Canada are required to carry **Hazardous Household Products (HHP) symbols** (**Table 2**). However, some products that contain only low concentrations of hazardous substances are simply required to carry "hazard statements," such as the following:

• Keep out of the reach of children.
• Do not store near food or beverages.
• Avoid contact with eyes, skin, and clothes.

Table 2 Hazardous Household Products Symbols

Symbol		The danger	Examples
explosive		This container can explode if it is heated or punctured. Flying pieces of metal or plastic can cause serious injuries, especially to the eyes.	water repellant for shoes or boots in an aerosol container, and spray paint in an aerosol container
corrosive		This product will burn skin and eyes on contact, or throat and stomach if swallowed.	battery acid, toilet bowl cleaner, and oven cleaner
flammable		This product, or its fumes, will catch fire easily if it is near heat, flames, or sparks.	contact adhesives, gasoline, and lighter fluid
poisonous/toxic		Licking, eating, drinking, or sometimes smelling this product will cause illness or death.	rat poison, bleach, windshield washer fluid, furniture polish, and some medications

Organic Solvents

Household chemicals that contain organic solvents are a particular concern (**Table 3**). A **solvent** is a substance that dissolves another substance—the **solute**—to form a solution. Any solvents that contain carbon (other than carbon dioxide) are called **organic solvents**. They are often flammable and toxic, and they pose a multitude of environmental and health hazards, including poisoning and skin, eye, lung, liver, and kidney damage. Common organic solvents include benzene, petroleum distillates, and phenol toluene (mineral spirits). Most chemical containers do not specifically state the presence of organic solvents, but the labelling may indicate their presence. A product may contain an organic solvent if it

- hardens or evaporates rapidly on the surface after application (polishes and waxes)
- has a strong "solvent" odour, such as a gas or kerosene odour
- contains petroleum distillates
- is labelled "flammable"
- has a warning that breathing the vapours may be harmful

Table 3 Products Likely to Contain Organic Solvents

Products that are generally 100% organic solvents	Products that may be partially solvent-based*
furniture stripper	furniture oils, polishes, and waxes
turpentine	shoe-care products
charcoal lighter fluid	spot removers
dry-cleaning fluids	rug and upholstery cleaners
paint thinner	adhesives
nail polish remover	metal and wood cleaners
degreasers	paints
lubricating oils	wood finishes, such as varnish, shellac, and stain
fuels	

* These products may be water-based or detergent-based instead.

DID **YOU** KNOW?

Not-So-Clean Cleaner
About 250 mL of trichloroethylene, a solvent that is found in some household cleaners, can contaminate about 14 million litres of water.

Acids and Bases

Most household cleaning agents are either acids or bases (**Figure 6**). Acidic compounds are generally found in tub, sink, and toilet-bowl cleaners. Bases are generally found in soaps and in glass and drain cleaners. The dangers posed by these substances must, by law, be indicated by both symbols and words on the containers. Why are acids and bases effective cleaners? How do they work? Both acids and bases are considered to be corrosive, and this is the key to their cleaning abilities. They can essentially "eat through" dirt and grime. Unfortunately, their corrosiveness is what makes them potentially dangerous as well, so they must be handled and stored safely at all times.

Figure 6 Corrosive substances, such as acids and bases, are found in many household products, including cleaners.

Acids

Acids are found in many household products, from salad dressing to car batteries, as well as in cleaning products. The word "acid" comes from the Latin word *acere*, which means "to be sour." All acids taste sour. (Of course, all acids are NOT safe to taste.) Common household acids, such as vinegar, yogurt, and lemon juice, obviously taste sour. An Aspirin (acetylsalicylic acid, or ASA) tablet also tastes sour if you keep it in your mouth for a while before swallowing it.

Chemically speaking, an **acid** is a substance that produces hydrogen ions, H^+, in solution. For example, when hydrogen chloride gas (the solute) dissolves in water (the solvent), hydrochloric acid is formed.

$$HCl_{(g)} \xrightarrow{H_2O} H^+_{(aq)} + Cl^-_{(aq)}$$

The hydrogen ions that are produced in this reaction make the solution behave like a typical acid. The more hydrogen ions produced, the more acidic the solution is. Five common acids are listed in **Table 4.**

C1: Chemicals in the Home: Good for Your Health?

Table 4 Some Common Acids

Common name	Chemical name	Formula
muriatic acid	hydrochloric acid	$HCl_{(aq)}$
battery acid	sulfuric acid	$H_2SO_{4(aq)}$
vinegar	acetic acid	$CH_3COOH_{(aq)}$
vitamin C	ascorbic acid	$C_6H_8O_{6(aq)}$
Aspirin	acetylsalicylic acid (ASA)	$C_9H_8O_{4(s)}$

Hydrochloric acid is a binary acid, which means that it contains only hydrogen and another non-metallic element. Sulfuric acid is an oxyacid. It consists of hydrogen bonded to a polyatomic ion that contains oxygen and a nonmetallic element. Acetic acid, vitamin C, and ASA are all organic acids. An organic acid consists of hydrogen bonded to an ion that contains carbon, more hydrogen, and oxygen.

Acids—particularly concentrated acids—are corrosive. It is this property that makes them effective cleaners. They react readily with dirt and thus remove it from a surface. The products of the reaction can then be wiped or rinsed away.

Bases

Solutions of **bases** feel slippery or soapy. This is because they dissolve the fatty acids and oils from your skin to form a kind of soap, which cuts down on the friction between your fingers as you rub them together. The ability of bases to react with fats and oils is what makes them effective cleaners.

Early soaps were very harsh on the skin and clothes due to their high base content. Even today, people with very sensitive skin must sometimes use a product that is not soap-based for bathing. All bases taste bitter. (Of course, most of them should NEVER be tasted!) The active ingredient in many medicines is a base. Why, then, are most cough syrups advertised as having a great taste? The taste comes from sweeteners and flavourings that are added to mask the bitterness of the active ingredient.

Bases are common components of many cleaning products, from glass sprays to drain cleaners (**Table 5**). Bases produce hydroxide ions, OH^-, in solution. Some bases do this directly through dissociation: they come apart in water. For example, when sodium hydroxide is dissolved in water, the sodium ion splits from the hydroxide ion as follows:

$$NaOH_{(s)} \xrightarrow{H_2O} Na^+_{(aq)} + OH^-_{(aq)}$$

Other bases, such as ammonia, actually react with water to produce hydroxide ions:

$$NH_{3(g)} + H_2O_{(l)} \longrightarrow NH_4^+_{(aq)} + OH^-_{(aq)}$$

Table 5 Some Common Bases

Chemical name	Formula	Use
sodium hydroxide	$NaOH_{(aq)}$	drain cleaners
potassium hydroxide	$KOH_{(aq)}$	soaps and cosmetics
aluminum hydroxide	$Al(OH)_{3(s)}$	antacids
ammonium hydroxide	$NH_4OH_{(aq)}$	glass cleaners
sodium hydrogen carbonate	$NaHCO_{3(s)}$	baking soda
potassium sulfite	$K_2SO_{3(s)}$	food preservatives

The Strength of Acids and Bases: The pH Scale

The **pH scale** is used to measure the strength of acids and bases. The pH scale indicates the concentration of hydrogen ions, with values ranging from 0 to 14. Most acids and bases can be measured using the pH scale. A strong acidic solution has a pH closer to 0, while a strong base has a pH closer to 14. The pH scale (**Figure 7**) is widely used to compare the pH of different substances.

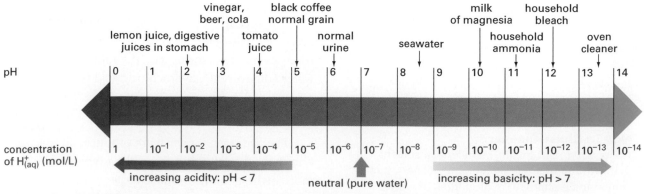

Figure 7 The pH scale is used to communicate a wide range of hydrogen ion concentrations, for a variety of substances.

Products at the two extremes of the pH scale (less than pH 1 or greater than pH 13) are extremely corrosive. Examples include sulfuric and hydrochloric acid at the low end, and caustic soda (sodium hydroxide) at the high end. Phosphoric and sulfamic acids, which are sometimes marketed as oven cleaners, usually fall between 1 and 2 on the pH scale. These are described as "safe" acids compared with the stronger acids, but they should still be handled cautiously and stored correctly.

Each pH unit represents a tenfold difference in the $H^+_{(aq)}$ concentration. It is this mathematical feature that makes the pH scale so compact. For example, a solution of pH 2 is not twice as acidic as a solution of pH 4, but a hundred, or 10^2, times more acidic. So, a slight difference in the pH of two solutions indicates a substantial difference in the concentration of $H^+_{(aq)}$.

Combining Chemicals

As mentioned, an acid adds hydrogen ions to a solution. At the same time, however, it removes any hydroxide ions that happen to be in the solution, because of the tendency of hydrogen ions to combine with hydroxide ions to form water.

$$H^+_{(aq)} + OH^-_{(aq)} \longrightarrow H_2O_{(l)}$$

So, when an acid is added to a basic solution (with a high pH), the solution becomes less basic and the pH changes. The pH becomes closer to 7, which is neutral.

Similarly, when a base is added to an acidic solution (with a low pH), the base increases the hydroxide ion concentration and thus reduces the hydrogen ion concentration. Again, the resulting solution is closer to neutral, and water is produced.

A reaction in which an acid and a base are mixed, resulting in a solution with a pH closer to 7, is known as a **neutralization reaction** or **acid–base reaction**. This type of reaction can be very useful if either an acid or a base is spilled. Adding the "opposite" substance will neutralize the spill and make it less dangerous (**Figure 8**).

Figure 8 Spilled muriatic (hydrochloric) acid can be neutralized by sprinkling horticultural lime over the spill.

C1.2 Activity COMBINING AN ACID AND A BASE

In this activity, you will observe what happens when you mix an acid and a base.

Materials
eye protection
lab apron
microtray
two 5-mL pipettes or medicine droppers
acidic household substance (such as vinegar) in a dropper bottle
basic household substance (such as a solution of baking soda or glass cleaner) in a dropper bottle
universal indicator solution (with colour chart)

 Acidic and basic substances may be corrosive. Handle them with care. Avoid contact with skin or eyes. Report any spills or splashes to your teacher immediately.

1. Put on your eye protection and lab apron.

2. Place about 3 drops of the acidic substance in a well of the microtray.

3. Add a drop of universal indicator solution. Record your observations.

(a) What is the pH of the acid?

4. Place about 3 drops of the basic substance in another well of the microtray.

5. Add a drop of universal indicator solution. Record your observations.

(b) What is the pH of the base?

6. Carefully place about 3 drops of the acidic substance into the well that contains the base. Swirl gently to mix. Record your observations.

(c) What is the pH of the mixture?

(d) What kind of reaction have you observed?

Some chemicals are extremely dangerous on their own. Chemical burns and poisonings are very real hazards. Accidentally mixing some household cleaners, however, can produce downright deadly reactions. Chlorine bleach and ammonia cleaners, such as Windex, pose a very serious threat if mixed together. Depending on the amounts of bleach and ammonia solution used, different reactions can occur. When equal amounts of bleach (sodium hypochlorite) and ammonia are combined, poisonous chlorine gas is produced.

$$2 \text{ NaOCl}_{(aq)} + 2 \text{ NH}_{3(aq)} \longrightarrow 2 \text{ NaONH}_{3(aq)} + \text{Cl}_{2(g)}$$

Chlorine gas was used as a chemical weapon during both world wars (**Figure 9**). Chlorine is a highly reactive nonmetal, with seven electrons in its outer shell. It has a strong tendency to "steal" an electron in order to have a complete outer shell of eight electrons. Chlorine will literally rip apart another molecule to obtain the last needed electron. If inhaled, this toxic gas tears into your nasal passages, trachea, and lungs. It causes massive cellular damage and, potentially, a very painful death.

 Never combine bleach and ammonia. The resulting reactions are extremely dangerous and potentially deadly!

Figure 9 Rarely has the science of chemistry been used with such unpleasant effects as when toxic gases were released on the battlefields during World War I.

C1.3 Investigation "GREEN CLEAN" VERSUS "PACKAGED POWER" >

If you watch television for even a short time during the day, you will likely be bombarded with advertisements for a multitude of cleaning products and their supposedly miraculous ability to clean and disinfect. However, it is not always in your best interest to be surrounded with these chemicals. Can more easily available and environmentally safer products do the same job? In this investigation, you will compare some commercially available cleaning products with nontoxic household chemicals that can be used as cleaners (**Figure 10**).

Figure 10 Which is more powerful: the "packaged power" or the "green clean"?

Inquiry Skills

- ⦿ Questioning
- ○ Hypothesizing
- ⦿ Predicting
- ⦿ Planning
- ⦿ Conducting
- ⦿ Recording
- ⦿ Analyzing
- ⦿ Evaluating
- ⦿ Communicating

Question

(i) Which cleaners work better: "green" cleaners or commercial cleaners?

(ii) Which cleaners are less expensive?

Prediction

(a) Predict answers to the Questions.

Materials
eye protection
lab apron
household rubber gloves
commercial glass cleaner (such as Windex)
commercial surface cleaner (such as Ajax or Tilex)

Materlals (continued)

commercial drain cleaner (such as Drano)
water
kettle
lemon juice
baking soda
vinegar
laboratory balance
4 pipettes with bulbs
microtray
universal indicator solution or pH paper
2 glass beakers smeared with vegetable oil
   or butter
2 lengths of blocked rigid plastic tubing
dirty sink or countertop
three 250-mL beakers
100-mL graduated cylinder
stirring rods
paper towels
spray bottles or wash bottles

 Windex is irritating to the eyes and skin. Splashes in the eyes or on the skin should be rinsed well with cool water. Wear eye protection.

Drano is corrosive and can cause eye and skin burns. It is irritating if inhaled, corrrosive to the skin, and may be fatal if swallowed. Avoid contact with eyes, skin, and clothing. Avoid breathing the vapour or spray mist. Use only in a well-ventilated area. Wear eye protection, a lab apron, and rubber gloves.

 Ajax is toxic if ingested and may cause irritation if it gets in the eyes. Do not mix Ajax with glass cleaners containing ammonia, because toxic chlorine gas will be produced. Wear eye protection.

Tilex is mildly irritating to the eyes and skin, and may cause nausea or vomiting if ingested. Splashes in the eyes or on the skin should be rinsed well with cool water.

Do not mix Tilex with toilet-bowl cleaners, acids, or ammonia, because hazardous gases will be produced. Wear eye protection.

Report any spills to your teacher immediately.

Procedure

1. Put on your eye protection and lab apron.

2. Your teacher will provide your group with the following cleaning tasks: two dirty beakers; a sink with soap scum or a greasy stain, or a countertop with residue; and two pieces of blocked tubing to simulate a blocked drain.

(b) Research recipes for "green" cleaners (such as water, lemon juice, baking soda, and vinegar) that can be used for each cleaning task. Each group will test a different recipe.

 www.science.nelson.com

3. Measure the quantity of each commercial or "green" cleaner you are going to test. Record the mass or volume in a table like **Table 6**.

4. Using a clean pipette, add 3 drops of your "green" cleaner to one well of a microtray. Add one drop of universal indicator solution (or dip a strip of pH paper in the cleaner). Compare the resulting colour with the pH chart. Record the pH of the cleaner.

5. Repeat step 4 with each commercial cleaner.

6. Clean one beaker with the commercial glass cleaner and the other beaker with your "green" alternative. Record the effectiveness of each cleaner on a scale of 1 to 5, with 1 being the least effective and 5 being the most effective. Also record your other observations, such as how much of each cleaner you used.

7. Repeat step 6, using the commercial surface cleaner on half of the dirty sink (or countertop) and your "green" alternative on the other half.

Table 6 Observations

Cleaning task	Cleaner used				
	Name	pH	Quantity (mL or g)	Effectiveness	Cost per use (¢/mL or ¢/g)
dirty beaker					
dirty sink					
blocked drain					

8. Repeat step 6, using the commercial drain cleaner on one blocked tube and your "green" alternative on the other blocked tube.

9. Tidy, rinse, and dry your work area. Collect used equipment, according to your teacher's instructions.

(c) Determine the cost per use for each commercial or "green" cleaner.

(d) Compare your results with the results of other groups by writing your results in a master table.

Analysis

(e) Answer the two Questions.

(f) Which "green" cleaners were the most effective? What properties of these cleaners allowed them to do the job?

(g) Which of the cleaners you tested are likely to be most corrosive?

Evaluation

(h) Compare your answers in (e) with your Prediction in (a). Account for any differences.

Synthesis

(i) Prepare a cost–benefit analysis of the cleaners you tested (see **Appendix A1**). Would you recommend the commercial cleaners, or are the "green" alternatives worth the effort? Consider cost, cleaning power, health risks, and corrosiveness in your recommendation.

Indoor Air Pollution: The Invisible Dangers

Surprisingly, Canadians have the greatest contact with potentially toxic pollutants in places that are generally considered to be unpolluted—their homes, workplaces, and motor vehicles. These pollutants are known as **indoor air pollution**. While people bring some chemicals into their homes deliberately, there are many other chemicals—from chloroform to carbon monoxide—that enter accidentally. The air inside homes is often more toxic than the air outside.

Pesticides, solvents, deodorizers, cleaners, dry-cleaned clothes, dusty carpets, paint, particleboard, and fumes from cooking and heating all contribute to indoor air pollution. If truckloads of dust with the same concentrations of toxic chemicals found in most carpets were deposited in a field, the field would be considered a hazardous waste site.

Chloroform

Chloroform is a gas that, in high concentrations, can cause cancer in animals. The main sources of chloroform in homes are showers, boiling water, and clothes washers. Chloroform is one of several trihalomethanes (THMs) that are produced by the addition of chlorine to water during the water treatment process. When the treated water is heated, the THMs evaporate into the air, where they can be inhaled. There is no firm evidence of chloroform causing cancer in humans, but it is listed as "potentially carcinogenic" because of its effects on animals. The only way to avoid inhaling chloroform is to make sure that kitchens, bathrooms, and laundry rooms are well ventilated.

Carbon Monoxide

Thanks to an increasing amount of media attention over the years, the danger of carbon monoxide poisoning is now common knowledge. This danger results from the incomplete combustion of fuels, such as the natural gas in furnaces and the gasoline in motor vehicles.

Carbon monoxide is a fairly common byproduct when any fuel is burned. Proper venting, however, usually takes care of it. This is one good reason to ensure that your furnace is properly maintained. If the exhaust vent becomes blocked and carbon monoxide begins to leak into your home, it can kill you in your sleep. Carbon monoxide is called the silent killer because it is an odourless, tasteless, and colourless gas. Its effects can range from increased fatigue and headaches to coma and death if the concentration becomes too high for an extended period of time. Fortunately, you can install carbon monoxide detectors in your home to warn of any potentially dangerous buildup (**Figure 11**).

Figure 11 It is wise to have a carbon monoxide detector on each floor of your home.

DID **YOU** KNOW?

Avoiding the Silent Killer
Normally, 100% of the blood's hemoglobin molecules bond with oxygen. Most home carbon monoxide detectors are set to sound an alarm if the concentration of carbon monoxide in the air corresponds to about 10% of the blood's hemoglobin molecules being bonded with carbon monoxide. At this concentration, most people will not notice the effects, so they are alerted to a problem before they do.

Minimizing Risk from Hazardous Materials

Many Canadian homes contain a wide range of hazardous chemicals. How do you reduce the risk of these chemicals? Start with prevention. Check to see if you (or a neighbour) already have what you need before you buy more, and buy the most appropriate, least hazardous product for the job. Buy only the quantity you need, and avoid organic solvents whenever possible.

What is the best way to deal with the chemicals that are already in your home? Safe use and storage are the top priority followed by proper disposal.

Disposal

Canadians have become accustomed to throwing unwanted items in the regular garbage. If we do this with hazardous chemicals, they are dumped in landfills. From there, they eventually leach into the soil and perhaps the ground water. They may even make their way into the drinking water supply.

Similarly, if you pour cleaning liquids or powders down the toilet, they flow through the wastewater treatment system and end up in local lakes and rivers. Pouring household chemicals into roadside storm sewers is even worse, as the sewer system delivers them directly into local surface waters. This allows pollutants to enter the drinking water supply very easily.

What, then, are good waste management strategies to use when disposing of household chemicals?

- Read the label. Some containers give advice for proper disposal. Unfortunately, most labels only include warnings, not disposal advice. These warnings should be a clue, however, that the chemicals should not simply be washed down the drain or thrown into the regular garbage.
- Use up as much of a chemical as possible. If you do not need all of it, perhaps a neighbour or friend could use the rest (**Figure 12**).

Figure 12 Share paint, if you have some left over.

- Recycle whenever possible. Some household hazardous waste centres accept and recycle opened cans of paint and other hazardous wastes. Many service stations accept used motor oil for filtering and reuse.
- While many chemicals can be safely stored in their original containers (with their labels intact), they should not be combined with other chemicals, even for disposal. Combining leftover chemicals can lead to unexpected and dangerous reactions.

- Most liquid wastes, such as latex paint and non-aerosol sprays, can be reduced through evaporation if you leave them outside (in a safe place), with the lid off. Do not leave more than one chemical outside at a time, because the chemical vapours could form a reactive mixture. When all the liquid has evaporated, a solid residue may remain. Wearing gloves, wipe out the residue with paper towels or rags, which should also be allowed to air dry outside. Check with your municipality to find out whether the empty container and the dried rags can be placed in the regular garbage.
- To completely empty a used aerosol can, take it outside and hold it upside down. Depress the button, pointing the spray nozzle toward paper towels or a rag (**Figure 13**). Place the empty container in the regular garbage (or, in some municipalities, in the blue box).

Figure 13 Completely discharge aerosol cans before throwing them in the garbage.

- It is important to remember that a container is rarely completely empty, even if you have used as much of the contents as possible. There is almost always some residue left. Careful handling and disposal of empty containers is still important. Never use an empty container from one chemical for another compound.
- Pesticides, herbicides, oil paints, paint cleaners, oil and transmission fluids, and batteries should never be disposed of through the sewer system, put into the regular garbage, or burned. Contact your local waste management facility to arrange for a pick-up or to find out where these compounds can be dropped off. Dumping hazardous wastes is illegal, and can result in a substantial fine.

- Large items, such as refrigerators and computers, often contain potentially hazardous substances. Therefore, they should not be dumped in a landfill. Urban municipalities may collect these items, so that the dangerous materials (such as the Freon commonly used as a coolant in fridges) can be safely removed and perhaps recycled. Rural municipalities may set aside one area of the local landfill site where fridges and other appliances can be dropped off and appropriately dealt with.
- If you are uncertain of how to deal with any potentially hazardous substance, contact your local waste management facility for disposal information. Most household chemicals should be taken to the hazardous waste section of a municipal transfer station.

DID **YOU** KNOW?

The 3H Program
The Recycling Council of Ontario has established a 3H program to go along with the now-famous 3Rs: Reduce, Reuse, and Recycle. The 3Hs are

Halt	Do you really need it? Is there a non-hazardous alternative?
Heed	Heed warnings and labels.
Handle	Take it to a depot for recycling and safe disposal.

Urban Chemical Waste Management

As you discovered in Unit B: Waste Management, most urban homes are connected to sewer systems that take liquid waste to municipal wastewater treatment facilities. These facilities were designed (often decades ago) to remove normal household wastes, such as food scraps, human waste, and detergent residues, from the wastewater. The treated water is then released into a nearby river, lake, or ocean. Waste treatment systems were not designed to remove the wide range of substances—from latex paint to unwanted medications—that we sometimes pour down the drain. While the waste water treatment facilities can handle small amounts of household chemicals (such as regular cleaners and the occasional cup of water used to clean latex paint from a brush), large quantities are not always removed.

There are some cleaners that, in small quantities, can be safely poured down the drain. If a cleaner is designed for use with water or on sinks, toilet bowls, and tubs, you can usually assume that it can be poured down the drain. This should, however, be done with a lot of water. Small quantities of antifreeze can also be poured down the drain. Larger quantities are toxic to fish, so they should be dropped off at a hazardous waste disposal site. (If you are on a septic system, never pour chemicals down the drain.)

Rural Chemical Waste Management

While some rural homes are connected to main sewer lines, many are not. These homes are most likely connected to a septic system made up of a septic tank and a drainage field.

Septic systems are damaged by chemical wastes, so drain disposal is not an option. The effectiveness of a septic system can be seriously damaged by disinfectants (which kill the necessary bacteria), substances that do not mix with water, and heavy loads of phosphate-containing detergents.

Careful disposal of hazardous chemicals is particularly important in homes with holding tanks or septic systems. Use up chemicals completely, and take leftover chemicals to local waste management facilities.

C1.4 Activity | MANAGING CHEMICAL WASTE AT HOME

Go back to the table of chemicals that you compiled in C1.1 Activity: Mapping Household Chemicals. From this table, select (if possible) one organic solvent, one acid, one base, and at least one other product that has a warning on its label.

For each of the four products, answer the following questions.

(a) How and where should it be safely stored?
(b) Assuming that you need this product (or one that fulfills its function), what could you do to minimize the health risks in your home?
(c) How and where should any unused product be disposed of?
(d) What are the dangers of improper disposal of the substance?

✔ Check Your Understanding

1. (a) List at least six potentially hazardous chemicals that are commonly found in the home.
   (b) Which of these chemicals are likely to be corrosive?

2. What group of substances do gasoline and nail polish remover belong to?

3. (a) Suggest a use for a household cleaner with a pH of 10.
   (b) Why is the cleaner suitable for this use?
   (c) What would happen to someone who accidentally swallowed the cleaner?

4. What type of reaction is likely to occur when an acid and a base are combined?

5. What are some of the physical symptoms that might indicate high levels of indoor air pollution?

6. What kind of safety information is missing on the labels of most cleaning products?

7. Suggest three "green" alternatives to commercial cleaners.

8. (a) Why is carbon monoxide called a "silent killer"?
   (b) Name two things you can do to protect yourself from carbon monoxide poisoning in your home.

9. (a) Under what circumstances can excess chemicals be poured down the drain?
   (b) Why should other chemicals not be poured down the drain?
   (c) List at least three substances that should not be poured down the drain.

10. How should motor oil be disposed of?

CASE STUDY

Household Cleaners

A CBC television program called *Marketplace* aired a story about society's obsession with cleanliness. We want our whites whiter and our bathrooms and kitchens disinfected like a hospital (**Figure 14**). The chemical industry has answered. Today's cleaning products promise faster, easier, and better results, with no scrubbing. Is our clean streak harming our kids, however?

Shawn Ellis, a toxicologist, has begun marketing his services to anxious homeowners. He tests the air in people's homes to see how many chemicals and particulate matter may be floating in the air. Ellis tests for all kinds of substances, including mould, moisture, and chemicals. "Some of my clients, using cleaners, especially if it's a combination of cleaners, can actually feel dizzy or have headaches." The cleaners he is talking about are common household cleaners. "I think the majority of the awareness of cleaning products in people's homes are that a cleaning product is natural and safe. I don't think people consider cleaning products chemicals," Ellis said. The advertising for cleaners promotes a feeling of safety. The come-on to parents has babies and young children looking adorable—and vulnerable. It's a parent's job to keep them free from germs. Last year, Canadians spent more than $275 million on household cleaning products.

Kathy Cooper—a senior researcher with the Canadian Environmental Law Association—says there is a lot we don't know about the chemicals in our cleaners. Companies are not required to tell us. "For cleaning products in particular, the only thing the label will tell you is whether it is seriously toxic ... if you swallow it or get it in your eye, or will the container blow up ... but you don't have any information about long-term toxicity," Cooper told *Marketplace*. If you look at the label of your favourite floor cleaner or furniture polish, you will not see much in the way of ingredients. This is because companies are protected by trade secrets. If you do see an ingredient, it is listed because it could blow up or poison you. Many other chemicals are not even listed. "If you had the kind of labelling laws that they have in Europe, where it would tell you that 'this product contains something that may cause cancer' and another similar product that does the same job doesn't, you might not buy the product that contains the carcinogen," said Larry Stoffman, an international expert on chemical hazards information.

(Adapted from CBC *Marketplace*, aired March 11, 2003.)

(a) What strategies do marketing companies use to convince consumers that they need a particular cleaning product?

(b) According to Shawn Ellis, why do people accept commercial cleaning products?

(c) Explain how product labelling in Canada differs from product labelling in Europe.

(d) Should companies be required to inform consumers if their products contain a carcinogen? Explain your answer.

(e) Do you think Canada should have better labelling laws for all cleaning products? Why or why not?

(f) Are Canadians spending too much money on unnecessary cleaning products?

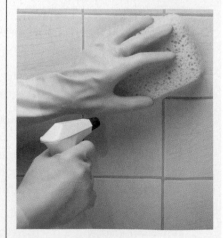

Figure 14 We sometimes forget that cleaners contain chemicals that can harm us.

CS

Going Overboard in Our Quest for Cleanliness?

The array of commercial cleaners on the market today is overwhelming. From vinegar-spray glass cleaners to heavy-duty drain cleaners, there are products available for just about every cleaning job imaginable. Moreover, there is not just one product—you can choose from pine-scented, lemon-scented, spring-flower-scented, or unscented. Are you looking for a product that is specially designed to accomplish one specific task, or a multi-purpose cleaner? Do you want an anti-bacterial cleaner? The choices are getting harder and harder to make. Are Canadians, in general, buying and using too many cleaners in an attempt to keep our homes as clean as possible (**Figure 15**)?

Figure 15 Is this special spray for cleaning glass really necessary?

Decision-Making Skills

- Define the Issue
- Identify Alternatives
- Research
- Analyze the Issue
- Defend a Decision
- Evaluate

Statement: Canadians are going overboard in our quest for cleanliness.

1. What is the issue under consideration? Working in a small group, write down what you think the issue is.

2. How do you think your classmates will feel about the issue? There will be a vote at the end of the activity. Will most people vote "for" or "against" the statement?

3. Reflect on what you have learned so far in this topic. Decide whether you will support or oppose the statement.

4. Collect further evidence to support your position and to counter the other side's arguments. Use **Table 7** to help you get started. Remember to record your sources of information.

 www.science.nelson.com

5. Assemble your information into a short speech, stating and defending your position.

6. Hold a class debate, ending in a vote (see **Appendix A7**).

7. Did the vote go as you had expected? Was your prediction in step 2 correct? What reasons can you give for this?

Table 7 Arguments for Why Excessive Cleanliness Is Not Necessary

Proponents	Opponents
specialized products are not necessary for most cleaning tasks, soap and water will usually get the job done	excess cleanliness may lead to an increase in asthma and allergies
vinegar is an inexpensive, and effective disinfectant	household cleaners are expensive
dusting can be done effectively with a damp cloth	excessive cleaning takes up valuable time and energy
baking soda can be used as a mild abrasive cleaner	Canada does not have mandatory labelling laws, commercial products may contain harmful and/or toxic compounds

SUMMARY

- Studies indicate that "excessive cleanliness" can be bad for the health because of the toxicity of the chemicals used. Homes often contain a wide variety of potentially hazardous products. Hazardous household products must be labelled with HHP symbols.
- Water molecules are polar, and grease molecules are non-polar. Therefore, water is not a good solvent for grease, unless soap or detergent is added to form micelles around the grease droplets.
- Organic solvents are often both flammable and toxic.
- Most household cleaning products are either acids or bases, and are therefore corrosive. Acids are substances that produce hydrogen ions in solution. Bases are substances that produce hydroxide ions in solution. Bases break down fatty acids and oils. Acids and bases are common ingredients in many household cleaning products, from glass cleaners to drain cleaners.
- The pH scale represents the concentration of hydrogen ions in a solution and indicates how acidic or basic a solution is. The pH scale uses values from 0 to 14 with 0 being the most acidic and 14 being the most basic. The midpoint (7) is neutral: neither acidic nor basic. The higher the concentration of hydrogen ions present, the lower the pH value and the more acidic the solution. Each pH unit represents a tenfold change in the concentration of hydrogen ions.
- Most household chemicals should never be mixed, because dangerous reactions may occur. When an acid is mixed with a base, however, a neutralization reaction occurs.

- Indoor air often contains more toxic pollutants than outdoor air does. Pollution from household cleaners can be reduced by choosing less harmful alternatives, such as vinegar, hot water, and baking soda.
- Carbon monoxide is a potentially deadly, colourless, odourless, and tasteless gas. It is produced through incomplete combustion, which can occur in furnaces and vehicles.
- When disposing of household chemicals, follow the instructions on the label or contact your local waste management facility. Many household chemicals require special disposal and should not be poured down the drain or thrown in the regular garbage.
- In urban centres, most homes are connected to a sewer system. Wastewater is treated and released to local waterways, but many chemicals in the water eventually end up in the environment.
- In rural areas, many homes have septic systems. Septic systems should be kept free of almost all chemicals.
- Choosing a household cleaning product requires research and consideration of what the product is being used for.

Key Terms

polar molecule	solvent
non-polar molecule	solute
corrosive	base
Hazardous Household Products (HHP) symbol	pH scale
	neutralization reaction/
organic solvent	acid–base reaction
acid	indoor air pollution

ASSESSMENT

Understanding Concepts

1. Generally, what types of compounds are household cleaners?

2. Do all household chemicals on the market have labels with hazardous household product symbols? Why or why not? If not, why might this be a safety concern?

3. Organic solvents tend to be hazardous chemicals.
   (a) What element is found in all organic solvents?
   (b) What information on the label is a clue that a substance may be an organic solvent?
   (c) What are the common health hazards of organic solvents?
   (d) Why are organic solvents a safety concern?

4. Define and give an example of an everyday chemical that is
(a) an acid   (b) a base

5. How many times more acidic is a solution with a pH of 2 than a solution with a pH of 5?

6. Using an example, explain why mixing household cleaners is dangerous.

7. List four steps that you can take to reduce the hazardous household wastes in landfills.

8. "Consumers can directly and indirectly influence the decisions of manufacturers, regarding the types of products they make." Discuss this statement with a partner or in a small group. Together, compile a list of ways in which consumers can exert an influence.

Applying Inquiry Skills

9. In a "kitchen sink" experiment, a student mixes vinegar with soap.
(a) Predict what you would expect to observe.
(b) Classify this type of reaction.

10. An old car battery, which has been sitting unused in a garage, starts to leak fluid onto the floor.
(a) Predict the approximate pH of the leaking substance.
(b) Suggest a method to clean up the spill. Include safety precautions.
(c) What should be done with the battery?

Making Connections

11. Research CLR. What is it? What type of chemical is it? How does it work? Are there any hazards associated with its use? What are the environmental impacts of using it? Are there any alternatives? Write a brief report of your findings.

 www.science.nelson.com

12. Research carbon monoxide poisoning. How many people are treated for carbon monoxide poisoning each year in Canada? How do these poisonings occur? How many people are killed each year from carbon monoxide poisoning? How could these deaths have been prevented? What steps can you take to improve the air quality in your home? Write a one-page brochure that could be given to consumers when they have new furnaces or fireplaces installed.

 www.science.nelson.com

13. Many household products have a limited amount of information on their labels. Sometimes the labels are not even clear about the specific chemicals that are in the products. As well, the precautions may be quite vague. Find one household product that provides insufficient information on its label. Contact the manufacturer by telephone, e-mail, or letter. Find out the best person to contact about your concerns, and express your concerns politely and clearly. Specify what action you would like the company to take.

14. Research two hazardous household products that are commonly used in the home. In an illustrated report, identify the warnings that are given on the labels, any disposal information, and the hazardous chemicals in each product. Recommend the proper disposal for each product.

 www.science.nelson.com

15. Conduct a cost–benefit analysis of disposal of hazardous household waste in the regular garbage, compared with disposal at an identified waste disposal facility. Make recommendations based on your analysis, and present them in an appropriate format.

16. Choose a specific career related to the use of chemicals in the home, such as pest exterminator, interior decorator, or gardener. Collect information on the educational and personality requirement for your career. Write a brief account of what a typical home visit might entail.

 www.science.nelson.com

Reflecting

17. Most household products do not give any instructions for proper disposal. Why do you think this is the case? What steps, if any, should be taken to rectify the omission? What can you do about it?

C2 Chemicals *in the* Workplace: MANAGING *the* RISKS

Firefighter Peter McGough, a 28-year veteran with the Kitchener Fire Department, observed that an unusually high number of men from his shift were dying—all from cancer.

"David died within 20 days of his last day at work. He went off sick, and he died shortly after that. He was 32. Ed Steely, he lasted a year. He was in his early 50s. Myself and John Devault, he was president of our association, we started looking into this. John developed cancer and died a year and a half after that. We were all on the same shift," McGough says.

McGough checked the records. The men dying of cancer had one thing in common: they had all fought the same fire—a huge chemical factory blaze in 1987 (**Figure 1**). The chemical fire raged all night and took several days to clean up.

Firefighters frequently risk their lives to save the lives of others. They are trained to avoid being trapped in a burning building or crushed under a collapsing roof. Now, however, there is evidence that firefighters face another serious risk: the risk of getting brain cancer or leukemia. The risk is so real that, in Ontario, these cancers are treated as workplace injuries in firefighters.

(a) What are "workplace injuries"? Why are they considered separately from other injuries?

Eleven of 14 recent studies on the mortality of firefighters found an increased risk of brain cancer. (Interestingly, similar studies conducted before the widespread use of plastics in the 1950s did not find this increased risk.) Most compensation claims (applications for money to help firefighters and their families) for leukemia and brain cancer are from firefighters who have been on the job for over 20 years. Claims for these cancers in much younger firefighters, however, are beginning to appear. The assumption that cancers are caused by exposure to toxic fumes and smoke over long years of service may no longer be valid. New evidence now suggests that cancers can begin very soon after exposure to toxic fumes. It is possible that some of the newer chemicals to which firefighters are now exposed might be causing cancers to develop much more quickly than in the past.

Many workplaces contain a wide array of chemicals. Because employees generally have little control over the substances they are exposed to, there are very strict rules in Canada to control the storage, use, and disposal of all kinds of chemicals. Whether you are changing the toner cartridge in a photocopier or fighting a blazing chemical fire, there are safety guidelines for your protection at work.

(b) What kinds of hazardous substances are you exposed to, at school or at work? What control do you have over this exposure?

Are some risks in the workplace acceptable? Who should decide what is acceptable and what is not? Who is responsible for workers' safety? What role should employers take in minimizing the risks to their employees? What regulations are in place to ensure workers' safety?

Figure 1 Is it possible that a single exposure to chemicals used to make floral foam caused the death of three of the 69 firefighters present, and the illness of at least 12 others?

Science & Technology

Staying Safe at Work

Workers in virtually every occupation are exposed to chemicals, from workers in seemingly safe offices to firefighters in burning buildings. Since the late 1980s, an attempt has been made to reduce the risk of chemical exposure by the implementation of the **Workplace Hazardous Materials Information System** (**WHMIS**). Prior to 1986, the financial cost of work-related accidents and health problems in Canada was millions of dollars every year. One of the main reasons for this high cost was believed to be the lack of readily available information on chemicals in the workplace.

Chemical Information and Training

Exposure to some hazardous materials can contribute to serious health problems, such as rashes, burns, kidney and lung damage, sterility, and cancer. Other hazardous materials can cause fires or explosions, which can result in damage to both people and property. WHMIS was created by representatives from government, industry, and labour. They hoped that it would inform both workers and employers about the potential dangers of hazardous materials and help them prevent injury, illness, or death. WHMIS officially became law in 1988. The following regulations are included under the WHMIS legislation:

- Canadian chemical suppliers must label their products and must provide a **material safety data sheet** (**MSDS**) for their customers.
- The MSDS must be available wherever the product is stored, transported, or used (including school science labs).
- Employers are responsible for providing training for all workers who are exposed to hazardous materials in the workplace, and for making sure that all hazardous materials are properly labelled.
- Workers who handle or encounter hazardous materials are required to participate in a WHMIS training program, to learn about MSDS information that will help them work safely with these hazardous materials.

C2.1 Activity   CHEMICAL PRODUCT LABELS

All chemicals should be properly labelled, as shown in **Figure 2**. What information is included, and what does it mean?

Materials
a variety of chemical containers with
original labels

Look at the containers that your teacher has displayed. Record the name of each product and any listed ingredients, warning symbols, and written instructions regarding its use and disposal.

(a) What do you think the symbols on each product mean?
(b) What safety precautions, if any, should be followed when using each product?
(c) Which product would you feel most comfortable using? Which product would you rather avoid? Explain why.

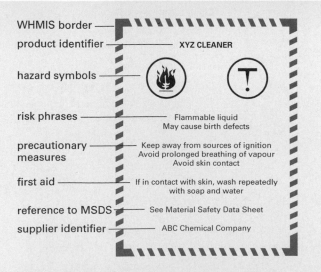

Figure 2 To meet WHMIS regulations, every chemical container must have a supplier label that identifies the product and provides safety warnings and precautions, as well as first-aid procedures in case of an accident.

WHMIS Classes and Symbols

WHMIS covers six broad classes of hazardous materials, lettered A through F. Class D is further divided.

Each type of hazardous material has its own symbol (**Table 1**).

Table 1 WHMIS Symbols, Classes, and Descriptions

Class A: Compressed Gas

This class includes compressed gases, dissolved gases, and gases that are liquified by compression or refrigeration. Examples: gas cylinders that contain acetylene for oxyacetylene welding and oxygen for water disinfection

Class B: Flammable and Combustible Material

The materials in this class are solids, liquids, and gases that are capable of catching fire or exploding in the presence of a source of ignition. **Flammable** liquids, such as acetone, are more easily ignited than **combustible** liquids, such as kerosene. Examples: white phosphorus, acetone, and butane

Class C: Oxidizing Material

This class includes materials that provide oxygen or similar substances and that increase the risk of fire if they come in contact with flammable or combustible materials. Examples: sodium hypochlorite, perchloric acid, and inorganic peroxides

Class D, Division 1: Toxic Material—Immediate and Serious

Materials that cause immediate and serious toxic effects are included in this division. Small amounts of these materials can cause death. Examples: sodium cyanide and hydrogen sulfide

Class D, Division 2: Toxic Material—Long-Term Concealed

This division consists of materials that cause immediate eye or skin irritation or long-term effects (such as birth defects, sterility, or cancer) in a person repeatedly exposed to small amounts. Examples: acetone (irritant), asbestos (carcinogen)

Class D, Division 3: Biohazardous Infectious Material

This division consists of biohazardous infectious materials: materials that contain harmful microorganisms. Examples: cultures or diagnostic specimens that contain *salmonella* bacteria or the hepatitis B virus

Class E: Corrosive Material

This class includes acidic or caustic materials, which can destroy the skin or eat through metals and some other substances. Examples: muriatic acid and lye

Class F: Dangerously Reactive Material

The materials in this class can undergo dangerous reactions if they are subjected to heat, pressure, or shock, or allowed to contact water. Examples: nitroglycerine, some plastic monomers, and some cyanides

Material Safety Data Sheets

Every potentially hazardous material in a workplace should be accompanied by a material safety data sheet (**Figure 3**). An MSDS contains a variety of useful information, from the various names by which the substance is known, to instructions for treating someone who has been exposed to the chemical.

Material Safety Data Sheet

PRAXAIR

I. PRODUCT INFORMATION

PRODUCT IDENTIFIER:	Propane
TRADE NAME:	Liquefied Petroleum Gas
CHEMICAL IDENTITY:	Propane
SYNONYMS:	Dimethylmethane, Pro... Propyldihydride
FORMULA:	C3H8
CHEMICAL FAMILY:	Alkane
SHIPPING NAME:	Liquefied Petroleum Gas,‡ or Propane

SUPPLIER/ MANU...
Praxair Canada I...
1 City Centre...

V. REACTIVITY DATA

STABILITY: UNSTABLE ( ) STABLE (x)

CONDITIONS OF CHEMICAL INSTABILITY:
See Section VII.

INCOMPATIBLE PRODUCTS:
Oxidizing agents, chlorine dioxide.

HAZARDOUS DECOMPOSITION PRODUCTS:
Thermal decomposition or burning may produce CO/CO2.

HAZARDOUS POLYMERIZATION:
MAY OCCUR ( ) WILL NOT OCCUR (x)

VII. PREVENTATIVE MEASURES

PERSONAL PROTECTION:
RESPIRATORY PROTECTION:

Select in accordance with the provincial regulations or guidelines. Selection should also be based on the current CSA standards Z94.4, "Selection, care and use of respirators." Respirators should be approved by NOSH and MSHA.

PROTECTIVE GLOVES: Preferred for cylinder handling and to prevent liquid exposure.

EYE PROTECTION: Select in accordance with the current CSA Standard Z94.3, "Industrial eye and face protection", and any provincial regulations or guidelines.

OTHERS: Metatarsal shoes for cylinder handling. Protective clothing where needed. Select in accordance with the current CSA standard Z195, "Protective foot wear", and any provincial regulations or guidelines.

SPECIAL HANDLING AND STORAGE REQUIREMENTS:

DANGER: Flammable, liquefied gas under pressure. Use piping and equipment adequately designed to withstand pressures to be encountered. May form explosive mixtures with air. Ground all equipment. Only use spark proof tools and explosion-proof equipment. Keep away form heat, sparks and open flames. Store and use with adequate ventilation at all times. Use only in a close system. Close valve when not in use and when empty. Keep away from oxidizing agents.

Figure 3   This MSDS for propane includes information that will be valuable to people working with the chemical.

C2.2 Activity   MSDS SAFETY CARDS   >

In this activity, you will create a set of quick-reference safety cards for the grade 9 and/or 10 science course. These cards could be a resource for the science teachers at your school and may be shared with the grade 9 and 10 students.

Materials
12 cm by 20 cm blank index cards
alphabetical dividers
index card box
grade 9 and/or 10 science textbook
school MSDS binder (or computer and MSDS CD)

1. Your teacher will assign you a portion of the textbook. Go through your assigned portion, and make a list of all the chemicals that are used in the activities and investigations.

2. As a class, combine all the lists into one master list. Organize the master list in alphabetical order, so that each chemical is listed only once.

3. Divide the master list equally among groups of two to four people.

4. Once your group has its list of chemicals, look up the MSDSs. Summarize the MSDS information on the cards, under the following headings:
   - Product Name and Formula
   - Hazard Ratings (health hazard, specific hazard, fire hazard, and reactivity)
   - Physical Data (appearance, odour, and solubility in water)
   - Fire and Explosion Hazard Data
   - Reactivity Data
   - Toxicological Properties
   - Exposure Time/Concentrations that Present a Safety Risk
   - Preventative Measures
   - First-Aid Instructions

5. Highlight the information that students should have before they use each chemical.

6. Place all your safety cards in alphabetical order in the box.

(a) How do the safety cards differ from the MSDSs?

(b) How do the safety cards differ from the labels on the containers?

(c) Why would these safety cards be helpful in the science classroom? How might students use them?

(d) Did you learn anything unexpected while completing this activity? Explain.

Some Common Reactions

Many jobs involve chemical reactions. For example, a welder uses an acetylene torch to join two pieces of steel, and a polymer chemist develops a new type of plastic. Whenever a new substance is formed by the reaction of chemicals, a chemical change has taken place. You should be familiar with all the clues that a chemical change has occurred (**Figure 4**).

There are five general types of chemical reactions: **synthesis, decomposition, single displacement, double displacement**, and **combustion** (**Table 2**).

A new colour appears.

There is a change in temperature.

Bubbles of gas are formed. A new odour may be noticed.

A solid material (called a precipitate) forms in a liquid.

The change is generally difficult to reverse.

Figure 4 These five clues indicate that a chemical change may have occurred and that the products are different from the reactants.

Table 2 Summary of Common Chemical Reactions

Type of reaction	General formula	Example	Description
synthesis	$A + B \rightarrow AB$	$4\,Fe_{(s)} + 3\,O_{2(g)} \rightarrow 2\,Fe_2O_{3(s)}$	Rust forms from iron and oxygen.
decomposition	$AB \rightarrow A + B$	$2\,H_2O_{2(l)} \rightarrow 2\,H_2O_{(l)} + O_{2(g)}$	Hydrogen peroxide decomposes into water and oxygen.
single displacement	$A + BC \rightarrow B + AC$	$2\,Na_{(s)} + 2\,H_2O_{(l)} \rightarrow$ $2\,NaOH_{(aq)} + H_{2(g)}$	Sodium metal reacts violently with water to produce basic sodium hydroxide and hydrogen gas.
double displacement	$AB + CD \rightarrow AD + BC$	$2\,NaCl_{(aq)} + Pb(NO_3)_{2(aq)} \rightarrow$ $PbCl_{2(s)} + 2\,NaNO_{3(aq)}$	Sodium chloride and lead nitrate react to form lead chloride and sodium nitrate.
combustion	hydrocarbon $+ O_2 \rightarrow$ $CO_2 + H_2O$	$CH_{4(g)} + 2\,O_{2(g)} \rightarrow$ $CO_{2(g)} + 2\,H_2O_{(g)}$	Methane burns in the presence of oxygen to produce carbon dioxide and water.

Look at **Table 2** (on the previous page).

(a) Rewrite the word equation for each reaction, filling in the blanks.

(b) Classify each reaction as one of the five types of reactions:

(i) hydrochloric acid + zinc → zinc chloride + _____

(ii) sodium carbonate → sodium oxide + _____ **(Figure 5)**

(iii) silver nitrate + potassium iodide → potassium nitrate + _____

(iv) paraffin wax + oxygen → _____ + _____

(v) potassium + chlorine → _____

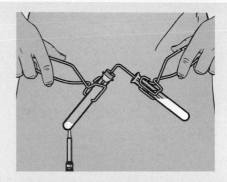

Figure 5 The liquid in the test tube is limewater. This gives a clue about one of the products of the reaction.

A Workplace Hazard: Fire

Imagine a welder's torch, a roaring steel furnace, and a forest fire (**Figure 6**). They look like very different reactions, but they are all forms of burning, or combustion. There are three main components in any fire: a fuel, heat, and oxygen. Most fires begin with a combustible or flammable material that is exposed to an ignition source, such as a smouldering cigarette in a couch cushion or a spark near the bedding of a hospital patient receiving oxygen.

Figure 6 British Columbia's forest fires in 2003 were a vivid example of how fuel, heat, and oxygen can combine into an uncontrollable blaze.

Unlike rusting, which is a slow oxidation reaction, combustion is a very rapid oxidation reaction that releases a tremendous amount of heat energy. Reactions that give off energy are called **exothermic reactions**. (Reactions that absorb heat are called endothermic reactions. For example, the reactions in chemical "icc" packs are endothermic reactions.)

Flammable materials are relatively easy to ignite. They can pose a serious danger if they are not stored properly. Although a source of ignition is usually required, fires can start with no initial spark or flame, which is called spontaneous combustion. For a fire to take hold fully, a sufficient supply of oxygen is also necessary. In general, a minimum concentration of 15% oxygen is required for flaming combustion. Smouldering can occur, however, with as little as 3% oxygen. The oxygen content of normal air is approximately 21%—more than enough to support flaming combustion.

DID **YOU** KNOW?

Flashpoint
The flashpoint is the lowest temperature at which a flammable substance will release vapours that will burn if a flame or spark is present. The flashpoint of gasoline is around −40°C. This means that gasoline evaporates to form a flammable mixture with air at any temperature above −40°C.

Combustion Reactions

A **complete combustion** reaction produces carbon dioxide and water—both relatively harmless substances.

methane + oxygen → carbon dioxide + water
$$CH_{4(g)} + 2\ O_{2(g)} \rightarrow CO_{2(g)} + 2\ H_2O_{(g)}$$

ethane + oxygen → carbon dioxide + water
$$2\ C_2H_{6(g)} + 7\ O_{2(g)} \rightarrow 4\ CO_{2(g)} + 6\ H_2O_{(g)}$$

Sometimes, when a substance is burned in insufficient oxygen, a more dangerous product—carbon monoxide—is also produced. This reaction is known as **incomplete combustion**.

ethane + oxygen → carbon dioxide + water + carbon monoxide

$$C_2H_{6(g)} + 3\ O_{2(g)} \rightarrow CO_{2(g)} + 3\ H_2O_{(g)} + CO_{(g)}$$

When a carbon-containing compound is burned in a very small amount of oxygen, the incomplete combustion reaction also produces carbon. You may have seen a black coating on the bottom of a flask that has been heated over a sooty flame (**Figure 7**).

ethane + oxygen → carbon dioxide + water + carbon monoxide + soot

$$3\ C_2H_{6(g)} + 6\ O_{2(g)} \rightarrow CO_{2(g)} + 9\ H_2O_{(g)} + CO_{(g)} + 4\ C_{(s)}$$

Figure 7 A black deposit of carbon (soot) indicates incomplete combustion due to a lack of oxygen.

Common combustion reactions include the burning of gasoline in vehicle engines, natural gas in home and office furnaces, and coal for the generation of electricity. Coal generating stations are among the largest sources of carbon dioxide emissions in Canada. They are slowly being phased out in this country in favour of cleaner sources of energy, but are still widely used in some parts of the world.

Categories of Fire

Fires are classified according to the type of fuel involved. The classification of a fire can be very important because it determines how the fire must be extinguished.

- Class A fires are typical house fires, occurring with combustible materials such as wood, cloth, paper, and upholstery. These fires are generally fought with water.
- Class B fires occur with combustible or flammable liquids, such as gasoline, jet fuels, diesel oil, fuel oil, paints, thinners, solvents, lubricating oils, and greases. A class B fire actually occurs in the fuel vapours above the liquid. A fire extinguisher that produces an aqueous film-forming foam (AFFF) must be used to put out a class B fire.
- Class C fires involve electrical equipment and wiring. Dry chemicals are used to extinguish electrical fires, to cut off the oxygen supply. Carbon dioxide extinguishers can also be used. A class C fire can be extremely dangerous, since it presents the additional risk of electric shock. As well, toxic fumes may be produced from the burning electrical insulation.
- Class D fires involve combustible metals, such as sodium, potassium, and magnesium. These metals react violently with water and air. A metal/sand extinguisher (usually applied with a scoop or a shovel) is used to put out a class D fire. It works by cutting off the oxygen and smothering the reaction.

Extinguishing a Fire

If you discover a fire, the first thing you need to do (if possible) is to alert everyone else in the building and make sure that you all get out quickly. Then you need to call the fire department. Some workplaces have employees who are specially trained to handle fires until the firefighters arrive. Here are some of the techniques that these specially trained employees and firefighters might use to slow or stop a fire.

- *Remove the fuel.* This is especially true for liquid fires (class B). Move any additional fuel sources as far away from the fire as possible (**Figure 8**).

Figure 8 Firefighters have used heavy equipment to clear a firebreak—removing a strip of vegetation in the fire's path. Doing this deprives the advancing fire of fuel so that it cannot spread in that direction.

- *Remove or reduce the heat.* Cooling down an area to a temperature that slows combustion will help to extinguish the fire. Water is the most commonly used cooling agent.
- *Remove the oxygen.* You cannot technically remove oxygen, since it is naturally present in the surrounding air. You can take steps, however, to block the fire's access to oxygen. For example, a carbon dioxide extinguisher displaces the air (and its oxygen) with carbon dioxide. This starves the fire. Without sufficient oxygen, the combustion process cannot continue. Every home should have a fire extinguisher on every floor, including one in the kitchen. If you do not have a fire extinguisher, a small kitchen fire can often be extinguished by dumping baking soda (sodium hydrogen carbonate) on it. Baking soda releases carbon dioxide as it heats, which displaces oxygen and thus puts out the fire.

Firefighting: A Hazardous Career

Fighting fires is a dangerous job, due to both the physical surroundings and the chemical byproducts of combustion. Firefighters must be protected from the heat of a fire, from falling debris, and from the gases that are produced by the fire. Protective clothing helps to shield them from the heat and from falling debris. Breathing apparatus is a "must," since fires produce gases that reduce the amount of oxygen available for breathing. Furthermore, the high

levels of carbon dioxide and carbon monoxide can quickly overcome a firefighter, leading to disorientation or unconsciousness. Carbon dioxide is a colourless and odourless gas, which can make it very dangerous. It can reach high concentrations without anyone being aware of its presence. At sufficiently high concentrations, it can actually suppress breathing, causing death through asphyxiation.

Incomplete combustion produces another dangerous gas—carbon monoxide. As you have learned, carbon monoxide is a odourless, colourless, and tasteless gas. It can be fatal in much lower concentrations than carbon dioxide. A person who is exposed to a concentration of just over 1% carbon monoxide in air will become unconscious and likely die within minutes if not removed from the area.

The danger of carbon monoxide is due to the fact that a carbon monoxide molecule is very similar in shape to an oxygen molecule (**Figure 9**). When carbon monoxide enters the bloodstream through the lungs, it has an even higher attraction than oxygen to the hemoglobin in the red blood cells. Even worse, once the carbon monoxide attaches to the red blood cells, it does not readily detach again. This essentially decreases the body's ability to deliver oxygen to the tissues. If the body accumulates too much carbon monoxide, the organs become starved for oxygen. This causes a victim to become very sleepy, slip into a coma, and possibly die.

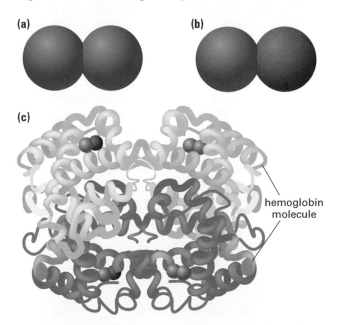

Figure 9 Because the oxygen molecule **(a)** and the carbon monoxide molecule **(b)** are so similar in shape and size, they can both fit into an oxygen-delivering hemoglobin molecule **(c)** the same way.

Unlike carbon dioxide, carbon monoxide can be highly explosive under certain conditions. If the concentration of carbon monoxide in air becomes high enough, an open flame or even a spark can set off a violent explosion.

Hydrogen sulfide, $H_2S_{(g)}$, is another dangerous gas that is produced in some fires. Hydrogen sulfide is a colourless gas that smells like rotten eggs. It can be produced naturally by rotting foods and sewage, and also by burning cloth and leather. Firefighters must take extra care when fighting fires that involve cloth and leather, and that occur around sewage systems or in areas where there has been a sewage spill. Air that contains relatively low concentrations of hydrogen sulfide (as little as 4.3%) can be violently explosive in the presence of a flame. Hydrogen sulfide is also extremely poisonous if inhaled. At concentrations as low as 0.07 to 0.10%, a person may rapidly lose consciousness, stop breathing, and possibly die after one breath.

As a fire burns, it rapidly consumes the available oxygen in the space. This is one of the primary reasons why firefighters wear self-contained breathing apparatus. If the concentration of oxygen drops to 15%, a person may become dizzy, experience an increase in heart rate, and hear a buzzing sound in the ears. If the concentration drops to 9%, the person may lose consciousness. Below 7%, death may occur.

✔ Check Your Understanding

1. List at least four health problems that can be associated with exposure to hazardous chemicals.

2. (a) What does WHMIS stand for?
   (b) Why were WHMIS regulations introduced?
   (c) What are the major requirements of WHMIS regulations?

3. Match each WHMIS symbol with the correct description.

Symbol	Description
(a)	(i) flammable material
(b)	(ii) corrosive material
(c)	(iii) compressed gas
(d)	(iv) oxidizing material
(e)	(v) toxic material

4. For each symbol in question 3, describe the safety precautions you would take when working with the chemical.

5. List at least five pieces of information you would expect to find on an MSDS.

6. What are three clues that a chemical reaction has occurred?

7. Classify each reaction as a combustion, synthesis, decomposition, single displacement, or double displacement reaction.
   (a) $2\ NaHCO_{3(s)} \rightarrow CO_{2(g)} + H_2O_{(l)} + Na_2CO_{3(s)}$
   (b) $2\ H_{2(g)} + O_{2(g)} \rightarrow 2\ H_2O_{(l)}$
   (c) $CaCO_{3\ (s)} \rightarrow CaO_{(s)} + CO_{2(g)}$
   (d) $C_3H_{8\ (g)} + 5\ O_{2\ (g)} \rightarrow 3\ CO_{2(g)} + 4\ H_2O_{(l)}$
   (e) $NaOH_{(aq)} + HCl_{(aq)} \rightarrow H_2O_{(l)} + NaCl_{(aq)}$

8. Define an exothermic reaction.

9. Name the products of
   (a) complete combustion
   (b) incomplete combustion

10. Why can incomplete combustion be dangerous or even deadly?

11. (a) What class of fire is most likely to be fought using water?
    (b) Why would you not use water to fight a class C fire?

12. (a) What materials can produce hydrogen sulfide gas when they burn?
    (b) In what other ways is hydrogen sulfide produced?
    (c) Why is hydrogen sulfide dangerous?

13. How can carbon dioxide be dangerous in a fire?

Society & the Environment

Chemicals in the Office

While an office may seem like one of the safest places to work, there are dangers lurking (**Table 3**). In a crowded office without adequate ventilation, the concentration of carbon dioxide can rise above normal and begin to cause physical symptoms (such as headaches and drowsiness) in the employees. If there is a problem with the furnace, the carbon monoxide concentration in the office may also be unacceptably high.

As well, there is the danger of volatile organic compounds (VOCs) permeating the work environment. VOCs are potentially toxic compounds that may be released by photocopiers (**Figure 10**), carpets, furniture, paints and varnishes, and many other sources. It is particularly important for buildings to be well-ventilated when any construction or redecorating work is in progress. Similarly, offices that are part of a manufacturing facility are vulnerable to air contamination from the factory floor. Again, proper ventilation is key to preventing this.

Biological contaminants are another concern. Moulds and fungi can grow in ventilation systems and insulation, and in damp walls, carpets, drapes, and furniture. Spores from these organisms can lead to illness. Moulds are one of the most difficult contaminants to remove.

In older buildings, dust and asbestos can pose serious health risks, ranging from skin irritations to lung cancer.

As recently as 15 years ago, smoking was allowed in many offices. There are now laws that ban smoking in most workplaces, resulting in much cleaner air.

Not all the pollution in an office comes from the building itself. Gases may leak into the building from the outside environment. If the air intake for the ventilation system is located where vehicles are often idling, such as in a shipping area, the exhaust from the vehicles can circulate through the building. Most building codes and regulations prohibit such poor design, but even open windows can allow vehicle exhaust into a building.

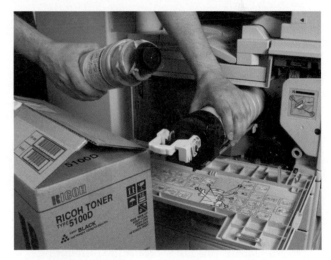

Figure 10 Even something as mundane as changing the toner in a photocopier should be done according to instructions, to avoid sending dust particles into the air.

Table 3 Causes of Office Air Contamination Resulting in Physical Symptoms

Causes	Percentage of total cases (%)
inadequacies in the ventilation system: insufficient fresh air intake; poor temperature and humidity control; poor venting of internally produced fumes	52
internal contaminants: photocopiers; cleaning chemicals; kitchen smells; furnace exhaust	18
outdoor contaminants: close proximity of the outdoor air intake to garages, loading docks, building exhausts, and outside construction projects	10
biological contaminants: poor maintenance of heating, ventilation, and air conditioning system, resulting in stagnant water in condensation pans where fungi and bacteria can grow; water damage to carpets, causing mould to grow	5
building and interior materials: paints; new carpeting; carpet adhesives	4
unknown	11

(Adapted from *Office Indoor Air Quality*, a Web page produced by MFL Occupational Health Centre, Inc.: http://www.mflohc.mb.ca)

C2.4 Activity CHEMICALS IN THE WORKPLACE

Firefighters are not the only workers who come in contact with potentially dangerous chemicals on a regular basis. In this activity, you will choose another job in which workers regularly deal with chemicals and research the possible health hazards and preventive measures.

1. Choose a company whose employees regularly deal with chemicals. Focus on a particular job within this company.

2. Arrange an interview with the employer or manager. Prepare an interview script that contains some or all of the following questions, plus some questions that you write yourself.
   • What are the dangers of the job?
   • Are there any other hazards besides chemicals, such as noise and radiation?
   • Is safety training provided? When?

• Do you have safety meetings?
• Is there any safety gear that an employee would be expected to wear? Do you provide training in how to use this safety gear? When?
• Are employees trained in emergency procedures, such as procedures for fires and chemical spills? When?
• Where are fire extinguishers, first-aid kits, and other emergency equipment located?
• What is the procedure if someone gets hurt? Who is responsible for first aid?
• What are the employee's health and safety responsibilities?
• Who can answer health or safety questions?

3. Present your findings like a Frequently Asked Question (FAQ) Web page or on a poster.

Explore *an* Issue

Sick Building Syndrome

You may have heard the term "sick building syndrome." What is a syndrome, and who or what is sick? You will look into the causes and impacts of this fairly recent phenomenon, and decide whether it is a serious concern.

1. Conduct research on sick building syndrome (SBS) to answer the following questions.

 www.science.nelson.com

(a) What is SBS?
(b) Identify common sources of contamination, including specific chemicals.
(c) Describe the physical symptoms experienced by employees who suffer from SBS.
(d) Are there other possible explanations for the health problems experienced by employees?
(e) Does SBS affect all the employees who work in the same office? If not, how can this be explained?

Decision-Making Skills
● Define the Issue   ● Analyze the Issue
○ Identify Alternatives   ○ Defend a Decision
● Research   ● Evaluate

(f) Not everyone agrees that sick building syndrome actually exists. What evidence can you find to support its existence?
(g) How can the effects of SBS be minimized or eliminated?

2. Prepare a cost–benefit analysis on "curing" a building of SBS (see **Appendix A1**).

3. Use your findings to write a brochure that could be handed out to new employees by the Health and Safety Committee of a large office-based company. Your brochure should inform employees about the existence of SBS, possible causes, and symptoms to look out for. As well, your brochure should include the employer's responsibilities and changes to expect once a complaint has been made.

SUMMARY

- WHMIS was implemented in 1988 to inform employers and employees about potential workplace dangers and ways to prevent them.
- An MSDS contains all the chemical and safety information about a chemical. It should be available wherever the chemical is stored, used, or transported.
- There are five basic types of chemical reactions:
  - synthesis: $A + B \rightarrow AB$
  - decomposition: $AB \rightarrow A + B$
  - single displacement: $A + BC \rightarrow B + AC$
  - double displacement: $AB + CD \rightarrow AD + BC$
  - combustion: hydrocarbon $+ O_2 \rightarrow CO_2 + H_2O$
- Combustion (burning) is an exothermic reaction that requires a fuel, oxygen, and heat. Fires can be extinguished by removing one of these three components. Flammable and, to a lesser extent, combustible materials are prone to ignite and burn. Incomplete combustion produces poisonous carbon monoxide gas and sometimes solid carbon (soot).

- Firefighting is a hazardous job due to the physical demands and the exposure to chemicals. Inhaling toxic vapours has recently been linked to increased cancer rates in firefighters.
- The office environment can be a source of chemical contamination due to the release of vapours from furniture and building materials, and the high concentration of carbon dioxide caused by overcrowded spaces and/or inadequate ventilation systems.

Key Terms

Workplace Hazardous Materials Information System (WHMIS)
material safety data sheet (MSDS)
flammable
combustible
synthesis reaction

decomposition reaction
single displacement reaction
double displacement reaction
combustion reaction
exothermic reaction
complete combustion
incomplete combustion

ASSESSMENT

Understanding Concepts

1. How are the WHMIS symbols and the HHP symbols similar? How are they different?

2. A chemical product has the label shown in **Figure 11**.
   (a) Is this substance a solid, liquid, or gas at normal temperatures?
   (b) What hazard(s) does sodium hydroxide pose?
   (c) If you were using this chemical, what safety precautions should you take?
   (d) Where would you find more detailed information about sodium hydroxide?

3. After scrubbing clean a dirty kitchen pot, you leave a steel wool pad in a saucer of water overnight. In the morning, the part of the silver-coloured steel wool that was under the water appears brown and flaky.
   (a) Has a chemical reaction occurred? How do you know?

Figure 11

(b) What is the brown flaky material?

(c) Write the word equation for this reaction.

4. **(a)** Suggest a chemical hazard that might be encountered by both a firefighter and an office worker.

(b) What is a likely cause of this hazard for each worker? Classify the reaction(s).

(c) What can be done to minimize the risk for each worker?

5. List two methods that you could use to "starve" (extinguish) a fire. How do these methods work?

6. **(a)** What is a class A fire?

(b) What is the best way to fight a class A fire? Why?

7. Give an example of

(a) a corrosive compound

(b) a fuel

(c) a product of complete combustion

(d) a common indoor air contaminant

(e) a polar molecule

(f) an organic solvent

Applying Inquiry Skills

8. In a lab demonstration, a raw egg is placed in a beaker of vinegar. (Vinegar is a solution of acetic acid, CH_3COOH.) Bubbles of gas are observed leaving the surface of the egg. After several hours, the eggshell (which is composed of calcium carbonate, $CaCO_{3(s)}$) has disappeared.

(a) Did a chemical reaction occur? Give reasons for your answer.

(b) What gas was probably produced during this reaction? What test could be used to identify the gas?

(c) Three new compounds are produced. One of these chemicals is water. Write the word equation and chemical equation to represent the reaction.

(d) How would you modify the experiment to identify the gas produced?

Making Connections

9. Firefighting is an essential service, and a very rewarding career. Firefighters' salaries are above the average salaries for Canada. Firefighting has always been known as a dangerous job, but there is mounting evidence that firefighters are exposed to new and deadly hazards. Do the benefits of being a firefighter outweigh the drawbacks? Make a decision, backing your arguments with evidence.

10. There are photocopiers in every office and many homes in Canada. They are useful, relatively inexpensive, and easy to use. Is there a downside to their widespread use, however? Do they contribute to indoor air pollution? Research the chemicals that are used in photocopiers. Is there any evidence that these chemicals cause harm? Weigh the pros and cons of photocopiers, and decide whether you would like to have one in a home office. Present your findings and decisions in a brief report, using a medium of your choice.

 www.science.nelson.com

11. Imagine that you work at a company that deals with potentially dangerous chemicals, and that you are injured by direct contact with one of these chemicals.

 www.science.nelson.com

(a) Create a specific scenario. Include your job, the company and type of workplace, the chemical involved, the situation, and the type of injury.

(b) Research your rights and responsibilities as an injured employee.

(c) Research your employer's rights and responsibilities.

(d) What do you think would be a fair outcome?

(e) What could be done to avoid this type of situation occurring again, to you or another employee?

Reflecting

12. When you buy or use an item, do you consider the effects it may have on your health? Why or why not?

13. You will soon be choosing a career path. How might an understanding of chemicals in the workplace affect your decision?

Chemicals *in* Industry:
PUTTING CHEMICALS *to*
WORK

A much-awaited family holiday is just beginning for Lara and Ben. They have arrived at an "unspoiled tropical paradise" and are looking forward to spending time on the beautiful beaches and swimming in the clear blue ocean waters. They wake up early in the morning and quickly put on their swimsuits, cover themselves with sunscreen, and head out to the beach. There are only a few other people already out, but the family notices that there is a lot of garbage scattered along the shoreline (**Figure 1**). Plastic pop bottles, empty fast-food containers, bits of rope, and other unidentifiable pieces of plastic litter are coating the soft white sand. They are disappointed that this isolated island is not as clean as they had expected. Undeterred, they decide to go swimming anyway. Once in the ocean, their spirits are lifted. The water is warm, and the salt makes their bodies feel light and buoyant. Even in the water, though, pieces of plastic come floating by. A little later, they notice cleanup crews coming along the beach, picking up all the garbage. Now the beautiful beach is clean and sparkling.

Early the next morning, they return to the beach. They find it covered in litter once again. More plastic garbage has been washed up by the tide overnight. This pattern repeats itself for the rest of their holiday.

When Ben and Lara return home, they are relaxed and happy. They have a new awareness of the impact of pollution, however—even in isolated parts of the world. The pristine beaches they were expecting to see no longer exist. They wonder if there is anything they can do to make the oceans cleaner.

(a) What could Ben and Lara do to reduce the amount of pollution entering the oceans?

Scientists have been studying the oceans intensively over the past century. Despite this fact, the oceans are often viewed as the last unexplored and unspoiled frontier. Unfortunately, humans are having a dramatic impact on this mysterious and pristine environment. The oceans are becoming increasing polluted with waste materials, from polychlorobiphenyls (PCBs) to plastics.

Scientists have collected surface-water samples in order to compare the mass of plastics in a given volume of water with the mass of plankton (small aquatic organisms). Their findings are shocking: the mass of the plastics is six times the mass of the plankton. Not only is this garbage unsightly, but it is also very dangerous to marine life. Many organisms mistake small pieces of plastic for food and ingest them. Animals have been found with pieces of fishing nets and other unidentified pieces of plastic in their stomachs. Adult albatrosses collect pieces of plastic to feed to their young. The babies' stomachs fill up with the plastics, so the babies no longer beg for food. Feeling full, they eventually die of starvation.

Dealing with the problem of plastic pollution is difficult. The oceans are very large and very deep, making manual cleanup virtually impossible. The use of biodegradable plastics may seem like a good idea, but the low ocean temperatures slow the

Figure 1 Plastics, which make up 86% of the debris in the oceans, can now be found littered along some of the most remote beaches in the world.

decomposition process considerably. The solution to the problem will likely have more to do with disposal methods than with the plastics themselves.

(b) Are plastics a pollution problem on land?

(c) What other environmental problems result from our use of plastics?

In many ways, chemicals have dramatically improved the standard of living of many people around the world. They have found their way into almost all aspects of our lives (**Figure 2**). As a result, our lives are easier, or at least more convenient. Many chemicals carry an environmental cost, however, and some pose a health risk for people who work in industry.

While disposing of plastic waste is a serious problem, plastics are extremely versatile and useful. What are the advantages of using plastics, compared with using other materials? What other materials might be used instead of plastics? When are other materials better than plastics? What are industries doing to reduce the amounts of wastes and pollution they create, and how successful are their efforts? What responsibilities do individuals share in waste production? How can we, as individuals, reduce the waste that is produced by large industries?

Figure 2 Many parents could not imagine caring for a baby without the advantages of today's plastics.

C3.1 Activity | WASTE FROM MANUFACTURED PRODUCTS

When you buy a product, it is easy to not think about its production. This activity encourages you to think about the processes used to make a variety of products—both plastic and non-plastic.

1. In a small group, brainstorm a list of common, everyday manufactured products. Choose at least one product from each of the following categories: food, clothing, health, energy, communications, appliances, transportation.

2. For each product you chose, use a table like **Table 1** to summarize and analyze the sources of waste, from the raw material stage to the final used product. Use the following guidelines to help you.

   • Manufactured product: Identify and describe the product. Indicate where and, if possible, when it was made.

Table 1 Manufactured Product Analysis

Manufactured product	Sources of waste
Source(s) of raw materials	
Level(s) of processing	
Life span and final destination	
Wastes produced	
Reduce, reuse, recycle	

• Source(s) of raw materials: What raw materials were used to manufacture the product? For example, did the raw materials come from agriculture, fishery, forestry, petroleum, or mining?

• Level(s) of processing: Is the product a primary product (such as a fruit or vegetable), or has it undergone secondary and/or tertiary processing?

• Life span and final destination: Is the product consumed over the short, intermediate, or long term? Short term is measured in days, and long term is measured in years. Estimate how long the product should last under normal usage. What is the likely final destination of the product or its parts?

• Waste produced: Identify and briefly describe the potential sources of waste at all stages, from the raw materials to the final used product.

• Reduce, reuse, recycle: Can your consumption of the product be reduced? Can the product or its parts be recycled or reused?

3. Analyze the "Reduce, reuse, recycle" information for all the products you chose. Are there any trends? Make a general statement about your overall consumption of manufactured products.

The Plastics and Pulp and Paper Industries

Two huge industries that use vast quantities of chemicals during production are the plastics industry and the pulp and paper industry. The plastics industry uses organic chemicals from oil and gas as raw materials. The pulp and paper industry's raw material is mostly wood. The chemicals are used to process the wood into its many end products.

The Plastics Industry

Plastics are used in just about every aspect of modern life: in food packaging, in clothing, and even in school supplies. The use of plastic packaging has led to a food spoilage rate of less than 3% in Canada—one of the lowest rates in the world.

Plastics are formed from the polymerization (joining together) of small organic molecules derived from oil, natural gas, and/or coal. Plastics, which are a class of synthetic **polymers**, are primarily composed of long carbon and hydrogen chains. Some plastics also contain oxygen, nitrogen, fluorine, chlorine, silicon, phosphorus, and sulfur. For example, polyvinyl chloride (PVC) contains chlorine, nylon contains nitrogen, and Teflon contains fluorine.

The manufacture of plastics is a very efficient process, in terms of the amounts of raw materials used. The manufacture of all plastics in Canada consumes just 2% of this country's oil and natural gas resources, although moving oil and gas around can be a hazardous business (**Figure 3**).

The basic process that is used to make plastics is very simple. It involves combining small molecules into larger molecules, which are linked together to make strong, flexible materials. This process requires far less energy than the processes that are used to make most alternative materials, as you will see when you investigate the pulp and paper industry. Because plastics can be formed into very thin sheets, the mass of packaging materials can be significantly reduced, which reduces shipping costs.

Obtaining the Raw Materials

Hydrocarbons from crude oil are separated into molecules of different sizes. Very small molecules are generally needed for making plastics. Larger molecules can be heated in a process known as cracking, which breaks them down into smaller molecules. For example, octane, C_8H_{18}, and other large hydrocarbons are broken into smaller hydrocarbons such as ethene, C_2H_4, propene, C_3H_6, and butene, C_4H_8. These small molecules are called **monomers**.

Figure 3 In 1989, an oil tanker broke up and sank in Prince William Sound, off the coast of Alaska, releasing about 40 000 t of oil into the water. Years later, after a massive cleanup effort, the effects of the spill are still being monitored.

DID **YOU** KNOW?

Plastic Packaging Pluses
If other packaging materials (such as paper or cardboard) were used instead of plastics, the volume of packaging waste would increase by 250%, the weight of packaging waste would increase by over 400%, energy consumption would increase by over 200%, and overall packaging costs would rise by 210%.

Sometimes the monomers are reacted with other chemicals, such as chlorine, to form compounds with slightly different properties.

Reacting the Monomers

The monomers are reacted together to form long polymer chains. Different combinations of monomers yield different polymers. There are two classes of plastics: addition polymers and condensation polymers. Each class is produced using different raw materials and different reactions.

Addition polymers are formed through addition reactions of small monomer subunits that contain double or triple carbon–carbon bonds. These multiple bonds make the molecules fairly unstable and quite reactive. When the multiple bonds are broken and the molecules linked to other, similar molecules, the resulting compound is much more stable. This is why plastics last for such a long time and why they can be used to store so many different substances.

Polyethene, more commonly known as polyethylene, is a polymer that is formed through addition reactions of ethene molecules (**Figure 4**).

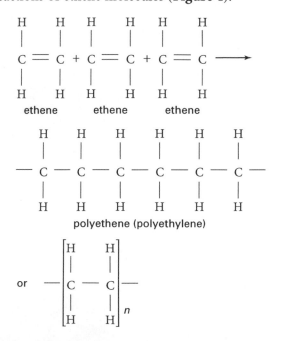

Figure 4 Polyethene is used for insulating wires and for making plastic containers.

Polypropylene (polypropene) is formed in the same way, with propene molecules as the monomers. Polypropylene is commonly used in carpet fibres, microwavable containers, and external medical splints and braces.

The long molecules in a polymer are held together by numerous **intermolecular forces**. These forces between molecules are much weaker than the permanent covalent bonds that occur within molecules. (They are also weaker than the ionic bonds that hold together ionic compounds.) These intermolecular forces are a result of the attraction between the temporary negative region of one molecule and the temporary positive region of a nearby molecule due to the random motion of electrons (**Figure 5**).

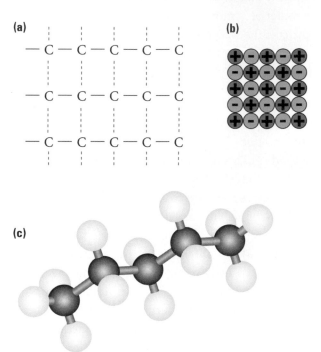

Figure 5 **(a)** Intermolecular forces act between separate molecules. **(b)** Ionic bonding holds together the ions of ionic compounds. **(c)** Covalent bonding holds together the atoms that make up a molecule.

These forces, which are still fairly weak, allow the chains to slide along each other, making the plastic flexible and stretchable. Some monomer units may, after forming a polymer, still contain reactive double bonds. This allows for the creation of **crosslinks** with adjacent polymers and, consequently, a more stable structure. The more crosslinks that form, the more rigid the plastic is.

Condensation polymers are formed by joining smaller molecules through the removal of a water molecule. A hydrogen atom, H, is taken from one molecule, and a hydroxide group, $-OH$, from another molecule. The two monomers join where the H and $-OH$ used to be. Polyamides and polyesters are examples of condensation polymers (**Figures 6** and **7**).

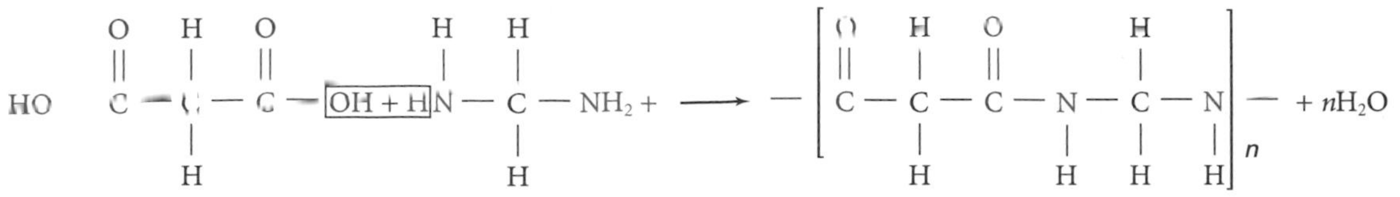

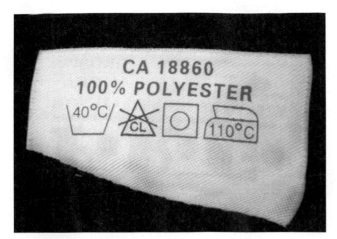

Figure 6 This is an example of a condensation reaction that forms a polyamide.

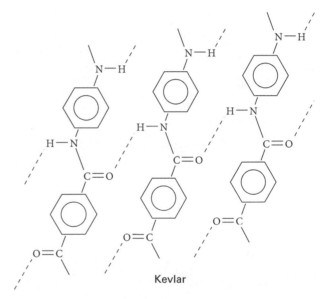

Figure 7 This label indicates that the garment is made of a synthetic polymer.

A form of strong intermolecular bonding, called **hydrogen bonding,** holds together condensation polymers. This bonding occurs because many condensation polymers contain $-OH$, $=O$, or $-NH$ groups. The oxygen and nitrogen molecules exert a very strong pull on nearby electrons, so the $-O$, $=O$, or $-N$ atoms often have a slight negative charge. This leaves a hydrogen atom on the same molecule with a slight positive charge. The positive areas of one molecule are attracted to the negative areas of another molecule. If the molecules have many negative $-OH$, $=O$, or $-NH$ groups and many

positive hydrogen atoms, multiple hydrogen bonds dramatically increase the strength of the polymer fibres.

Kevlar is a condensation polymer with a strong network of hydrogen bonds (**Figure 8**). It was created for its special properties: it is stronger than steel and heat-resistant, yet it is light enough to wear.

Kevlar

Figure 8 Kevlar is found in aircraft parts, sports equipment, protective clothing for firefighters, and bulletproof vests for police officers. The dashed lines represent hydrogen bonds. The many hydrogen bonds in this compound make it extremely strong.

C3.2 Activity | MODELS OF MONOMERS

Materials
molecular model kit

1. Build four or more models of ethene (**Figure 9**).

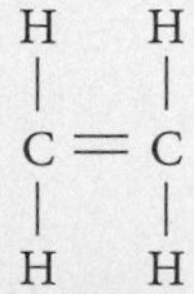

$$
\begin{array}{c}
H \quad\ H \\
| \qquad | \\
C = C \\
| \qquad | \\
H \quad\ H \\
\text{ethene}
\end{array}
$$

Figure 9 You will need at least four models of this structure.

2. Link the models together to form an addition polymer.

(a) What is the name of this polymer?

3. Design and construct a monomer that is capable of linking within a main polymer chain, and also linking across to a neighbouring polymer chain. Demonstrate your monomer's ability to form crosslinks.

The Final Touches

Other chemicals are sometimes added to polymers to modify their properties. These additives are used to alter and improve the mechanical, physical, or chemical properties of a plastic. They may also be used to protect the plastic from the degrading effects of light, heat, or bacteria, or to change the appearance of the plastic.

Many polymers are shaped in moulds (**Figure 10**). Other polymers are heated and drawn out into long threads, in a process called extrusion (**Figure 11**). Extrusion causes the polymer chains to orient themselves lengthwise along the direction of the stretch. Crosslinks are formed between the chains, giving the fibres added strength. The fibres may be used to make fabrics for clothing or strands of strong, rot-resistant rope.

Figure 10 Melted plastic is poured into or over a mould and allowed to cool, taking the shape of the mould.

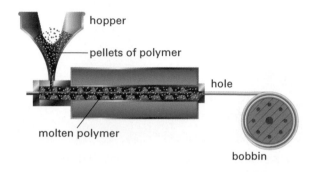

Figure 11 To make a polymer into a fibre, the polymer must first be heated and melted. The molten polymer is then placed in a pressurized container and forced through a small hole to produce a long strand, which is then stretched.

C3.3 Activity CLASSIFYING PLASTICS >

In recent times, Canadians have begun throwing away massive quantities of plastics. To reduce the quantities of plastics going to landfill sites, communities are starting to implement recycling programs. Because different types of plastics are made of different components, effective recycling requires the different types of plastics to be identified and separated. To help with the identification, the Society of the Plastics Industry, Inc. (SPI) established an identification coding system (**Figure 12**) in 1988.

Figure 12 The triangular symbol on a plastic container allows you to identify the kind of plastic from which it was made.

The different composition, bonding, and structure of different plastics can be used to identify them. In this activity, you will differentiate among several samples of unknown plastics by their density (by placing them in liquids of different densities), flame colour (a green flame indicates chlorine), solubility in acetone, and resistance to heating. You will then use your results to identify the plastics and their SPI codes.

Question
What is the SPI code for each of the six unknown plastic samples?

Materials
eye protection
lab apron
1 cm by 1 cm samples (unknown) of the six
    categories of plastics, each cut into an
    identifiable shape

Materials (continued)

three 250 mL beakers
water
glass stirring rod
tongs
paper towel
60 g 2-propanol (rubbing alcohol)
electronic balance or triple-beam balance
corn oil
15 cm copper or nichrome wire
cork or rubber stopper
Bunsen burner
50 mL nail polish remover, containing acetone
100-mL beaker
utility stand with clamp
hot plate

Procedure

Part 1: Testing for Density

1. Put on your eye protection and lab apron.

2. Obtain one sample of each of the six unknown plastics.

3. Place all six samples in a 250-mL beaker that contains 100 mL of water, and stir with a stirring rod. Allow the samples to settle. Use tongs to separate the samples that float from the samples that sink. Dry each sample with a paper towel.

4. Prepare an alcohol solution by measuring 60 g of 2-propanol in a 250-mL beaker and adding water to make a total of 100 g. Mix well.

    2-propanol is highly flammable, so it must be kept well away from open flames.

5. Take any samples that floated in the water, and place them in the alcohol solution. Stir, and then allow the samples to settle. Use tongs to separate the samples that float from the samples that sink. Dry each sample with a paper towel.

6. Take any samples that floated in the alcohol solution, and place them in a 250-mL beaker that contains 100 mL of corn oil. Stir, and then allow the samples to settle for a few minutes. Note any samples that sink.

Part 2: Testing for Flame Colour (Teacher Demonstration)

 The fumes that are produced by burning plastic may be toxic, so the flame tests will be carried out in a fume hood by your teacher.

7. Your teacher will use the samples that sank in water and test each one for flame colour in a fume hood. Your teacher will touch the hot end of the copper wire to each sample so that a small amount melts and attaches to the wire. Your teacher will then hold the melted sample in a flame. Record the colour of the flame.

Part 3: Testing with Acetone

8. Ensure that all open flames are extinguished. Obtain a fresh sample of any plastic that did not burn with a green flame in step 6. Place each of these fresh samples in a 100-mL beaker that contains 50 mL of nail polish remover (acetone solution). Watch the sample for a few minutes, and note any colour change. Remove the sample with tongs, and test it for increased softness.

    Acetone is highly flammable and must be kept well away from open flames. Use only in a well-ventilated area.

Part 4: Testing for Resistance to Melting

9. Place 125 mL of water in a 250-mL beaker. Use a utility stand and clamp to support the beaker on a hot plate (**Figure 13**). Heat the water until it comes to a rolling boil.

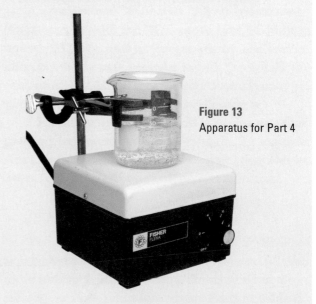

Figure 13
Apparatus for Part 4

Use tongs to test each sample for softness. Then place any sample that did not burn with a green flame in step 6 into the boiling water. Keep the water at a boil for a few minutes. Note any change in the shape and softness of the sample.

10. Dispose of the waste materials as directed by your teacher.

(a) Copy **Table 2** into your notebook, and complete it with your own observations.

Analysis

(b) From your observations in **Table 2** and the flowchart in **Figure 14**, identify and suggest SPI codes for each of the six samples you tested. Your teacher will provide you with a table that gives the properties and end products of plastics, identified by their SPI codes.

Evaluation

(c) Obtain the actual SPI codes for each sample from your teacher, and evaluate the reliability of your results.

(d) Suggest any changes to the Procedure that would improve the reliability of your results.

Synthesis

(e) Identify some environmental issues related to the growing use of plastics, such as the consumption of fossil fuels and the disposal of waste plastics. Suggest alternative materials that could be used instead of synthetic polymers such as polyester fabrics, plastic cutlery, Styrofoam cups, and disposable diapers.

(f) Recycling only works if the "raw" material, such as plastic, is made into a product and used again. Research at least three products that are made with recycled plastics. Create a table that includes the source of "raw" material, the treatment it receives, and the cost per kilogram to make the new product.

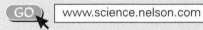
GO   www.science.nelson.com

(g) What programs are available for recycling plastics in your community? To what extent do you and your family recycle plastics?

Table 2 Summary of Observations

Sample tested	Density	Flame colour	Acetone	Melting
example	sinks in water	no green flame	no increased softness	increased softness
1				
2				

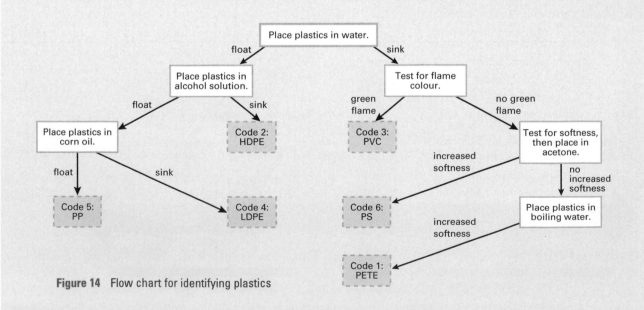

Figure 14 Flow chart for identifying plastics

Disposal of Plastics

While using plastics for packaging has tremendous advantages, there is still the issue of disposal. There are several options for dealing with plastics once they have reached the end of their useful life. Some of these options are more acceptable than others.

Improper Disposal: Pollution

Despite the low weight and volume of plastics, and our ability to recycle many of them, much of the plastics that are produced end up in the environment. As mentioned earlier, waste plastics are unslightly, damage habitat, and can be deadly to wildlife when ingested. Improper and careless disposal has helped to give plastics a bad name. Can this, however, be seen as a social problem requiring public education, rather than a problem with the plastics themselves?

Responsible Disposal

What happens to all the plastic packaging when it is removed (**Figure 15**)? The Canadian plastics industry is aware of the problems associated with the disposal of its products. The Environment and Plastics Industry Council is an industry initiative that focuses on reducing the amount of plastics entering the waste stream. They believe in a five-part integrated approach.

Figure 15 Perhaps the use of plastics for packaging is getting out of hand.

- *Making less (or using less)*: Thanks to thinner, stronger plastics, pop bottles and grocery bags now contain far less plastic than they did in the past. Thinner plastic products have led to a 40 000 000-kg decrease in the amount of plastics produced and a savings of 350 000 barrels of oil each year in Canada alone, compared to the amounts used 20 years ago.

- *Reuse*: Shipping crates for soft drinks, dairy products, and bakery goods are examples of products that are being designed for long-term use.
- *Recyling*: Household plastic recycling is becoming increasingly common, as the popularity of "blue box" programs increases across the country. The plastics industry has always recycled the plastic scraps that are produced during the manufacturing process, but now more "used" plastics can be recycled. The plastic bottles that we recycle are crushed, chopped into flakes, and eventually spun into fibres (fibrefill). These fibres are used to make clothing and home products, such as carpeting.

As well, there is an increasing demand for plastic lumber (**Figure 16**). Several companies are now using milk jugs, shopping bags, reclaimed wood, and industrial stretch wrap to make a lumber substitute.

Figure 16 Recycled plastic and wood waste can be combined to produce an attractive alternative to traditional lumber.

Beside the Don Valley Parkway in Toronto is a very unusual use of recycled plastics. They have been made into a soil substitute and are used in an art structure called *The Elevated Wetlands* (**Figure 17**).

- *Resource recovery*: Eventually, no matter how effectively plastics are used and reused, some of them will reach the end of their useful life and need to be disposed of. There are two options left: resource

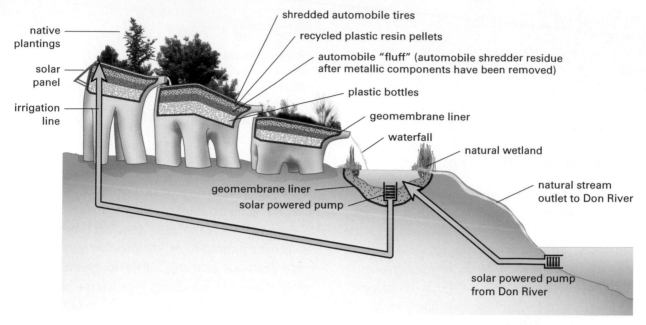

Figure 17 *The Elevated Wetlands* is a series of plastic structures that contain recycled plastics as a soil substitute. Polluted water, piped up from the nearby Don River, is purified as it flows through *The Elevated Wetlands* and returns to the river much cleaner than before.

recovery or retention in landfills. Resource recovery is probably the most controversial method of waste management, using plastics as a fuel to produce usable energy. This process could reduce the amount of plastics ending up in landfills by up to 90%, but there is a real concern about the environmental impact of the incinerators. While new and improved incinerators are being designed, there is still fear that they could release harmful chemicals. This concern has kept resource recovery from being widely used.

• *Retention in landfills:* The final destination for used plastics is a landfill. Plastics are very stable, however. Once they enter a landfill, they stay there, essentially unchanged, for decades or centuries. With the increasing difficulty in finding landfill space that is acceptable to everyone, this is not a desirable option.

Biodegradable Plastics

The use of **biodegradable plastics** (plastics that break down to some extent due to microbial action) has slightly decreased the amount of waste plastics entering landfill sites or polluting the environment. Some of these special polymers are made from a mixture of plant-based compounds and "regular" plastics. They are the same as conventional plastics in almost every way, except that they do not last as long. Although biodegradable plastic products only make up 10 to 20% of the plastics in use at the present time, they have some interesting and important uses:

• medical and dental implants (such as sutures, staples, pins, clips, and screws), and devices that are designed to release a measured dose of medicine slowly
• hospital laundry bags and hamper liners that break down completely during the hot washing and disinfection process
• fabrics that are used as industrial wipes, filters, and geotextiles for erosion control and landscaping
• personal hygiene products, such as tampon applicators and the plastic liner of disposable diapers
• agricultural products, such as agricultural mulch films, seeding strips and tapes, and fertilizer bags
• composting bags for yard waste and food scraps
• single-use food-service items, such as plastic cups, straws, plates and cutlery, collected in compostable plastic bags

While biodegradable plastic containers at first seemed to be a space-saver in landfill sites, the early products were not a big advantage. The little shreds of plastic that remain take up almost the same space as non-biodegradable plastics. More recent developments, involving the use of plant starches for 100% of the plastics, seem to be more promising.

Why is littering so widespread? A glance at any local roadside, schoolyard, or park is likely to show discarded water bottles, broken sunglasses, the tops from disposable coffee cups, and the wrappers from cigarette packages (**Figure 18**). What can you do to reduce the amount of litter that is dropped in your community?

(a) In a group, brainstorm how you might reduce the amount of litter dropped in a certain area of your community.

(b) Conduct research (perhaps an observational study or a survey) to help you decide on a strategy. Your strategy might include a news conference, a commercial, or an information pamphlet for the community.

(c) Carry out your strategy.

(d) Follow the success of your strategy. Did it help to reduce the amount of littering? Why or why not?

Figure 18 Plastics are one of the worst types of litter because they do not break down.

The Pulp and Paper Industry

Although the explosion of computer technology was accompanied by a call for "the paperless office," society's reliance on paper seems to be more entrenched than ever. Pulp and paper manufacturing is one of the world's largest industries, and Canada is one of the world's largest producers. In 1991 alone, Canada shipped over 29 million tonnes of pulp and paper products.

The Paper-Making Process

The forest products industry, as a whole, is a very heavy user of energy. In the mid-1990s, the manufacture of pulp and paper consumed about 20 PJ of energy (1 PJ = 1×10^{15} J). About half of this energy is produced by burning wood residue and sawdust—a practice that has a considerable environmental impact.

Almost all the paper that is made in Canada comes from the processing of wood (**Figure 19**): whole trees, waste from sawmills, and recycled paper. Wood is essentially cellulose fibres (natural polymers made up of many glucose monomers) that are held together by a glue-like substance called lignin. Paper makers only need the cellulose fibres.

There are two widely used processes for preparing pulp to make paper: chemical pulping and mechanical pulping.

Chemical Pulping

There are two main types of chemical pulping. The oldest type is the sulfite process, which uses sulfur dioxide in the wood digester. Sulfur dioxide is an acid gas that is very toxic and irritates the mucous membranes of the eyes, nose, and throat. When released into the atmosphere, sulfur dioxide acts as a greenhouse gas and contributes to global warming. Most sulfite mills produce pulp for newsprint manufacturing.

In the late 1970s, **Kraft pulping** was developed in Germany. (The word "Kraft" comes from the German word for "strong.") In Kraft pulping, a basic solution of sodium sulfide is added to a mixture of water and wood chips. Sulfur is the active agent that separates the fibre from the rest of the material in the wood chips. Unfortunately, Kraft pulping yields less than 50% of the tree for use in the paper-making process. One advantage of Kraft pulping is that it can use pine trees for pulp, unlike the sulfite process.

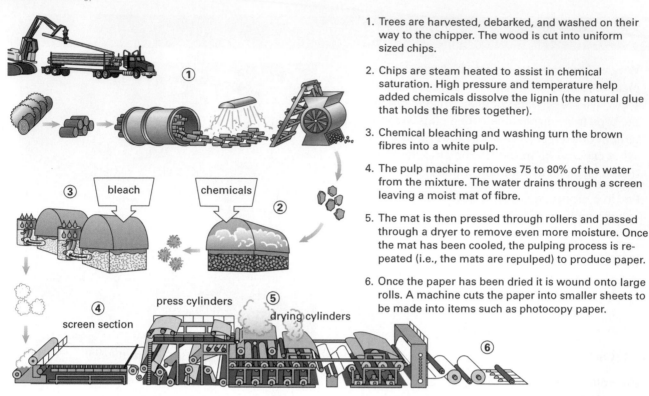

1. Trees are harvested, debarked, and washed on their way to the chipper. The wood is cut into uniform sized chips.

2. Chips are steam heated to assist in chemical saturation. High pressure and temperature help added chemicals dissolve the lignin (the natural glue that holds the fibres together).

3. Chemical bleaching and washing turn the brown fibres into a white pulp.

4. The pulp machine removes 75 to 80% of the water from the mixture. The water drains through a screen leaving a moist mat of fibre.

5. The mat is then pressed through rollers and passed through a dryer to remove even more moisture. Once the mat has been cooled, the pulping process is repeated (i.e., the mats are repulped) to produce paper.

6. Once the paper has been dried it is wound onto large rolls. A machine cuts the paper into smaller sheets to be made into items such as photocopy paper.

Figure 19 The pulp and paper process

Another advantage is that up to 98% of the pulping chemicals can be recycled within the facility. Kraft pulping produces exceptionally strong, dark fibres. Some of these fibres are used as they are, and some are bleached with chlorine compounds or other chemicals.

Mechanical Pulping

In **mechanical pulping**, the trees are physically ground down with grindstones while steam is pumped into the system. Mechanical pulping yields up to 90% of the tree's mass but uses a large amount of water and energy. The resulting fibres are lighter in colour than the fibres produced in Kraft pulping, and they can be whitened with non-chlorine compounds, such as hydrogen peroxide, $H_2O_{2(aq)}$. The fibres are weaker, however, and tend to discolour over time. For these reasons, they are used to make newsprint.

Bleaching

During the bleaching process, the pulp goes through three to five stages of bleaching and washing, depending on the desired whiteness of the finished stock. Because of the multiple washes, the bleaching process uses a lot of water.

In the past, elemental chlorine, $Cl_{2(g)}$, was the most commonly used bleach for whitening the wood pulp. As the chlorine reacted with the pulp, however, many complex chemicals were formed. Perhaps the most notorious of these chemicals was dioxin—one of the most carcinogenic substances known. Studies of fish populations downstream of North American pulp mills showed dangerously high levels of dioxin in fish tissue, leading to bans on the human consumption of these fish. Fortunately, research has revealed several economically viable alternatives to elemental chlorine. Three of these alternatives are described below.

- **Elemental chlorine free** (ECF) bleaching is a process in which pulp is bleached without elemental chlorine gas. This process uses chlorine compounds such as chlorine dioxide, $ClO_{2(g)}$, however some elemental chlorine is still found in chlorine dioxide mills. Proponents of ECF point out that the trees themselves contain chlorine, so it is not possible for a process to be 100% chlorine free. While the production of toxic byproducts is reduced by using ECF, the problem is not eliminated.

- **Totally chlorine free** (TCF) bleaching uses virgin (new) pulp, bleached without any chlorine, either in the elemental form or in compounds. Whitening of the fibres is accomplished by oxidation, using ozone and hydrogen peroxide. As mentioned above, however, trace amounts of naturally occurring chlorine may be present

- **Process chlorine free (PCF)** bleaching is a recycling process that uses no chlorine compounds. The original paper may, however, have been bleached with chlorine. Only when no virgin pulp is ever bleached with chlorine will PCF products be entirely chlorine free. PCF products are considered to be the most environmentally friendly because they combine the benefits of recycling with the benefits of oxygen-based (rather than chlorine-based) bleaching.

The use of chlorine has largely been replaced, in both North America and Europe, with less toxic processes such as these three alternatives. In Canada, the release of dioxins and related compounds from pulping facilities has been almost totally eliminated since 1997.

Recycling in Canada

For decades recycled paper from cities and towns, and wood residues (such as sawdust, wood chips, and shavings from lumber operations) have been used as sources of fibre for paper manufacturing. In fact, recycling in Canada is almost 200 years old. Used linen and cotton rags were collected in Montreal and Quebec City in 1805 and shipped to Canada's first paper mill in St. Andrews, Quebec where they were used to make newsprint and wrapping paper.

The paper industry today produces more products from recycled materials because of the availability of such materials and economic considerations.

Using recycled materials also creates 73% less air pollution than using virgin fibres.

Currently, just over 10% of paper packaging made in Canada is made from freshly-cut trees; almost 90% of all paper-based packaging (such as corrugated boxes or containerboard, folding cartons or boxboard, and Kraft paper bags) is now made from recycled fibres or wood residues. **Table 3** shows the national average percentages for the sources of fibres by packaging materials. Approximately 63% of all such packaging shipped domestically was produced from recycled fibres.

Table 3 Sources of Fibres for Canadian Paper Packaging (Average Percentages)

Source	Containerboard	Boxboard	Kraft papers
recycled fibre	58	92	19
wood residues	29	7	36
logs	13	1	45

Source: http://www.ppec-paper.com

C3.5 Investigation — WHAT FACTORS DETERMINE PAPER QUALITY? >

Many of the paper products you use today are made from recycled paper. You can use a similar process to make paper at home or in the laboratory (**Figure 20**).

The materials required and the general steps for making paper are given below. You can vary the materials and steps, however, depending on the resources that are available.

Inquiry Skills

- Questioning
- Hypothesizing
- Predicting
- Planning
- Conducting
- Recording
- Analyzing
- Evaluating
- Communicating

Materials
fibre source (such as newspaper, used writing paper, or dryer lint)

warm water
blender or food processor
plastic spatula
large tray or pan
framed screen (such as a fly screen or pantyhose)
rolling pin or another tool for rolling
oven or iron (optional)

Figure 20 Paper can be made using ordinary materials and equipment.

General Steps for Making Paper
- Put on your eye protection and lab apron.
- Shred or tear used paper or another fibre source into small pieces.
- Soak the fibre-source pieces until they are soggy.
- Put the fibre-source pieces in the blender (one-half to one-third full), and add water (about two-thirds full). Put the lid on the blender. Blend the mixture to make pulp.

 Do not put your fingers in the blender. The blades are very sharp.

- Pour the pulp mixture into the tray. Use the plastic spatula to scrape out the pulp.
- Submerge the screen into the pulp mixture. Lift out the screen, keeping it horizontal.
- Allow the water to drain. Use the rolling pin to remove excess water from the screen. Carefully peel the sheet of paper from the screen.
- Dry the paper completely by hanging it up, placing it in a warm oven, and/or ironing it using a medium setting on the iron.

In paper making, the quality of the finished product is determined by a number of factors that can be controlled. In this investigation, you will define one or more characteristics of the paper you want to produce and experiment to determine which factors produce the best quality paper with these characteristics.

Procedure
1. Determine one or more characteristics that you want your paper to have. Consider characteristics such as whiteness, brightness, strength, smoothness, softness, rigidity, and flexibility.

2. Establish a criterion (or criteria) to measure your chosen characteristics as objectively as possible.

3. Identify factors that could potentially affect the characteristics you have identified. Depending on the characteristics, these factors might include
   - the fibre source
   - the proportion of different fibres in the pulp mixture
   - the amount of water or the thickness of the pulp mixture
   - the temperature of the water
   - the time of the pulping process
   - the type and repetition of the bleaching process
   - additives (such as starch, glue, and dye)
   - the pressure of the rolling process
   - the temperature of the drying process
   - the presence or absence of contaminants

 Chlorine (household) bleach is corrosive. It can burn skin and cause eye damage. Wear eye protection, a lab apron, and gloves when handling chlorine bleach.

Feel free to identify any other factors that you think might affect the quality of the paper.

(a) Write a question that you will attempt to answer in this investigation. Your question should relate the factor in the paper-making process to the characteristics of the paper. It should be written in the form "How does [the independent variable] affect [the dependent variable]?"

(b) Create a hypothesis that explains why the factors you have chosen will affect the characteristics of the paper.

(c) Make a prediction about how variation of the factors will affect the characteristics of the paper.

(d) Design an experiment to determine how the factors you identified in step 3 will affect the characteristics you identified in step 1. Identify the dependent and independent variables, as well as the variables that should be controlled.

(e) Decide on the steps you will use by clearly defining and refining the general steps provided. Write a detailed procedure for your experimental design. Include a list of required materials, and note all appropriate safety precautions.

4. Do not continue until you have obtained your teacher's approval. When you have your teacher's approval, carry out your experiment and carefully record your observations in an appropriate table. Remember to save your paper products as evidence.

(f) Describe the criteria you used to measure each characteristic of your paper. For example, if you chose to look at strength, how will you objectively measure and compare the strength of the different papers?

Analysis

(g) Summarize the observations you recorded in your table.

(h) Based on your observations, write a conclusion that answers your question in (a).

Evaluation

(i) Was your prediction correct?

(j) Was your hypothesis supported by your observations? What evidence did you use to support or reject your hypothesis?

(k) Evaluate your observations and the procedure you used. Identify any potential flaws in your experimental design and procedure, and suggest possible improvements.

(l) Suggest other possible hypotheses that might explain your observations.

Synthesis

(m) Based on your knowledge of the paper-making process and your experiment, how might the quality of the paper produced influence a mill's impact on the environment?

✔ Check Your Understanding

1. What type of bonds must be present in the monomer units in order to form addition polymers?

2. Why are polymers more chemically stable than their monomer units?

3. Draw diagrams to show how each hydrocarbon would form an addition polymer.

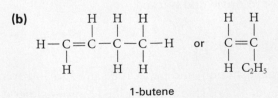

(a) chloroethene

(b) 1-butene

4. What atoms must be present in the monomers of a condensation polymer?

5. List the advantages and disadvantages of using plastic packaging over using cardboard.

6. Using an example, explain how the properties of a synthetic polymer are related to its structure.

7. (a) Suggest four strategies that consumers could use to reduce the amount of plastics going to landfill sites.
   (b) Which, if any, of these strategies is not environmentally friendly?

8. The Environment and Plastics Industry Council proposes incinerating plastics to produce energy. What is a potential drawback to this proposal?

9. Briefly describe the steps that are involved in industrial paper making.

10. Compare and contrast the two most widely used pulping processes. Which process would you consider to be more environmentally friendly? Explain your choice.

Paying for Pulp and Paper Pollution

The pulp and paper industry has long been an environmental concern, from the logging of trees to the use of chemicals that make their way back into the environment as a result of the paper-making process. These chemicals are released through discharge pipes into the water, from chimneys into the air, and as truckloads of solid waste (**Figure 21**).

Figure 21 Pulp and paper mills invariably have a huge effect on the environment.

Water Pollution

Paper mills are huge consumers of water. This consumption can lead to low water levels in nearby waterways. The returned water may cause three types of pollution:

- **Thermal pollution:** This occurs when the water returning to the rivers is warm. Warmer water contains less dissolved oxygen than cooler water. Increased temperatures affect the species of plants and animals that can survive in the water.
- **Physical pollution:** The release of suspended solids into the water blocks the light, and so prevents plants from photosynthesizing and producing oxygen.
- **Chemical pollution:** This causes several problems. Organic matter in the wastewater feeds bacteria, which quickly multiply and use up much of the oxygen in the water. This has negative effects on fish and other organisms that also require oxygen from the water. Any nitrates or phosphates that are dissolved in the wastewater act as fertilizers for algae and other aquatic plants, resulting in an algal bloom that dies off and, in decomposing, reduces the amount of oxygen available to other organisms. Furthermore, in the past, contaminants including dioxins were released in the wastewater. These contaminants build up in the fish and make them unsafe for human consumption.

Studies have shown a decrease in the reproductive rates of zooplankton, invertebrates, and shellfish—all important food sources for local fish—downstream from the discharge pipes of paper mills. Studies have also shown evidence of genetic and immune system damage in fish populations. Switching from chlorine bleaching significantly improves the quality of water downstream and lowers the dioxin content of resident fish. Most Canadian mills have made this switch.

Air Pollution

Pulp and paper mills also produce a significant amount of air pollution, including carbon dioxide (a greenhouse gas that contributes to global warming), fine particulates, and dangerous carcinogens (such as dioxins and furans). In 1995, Canadian pulp and paper mills released about 77 000 t of sulfur oxides (a gas that contributes to acid precipitation). In the same year, 90 000 t of fine particulates were released. Environmental groups are concerned that this is only part of the story, since many emissions are not recorded and tracked.

Solid Waste

Canadian pulp and paper mills produce, on average, about 40 t of sludge (also called biosolids) per day. The sludge is generally burned, which releases pollutants into the air, or shipped to a landfill, where leaching can result in soil and water pollution. Many companies are trying to find ways to market the biosolids as fertilizer, but so far this has met with limited interest. Extensive testing would be needed to confirm that the biosolids are safe to use.

Pollution Control Regulations

While pulp and paper manufacturing is one of the world's largest industries, it has also historically been one of the world's worst polluters. In fact, it is the third most polluting industry in North America. After years of having very few laws governing the operation of pulp and paper mills, there are now specific federal regulations to help reduce the amount of pollution they create. In 1992, the Pulp and Paper Effluent Regulations and the Pulp and Paper Defoamer and Wood Chips Regulations were added to the Canadian Environmental Protection Act. One of the aims of these regulations was to reduce the amount of dioxins and furans released by pulp mills, largely as a result of using elemental chlorine as a bleach. Regulations were also added to the Fisheries Act to reduce the total suspended solids (TSS) entering the environment and to monitor the amount of organic matter released by pulp and paper mills into receiving waterways.

In response to these regulations, the Canadian pulp and paper industry has almost completely replaced elemental chlorine with other bleaching agents. In addition, the wastewater (effluent) from paper mills is now treated to remove debris and organic matter, and allowed to cool before being returned to the environment (**Figure 22**).

The reduction in pollution has been dramatic. As of 2003, the following results have been reported:

- There has been a 99% reduction in the formation of furans and dioxins from paper processing since 1988.
- The reduced pollution has resulted in the lifting of fin fish consumption advisories and the reopening of half of the local shellfishery areas.
- Carbon dioxide emissions have decreased by 28% from 1990 levels.
- There has been a 94% reduction in the amount of organic materials and a 70% reduction in the amount of total suspended solids released into the water.
- Initiatives by the pulp and paper industry have resulted in a 30% reduction in water consumption since 1989 (**Figure 23**).

Figure 22 Wastewater cools in large tanks before being returned to local waterways.

Figure 23 Modern paper mills are significantly cleaner than those built twenty or more years ago. The pulp and paper industry has made huge strides in reducing pollution.

Explore *an* Issue

Should Everybody Pay for Paper Pollution?

When we consume goods and services, we indirectly contribute to the pollution and wastes that the industries produce. Some people argue that those who consume the most goods and services should also contribute most to preventing and cleaning up the pollution caused by manufacturing the goods and providing the services—a "polluter pay" system. So, can a pollution tax on paper be justified?

1. Imagine that you are a member of a federal government task force, created to study the pollution problem associated with the pulp and paper industry and to make recommendations. The task force includes the following members:
   - a representative from each of Environment Canada, Natural Resources Canada, and Industry Canada
   - two representatives of the pulp and paper industry
   - two representatives of consumer advocacy groups
   - two representatives of environmental advocacy groups

2. Each member of your group will assume the role of one of the members of the task force. Elect someone to be a chairperson, a recorder, and any other role that you consider important.

3. Depending on whether you accept or reject the idea of a "polluter pay" system, complete *one* of the following tasks. As a group, decide which of the two tasks you will complete.

Task 1

Since you accept the idea of a "polluter pay" system, the mission of your task force is to design a taxation plan aimed at financing the prevention and cleanup of pollution from the pulp and paper industry.

4. Use the Internet and other resources to research the position of the government department or organization that you represent. Summarize the position in point form and share it with your group.

 www.science.nelson.com

Decision-Making Skills

- ● Define the Issue
- ● Identify Alternatives
- ● Research
- ● Analyze the Issue
- ● Defend a Decision
- ● Evaluate

5. As a group, propose a suitable paper tax structure based on the "polluter pay" system.

6. Design a plan that includes the projected revenue from your tax structure, the proposed strategies aimed at addressing the pollution problems, and how the funds collected by your tax will be allocated to the various strategies.

Task 2

Since you do not accept the idea of a "polluter pay" system, the mission of your task force is to propose an alternative solution to the problem. In your solution, you must consider the following criteria:

- How will your solution be funded? No additional taxation is permitted, and federal government funding is limited to existing budgets.
- Implementation of your solution must be achievable over the next 10 years.
- Your solution may be a single strategy or a combination of several strategies.
- Your solution may include existing technologies or technologies that are currently being developed.

7. Use the Internet and other resources to research a possible strategy that would be acceptable to the government department or organization that you represent. Summarize the strategy in two paragraphs, and present it to your group.

 www.science.nelson.com

8. As a group, evaluate each of the proposed strategies. Accept or reject each strategy as part of the overall solution. Justify your decision to accept or reject each strategy.

9. Prepare a report that presents the final solution proposed by your task force. The report does not have to represent the position of every member of your task force, but it should represent a consensus.

C3 SUMMARY & ASSESSMENT

SUMMARY

- Pollution of the oceans by carelessly discarded plastic is a serious threat to wildlife.
- Plastics are manufactured by a process called polymerization. In this process, small hydrocarbon monomers (extracted from crude oil) are joined together to create polymers.
- Addition polymers are formed by joining monomers that contain double or triple carbon bonds.
- Condensation polymers are formed by joining monomers through the removal of hydrogen and oxygen atoms, which combine to form water molecules.
- The plastics industry uses only 2% of Canada's annual oil and natural gas consumption.
- Polymer molecules are held together by intermolecular forces (including hydrogen bonding), and through the formation of crosslinks.
- Plastics can be identified by density, flame colour, softening in various solvents, and heat resistance.
- Plastics are very stable, which is both an advantage (they can be used for many different purposes) and a disadvantage (they do not break down easily). Strategies to reduce the amount of waste include using less plastic per product, reusing products, recycling used plastics into different products, developing biodegradable plastics, incinerating used plastics to produce energy, and sending plastics to landfill sites.
- Canada is one of the world's largest producers of pulp and paper.

- There are two main processes for preparing pulp to make paper: chemical pulping and mechanical pulping. There are two main types of chemical pulping: the sulfite process and Kraft pulping. Mechanical pulping uses grindstones to grind up the wood chips into usable fibres.
- Pulp and paper mills cause thermal, physical (sediments), and chemical pollution in nearby waterways. They release carbon dioxide, fine particulates, and carcinogens into the air. The sludge they produce poses a disposal challenge. Recent legislation has tightened environmental standards, resulting in cleaner water, healthier fish, and reduced carbon dioxide emissions.
- More environmentally friendly strategies for bleaching are now ECF, TCF, and PCF bleaching.

Key Terms

plastic	**mechanical pulping**
polymer	**elemental chlorine**
monomer	**free (ECF)**
addition polymer	**totally chlorine**
intermolecular force	**free (TCF)**
crosslinks	**process chlorine**
condensation polymer	**free (PCF)**
hydrogen bonding	**thermal pollution**
biodegradable plastic	**physical pollution**
Kraft pulping	**chemical pollution**

ASSESSMENT

Understanding Concepts

1. **(a)** Draw diagrams to show how butene monomers join to form a polymer. Use at least three 2-butene monomers in your example (**Figure 24**).

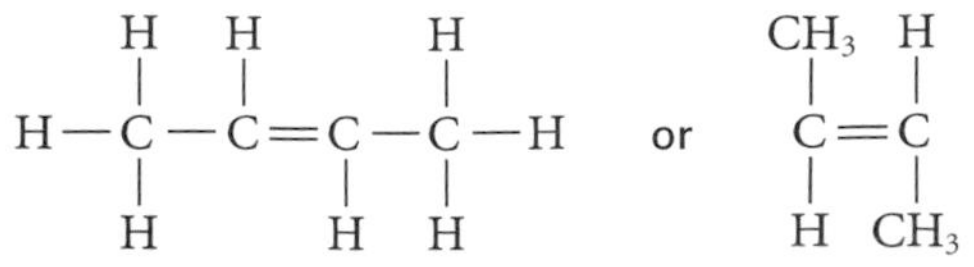

Figure 24

2-butene

(b) What type of polymer is formed by the reaction in **(a)**?

2. **Figure 25** on the next page shows the reaction between di-ethanoic acid and 1,2-ethanediol.
   (a) Draw a diagram to show how these monomers form part of a polymer.
   (b) What kind of reaction is this?
   (c) What other product is formed?
   (d) What kinds of forces might form between the molecules in the polymer?

HO OCCH₂CH₂CO OH + H OCH₂CH₂O H +HO OCCH₂CH₂CO OH $\longrightarrow$ _____ + _____

di-ethanoic acid   1,2-ethanediol

Figure 25

3. What are some of the advantages of using plastics for packaging over using cardboard or other materials?

4. Describe the options for dealing with plastics once they have reached the end of their useful life.

5. Outline the steps involved in making paper.

6. List at least three environmental concerns associated with the pulp and paper industry.

7. Describe the differences between Kraft pulping and mechanical pulping. Give one advantage and one disadvantage of each process.

8. Briefly describe how wastewater (effluent) from pulp and paper mills is treated.

9. **(a)** What are biosolids?
   (b) What is one potential use for biosolids?
   (c) What are the concerns about using biosolids?

10. Using the Key Terms listed on page 195, create a concept map for this topic. Indicate connections between related terms.

Applying Inquiry Skills

11. Use a molecular model kit to illustrate why plastics are generally solid, while the monomers they are made from are gases or liquids.

Making Connections

12. Contact your local recycling organization and find out which plastics can be recycled in your area. Is there any other option for the plastics that cannot be recycled, besides sending them to a landfill?

13. Research the use and effectiveness of biodegradable plastics. Select a product for which a biodegradable plastic would be appropriate. Create a marketing piece (AV presentation, brochure, etc.) to pitch your biodegradable product to a potential customer.

 www.science.nelson.com

14. **(a)** What are some of the reasons for the increased use of paper in our current "electronic age"?
    (b) Using a medium other than paper, create a table outlining steps that could be taken, both by individuals and by society to reduce the reliance on paper.

15. Investigate at least two pulp and paper companies (one in Canada and one outside North America) to see what actions they have taken to reduce their impact on the environment. Present your findings in a medium of your choice.

 www.science.nelson.com

16. Compare the efficiency of plastics production with the efficiency of paper production.

17. The plastics industry and pulp and paper industry are not the only industries that cause pollution. Imagine that you are the vice president of a mining company. Prepare a multi-media report for a community meeting about how your company is changing its practices to reduce the various types of pollution that it currently produces.

 www.science.nelson.com

18. In 1984 a leak of methyl isocyanate from Union Carbide's manufacturing facility in Bhopal, India, killed 3800 people and disabled nearly 3000 others. Research this disaster, including what caused it and what has been done since to avoid a similar incident. Present your findings in the format of your choice.

 www.science.nelson.com

Chemicals *in the* Environment: BALANCING COSTS *and* BENEFITS

Derrik and Damian take Damian's dog, Oliver, for a walk in the local park almost every day. They know that both they and Oliver benefit from the exercise, but they sometimes wonder whether the park is a healthy place for Oliver to play. In the winter, the salt on the path gets in his paws and makes him limp. They need to wash off the salt when they get home, before Oliver can lick it off.

In the spring, Oliver loves running on the new grass. Sometimes, however, the grass has warning signs: "Keep off. Pesticides in use." The boys wonder how safe these chemicals are, if people are not allowed to walk on the grass.

As spring turns into summer, the park becomes a busy place. The gardens are in full bloom, boosted by regular applications of fertilizer. Children and dogs play on the lush green grass. Oliver is attracted to the smell of food grilling on the charcoal-burning barbecues and to the children playing on the newly painted swing sets. Everyone is enjoying the fresh air (**Figure 1**). Not many people stop to wonder, as Derrik does, why some of the trees appear to be dying. He has heard that acid rain is killing trees in parts of Canada, and is concerned that this might be the problem here.

Figure 1 Even a place as apparently clean as this park experiences the effects of chemicals.

(a) List all the chemicals that are entering the environment in this park. Are they all necessary? Which chemicals are dangerous? Are there alternatives?

Every hour of every day, chemicals are being pumped into the environment. Some of these chemicals are intentionally used for a specific purpose, like fertilizer to help crops grow, or salt to give traction on icy roads.

The sources of many chemicals, and their impacts on the environment, are fairly well understood. For example, scientists have been studying acid precipitation for years. The combustion of fossil fuels causes most of the acid precipitation that has a negative effect on aquatic and terrestrial ecosystems.

(b) What can you do to reduce the combustion of fossil fuels, to limit the resulting acid precipitation?

Similarly, the source of road salt is no mystery: about 5 million tonnes of road salt are applied to Canada's roads every winter. In a country known for its long harsh winters, salt is the most inexpensive and readily available chemical for de-icing our roads. While the use of salt has definite safety and economic benefits, it also has a cost. Salt buildup leads to the corrosion of vehicles and buildings, and is known to have a negative impact on the environment. In 2001, Environment Canada recommended that road salt be listed as a toxic substance. While road salt has not been banned, municipalities are being encouraged to find ways to use less salt on their roads.

(c) Sand is sometimes used to help improve traction on icy roads. It is natural and non-toxic. Why is sand not used exclusively?

What are the benefits and drawbacks of using salt on our roads and walkways in the winter? How do you contribute to the production of acid precipitation? What other chemicals do you add to the environment during your daily activities. How do these substances affect the environment?

Science & Technology

Chemicals in the Air, Water, and Ground

Every time a home furnace kicks in, a can of antifreeze spills, or a spray of insecticide drifts over a garden fence, the environment receives a dose of chemicals. In this topic, you will look at a few of these chemicals: what produces them, what effects they have, and what can be done to minimize their effects.

Acid Precipitation

The battle against **acid precipitation** (commonly called acid rain) has been raging for years. In the 1970s, environmentalists sent out warnings that smokestacks and tailpipes were emitting chemicals that were increasing the acidity of rain and snow. Since then, laws have been passed to control the amounts of chemicals (such as sulfur dioxide and the nitrogen oxides) that can be released by electricity generating plants, vehicles, and manufacturing facilities. The battle against acid precipitation is not over yet, however.

The Chemistry of Acid Precipitation

While the pH of pure water is 7 (see **Figure 7** on p. 152), normal precipitation has a pH of around 5.6. This slightly acidic value is due to carbon dioxide from the air that reacts with water droplets to form carbonic acid. The pH of acid precipitation, though, can be as low as 4.2. What makes acid precipitation so acidic?

Acids are compounds that, when mixed with water, produce hydrogen ions, H^+. For example:

$$HCl_{(aq)} \rightarrow H^+_{(aq)} + Cl^-_{(aq)}$$

Acid precipitation is caused by emissions of sulfur dioxide and nitrogen oxides. Although these chemicals exist naturally, over 90% of sulfur dioxide emissions and 95% of nitrogen oxide emissions are the result of human activities, such as fuel combustion in vehicles, coal-burning power plants, and metal smelting (**Figure 2**). These chemicals travel through the atmosphere, where they react with water molecules to form corrosive acids—mostly sulfuric acid and nitric acid. The acids then fall to Earth as rain, snow, or fog. Once on the ground, the acids are absorbed into plant roots and transported to aquatic ecosystems.

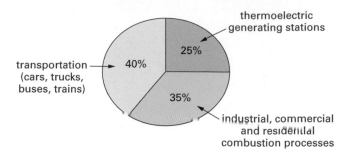

Figure 2 Sources of nitrogen oxides from human activities

Sulfuric Acid Production

Fossil fuels, such as coal and petroleum, were formed over millions of years from once-living plants and animals. When the ancient organisms died, the carbohydrates that they contained were transformed into hydrocarbons. The ancient organisms also contained proteins, however, and these proteins contained sulfur and nitrogen. The sulfur, therefore, remains as a contaminant in fossil fuels. When the fossil fuels are burned, the sulfur is heated to very high temperatures and reacts with oxygen in the air.

$$S_{(s)} + O_{2(g)} \rightarrow SO_{2(g)}$$

Sometimes the sulfur is present in the fuel as hydrogen sulfide, which can also react with oxygen.

$$2\,H_2S_{(g)} + 3\,O_{2(g)} \rightarrow 2\,SO_{2(g)} + 2\,H_2O_{(l)}$$

As you can see, both reactions produce sulfur dioxide, $SO_{2(g)}$, which reacts with oxygen in the atmosphere to form sulfur trioxide.

$$2\,SO_{2(g)} + O_{2(g)} \rightarrow 2\,SO_{3(g)}$$

The sulfur trioxide then combines with atmospheric water to produce sulfuric acid.

$$H_2O_{(l)} + SO_{3(g)} \rightarrow H_2SO_{4(aq)}$$

Nitric Acid Production

The high temperatures inside automobile engines allow atmospheric oxygen and nitrogen to react, producing nitrogen oxides.

$$N_{2(g)} + O_{2(g)} \xrightarrow{\text{heat}} 2\,NO_{(g)}$$

$$2\,NO_{(g)} + O_{2(g)} \rightarrow 2\,NO_{2(g)}$$

When nitrogen dioxide comes in contact with water, a solution of nitric acid is formed.

$$3 \text{ NO}_{2(g)} + \text{H}_2\text{O}_{(l)} \rightarrow 2 \text{ HNO}_{3(aq)} + \text{NO}_{(g)}$$

The Impact of Acid Precipitation

Acid precipitation is a problem across large sections of Canada. More than 80% of all Canadians live in areas that are polluted by acid precipitation. About 96% of the land in eastern Canada that is considered to have a high capability for forestry is subjected to excess levels of acid precipitation.

As acidic precipitation falls to the ground, it can cause various problems. It damages the leaves of plants (**Figure 3**), harms aquatic organisms by changing the pH of surface water, and leaches nutrients out of the soil. It also increases the rate of erosion of exposed rock, metal, and mortar.

Figure 3 Acid precipitation damages the leaves of many trees, including the sugar maple.

Canada's northern forests have experienced a noticeable decline in growth over the last 30 years. This decline coincides with rapidly increasing industrialization and urbanization. In eastern Canada, the maple sugar industry is an integral part of the economy and the culture. In recent years, most likely due to high levels of acid precipitation, the growth rate of sugar maple trees has slowed significantly and many trees have died. This has resulted in poor sap production, leading to hard times for the maple sugar industry. Changes to the environment often occur slowly, over time. The cumulative damage, however, can eventually have a major impact.

Acid rain causes an estimated $1 billion worth of damage in Canada every year. As well as the damage to forests, a large portion of the Maritime salmon habitat has been lost, and there has been considerable damage to buildings and national monuments.

Unless further reductions in sulfur dioxide and nitrogen oxide emissions are made in both Canada and the United States, the damage to forest and aquatic ecosystems will continue.

Aquatic Organisms

Most aquatic organisms—both plants and animals—thrive in an environment with a pH near 7. When the pH decreases significantly, the organisms are less able to survive. In particular, the very young fish die off. A decrease in reproductive success usually follows and, in severe situations, entire populations can be lost (**Figure 4**).

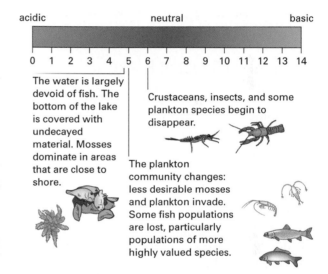

Figure 4 This diagram shows the impact of pH on aquatic organisms in a lake.

Terrestrial Organisms

Terrestrial animals that depend on aquatic ecosystems are also affected. Waterfowl, for example, depend on aquatic organisms for nourishment and nutrients. As these food sources are reduced or eliminated, the quality of the habitat declines and the waterfowl are less able to raise their young successfully.

The effect of acid rain is less direct for plants and animals on land, but no less damaging (**Figure 5**).

One of the more direct concerns for humans is the impact of acid precipitation on toxic metals. The increased acidity of local water, if not adjusted at a water treatment facility, causes toxic metals, such as copper and lead, to leach from water pipes into drinking water. The toxic metals can accumulate in the body, causing chronic, long-term health effects, particularly in young children.

Some toxic elements, such as aluminum, become more soluble. High soil aluminum concentration can prevent the uptake of nutrients by plants.

The protective waxy surface of leaves is damaged, lowering disease resistance.

Habitat damage and declining food supplies affect the health of an animal population, leading to a decline in the survival of offspring.

Plant germination and reproduction are reduced.

Nutrients are lost from the soil.

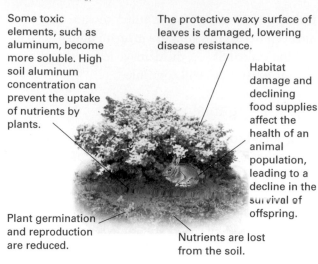

Figure 5 As in aquatic ecosystems, the effects of acid rain on one organism is likely to have an impact on another organism.

The Buffering Effect of Rocks

Not all bodies of water are equally affected by acid precipitation. The impact varies, depending on the type of rock underneath the lake or stream. In some areas, the bedrock reacts with the acid in a neutralization reaction. This has the effect of keeping the pH close to 7—a healthy pH for fish and other aquatic organisms.

- limestone/calcium carbonate, $CaCO_{3(s)}$:

$$CaCO_{3(aq)} + 2\,H^+_{(aq)} \rightarrow CO_{2(g)} + H_2O_{(l)} + Ca^{2+}_{(aq)}$$

- dolomite, $CaMg(CO_3)_{2(s)}$:

$$CaMg(CO_3)_{2(s)} + 4\,H^+_{(aq)} \rightarrow 2\,CO_{2(g)} + 2\,H_2O_{(l)} + Mg^{2+}_{(aq)} + Ca^{2+}_{(aq)}$$

Clay soils also neutralize the acid from acid precipitation. Clay soils contain minerals that have negative charges on their surfaces. These negative charges attract positive ions—often sodium ions, $Na^+_{(aq)}$, and potassium ions, $K^+_{(aq)}$—to form ionic compounds. The ionic compounds then react with the hydrogen ions, $H^+_{(aq)}$, of acid precipitation. An ion exchange (single displacement reaction) takes place, releasing sodium and potassium ions into the water, and taking up the hydrogen ions to become part of the ionic compounds. As the hydrogen ions are no longer in solution, they do not make the water acidic.

Thus, in areas where the rock or soil is limestone, dolomite, or clay, the impact of acid precipitation is reduced (**Figure 6(a)**). This does not happen in areas where the bedrock is granite (**Figure 6(b)**).

Figure 6 These two lakes illustrate the influence of rock type on the acidity of water. Lake **(a)** is in an area where the bedrock is limestone, so the acid precipitation has little impact on the pH of the lake water. The limestone has a buffering effect. The bedrock under lake **(b)** does not have the ability to neutralize acid precipitation, so the lake water is too acidic to support aquatic life. While this lake may appear to be beautifully clean and clear, it is effectively dead.

Granite, like many other types of rock, does not undergo acid–base reactions, and therefore it does not neutralize acid precipitation. Consequently, acid precipitation that falls in a granite area has a much more harmful effect than acid precipitation that falls in a limestone or clay area.

While the buffering effect protects lake water, the rocks are very slowly corroded in their reaction with the acid precipitation. This is generally unnoticeable in natural rock formations, but it is very noticeable when buildings and statues are corroded. In some parts of the world, acid precipitation is causing irreversible damage to historically valuable structures.

Melting the Ice on Canadian Roads

Road salt (sodium chloride, NaCl) lowers the freezing point of water. A solution of salt and water is known as brine. While pure water freezes at 0°C, a 10% solution of $NaCl_{(aq)}$ (10 g of NaCl in 100 mL of solution) freezes at −6°C. A more concentrated brine solution has an even lower freezing point. The lowest temperature at which sodium chloride will melt ice is −21.12°C. Road salt is most effective, however, at temperatures just below 0°C. Fortunately, these are the temperatures at which most snowstorms occur. Why does salt dissolve in water, and why does it lower the point at which water freezes?

Water: A Polar Molecule

Water, H_2O, is a molecule that is held together with **covalent bonds**. This means that the two hydrogen atoms share pairs of electrons with the oxygen atom. The sharing is not equal, however. Oxygen is a larger and electrically stronger atom, and therefore it pulls the electrons from the hydrogen atoms closer to itself (**Figure 7**). This gives the oxygen a slightly negative charge. The hydrogen atoms, on the other hand, almost lose their electrons and take on a slightly positive charge. Thus, the bonds between the hydrogen atoms and the oxygen atom are more specifically called **polar covalent bonds.**

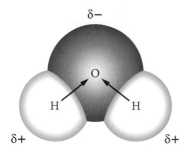

Figure 7 Oxygen, being more electronegative than hydrogen, attracts the electron pair in each bond toward itself, as indicated by the arrows.

Overall, a water molecule is considered to be a polar molecule: it has opposite charges at opposite ends. Because of their polarity, water molecules are attracted to each other and to other polar molecules. The positive end of one molecule is attracted to the negative end of a neighbouring molecule (**Figure 8**).

Water interacts in a similar way with compounds, such as road salt, that are held together with **ionic bonds.** (As you may know, ionic compounds are made up of positively and negatively charged ions.) The

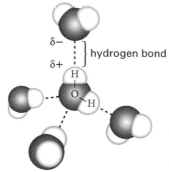

Figure 8 Hydrogen bonding between water molecules.

negative (oxygen) end of a water molecule is attracted to the positive (sodium) ion and pulls it away from its crystal structure. At the same time, the positive (hydrogen) ends of the water molecule pull at the negative (chloride) ions in the salt crystal. Ion by ion, the water pulls the salt crystal apart (**Figure 9**).

Figure 9 Water is able to dissolve ionic compounds, such as salt, because of the attractions between the polar water molecules and the charged salt ions.

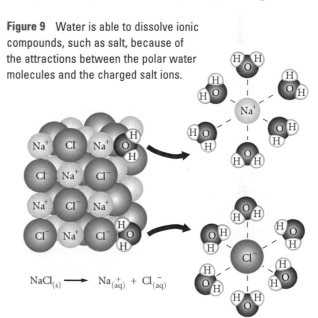

$$NaCl_{(s)} \longrightarrow Na^+_{(aq)} + Cl^-_{(aq)}$$

DID **YOU** KNOW?

De-Icing Airplanes
Just as sodium chloride is used for roads, hot solutions of other de-icing compounds (such as ethylene and propylene glycol) are sprayed onto the wings and body of an airplane prior to take-off during cold, wet weather. The liquid coating prevents ice from forming and building up on the wings and body: a dangerous situation because the ice could interfere with the flow of air over the wings. Most airports now recover much of the de-icing solution so that it can be used again. Some of the de-icing solution runs off the planes and into the ground, however, where it can contaminate local ground water.

C4.1 Activity | MODELLING THE DISSOLVING PROCESS

A scientific concept, such as dissolving, is often easier to understand if you make a model of it. For this activity, you will use whatever materials are available to model the dissolving process.

Possible Materials

molecular model kits
coloured marshmallows and toothpicks
modelling clay

1. Make models of water molecules and a salt crystal.

2. Use your models to show how water molecules and a salt crystal dissolve in each other.

(a) What are the differences between a salt crystal and a water molecule, at the atomic level?

(b) In your own words, explain how salt prevents ice from forming as the temperature drops below freezing.

(c) Compare the process of salt dissolving in water with the process of ice melting in the presence of salt.

The Effects of Salt in Water

Just as liquid water dissolves salt crystals, the ions from the salt crystals prevent ice crystals from forming. The dissolved sodium ions, $Na^+_{(aq)}$, and chloride ions, $Cl^-_{(aq)}$, attract water molecules to themselves. These little clumps of water molecules surrounding an ion prevent other water molecules from joining into the ice structure. The resulting salt water, or brine, then continues to melt built-up snow and ice. Once the brine gets under the ice, ploughs can break up the ice and move it off the roads. This is why crews are sent out to salt the roads at the beginning of a snowstorm, rather than toward the end.

Unfortunately, the use of salt has many negative impacts: it damages soil and vegetation, contaminates surface and ground water, and speeds up the corrosion of metals, concrete, and other materials. As well, many animals are attracted to the salt on roads, frequently resulting in their being hit by fast-moving vehicles.

Impacts of Salt on Plants and Animals

Many plant species are sensitive to salt and unable to survive a dramatic increase in salinity. Over time, the use of salt can change the distribution of plant species in places where they have grown for hundreds of years (**Figure 10**). In some cases, this results in a loss of food and cover for local animal populations, which can lead to a significant decrease in their numbers.

In unpolluted bodies of fresh water, the concentration of chloride ions is very low—usually around 50 mg/L. In areas where salt is heavily applied, chloride ion concentrations in surface water can reach 18 000 mg/L (18 g/L). Where salt is stored, chloride ion concentrations are even higher: up to 82 000 mg/L (82 g/L). These high concentrations are generally found during winter or spring thaws, although high concentrations often persist throughout the summer. Small bodies of water, such as ponds and local streams, are most at risk, along with parts of lakes near large urban areas.

Chloride ions may slow the growth of some species and affect their rates of reproduction. The loss of sensitive species affects the populations of dependent organisms higher up the food chain, including local fish populations. For example, if some species of aquatic plants are killed by high salt concentrations, there is not enough food for the herbivores in the area so they, too, begin to die off. The carnivores, in turn, are affected, causing an overall decline in the number of organisms in the ecosystem.

Figure 10 Terrestrial plants can be damaged by salt spray on their leaves and by high salt concentrations in the ground water.

Another danger is that sodium ferrocyanide is often added to road salt. Sodium ferrocyanide is a chemical that helps to prevent caking and inhibits corrosion. In the presence of sunlight, however, it can break down, producing toxic cyanide. Cyanide is lethal to most animal species, and it has a particularly damaging effect on fish and amphibians.

Salt and Corrosion

One of the main economic downsides of using road salt is the corrosion of vehicles and reinforced concrete structures.

Corrosion is defined as the wearing away of a metal (or another substance) by a chemical agent (usually oxygen) or process.

Corrosion is an electrochemical reaction, which means that electrons are transferred among the various reactants. For the electrons to be able to move, they need to be in a solution that conducts electricity—a solution that contains ions. Substances that form ions in solution are called **electrolytes**. Solutions of electrolytes can conduct electricity because of the ions. Pure water contains hardly any ions, so it is a non-electrolyte.

Electrolytes and Corrosion

When ionic compounds dissolve in water, the number of ions increases dramatically. More ions result in better conductivity. Salt is not the only substance that improves conductivity, however. Even non-ionic compounds, such as carbon dioxide, can react in water to form a solution that contains ions. When water combines with atmospheric carbon dioxide,

it reacts to form carbonic acid, $H_2CO_{3(aq)}$, which is an electrolyte. Some of the carbonic acid molecules then split into hydrogen ions, $H^+_{(aq)}$, and carbonate ions, $CO_3^{2-}_{(aq)}$. This reaction occurs naturally as rain falls through air, resulting in slightly acidic precipitation. Road salt, NaCl, is also an electrolyte.

If a solution that contains an electrolyte, such as carbonic acid or road salt, comes in contact with iron or steel, the metal is slowly eaten away. The metal is replaced with a brittle, flaky reddish-brown compound—rust. Rust is mostly iron(III) oxide, $Fe_2O_{3(s)}$ (**Figure 11**). Rust forms as a result of a chemical reaction between iron and oxygen, in the presence of water.

$$4 \ Fe_{(s)} + 3 \ O_{2(g)} \longrightarrow 2 \ Fe_2O_{3(s)}$$
$$\text{rust}$$

This explains why cars are so susceptible to rusting in Canada, compared with warmer and drier locations.

Figure 11 Cars have steel frames and bodies. Steel contains iron, which rusts when exposed to water and oxygen.

C4.2 Investigation | CONDUCTIVITY OF SOLUTIONS

In this investigation, you will use your knowledge of ionic and molecular substances to predict which substances will conduct electricity when dissolved in water. You will then test your predictions, and try to explain why some substances are electrolytes and some are not.

Question

Which of the following substances will dissolve in water to conduct electricity: table salt, $NaCl_{(s)}$; road salt, $NaCl_{(s)}$; sugar, $C_{12}H_{22}O_{11(s)}$; baking soda, $NaHCO_{3(s)}$; distilled water, $H_2O_{(l)}$; lye, $NaOH_{(s)}$; hydrochloric acid, $HCl_{(aq)}$; oxygen, $O_{2(g)}$; carbon dioxide, $CO_{2(g)}$?

Predictions

(a) Classify each substance to be tested as molecular or ionic.

(b) Predict an answer to the Question.

Materials

eye protection
lab apron
conductivity apparatus
spot plate
solids to be tested:
    table salt, $NaCl_{(s)}$
    road salt, $NaCl_{(s)}$
    sugar, $C_{12}H_{22}O_{11(s)}$
    baking soda, $NaHCO_{3(s)}$
liquids to be tested, in dropper bottles:
    distilled water, $H_2O_{(l)}$
    1-mol/L sodium hydroxide solution, $NaOH_{(aq)}$
    1-mol/L hydrochloric acid, $HCl_{(aq)}$
    water that contains oxygen, $O_{2(aq)}$
    water that contains carbon dioxide, $CO_{2(aq)}$
5 toothpicks (preferably the kind with a flat end)

 Sodium hydroxide and hydrochloric acid are corrosive. Avoid contact with skin and eyes. Wear eye protection and a lab apron. Use only a very small amount of each substance. If either substance gets on your skin, wash it off with plenty of cool water. Report any spills to your teacher immediately.

Procedure

1. Prepare a table to record your observations of conductivity for the nine substances to be tested.

2. Put on your eye protection and lab apron.

Inquiry Skills

○ Questioning   ○ Planning   ● Analyzing
○ Hypothesizing   ● Conducting   ● Evaluating
● Predicting   ● Recording   ● Communicating

3. Number nine wells in the spot plate to correspond with your table.

4. Using a clean pipette, place about 5 drops of distilled water in each of the first seven wells. Leave the first well as a control.

5. Place a few grains of table salt in the second well, road salt in the third well, sugar in the fourth well, and baking soda in the fifth well, using a different toothpick for each substance. Stir each mixture with its own toothpick.

6. Using a clean pipette, place 2 drops sodium hydroxide in the sixth well and 2 drops of hydrochloric acid in the seventh.

7. Your teacher will prepare solutions of oxygen and carbon dioxide by bubbling these gases through distilled water. Using clean pipettes, place about 7 drops of oxygenated water in the eighth well and 7 drops of carbonated water in the ninth well.

8. Using the conductivity apparatus, test each solution. Record your observations in your table.

9. Dispose of the contents of the spot plate in the sink, and flush with lots of water. Clean up your work area.

Analysis

(c) Answer the Question.

(d) Do you detect any relationship between the conductivity of a substance and its ionic or molecular nature?

Evaluation

(e) How confident are you in your observations and analysis? Is there anything you can suggest to improve this investigation?

(f) Compare your answers to (b) and (c). For which substances was your prediction correct? For which substances was your prediction incorrect?

Synthesis

(g) Try to account for the observations that did not match your predictions.

Sodium chloride is a very soluble compound. When placed on ice, it immediately dissolves in the surface moisture and begins to melt the ice. The resulting solution—brine—dissolves more salt to create more brine, which then melts more ice, and so on. Sodium chloride is not the only substance that can melt ice, however (**Figure 12**).

Figure 12 There are other substances, besides sodium chloride, that can lower the melting/freezing point of water. Some products, such as this one, are a mixture of several compounds.

In fact, because of its corrosive properties and its danger to living things, sodium chloride is not an ideal choice for use on icy roads. For years, researchers have been looking for viable alternatives. Unfortunately, there is no single best alternative. (Strictly speaking, not all ice-control agents melt ice, but all can be used to make icy roads less dangerous.)

There are many variables that need to be taken into consideration when choosing an ice-control agent, including road surface and air temperatures, traffic speed and volume, as well as the effectiveness of the agent for melting ice. In this investigation, you will look at the last of these variables.

Inquiry Skills

○ Questioning	● Planning	● Analyzing
● Hypothesizing	○ Conducting	● Evaluating
● Predicting	● Recording	● Communicating

Question

How do the following ice-control agents compare with sodium chloride for melting ice: calcium chloride, magnesium chloride, calcium magnesium acetate, potassium acetate, sand, urea?

Predictions

(a) What characteristic of a compound might affect how effective it is for melting ice? (You might consider the number of atoms or ions in each molecule, or the number of ions it forms when it dissolves.)

(b) Predict an answer to the Question, using the characteristic you selected in **(a)**.

Materials

eye protection
lab apron
2 Styrofoam cups
crushed ice
electronic balance
teaspoon
2 funnels supported by retort stands
masking tape
two 100-mL graduated cylinders
sodium chloride, $NaCl_{(s)}$
calcium chloride, $CaCl_{2(s)}$
magnesium chloride, $MgCl_{2(s)}$
calcium magnesium acetate, CMA
potassium acetate, $KCH_3COO_{(s)}$
sand, $SiO_{2(s)}$
urea, $(NH_2)_2CO_{(s)}$
stopwatch
graph paper

 Calcium chloride is corrosive. Do not touch it with your hands. If it does get on your skin, rinse your skin well with cool water and inform your teacher.

Procedure

(c) You are going to compare how fast sodium chloride melts 100 g of ice with how fast one of the other substances melts the same mass of ice. You can use the materials listed or other materials, and the setup shown in **Figure 13**. Write a detailed procedure to be followed. In your procedure, identify the dependent, independent, and controlled variables, and include safety precautions and disposal directions. Prepare a table like **Table 1** to record your observations. Your teacher will assign test substances to each group. When your teacher has approved your procedure, conduct your experiment.

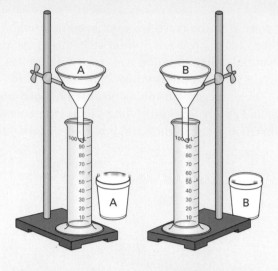

Figure 13 Setup for catching the meltwater

Table 1 Comparing Melting Rates

Time (min)	Volume of water + sodium chloride (mL) in cup A	Volume of water + other ice-control agent (mL) in cup B
1		
2		
3		
15		

(d) Using a table similar to **Table 2**, your teacher will provide you with the observations from your classmates. If necessary, calculate averages.

Analysis

(e) Plot your data from **Table 2** on a line graph of time versus water volume. Use a different colour for each ice-control agent you tested. Include a title, and label the axes.

(f) Which ice-control agent resulted in the fastest melting rate? Which resulted in the slowest melting rate?

(g) Answer the Question at the beginning of the investigation.

(h) Your teacher will provide you with the cost per gram of each substance. Use this cost to estimate which ice-control agent would be most economical for use on local roads.

Evaluation

(i) How confident are you in your experimental design and observations for this investigation? Are there any improvements you would make?

(j) Compare your Prediction in **(b)** with your answer in **(g)**. Account for any differences.

(k) Is it necessary that all groups follow the same procedure? Why or why not? How could you improve the experimental design?

Table 2 Melting Rate of Ice with Various Ice-Control Agents

| Time (min) | Volume of meltwater (mL) with | | | | | | |
	$NaCl_{2(s)}$	$CaCl_{2(s)}$	$MgCl_{2(s)}$	CMA	$KCH_3COO_{(s)}$	$SiO_{(s)}$	$(NH_2)_2CO_{(s)}$
1							
2							
3							
15							

1. **(a)** Which chemicals, when discharged into the atmosphere, result in acid precipitation?
   (b) What processes release these chemicals?

2. Why do fossil fuels contain sulfur?

3. Give an example of a negative effect of acid precipitation on the environment.

4. **(a)** Why do some types of rock reduce the effect of acid precipitation?
   (b) What is the reaction between the rock and the acid precipitation called?

5. Would a gravestone made of granite be more or less susceptible to damage by acid precipitation than a gravestone made of limestone (**Figure 14**)? Explain your answer.

6. Why is finding a suitable ice-control agent particularly important in Canada?

7. **(a)** How are the bonds in a water molecule different from the bonds in a crystal of sodium chloride?

(b) Given this difference, what characteristic of water makes water a good solvent for salt?
(c) How does road salt work, on the molecular level, to prevent ice formation?

8. **(a)** Why does salt speed up corrosion?
   (b) Explain how some molecular compounds can speed up corrosion. Give two examples of molecular compounds that can speed up corrosion. What do these compounds have in common?

9. List at least four other substances that are possible alternatives to sodium chloride for preventing ice formation. Briefly describes the benefits and drawbacks of each substance.

Figure 14 Which gravestone—**(a)** made of granite or **(b)** made of limestone—would suffer the most from the effects of acid precipitation?

Choosing the Best Ice-Control Agent

Sodium chloride, as you discovered in C4.3 Investigation: Testing Ice-Control Agents, is not the only substance that melts ice. Would any of the other substances you investigated be suitable for use as an ice-control agent on roads? One or more of them would likely be effective, but would they be "better" than sodium chloride? This is not an easy question to answer. Many factors need to be considered, including the effect on the environment.

Environment Canada has done some research over the past few years on the impact of road salt on the environment. As a result, some new techniques have been developed to reduce the amount of salt used. These techniques include spraying the roads with brine (a mixture of salt and water) just before a snowstorm and mixing sodium chloride with other substances to prevent the salt from clumping.

Table 3 compares some advantages and disadvantages of various ice-control agents and other substances that can make icy roads less dangerous.

Table 3 Alternatives to Using Sodium Chloride on Roads

Agent	Advantages	Disadvantages
sand, clay, kitty litter, and ashes	• provide traction • are non-toxic and inexpensive	• do not accelerate the melting of snow and ice • remain on the surface after snow and ice melt
calcium chloride, $CaCl_{2(s)}$	• melts snow and ice eight times faster than sodium chloride, NaCl • is effective to $-30°C$ • is less corrosive than NaCl	• damages vegetation and wildlife • costs more than NaCl
calcium magnesium acetate, CMA	• is biodegradable • is safe for use on concrete • is less effective than NaCl	• is only effective at temperatures above $-6°C$ • costs up to 20 times more than NaCl
magnesium chloride, $MgCl_{2(aq)}$	• can be sprayed in solution onto roads prior to a storm to prevent ice from attaching to the pavement • is less corrosive than NaCl	• costs at least five times more than NaCl • leaves a sticky black residue • is only effective to $-15°C$
urea, $(NH_2)_2CO_{(s)}$	• does not damage vegetation (is a component of fertilizers) • is non-corrosive	• is only effective above $-4°C$ • can pollute waterways
potassium acetate, $KCH_3COO_{(s)}$	• is relatively environmentally friendly • causes minimal corrosion	• costs 20 times more than NaCl
brine, $NaCl_{(aq)}$ (same chemical as road salt, but less is used)	• is applied before a storm as brine, to prevent ice from attaching to the pavement • can dramatically reduce the amount of NaCl used	• damages roadside vegetation • is corrosive
"Magic-0" (mixture of beer byproducts and $MgCl_2$)	• is biodegradable, non-toxic, and does not pollute waterways • works at lower temperatures • bonds to surfaces to prevent initial ice buildup • is more effective than NaCl	• costs significantly more than NaCl
calcium magnesium propionate (CMP)	• is inexpensive • is produced from agricultural wastes • is environmentally friendly • performs well in colder temperatures	• is still in the testing stages
Grasscrete (vegetation breaks between solid surfaces)	• is environmentally friendly • does not require any chemical • prevents sheet ice from forming, making the surface less slippery	• is practical only on a small scale, for driveways, sidewalks, and parking lots

Ice Control

Local municipalities are generally responsible for deciding which ice-control agents should be used on their roads (**Figure 15**). There are many factors to consider:

- local climate and weather conditions
- traffic patterns
- availability and cost of distribution vehicles
- financial cost, comparative effectiveness, and community and environmental impact of available ice-control agents and techniques

Figure 15 Spreading ice-control chemicals is expensive, so it needs to be done as efficiently as possible.

Imagine that you are a municipal employee. You have been asked to research the available ice-control agents and make a recommendation to your municipal council about which ice-control agent should be used on municipal roads (**Figure 16**). To prepare your recommendation, you should go through the following steps.

DID **YOU** KNOW?

The True Cost of Salt
The US Environmental Protection Agency reports that the real cost of using road salt is 15 times the cost of purchasing and applying it. This includes environmental damage as well as damage to roads and vehicles.

Decision-Making Skills

○ Define the Issue ● Analyze the Issue
● Identify Alternatives ● Defend a Decision
● Research ○ Evaluate

1. Research the factors listed, using print and electronic resources and the results of your primary research (such as Investigation C4.3: Testing Ice-Control Agents).

    GO | www.science.nelson.com

2. Decide how you will weight the costs of the available ice-control agents and techniques.

3. Compile your collected data (including your results from C4.3 Investigation: Testing Ice-Control Agents) into tables. Remember to cite your sources.

4. Select what appear to be the best three options. Complete a cost–benefit analysis to decide which of these three options is the best choice (see **Appendix A1**).

5. Plan how you will communicate your decision to the municipal council (your classmates).

6. Finally, make your presentation to the council.

Figure 16 Blizzard conditions can cause slippery roads and poor visibility. Which ice-control agent should be used on a municipal road such as this one?

SUMMARY

- Acid precipitation results from the release of sulfur dioxide and nitrogen oxides into the atmosphere. When these compounds react with atmospheric water, corrosive acids are formed.
- Acid precipitation damages exposed rock, metal, and mortar. As well, it reduces the pH of aquatic ecosystems and ground water, which has been associated with a decrease in the reproductive success of many organisms.
- The impact of acid precipitation varies depending on the type of bedrock. Because of neutralization reactions, limestone areas are less affected than granite areas.
- Water is a polar molecule: it has opposite charges at opposite ends. Dissolved ionic compounds, such as sodium chloride, interact with the polar water molecules to prevent the formation of ice crystals. This has the effect of lowering the freezing point of the water.

- Sodium chloride (road salt) is the chemical that is most commonly used for road de-icing in Canada. It is cheap and relatively effective, but it damages vegetation, contaminates surface and ground water, and speeds up the corrosion of metals.
- Corrosion is a chemical reaction that involves a metal, water, oxygen, and an electrolyte (often an ionic compound such as sodium chloride). The electrolyte allows electrons to transfer from one substance to another. The corrosion of iron results in the production of rust and weakens the metal considerably. Road salt is a common electrolyte, but some covalent compounds (acids) can also form ions in solution. Both salt and acids produce corrosive solutions.

Key Terms

acid precipitation	ionic bond
covalent bond	corrosion
polar covalent bond	electrolyte

ASSESSMENT

Understanding Concepts

1. (a) Normal precipitation is slightly acidic. Why? What is the pH of normal precipitation?
   (b) What is acid precipitation, and what causes it? What pH range defines acid precipitation?
   (c) What are the three main sources of the chemicals that cause acid precipitation?

2. Explain how each acid is produced.
   (a) sulfuric acid
   (b) nitric acid

3. List three Canadian industries that are being adversely affected by acid precipitation.

4. List the effects that acid precipitation can have on aquatic and terrestrial ecosystems.

5. (a) Why do the effects of acid precipitation vary from location to location in Ontario?
   (b) What type of reaction reduces the effects of acid precipitation on aquatic ecosystems?

6. Explain why water, H_2O, is a polar molecule and nitrogen gas, N_2, is not.

7. Using diagrams, explain how sodium chloride prevents the formation of ice.

8. How does corrosion occur? Include an equation in your explanation.

9. (a) What are electrolytes?
   (b) How do electrolytes influence corrosion?

10. Give at least two reasons why the life span of vehicles in California might differ from the life span of vehicles in Ontario.

11. When salt concentrations rise in an aquatic ecosystem, some species start to experience a decrease in reproductive success.
   (a) Using minnows as an example, describe how this will affect a species over several generations.
   (b) How might a decrease in the population of minnows affect the population of trout?
   (c) Why might people who fish as a sport be concerned about the use of salt on roads near their favourite fishing holes?

Applying Inquiry Skills

12. A community wishes to reduce its use of sodium chloride as an ice-control agent. Design a pilot project to test three of the alternatives you tested in Investigation C4.3: Testing Ice-Control Agents. Your pilot project should cover one season of road treatment. Outline how the three alternatives will be tested and compared with the traditional ice-control agent, sodium chloride. What factors need to be evaluated before a change is made? Should one chemical be used, or is a combination of the three a wiser solution?

13. A student predicts that spraying a solution of brine on a road before a snowstorm will be more effective than sprinkling solid salt on the road during a snowstorm.
    (a) Write a question for an experiment that addresses the prediction.
    (b) Create a hypothesis to explain the chemistry behind the prediction.
    (c) Write an experimental design to test the prediction and answer your question. (The experiment could be performed in an outdoor setting.)
    (d) Predict the impact on nearby aquatic ecosystems if brine spraying were used instead of solid salt.

14. Using a molecular model kit and other materials as necessary, make at least four models of water molecules and one model of an ionic compound, such as salt. Arrange some or all of these models to illustrate
    (a) the molecular structure of liquid water
    (b) how water dissolves an ionic compound

15. A yellow haze sits over many large cities, so that a clear sky is not visible, day or night.
    (a) Find out what chemicals cause this haze. Where do these chemicals come from?
    (b) Investigate the efforts of at least three different cities to reduce air pollution. Are these cities having any success?

    (c) Compile your findings in a letter to the mayor of your nearest big city. Highlight suggestions for how the city council could work toward reducing pollution over the city.

 www.science.nelson.com

Making Connections

16. (a) Research the MSDSs for at least four of the alternative ice-control agents listed in **Table 3**, on page 208. Note any issues related to the safe handling of these ice-control agents.
    (b) On the basis of safety alone, which ice-control agent is the best?

 www.science.nelson.com

17. Describe at least two situations in which the ice-control agents listed in **Table 3**, on page 208, would not be suitable for Ontario roads.

18. Road salt is not the only chemical that can cause environmental damage. Chemical fertilizers, widely used to give us greener lawns, brighter flowers, and better crop production, can also have negative effects on the environment.
    (a) Research the common chemicals that are found in fertilizers. Find out how these chemicals can have such positive effects on gardens and fields but such negative effects on the natural environment. Also find out what the following terms refer to: runoff, eutrophication, algal bloom.
    (b) Prepare a cost–benefit analysis on the use of fertilizers on either gardens or farm fields.

 www.science.nelson.com

Reflecting

19. What have you learned in this topic that might affect how you choose to remove ice from your sidewalk or pathway next winter?

Unit C Task & Summary

TASK: Factors That Affect Plant Growth

Plants are greatly affected by their environment. The addition of fertilizers encourages them to grow faster, while other chemicals inhibit their growth. They may also be affected by their growing medium: sandy soil, clay, peat, vermiculite, or synthetic soil.

In this investigation, you will design and carry out an experiment to determine the effects of environmental chemicals or the growing medium on plants. For example, you could determine to what extent plant growth is affected by salinity, pH, or any other chemical factor. Alternatively, you could compare growth in a variety of mediums, including a medium made from recycled plastics.

Once you have identified the optimum growing conditions, you will prepare either a formal lab report or a presentation to advise gardeners on how to grow the healthiest plants.

Questions

(i) How does salinity affect plant growth?

(ii) How does pH affect plant growth?

(iii) What other chemical factors affect plant growth?

(iv) What is the best growing medium for plants?

Part A: Writing a Proposal

(a) Plan an experiment to answer one of the Questions above. Your first step will be to research (using print and/or electronic media) the effects of the factor you have chosen on plant growth. As you research these effects, try to find scientific explanations for them. Keep notes, including all relevant sources of information.

 www.science.nelson.com

(b) Write a proposal for your experiment (see **Appendix A7**). Also include a bibliography, in which you will properly cite your sources of information.

Part B: Carrying Out Your Experiment

When your teacher has approved your proposal, carry out your experiment. Remember to follow all appropriate safety precautions. Record any changes that you make to your procedure, as well as both qualitative and quantitative observations.

Analysis

(c) Interpret your observations to answer the Question.

Evaluation

(d) Why did you need to use more than one seedling for each treatment? What number of seedlings would you suggest using if you were going to repeat the experiment? Why?

(e) Growth rates can be measured using several features of a plant. Explain which feature is the most convenient. Explain which feature gives the most valid measurement of growth.

(f) How confident are you in your experimental design and procedure? Is there any reason to doubt the validity of your observations? If so, what would you change to improve the quality of the data collected?

(g) If you are confident in your observations and Analysis, compare your answer in **(c)** to the prediction you wrote for your proposal in **(b)**. Account for any differences.

(h) How did your results compare with the results of other groups in your class and with the results of previously published experiments? Suggest reasons for any differences.

Synthesis

(i) Explain how your results might be useful to

    (i) a farmer growing field crops

    (ii) the operator of a greenhouse

    (iii) the operator of a hydroponics operation

Part C: Presenting Your Findings

(j) Prepare either a formal lab report *or* a presentation for gardeners.

- If you choose to write a lab report follow the guidelines in **Appendix A7**.

- If you choose to make a presentation, select an appropriate medium (such as a booklet, a video, or a Web page) for communicating with gardeners. Share your findings on how to grow the healthiest plants.

SUMMARY

Throughout this unit, you have had opportunities to

- demonstrate your understanding of the properties, benefits, and hazards of everyday chemicals, as well as the safe use of these products at home, in the workplace, in industry, and in the environment
- use experiments and electronic or print resources to investigate the properties of everyday chemicals safely

- weigh the advantages and disadvantages of using common chemicals in everyday life, and analyze the environmental and economic impacts of their use

Copy the following graphic organizer into your notebook, and use it to help you summarize your understanding of the key concepts in each of the four major topics. Add the key concepts related to the topic that you chose for your Unit Task.

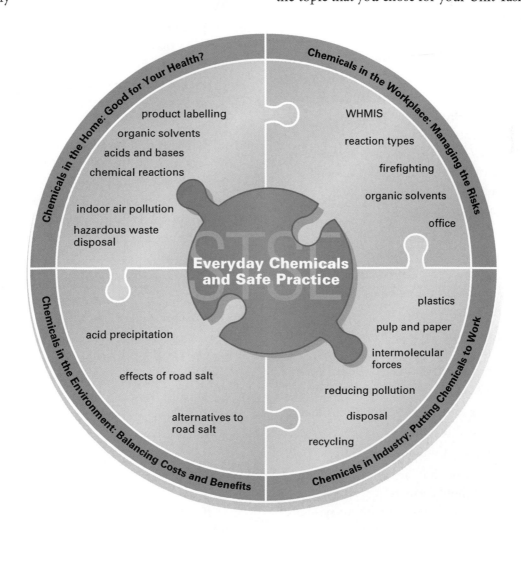

Unit C Review

Understanding Concepts

1. Many household cleaners carry this symbol:

   (a) What does this symbol mean?
   (b) What precautions should you use when handling a cleaner with this symbol?

2. Write the general formula for each type of reaction, and give an example as a word equation.
   (a) synthesis
   (b) decomposition
   (c) single displacement
   (d) double displacement
   (e) combustion

3. (a) What is an organic solvent? Give two examples.
   (b) Why are organic solvents especially dangerous?
   (c) What types of products are likely to contain organic solvents?
   (d) What alerts a consumer to the presence of an organic solvent in a household product?
   (e) How should organic solvents be stored?

4. Define and give an example of
   (a) an acid
   (b) a base

5. Most cleaning products are either acids or bases. Briefly explain how acids and bases work to clean surfaces.

6. (a) What type of reaction is likely to occur if you mix an acid and a base?
   (b) Write a word equation and a chemical equation for an example of this type of reaction.

7. What three factors must be present for a fire to start and continue burning?

8. What is the best way to fight a class A fire? Why?

9. (a) Which type of symbols are used on the labels of most household cleaners?
   (b) How do household cleaners with no symbols on their labels warn of any safety risks or precautions?

10. (a) Describe the physical properties of carbon monoxide.
    (b) What reaction produces carbon monoxide?
    (c) What effects can carbon monoxide have on a person?
    (d) What can be done to reduce the dangers of carbon monoxide poisoning in a home?

11. (a) When can carbon dioxide be considered an indoor air pollutant?
    (b) What could be done to remedy this situation?

12. Explain how you should safely dispose of
    (a) an almost-empty can of latex paint
    (b) a bottle of bathroom tile cleaner that you cannot use because it makes you cough
    (c) half a bottle of mineral spirits
    (d) a used-up aerosol can of pet flea spray

13. (a) What raw material is the original source of most plastics?
    (b) What are the two main types of reactions that are used to form polymers? Write a word equation for a reaction that produces a polymer.

14. What is the purpose of SPI codes on containers?

15. (a) In terms of disposal, what is the main problem with the use of plastics?
    (b) Suggest how this problem can be addressed
       (i) by plastics manufacturers
       (ii) by food-packaging companies
       (iii) by consumers

16. (a) Describe at least three major environmental concerns with paper processing.
    (b) What is the pulp and paper industry doing to address these concerns?

17. The pH of normal, unpolluted rain is approximately 5.6. Explain, using chemical equations, why normal rain is not neutral.

18. (a) What is the main source of sulfur dioxide?
    (b) What environmental problem does sulfur dioxide contribute to?

19. Explain why acid precipitation may eventually lead to a loss of fish species.

20. (a) How do soluble ionic compounds inhibit the formation of ice?
    (b) What property of water is important in this process?

21. **(a)** Why has sodium chloride historically been the de-icing chemical of choice in Canada?
    (b) Outline the environmental concerns regarding the use of sodium chloride on roads.
    (c) List at least three drawbacks to the alternative ice-control agent.

Applying Inquiry Skills

22. Design an experiment to compare the cleaning effectiveness of baking soda with the cleaning effectiveness of a commercial abrasive cleaning product, such as Ajax or Comet.

23. In a crowded office, the carbon dioxide concentration can increase to a dangerous level. Plants are nature's carbon dioxide removers.
    (a) Design an experiment to test the effect of the presence of plants on indoor air quality.
    (b) Research the best species of plants to use for your experiment.
    (c) What other airborne toxins can plants remove?

24. A new chemical warning system, with a colour-coded diamond, is being used in the United States. This system may be coming to Canada soon. Research this system, and create warning symbols for two everyday chemicals of your choice.

25. **(a)** Design an experiment to compare the corrosive effects of kitty litter, calcium chloride, urea, and sodium chloride.

    (b) Research the chemical structure of each compound. Use your findings to predict and explain the differences you expect to observe.

Making Connections

26. Create a brochure on the safe handling, storage, use, and disposal of a common household cleaner. In your brochure, recommend a "green" alternative to this cleaner. Include the method of preparation, necessary safety precautions, and a cost–benefit comparison.

27. Many cancers are now considered to be occupational diseases for firefighters. Why is the risk increasing? What compounds have been implicated as causing these cancers? Research the chemical structure and properties of one of these compounds. Present your findings in a brief report, highlighting the health effects of chronic (prolonged) and acute (concentrated) exposure to this compound.

28. Conduct Internet research on an indoor contaminant of your choice. What is the source of the chemical? What are the health concerns associated with the chemical? How can its presence and/or impact be minimized or eliminated? Create a Web page to communicate your recommendations.

29. Why does paper continue to be so popular in this electronic age? What steps could be taken to reduce paper consumption? Create a script for a television advertisement, encouraging people to save paper.

30. Weather conditions across Canada are variable. Research your area's local ice-management plan. What chemicals are used, and how are they applied? What changes, if any, have been made to the ice-management plan in the last 5 to 10 years? In your opinion, is this an appropriate strategy? Write an article for a local newspaper, to share this information with readers.

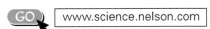

Extension

31. Look up the Canadian Environmental Protection Act. What is the definition of a toxic substance in the act? Using this definition, create an illustrated list of at least 10 toxic substances that you may encounter on a daily basis. Include precautions that you could take to avoid being poisoned by these substances.

Body Input
and
BODY FUNCTION

Faisan and Linda stopped at a corner store on the way to school. They were not there to buy junk food. Faisan had enjoyed a protein shake for breakfast. He wanted to buy the latest issue of his favourite body-building magazine. Linda, however, had skipped breakfast. She was dieting so that she could get into a new outfit she had bought after admiring something similar in a fashion magazine. As they leafed through the pages of the magazines, their eyes caught the captions in the advertisements (**Figure 1**) and scanned the photos of the models. Faisan and Linda sighed inwardly. Would their bodies ever be that perfect?

(a) List or bring in captions like those in **Figure 1**, related to losing weight or building muscle. Think about advertisements you have seen in the past week, in newspapers, magazines, and other media. How can you identify claims that are unrealistic? Suggest ways of responding to media pressure regarding the perfect body.

Is there such a thing as a perfect body? The media would have you think so. In the 2000s, typical female models are young, tall, thin, and beautiful (**Figure 2**), while typical male models are muscular and lean (**Figure 3**). How closely do these models resemble you? How closely do the models resemble themselves, considering

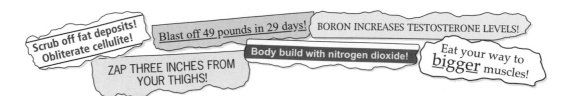

Scrub off fat deposits! Obliterate cellulite!

Blast off 49 pounds in 29 days!

BORON INCREASES TESTOSTERONE LEVELS!

ZAP THREE INCHES FROM YOUR THIGHS!

Body build with nitrogen dioxide!

Eat your way to <u>bigger</u> muscles!

Figure 1   Can the perfect body be bought?

Figure 2 The ideal female, as portrayed by the media

Figure 3 The ideal male, as portrayed by the media

that computer techniques can be used to enhance any image and edit out unwanted features? According to the media message, the perfect body will make you happy and successful, and it is possible if you spend enough money. Do you have enough money? Is the goal worth the price?

Today's perfect body would not have received a second glance 100 years ago! **Table 1** shows how the media image of the ideal female has evolved over time.

(b) How much attention should you pay to media messages, given how frequently they change?

(c) Predict the media ideal for males and females 50 years from now.

Table 1 The Evolution of the Media Image of the Ideal Female

Time period	The ideal woman	Typical models	
		Height (cm)	Weight (kg)
1800s	plump body and pale complexion, representing wealth, abundance of food, and a refined indoor lifestyle		
early 1900s	corseted "hourglass" look		
1950s–1960s	full-figured shape of Marilyn Monroe and gaunt Twiggy look	173	60
1970s–1980s	taller, thinner look with no visible body fat; muscles highly toned by exercise	173	53
early 1990s	waif-like, pre-teen look in adult women, found naturally in about 4% of women	179	50
late 1990s	narrow hips and large breasts—a rare combination without the help of breast implants, a common requirement for models in the 1990s	179	50
2000s	The average North American woman is 163 cm and 64 kg—15% to 20% heavier than a typical model.		

Figure 4 More than 50% of Canadians are overweight.

The overly muscular male ideal is reflected in toy trends. Consider the 1974 G.I. JOE action figure. If this toy were a real man, he would have a 79-cm waist, a 112-cm chest, and 30-cm biceps. The male equivalent of today's G.I. JOE action figure would have a 71-cm waist, a 127-cm chest, and 56-cm biceps! When college males were asked to choose images of their ideal body type, they chose images that had an average of 13 kg more muscle than their own bodies. Most fitness models have a muscular form that is attainable only with the use of steroids.

(d) With societal pressures to be thin, why are so many Canadians overweight (**Figure 4**)?

What determines your body shape? Body shape is predetermined, to a great extent, by genetics. Somatotyping is one way to assess body shape. A somatotype is a particular build or body type based on physical characteristics of slenderness, muscularity, and fatness. Three main body shapes are described in **Table 2**. Categorizing a person's body as a particular somatotype is helpful for providing diet and exercise counselling and for assessing activity preferences. For example, mesomorphs gain muscle size and strength more easily than ectomorphs. Because 30% or more of an endomorph's body weight may be fat, diet and exercise regimes are important for staying healthy.

Table 2 Somatotyping to Assess Body Shape

Ectomorph	Mesomorph	Endomorph
• frail, delicate body structure • relatively large skull • small face, sharp nose, long neck • long arms and long, thin legs • flat abdomen with hollow navel	• hard, muscular body • long, strong neck • broad shoulders and slender, low waist • muscular arms and legs	• soft roundness, with mass concentration near centre of body • large, round head and short neck • broad, thick chest and abdomen • short arms and legs

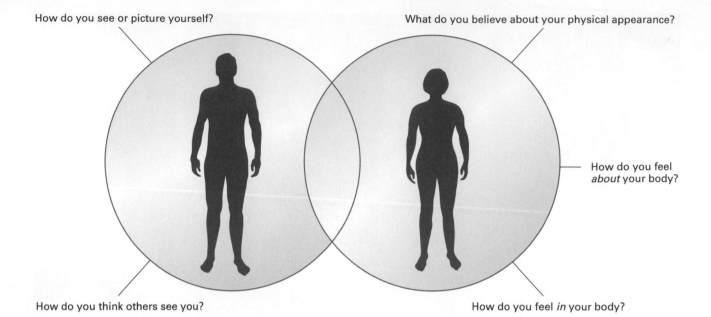

How do you see or picture yourself?

What do you believe about your physical appearance?

How do you feel *about* your body?

How do you think others see you?

How do you feel *in* your body?

Figure 5 What is body image?

(e) How would you assess your body shape, using somatotyping? How many of the descriptions fit you exactly? Identify limitations to this method for assessing body shape. Suggest other ways that body shape could be classified.

How do you feel about your body? Body image can be described as an inner view of the outer self (**Figure 5**). Body image is ever-changing. It is sensitive to changes in mood, environment, and physical experience. Media messages are only one influence on body image. Feedback from family and friends is equally important. Some of us accept our bodies and feel comfortable as we are. Many of us, however, are dissatisfied and feel our problems would be solved if only we could change our bodies.

DID **YOU** KNOW?

Dieting and the Media

In a recent poll by *People Magazine*, 80% of women reported that the images of women on television, in movies, and in fashion magazines and advertising made them feel insecure about their looks. In fact, 34% felt so insecure that they were willing to try diets that posed health risks, or undergo cosmetic surgery. Of the women surveyed, 93% indicated that they had made various and repeated attempts to lose weight, so that they could measure up to the media images.

(f) Having a positive body image means that your feelings about your body size and shape do not depend on other events in your life. Describe some guidelines that a person your age should use to maintain a positive body image.

Body image issues affect both genders. Although dissatisfaction is higher in females, one U.S. study found that 43% of men are obsessed with their body shape and size. This percentage is triple what it was 25 years ago! In a recent survey of high school students, two-thirds of both males and females believed that being thinner would have an impact on their lives. Most females believed that the impact would be positive, while most males believed that the impact would be negative.

(g) Assess how you project yourself to others. What stereotype does our society associate with your looks? How often do people project this stereotype onto you? Do you behave any differently in order to avoid provoking this stereotype? What skills do you use to break through this stereotype and show your real self?

(h) Think about any stereotypes related to your family's cultural background. Are there differences between these stereotypes and "typical Canadian" stereotypes?

Psychologists and counsellors agree that body image is directly related to self-esteem. In females, negative body image can be associated with weight fluctuations, depression, risk-taking behaviour, and suicide.

In your notebook, answer "yes" or "no" to each question in the following survey.

Body Image Survey

1. Do you weigh yourself often or try to control your weight?

2. Have you avoided sports because you do not want to be seen in gym clothes?

3. Does eating even a small amount of food make you feel fat?

4. Do you worry about your body not being small or thin enough?

5. Do you worry about your strength, or how toned and firm your muscles are?

6. Have you avoided situations where people could see your body?

7. Do you feel that your body is a disadvantage to you, socially or athletically?

8. Have you avoided wearing clothes that make you especially aware of your shape?

9. Do you compare your body with other people's bodies and feel inadequate?

This survey covers a broad range of issues. If you answered "yes" to most or all of the questions, however, you could benefit from the advice of a health professional. You may need help to control your fears or insecurities about your body image.

(a) Describe your feelings as you completed the survey.

(b) What gender differences would the answers show? Explain your thinking.

(c) Add three additional questions that you feel would improve the survey.

(d) What weaknesses do surveys, such as this one, have?

DID **YOU** KNOW?

Physical Activity and Body Image
People who are physically active are more likely to have a positive body image and a greater acceptance of themselves than people who are not physically active.

In males, negative body image can be associated with increased physical and verbal aggression and substance abuse. As well, males with poor body image are more likely to be bullies or victims of bullying. Serious examples of poor body image in both genders are the eating disorders anorexia nervosa and bulimia.

Your body image affects the lifestyle choices you make. Many of these lifestyle choices determine what enters your body. Do you have a balanced diet, or do you eat a lot of junk food? Do you need a mug of coffee to survive science class? Do you smoke? Do you have other non-food addictions? Like any well-tuned machine, your body functions on the fuel it burns. Going without breakfast has certain predictable effects on how Linda's body will function during the morning. Similarly, ingesting excess pro-

tein affects Faisan's body functions, though in different ways. To a great extent, you are what you eat.

(i) Write a reflective paragraph about how your body image affects your personal eating patterns.

Throughout this unit, you will make inferences about how eating patterns affect body function. Investigations will help you determine the nutrient and energy content in selected food samples, determine the effect of non-nutritive food additives, assess a variety of popular diets for their nutrient content, and evaluate strategies for monitoring and maintaining personal health.

The effect of body input on body functions cannot be judged by science alone. There are social and economic costs and benefits of certain eating behaviours, such as adopting a vegetarian diet or eating highly processed foods. The use of non-nutritive food additives to preserve and enhance foods also brings social and economic costs and benefits. Personal and societal factors, such as allergies, disease, and body image, affect our eating behaviours. Thus, science, technology, society, and the environment are all necessary perspectives in the study of how body input affects body function.

Questions to Think About ...

As you explore the topics in this unit, keep the following questions in mind:

- What are the principal food nutrients—their sources, basic chemical structure, and function in the body?
- What is the role of dietary fibre?

- How do certain factors contribute to the body's use of energy?
- What is the role and impact of non-nutritive food additives?
- How do diets that include excessive amounts of certain foods influence the balance of body functions?
- What are the causes and symptoms of eating disorders?

Food Becomes You:
Principal Food
Nutrients

The Real Thing?
Food Forms
and
Sources

STSE

Body Input
and
Body
Function

Weighty Issues:
Fad Diets
and Eating
Disorders

In Balance:
Energy Use

Read the Label:
Food
Additives

Unit Task Introduction

How does the food you eat affect the way your body functions? In this unit, you will compile a personal food and fitness diary for assessment. You will use your inquiry and communication skills to apply the broad concepts presented in the five topics. Read the description and requirements on pages 288 to 289 before you start the unit topics, so that you can prepare for the Unit Task as you progress through the unit.

Patricia has recently made an important decision—she has chosen to become a vegetarian. Her reasons are many. For some time, she has believed that raising animals for food is cruel. Reports in the newspaper horrify her: chickens packed so tightly in cages that they can hardly move, lobsters boiled alive, and cows fed growth hormones to produce more milk. Last year's science unit on ecology caused her to think more carefully about the environment. Doesn't land yield more food when it is used for farming rather than grazing? If humans ate energy producers rather than other energy consumers, wouldn't the food chain operate more efficiently? And what about other problems associated with raising animals for food, such as methane released by cows, animal wastes in the water table, and loss of topsoil from grazing?

Patricia's primary reason for choosing vegetarianism, however, is health. Her mother has high blood cholesterol levels and is overweight and diabetic. Patricia suspects that a vegetarian diet could help her avoid these health conditions.

(a) Discuss the basic motivations that people may have for choosing a vegetarian lifestyle. Can you add other motivations to Patricia's list?

(b) How can diet and health claims, like those mentioned above, be supported?

Some of Patricia's friends have made similar decisions. Reynah is a strict **vegetarian**, or vegan, which means that she eats only plant foods (**Figure 1**). As a Hindu, Reynah believes that killing animals brings bad karma, leaving one open to experiencing the same suffering in the future. Mathieu is an ovo vegetarian. He eats non-animal foods plus eggs. Sabeen, who is a lacto-ovo vegetarian, eats non-animal foods plus eggs and dairy products. Jennie is considered to be a semi-vegetarian because she chooses to eat free-range chicken and other humanely-treated

Figure 1 A vegetarian diet is not just vegetables!

animals when they are available. As a Muslim, Moe avoids meat from pigs and other carnivorous animals. Patricia's vegetarian friends all look healthy, although Mathieu seems to have a lot of intestinal gas and Reynah never has enough energy for lunchtime sports.

(c) What limitations could there be to maintaining a vegetarian eating pattern?

Patricia gets the most resistance to her decision from her family. "Three square meals a day!" and "Red blood cells need meat!" are her mother's favourite sayings. Patricia knows her parents are worried about her health. As a compromise, she agrees to visit a nutrition counsellor. Armed with current information on the principal food nutrients and the importance of fibre in the diet, she should feel comfortable about her decision.

(d) We all grow up with certain perceptions of what healthy eating means. What perceptions of healthy eating have you received from your family and friends?

(e) Vegetarianism is only one example of an altered eating pattern. What other examples can you think of?

DID **YOU** KNOW?

From One Hectare of Land...
One hectare of prime land can produce 44 000 kg of potatoes, 32 000 kg of carrots, 54 000 kg of tomatoes, or 280 kg of beef.

Food Nutrients

Food provides six main types of nutrients for the body: carbohydrates, proteins, lipids, minerals, vitamins, and water. These **nutrients** are edible chemicals that are broken down for the body's growth, maintenance, and energy. A certain amount of each nutrient is required daily to prevent deficiencies and to lower the risk of chronic or long-term diseases. Most nutrients are considered to be essential because the body is unable to synthesize them in sufficient quantities. Nonessential nutrients can be synthesized in the body from other nutrients. In 2002, scientists in Canada and the United States developed new daily nutrient recommendations, called **dietary reference intakes (DRIs)**.

Carbohydrates

Carbohydrates are used primarily as an energy source. Carbohydrate molecules contain carbon, hydrogen, and oxygen in fixed ratios. The basic carbohydrates are simple sugars called **monosaccharides**. (In Greek, *monos* means "single" and *saccharon* means "sweet thing.") Glucose (**Figure 2**) is the most important monosaccharide because it is used as a fuel by all cells. All usable carbohydrates are broken down, or metabolized, to form glucose during the digestive process. Other monosaccharides are fructose (fruit sugar) and galactose (a component of milk sugar).

When two monosaccharides bond together, they form a double sugar, called a **disaccharide**. Sucrose (table sugar) is a common disaccharide. When many monosaccharides bond together in long chains, the resulting complex sugar is called a **polysaccharide**. Starch is a polysaccharide. So is cellulose, which is also known as roughage, or **fibre**.

Grains, fruits, and vegetables are excellent dietary sources of carbohydrates (**Figure 3**). When your diet is rich in carbohydrates, your body extracts energy from them, saving protein for muscle building and body repair. Current North American guidelines recommend that carbohydrates, especially complex carbohydrates, provide 55% to 60% of your daily energy requirements. The DRI is 130 g/day, but more is required during infancy, pregnancy, and breast-feeding, when energy needs are higher.

Figure 3 Some sources of carbohydrates

Lipids

Like carbohydrates, **lipids** or fats are made up of carbon, hydrogen, and oxygen; however, fat molecules have a higher proportion of hydrogen atoms in their structure (**Figure 4**). Fats contain more chemical energy per gram than carbohydrates, and they are used by animals to store energy. Like carbohydrates, fats can be used for energy, allowing proteins to be used for other body functions. Fats have other important functions, too. They transport certain vitamins around the body, they are used by the body to synthesize chemical messengers, such as enzymes and hormones, and they are required for normal functioning of the cell membrane.

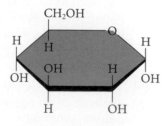

Figure 2 Glucose, $C_6H_{12}O_6$

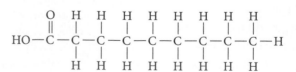

Figure 4 Fatty acid

Follow the links to *Canada's Food Guide to Healthy Eating*.

 www.science.nelson.com

(a) What recommendations does the Food Guide give? Why do you think the Food Guide recommends that you eat large amounts of some foods and smaller amounts of other foods?

(b) According to the Food Guide, which foods should be eaten in large quantities? Which foods should be eaten in smaller quantities?

(c) Describe the particular dietary needs and concerns of your age group.

(d) Write down everything you might eat on a typical day. Score yourself using the Healthy Eating Scorecard.

(e) Using Canada's Food Guide, create a table that lists what you might eat in one day if you were
(i) a meat eater
(ii) a lacto-ovo vegetarian

(f) Research the typical daily diet of a person from a country outside North America. Compare it with your diet. What are the similarities and differences? What accounts for the differences?

There are three main types of fats in foods: **saturated**, **monounsaturated**, and **polyunsaturated** fats. Foods also provide other types of fats, such as **cholesterol** and fats formed during food processing (**Table 1**). These molecules differ in the amount of hydrogen they contain. Saturated fatty acids contain the most hydrogen

Table 1 Fat Primer

Type of fat	Description
saturated	Saturated fats are usually solid at room temperature. Key food sources are animal fats: butter, lard, milk, cheese, cream, fats in meat and poultry, and palm and coconut oils. Saturated fats are closely associated with increased health risks. They can increase "bad" cholesterol levels (low-density lipoprotein or LDL cholesterol) and decrease "good" cholesterol levels (high-density lipoprotein or HDL cholesterol). Intake should be limited to no more than 10% of calories (adults: 20 g/day for females; 25 g/day for males).
monounsaturated	A key food source is olive oil. Other sources are canola or peanut oil, nuts, and seeds. Monounsaturated fats appear to lower LDL cholesterol levels in the blood, while increasing HDL cholesterol.
polyunsaturated	Polyunsaturated fats are found in oils that are liquid at room temperature: safflower, sunflower, corn, and other vegetable oils. Other food sources include soft margarines made from these oils, as well as nuts, seeds, and fatty fish, such as salmon, trout, mackerel, sardines, and tuna. These fats lower total cholesterol levels in the blood. Fish oil fats are omega-3 fats, which regulate blood pressure, and are important for brain function and cell building and repair.
cholesterol	Cholesterol occurs naturally in animals. About 80% of cholesterol is made by our liver, while the other 20% comes from food. Dietary cholesterol is LDL cholesterol, known as the "bad" cholesterol because it contributes to the formation of plaque in our arteries. HDL cholesterol is known as the "good" cholesterol because it can reverse the buildup of plaque in our arteries. Studies have shown that our blood cholesterol levels are more affected by the amount of saturated fats we eat than by the amount of cholesterol we eat. Cholesterol is found in all animal products, such as meat, poultry, eggs, milk, and cheese. Plant food sources do not contain cholesterol.
other	Other fats are found in human-made products. The process of hydrogenation (adding hydrogen atoms) produces trans fats, which act like saturated fats by increasing "bad" cholesterol and possibly decreasing "good" cholesterol. Examples of other fats are some margarines, shortening, some cheeses, and prepared baked foods, such as crackers, cookies, and pies.

atoms. Polyunsaturated fatty acids contain the fewest hydrogen atoms. One essential polyunsaturated fatty acid, linoleic acid, cannot be synthesized by the body and must be provided by the diet. Current North American guidelines recommend that dietary fats should supply no more than 30% of your daily energy requirements.

Proteins

Proteins provide the chemical building blocks for the growth and repair of body tissues and for the synthesis of hormones and enzymes. The basic component of a protein is an **amino acid** (**Figure 5**).

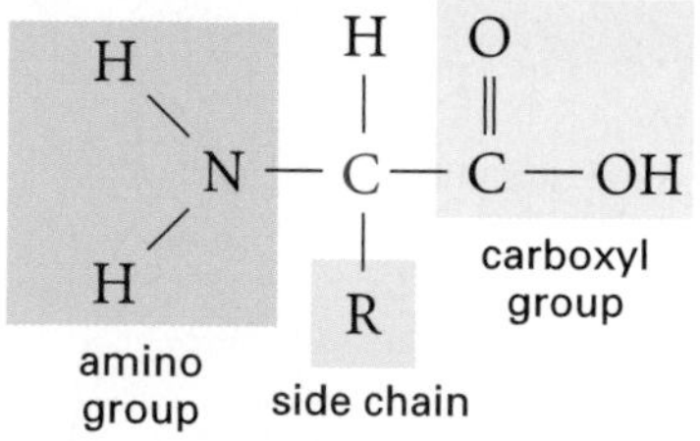

H
\
N — C — C — OH
/ |
H   R

amino group   side chain   carboxyl group

Figure 5 The generalized structure of an amino acid

Amino acids are small molecules that contain a central carbon atom attached to an amino group, a carboxyl group, a hydrogen atom, and a side chain. The structure of the side chain (the R group) distinguishes one amino acid from another. There are 20 different R groups, thus there are 20 different amino acids. Of these 20, eight are considered to be essential. Because the body cannot produce these eight essential amino acids from simpler compounds, they must be obtained from food.

Proteins are chains of amino acids (**Figure 6**). They differ from one another by the number and sequence of the amino acids they contain. A complete protein has all the **essential amino acids** in the correct proportions to support growth. Animal foods (such as beef, poultry, fish, and eggs) are sources of complete proteins. The proteins in many plants lack essential amino acids, so they are considered to be incomplete proteins. For example, the amino acids leucine and isoleucine are not present in grains, nuts, seeds, and vegetables, but they are present in legumes. Two other amino acids, methionine and tryptophan, are found in some vegetables but not in legumes. Vegetarians must carefully balance their cereal and legume intake in order to obtain all eight essential amino acids.

The human body has limited stores of protein. If few carbohydrates are present in the diet, the body converts proteins into energy. The DRI of proteins for adults is 0.8 g/kg/day (10%–35% of daily energy requirements). The DRI is higher during infancy, adolescence, pregnancy, and breast-feeding.

Minerals

Minerals are inorganic substances—that is, they do not contain carbon atoms bonded to hydrogen atoms. Although the body requires only small amounts of minerals, they perform many important functions (**Table 2**). Minerals are needed in all body structures and are attached to some vitamins and hormones. As well, they are involved in the transmission of nerve impulses and muscle contraction and are required to maintain the water and acid–base balance. Humans require 22 minerals. Because minerals cannot be made by the human body, they must be provided by foods or by supplements.

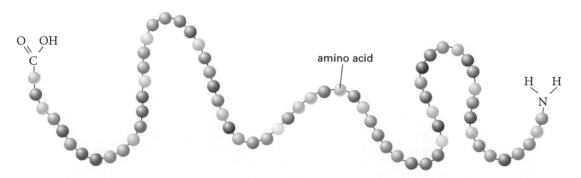

Figure 6 Proteins are amino acid chains. Each colour represents a different amino acid.

Table 2 Major Minerals

Mineral	Adult DRI	Functions	Dietary sources
calcium, Ca	1000–1200 mg	bone and tooth development and maintenance; muscle contraction; heartbeat regulation; nerve transmission; blood clotting; cell membrane permeability	milk, cheese, green leafy vegetables, whole-grain cereals, beans, hard water
fluoride, F	3 mg for females; 4 mg for males	bone and tooth structure	fluoridated water
iodine, I	150 μg	production of thyroid hormone; regulation of metabolism	seafood, kelp, iodized salt
iron, Fe	18 mg for females; 8 mg for males	transport of oxygen in the blood; DNA synthesis; energy conversion; growth	whole-grain cereals, nuts, green leafy vegetables, organ meats
magnesium, Mg	310–420 mg	bone and tooth formation; energy conversion; protein synthesis; nerve transmission, muscle contraction; maintenance of body temperature	whole-grain cereals, seafood, green leafy vegetables, meat, dairy products
phosphorus, P	700 mg	bone and tooth formation; muscle contraction; kidney function; nerve and muscle activity; blood clotting; heart rhythm	whole eggs, fish, meat, poultry, whole-grain cereals, dairy products
zinc, Zn	8 mg for females; 11 mg for males	digestion and synthesis of proteins; wound healing; development and growth of reproductive organs; insulin formation; immune function; bone formation	yeast, whole-grain cereals, liver, seeds, meat, seafood

Vitamins

Vitamins are organic chemicals that the body cannot synthesize, either at all or in sufficient quantities. Vitamins act as catalysts, aiding essential chemical reactions in the body. Vitamins help in regulating metabolism, converting fats and carbohydrates into energy, and forming bone and tissue (**Table 3**). Some vitamins (A, D, E, and K) are fat-soluble. These vitamins can be stored in the body's fat tissues, but excess amounts can accumulate and be toxic. Other vitamins are soluble in the water in foods. Water-soluble vitamins cannot be stored in the body, so they must be consumed daily. Excess amounts are excreted in urine. There is no energy value in vitamins. Ideally, vitamins are best obtained through a varied diet rather than in a supplement because there is little chance of taking too high a dose.

Several vitamins—including C, E, and beta carotene (the chemical parent of vitamin A)—have received attention recently for being antioxidants.

Research suggests that **antioxidants** are able to lessen the damage caused by a group of harmful molecules known as free radicals. Free radicals are found in ultraviolet rays, X-rays, and pollutants such as ground-level ozone, tobacco smoke, and car exhaust. Free radicals damage genetic information in body cells, causing mutations. As well, they may play a major role in the development of cancer, heart and lung disease, and even cataracts. They may also accelerate the aging process. By eating vegetables that are rich in antioxidants, you may live longer and have better health!

Water

Water plays an essential role in carrying nutrients and wastes from the cells and in regulating body temperature. Between 60% and 70% of your body weight is water. A person at rest loses about 1.5 L of water each day—more during physical activity or in

Table 3 Major Vitamins

Vitamin	Adult DRI	Functions	Dietary sources
A	700 µg for females; 900 µg for males	growth; vision; healthy tissue, skin, hair, and teeth; resistance to infection	milk, butter, eggs, liver, green and yellow fruits and vegetables
B₁ (thiamine)	1.1 mg for females; 1.2 mg for males	heart and cardiovascular system; growth; nervous system; energy production; digestion; brain function	whole-grain cereals, fish, lean meat, liver, poultry, milk, pork
B₂ (riboflavin)	1.1 mg for females; 1.3 mg for males	healthy skin; tissue repair; formation of antibodies and red blood cells	whole-grain cereals, yeast, milk, eggs, green leafy vegetables, lean meat
folic acid	400 µg	production of red blood cells and tissue cells; normal growth; healthy intestinal tract; energy production; brain function; possible reduction in risk of spinal cord defects during fetal development	yeast, green leafy vegetables, meat, whole-grain cereals
C	75 µg for females; 90 µg for males	wound healing; immune system; maintenance of healthy gums, skin, and blood	citrus fruits, berries, cabbage, potatoes, vegetables, tomatoes
D	5 µg	bones and teeth; growth; optimum calcium-phosphorus metabolism; heartbeat regulation, blood clotting	milk, cod-liver oil, tuna, salmon oil, eggs
E	15 µg	antioxidant; protection of cell membrane and tissues; maintenance of circulatory system	vegetable oil, whole-grain cereals, wheat germ, dark green leafy vegetables
K	90 µg for females; 120 µg for males	blood clotting (coagulation); bone formation and repair	dark green leafy vegetables, molasses, yogurt, alfalfa

hot weather. Guidelines recommend that adults consume the equivalent of eight glasses of water daily. Caffeine-containing beverages, such as coffee, tea, and cola, should not be included because caffeine is a diuretic, making you lose water. All foods contain water, varying from 98% in most fresh vegetables to about 4% in cookies. A great plus for water, in comparison to other fluids, is that it hydrates the body without providing extra calories.

Nutrient Information

Food labels provide three main sources of valuable information:
- the ingredients list
- the nutrition information panel
- claims such as "low fat" and "source of fibre"

The ingredients list, which is mandatory on all foods, lists the contents by weight, in descending order. As well, Health Canada now requires mandatory nutrition labelling on most prepackaged foods. The Nutrition Facts table (**Figure 7**) on prepackaged foods gives consumers some of the information they need to compare products and to make informed choices about food options.

It is important to realize that many food nutrients are interchangeable and can be used by the body to perform similar functions. Carbohydrates, fats, or proteins can be used by the body to fulfill its energy and carbon requirements. Fats or proteins can provide the components to synthesize important biological carbohydrates, such as glucose.

The nutrient information is based on a specified amount of food. Compare this to the amount you eat.

This number is the amount of the nutrient in the specified quantity of food.

The *Nutrition Facts* table will include this list of Calories and up to 13 nutrients.

Nutrition Facts Per 125 mL (87 g)	
Amount	% Daily Value
Calories 80	
Fat 0.5 g	1%
Saturated 0 g Trans 0 g	0%
Cholesterol 0 mg	
Sodium 0 mg	0%
Carbohydrate 18 g	6%
Fibre 2 g	8%
Sugars 2 g	
Protein 3 g	
Vitamin A	2%
Calcium	0%
Vitamin D	10%
Iron	2%

The % Daily Value gives a context to the amount of the nutrient in the specified amount of food. The Daily Values are based on recommendations for healthy eating.

Figure 7 Read the label.

D1.2 Activity WHAT'S IN A BURGER? >

Nadine and Troy both plan to eat burgers for lunch. Troy is preparing his in Foods class. Nadine is going to buy hers at a fast-food restaurant. The components of a hamburger— the bun, ground beef, lettuce, tomato, and dressing (**Figure 8**)—are rich in nutrients. In this activity, you will use food composition tables to compare the nutritional content of homemade and fast-food burgers (**Figure 9**).

Figure 8 Components of a hamburger

Question
What is the difference in the nutritional content of homemade and fast-food hamburgers?

Prediction
(a) Predict the relative content of the six main nutrients in each hamburger.

Procedure
(b) Consider all the components of a hamburger: bun, mayonnaise and other condiments, lettuce, tomato, and meat. Design a table to record the nutritional content of these components for both a homemade hamburger and a fast-food hamburger. Include the appropriate units.

(c) Research the components of both types of hamburgers, using food composition sources on the Nelson Web site.

 www.science.nelson.com

Figure 9 Are these two burgers equally good for you?

Analysis

(c) Visually display your results for each hamburger, using graphic format.

(d) What trends and patterns do you see?

(e) Recall the six nutrients you studied in this topic. What is the main source of each nutrient in a hamburger?

(f) Answer the Question.

Evaluation

(g) Evaluate your Prediction based on your Analysis.

(h) Describe any difficulties you experienced carrying out the Procedure. What could or should you have done differently?

Synthesis

(i) What implications do your findings have, considering the popularity of fast-food hamburgers?

(j) Complete a cost–benefit analysis on eating homemade versus fast-food hamburgers. Consider the full cost (time, energy, electricity, economy, environment, and health) in your analysis.

(k) Repeat the Procedure for one other food item, such as French fries, chicken nuggets, or a milkshake.

✔ Check Your Understanding

1. Compile a table of dietary reference intakes (DRIs) for all the nutrients mentioned in this section.

2. Define three types of carbohydrates, and give an example of each.

3. What are two main differences between saturated and unsaturated fats? Give two food sources for each.

4. Explain the difference between LDL and HDL cholesterols.

5. Why are fats important in a well-balanced diet?

6. Distinguish between essential and nonessential amino acids.

7. Why is milk considered to be a complete protein, while corn is an incomplete protein?

8. List the major vitamins and minerals that are found in whole grains.

9. Which nutrient category is considered to be inorganic, and why?

10. List six organs that require vitamins for healthy functioning.

11. What is an antioxidant? How is it thought to act in the body?

12. Justify the following statement: "Our bodies require eight glasses of water, or comparable fluid, each day."

13. Why should you read food labels?

Society & the Environment

Canada's Food Guide to Healthy Living displays four main food groups in the arc of a rainbow (**Figure 10(a)**). Recommended daily servings for each food group are summarized in **Table 4**. Your teacher will provide you with a copy of Canada's Food Guide.

Table 4 How Many Servings Do I Need?

Food group	Daily servings
grains	5–12
vegetables, fruit	5–10
milk products:	
ages 4–9	2–3
ages 10–15	3–4
adults	2–4
pregnant women	3–4
meat and alternatives	2–3

(a) What is the significance of the rainbow in the Food Guide? List the advantages and disadvantages of this design.

(b) Why do different people need different amounts of food? Use milk as an example.

(c) Explain how one food guide can suit the needs of such a diverse population (in age, activity, and health).

(d) Give examples of serving sizes for each food group.

(e) What three food groups are key sources of vitamin A? Why is this nutrient important?

(f) Give examples of "Other Foods," which are not part of any food group. How do we incorporate these foods into our diets?

(g) Andrew is an Olympic team rower. Describe how he could modify **Table 4** to meet his nutrient and energy needs.

(h) Describe your favourite pizza. List the main food items it contains. Estimate how much of each food item one serving contains, and calculate how many food group servings this serving provides.

(i) What is the "Vitality" component of the Food Guide and why is it important?

To be effective, a food guide must incorporate the unique dietary components of a specific population. Different societies have different food availabilities and preferences, dietary patterns, and cultural needs. Examine the food guides shown in **Figure 10**.

(j) List similarities and differences among the graphic designs of the four food guides shown in **Figure 10**. Which design do you consider to be the most effective, and why?

(k) What is the major difference between the Canadian and American guides?

(l) What is the major difference between the North American food guides and the Asian and Mediterranean food guides?

(m) Summarize the distinctive features of each food guide.

(n) Rank each diet according to the prevalence of
(i) fats
(ii) proteins
(iii) carbohydrates

(o) Canada's Food Guide is undergoing revisions. What changes would you propose and why?

(p) In a one-page position paper, argue for or against the following statement: "Canadians should change from the typical Western diet, which predisposes them to health risks and early death, in favour of a Mediterranean diet."

(a) The Canadian food guide

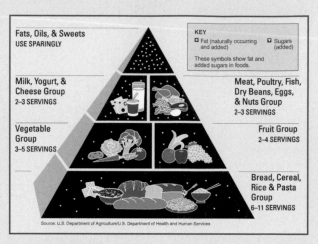

(b) The American food guide

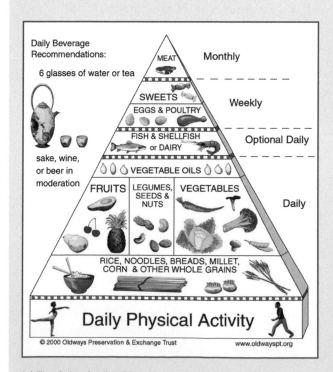

(c) The Asian food guide

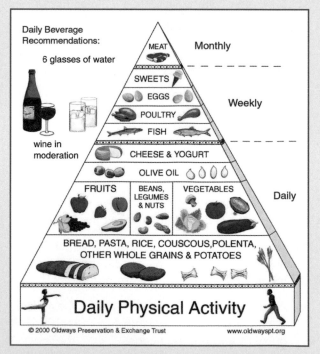

(d) The Mediterranean food guide

Figure 10

Planning a Vegetarian Diet

At the beginning of this topic, Patricia made a decision to become a vegetarian. You are now in a position to advise her. Using concepts you have learned in this topic, along with information in **Figure 11** and in articles on the Nelson Web site, you will prepare some dietary advice for Patricia.

1. Start by researching the advantages and disadvantages of a vegetarian diet. Search for information in newspapers, periodicals, CD-ROMs, and on the Internet. Keep in mind the different interest groups, such as nutritionists, medical scientists, and the agriculture and food industries.

 GO www.science.nelson.com

2. As background for your role as nutrition counsellor, describe the characteristics of a vegetarian diet. Also describe the basic motivations that people might have for choosing a vegetarian lifestyle.

3. Prepare a cost–benefit analysis for Patricia, based on the results of your research (see **Appendix A1**).

4. Identify six nutritional concerns for vegetarians. Explain how each concern can be overcome.

5. What alternatives to vegetarianism can you offer Patricia?

6. Plan a full day of vegetarian meals for Patricia: breakfast, lunch, supper, and snacks. Include recipes and a shopping list for the food required.

7. With your parent's approval, follow the plan that you prepared in question 6 for a few days.

Decision-Making Skills

- Define the Issue
- Research
- Defend a Decision
- Identify Alternatives
- Analyze the Issue
- Evaluate

Write a brief summary of your physical and emotional reactions to the vegetarian diet. *CAUTION:* Do not follow the plan if you have a medical condition that could make it harmful for you.

8. Step back from your role as nutrition counsellor, and reflect on what you have just learned about vegetarianism. Would you recommend vegetarianism? Explain your reasons.

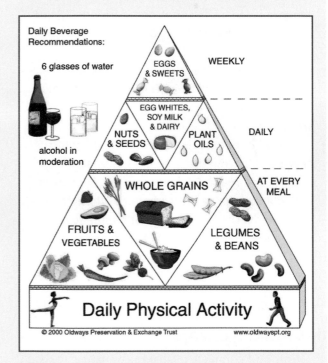

Figure 11 The vegetarian food pyramid

SUMMARY

- Your eating patterns directly affect your personal health and well-being. Food provides your body with the chemical constituents it needs for growth and repair. You can use food composition tables to estimate the nutrient content of food.
- New daily nutrient recommendations, called DRIs, are now recognized across North America.
- Carbohydrates provide your body with its basic fuel. They are composed of monosaccharides and disaccharides (simple sugars) and poly-saccharides (complex sugars and starches). Polysaccharides provide dietary fibre.
- Lipids, or fats, are excellent sources of energy. As well, they transport fat-soluble vitamins in the body, they are used to synthesize chemical messengers (such as enzymes and hormones), and they are required for the normal functioning of the cell membrane.
- Fats in foods may be saturated, monounsaturated, and polyunsaturated. Foods also provide other fats, such as cholesterol, hydrogenated fats, and trans fats.
- Proteins are composed of amino acids, which provide cells with the building materials needed to grow and maintain their structure. Nonessential amino acids can be created out of other chemicals in the body. The eight essential amino acids must be provided by the diet.

- Minerals are inorganic elements. They are required by the body in trace amounts.
- Vitamins are essential in minute quantities. They act as catalysts in the regulation of chemical processes. Some vitamins act as antioxidants.
- Water carries nutrients and wastes to and from the cells. As well, water helps to regulate body temperature.
- Food labels provide valuable information about ingredients, nutrients, and nutritional claims.
- *Canada's Food Guide to Healthy Living* recommends a certain number of daily servings from four food groups.
- Vegetarianism is an eating pattern that requires careful application of nutrition principles to maintain a balanced nutrient intake.

Key Terms

vegetarian	**saturated fat**
nutrient	**monounsaturated fat**
dietary reference	**polyunsaturated fat**
intake (DRI)	**cholesterol**
carbohydrate	**protein**
monosaccharide	**amino acid**
disaccharide	**essential amino acid**
polysaccharide	**mineral**
fibre	**vitamin**
lipid	**antioxidant**

ASSESSMENT

Understanding Concepts

1. Create and complete a table to compare the six main food nutrients. Use the following headings: Chemical structure, Function, and Sources.

2. Classify the fats in each food as saturated, monounsaturated, or polyunsaturated. Explain your classification.

salmon	whole milk
peanuts	theatre popcorn

3. Does corn-and-lentil soup contain complete or incomplete proteins? Explain.

4. Jenelle refuses to eat anything green. What nutrients may be missing from her diet?

5. Explain the observation that the dental cavity rate in children appears to parallel the consumption of bottled water.

6. Classify each food according to the main nutrients it provides.

steak	potato chips	butter
eggs	olive oil	spinach
whole-wheat bagel	banana	sugar
raisin bran cereal		

7. Using Canada's Food Guide, plan a daily menu for two 12-year-old boys. One boy plays soccer and swims. The other boy does not take part in many physical activities.

8. Compare and contrast the Canadian and Asian diets, using information in **Figure 10** (on p. 232).

9. Explain the advantages and disadvantages of
   (a) a vegetarian diet
   (b) a non-vegetarian diet

Applying Inquiry Skills

10. Select and remove three labels from food products. Fasten each label to the top of a piece of paper, and answer the following questions.
    (a) What are the first three ingredients mentioned? How are they related to the name of the product?
    (b) Calculate the percentage of your DRI that is provided by each nutrient in this product.
    (c) List each ingredient that cannot be considered a food nutrient.
    (d) Are any health claims mentioned? What are they?

11. Write down everything you eat on a typical day. Design a table to record the nutrient content of your daily diet. Use food composition tables to estimate the quantity of nutrients you consume. Analyze your diet according to the dietary reference intakes.

Making Connections

12. Your diet should contain a balance of the six main food nutrients. If your food intake is not balanced (e.g., you consume too much or too little of a particular nutrient), you may experience poor health or disease. Complete **Table 5** for each of the six food nutrients, using information on the Nelson Web site.

 www.science.nelson.com

Table 5 The Six Food Nutrients

Food nutrient	Symptoms of excess	Symptoms of deficiency	Sources of nutrient

13. For their products, many food companies prefer to use trans fats instead of oils to reduce costs, extend storage life, and improve flavour and texture. Give two examples of trans fats. Explain why Health Canada requires trans fats to be listed on labels.

14. In January 2003, for the first time, Health Canada regulations permitted labels to contain certain claims about diet–health relationships. Choose one of the following claims, and research the link between diet and the effect mentioned.

 www.science.nelson.com

   • A diet that is low in sodium and high in potassium may reduce the risk of high blood pressure.
   • A diet that is adequate in calcium and vitamin D may reduce the risk of osteoporosis.
   • A diet that is low in saturated fat and trans fat may reduce the risk of heart disease.
   • A diet that is rich in vegetables and fruit may reduce the risk of some types of cancer.

15. On a label, "calorie reduced" means 50% fewer calories than the regular product. "Low calorie" means less than 15 calories per serving. Interpret each of the following terms.

   low fat
   high source of fibre
   low in saturated fat
   very high source of fibre

 www.science.nelson.com

Reflecting

16. Assess your eating patterns, based on what you have learned in this topic. What influences your food intake? When do you eat? What are the strengths and weaknesses of your daily food consumption? What three changes could you make to improve your health and well-being? What challenges would you face in doing so?

Canadian astronaut Chris Hadfield grew up on a farm outside Milton, Ontario. His food came from the land. Dinner might have included a plump chicken with sage bread stuffing, mashed potatoes and gravy, corn on the cob dripping with butter, thick slices of beefsteak tomatoes, string beans, carrots, peas, bread and butter, and pickles (**Figure 1**). Dessert might have been apple pie with a slab of orange cheddar cheese on the side.

(a) Assess this menu according to Canada's Food Guide.

(b) Consider the different cultures that are represented in your class, and design three typical family dinners.

Hadfield sat down to a very different meal as the space shuttle *Endeavor* hurtled toward the International Space Station (ISS) in April, 2001 (**Figure 2**). On his tray was a selection of space food, coded in the following categories: thermostabilized (T), irradiated (I), intermediate moisture (IM), freeze dried (FD), rehydratable (R), natural form (NF), and fresh food (FF). All shuttle food is precooked or processed, so that it requires no refrigeration. It is ready to eat, or it can be prepared by adding water or heating.

(c) List examples of common foods that might fit into the above coded categories.

(d) Describe two primary restrictions on space food.

(e) Shuttle orbiter fuel cells produce electricity by combining hydrogen and oxygen. This reaction provides extra water for the astronauts. There is no extra water on the ISS because electrical power is generated from solar panels. How does the limited water supply affect food needs?

Figure 1 Dinner on the farm

Figure 2 Dinner in space

If food categories seem artificial on the space shuttle, consider the early days of space flight. *Mercury* astronauts (1961) consumed bite-sized cubes, freeze-dried powders (**Figure 3**), and semi-liquids stuffed in aluminum tubes. Improvements for *Gemini* astronauts (1965) included coating the cubes with gelatin and encasing freeze-dried foods in plastic containers to make reconstituting easier. By *Apollo* launches (1968), hot water was available, and astronauts were given a spoon bowl.

Figure 3 Nourishment in cubes and powders

(f) Hypothesize why coating food cubes with gelatin was an improvement.

(g) *Skylab*'s three-member team could "sit" around a table (1973). What were the advantages of this arrangement?

Few of us can be astronauts, but we have all benefited from the research and development of space products.

(h) List everyday foods that are the result of space research.

What's next in food science? The U.S. Air Force is developing a meal tablet called a Micro-MRE (Meals Ready to Eat). One Micro-MRE will contain enough calories to sustain a soldier on the battlefield for 24 h. A transdermal (skin) patch that will feed soldiers through their skin is also being developed.

(i) What are some advantages and disadvantages of nourishment through a transdermal patch?

(j) Suggest other food innovations for life in the twenty-first century. What are some advantages and disadvantages of these innovations?

How is the food you eat similar to space food? How is it different? How have our food forms and sources changed in recent years?

NEL

D2: The Real Thing? Food Forms and Sources **237**

Science & Technology

Food Terminology

What images come to mind when you think of food? When your grandmother was your age, she likely thought of fresh ingredients on a cutting board, the aromas of baking bread and simmering stews, and the final meal on a plate (recall **Figure 1**). With advances in technology, food is now big business, involving both agricultural and pharmaceutical industries. Food is no longer just raw ingredients from nature.

The term *organic* has been widely used since the 1940s to describe food production systems and their produce. All certified **organic foods** are produced according to specific rules, encompassing an ecological balance among the plants, animals, and people that make up the farm environment. Soil health is maintained using composted organic matter and crop rotations rather than synthetic pesticides and fertilizers.

The term *natural food* has been adopted by food corporations to describe processing rather than production methods. Although "natural" implies minimal processing and the absence of synthetic ingredients, there are no formal definitions, standards, or verification procedures. During some food processing procedures, nutrients are lost. Enriched or **fortified foods** have had some of their lost nutrients replaced in order to prevent nutritional deficiencies.

An increasing volume of the world's food supply is now produced using genetically engineered organisms (**Figure 4**). Foods that are derived from this type of biotechnology are referred to as genetically engineered foods (GEFs). In Canada, GEFs are considered to be one class of novel foods.

According to Canada's Food and Drugs Act, a **novel food** is

- a substance, including a microorganism, that does not have a history of safe use as a food
- a food that has been manufactured, prepared, preserved, or packaged by a process that has not been previously applied to the food, and causes the food to undergo a major change
- a food that is derived from a plant, animal, or microorganism that has been genetically modified such that it now exhibits characteristics that were not previously observed, or no longer exhibits characteristics that were previously observed

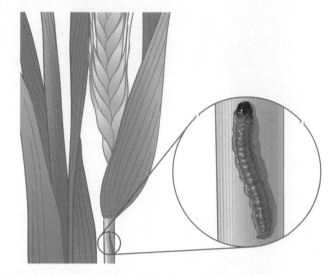

Figure 4 Wheat can be genetically engineered to resist insect attacks.

In recent years, researchers in the food and beverage industry have discovered certain components in conventional foods that appear to provide health benefits beyond their nutritional value. Foods that contain these components are called **functional foods**. Examples are shown in **Figure 5**.

A functional food can be a conventional food that is eaten as part of a regular diet. For example, ground flaxseed or flaxseed meal, sprinkled on cereal, is an example of a functional food. It contains the key component alpha-linoleic acid, which helps to reduce blood cholesterol. Other examples are listed in **Table 1**.

Figure 5 Are these products food or medicine?

Table 1 Some Functional Foods

Functional food	Key component(s)	Potential health benefits
black and green teas	catechins	reduces risk of cancer
broccoli	sulforaphane	reduces risk of cancer
fruits and vegetables	omega-3 fatty acids	reduces risk of heart disease
garlic	phytochemicals	reduces risk of cancer and heart disease
oats	soluble fibre and beta glucan	reduces cholesterol
soy foods	soy protein	reduces cholesterol
tomatoes	lycopene	reduces risk of cancer
yogurt	lactic acid bacteria	improves gastro-intestinal health

Nutraceuticals (a contraction of the words "nutrient" and "pharmaceutical") have been developed in recent years by the food and beverage industry. They are isolated or purified from foods and are generally sold in medicinal forms that are not usually associated with food. A nutraceutical must have a physiological benefit or provide protection against a chronic disease. For example, flaxseed oil is produced in Saskatchewan and sold internationally as a source of healthy fatty acids, to help reduce blood cholesterol.

More than half of Canadians use **natural health products (NHPs)**. Sales of NHPs are estimated to be a $3.4-billion industry. NHPs consist of molecules and elements that are found in nature. They are sold in dosage form to maintain or improve health and to treat or prevent diseases or conditions. NHPs may be absorbed into the body through the skin, nasal passages, or lungs, or taken orally. NHPs include herbal and homeopathic remedies, vitamin and mineral supplements, nutraceuticals, some cosmetics, and ingredients used in aromatherapy and sports nutrition (**Figure 6**). By the end of 2008, all NHPs sold in Canada will be licensed and assigned either a natural health or homeopathic products number.

Under the umbrella of NHPs are **dietary supplements**. This broad category includes any product that is taken by mouth and contains "dietary ingredients." Dietary ingredients are vitamins, minerals, herbs or botanicals, enzymes, amino acids, or other substances that are used to supplement the diet. Dietary supplements come in various forms, such as pills, tablets, capsules, liquids, or powders. In general, they are useful for individuals who are unable or unwilling to consume an adequate diet. Examples of recommended supplements are

Figure 6 Natural health products

- fluoride supplements for children who do not drink fluoridated water
- multivitamin–mineral supplements, not exceeding DRI, for children or elderly people who have poor eating habits, people who are recovering from surgery or serious illness, and people who are on severe weight-reduction diets
- vitamin B_{12} for children who are on vegetarian diets
- iron and folic acid during pregnancy
- calcium for post-menopausal women

High (above-DRI) doses of nutrients are regarded as drugs rather than as supplements. They should be taken with medical supervision.

Meal replacements are customized food products that must contain a minimum food energy value, a maximum amount of fat, and a specified amount and quality of protein and various vitamins and minerals.

D2.1 Activity | WHAT'S IN AN ENERGY BAR?

Sports nutrition products are marketed as healthy snacks in North America. Many people who would have reached for a chocolate bar 10 years ago now reach for an energy bar—to the tune of $609 million in 2003! In this activity, you will analyze the nutrient content of an energy bar (**Figure 7**).

Access information about an energy bar through the Nelson Web site.

 www.science.nelson.com

Figure 7 PowerBar is "created by athletes, for athletes."

(a) List the advertised features of this energy bar.

(b) What is the recommended intake and serving size?

(c) Create a table with the following headings: Calories, Fats, Proteins, and Carbohydrates. Record this nutritional information for an energy bar and for your choice of chocolate bar. In the last row of your table, record the DRI for each nutrient.

(d) Based on your data, summarize the nutritional value of each product. Include both strengths and weaknesses.

(e) In what situations would you recommend eating an energy bar? What precautions would you suggest?

(f) Name other customized food products or meal replacements that are pitched to athletes or active people.

The Role and Importance of Dietary Fibre

Two centuries ago, Sylvester W. Graham knew the importance of roughage, or dietary fibre, in the diet. Although his cracker is still with us, dietary fibre has passed in and out of favour with consumers. The fibre intake of North Americans steadily declined during the 20th century and is only now making a comeback.

The term "dietary fibre" generally refers to parts of fruits, vegetables, grains, nuts, and legumes that cannot be completely digested by humans. Meats and dairy products do not contain fibre.

There are two basic types of fibre: insoluble and soluble. Insoluble fibre (mainly cellulose) is essential to the cellular structure of plants. Insoluble fibre travels quickly as an undigested mass through the human digestive tract, collecting waste materials for removal. Good food sources of insoluble fibre are wheat and corn bran (**Figure 8**), whole-grain breads and cereals, vegetables, fruit skins, and nuts. Soluble fibre is found within plant cells and includes pectin, gums, and mucilages. Soluble fibre is partly broken down by bacteria in the large intestine, providing

Figure 8 Does a bran muffin a day keep the doctor away?

some energy. Sources of soluble fibre are fruits, legumes (dried peas, split peas, and lentils), nuts, seeds, and brown rice, as well as oat, barley, and rice brans.

Research has established that dietary fibre is a collection of elements with a variety of functions, rather than a single substance with a single function. Thus, a high-fibre diet has many benefits, as summarized here:

- promotes more frequent bowel movements and softer stools with increased mass, due to the presence of gas that is produced by bacterial action on the fibre
- stimulates peristalsis, or wavelike muscular contractions in the colon, preventing the two extremes of constipation and diarrhea
- renders the feces more acidic (from bacterial action), reducing the amount of potentially cancer-causing substances
- reduces the intestinal transit time of food contents, thereby reducing the possibility of harmful toxin formation

- increases the number of bacteria—which require nitrogen for their growth—in the large intestine, thereby reducing the amount of ammonia in the large bowel and the chances of cancerous mutations in cells
- reduces the absorption of cholesterol in the diet
- slows down the rate of absorption of sugars from the food in the digestive system
- increases the viscosity (thickness) of digestive matter, which indirectly reduces the need for insulin secreted by the pancreas

As well, research has indicated that a fibre-rich diet may help to prevent or control the following conditions: obesity, colon cancer, heart disease, gallstones, irritable bowel syndrome, diverticulosis, and diabetes.

Health professionals caution against making an immediate leap from a low-fibre diet to recommended levels, because increasing dietary fibre too rapidly can result in flatulence and cramping. Excessive consumption of fibre may irritate the delicate functioning of the digestive system, especially in people with weakened immune systems. An excessive intake of fibre may result in a loss of valuable minerals (such as calcium, phosphorus, magnesium, and potassium) due to the quick passage of food from the intestine. The DRI for fibre is 30 g.

D2.2 Activity   COMPARING BREAKFAST OPTIONS

Only 50% of Canadians eat breakfast every day, and 10% always skip breakfast. As the first meal of the day, breakfast provides the nutrients that are necessary to fuel mental performance, elevate mood, and help to control body weight. A well-balanced breakfast should include at least three of the major food groups. Dieticians suggest including carbohydrates for instant energy and proteins for increased alertness and a prolonged sense of fullness.

In this activity, you will compare three breakfast options (**Figure 9**): a glass of orange juice and a bowl of whole-grain cereal with a banana and milk; a homemade smoothie (125 g each of bananas, strawberries, yogurt, and orange juice); and reconstituted instant breakfast, made with 1% milk.

 www.science.nelson.com

Question
(a) Write a suitable Question.

Prediction
(b) Make a prediction that ranks the nutritive value of the three breakfast options.

Procedure
(c) Use a table like **Table 2** to compare the nutritional value of the three breakfast options.

(d) Create another table to compare the major vitamin and mineral content of the breakfast options. Include a column for "other" ingredients. For example, what other ingredients are listed on the package of the instant breakfast?

NEL

D2: The Real Thing? Food Forms and Sources   **241**

Table 2 Observations

Nutrient	Calories	Protein	Fat	Carbohydrate
DRI				
Option 1: juice, cereal, milk, banana TOTALS:				
Option 2: homemade smoothie TOTALS:				
Option 3: instant breakfast TOTALS:				

(a)  (b)  (c)

Figure 9 A Western breakfast takes many forms. It can be **(a)** a meal, **(b)** a meal in a glass, or **(c)** an instant, packaged pouch.

Analysis

(e) Answer your Question.

(f) Rank each breakfast option according to fibre content and fat content.

Evaluation

(g) Was your Prediction correct? Explain.

(h) Summarize the advantages and disadvantages of each breakfast option.

(i) If you were to repeat this activity, how would you modify it?

(j) Make a conclusion about the nutritional value of the breakfast options you compared.

(k) Predict the results if a doughnut and coffee were a fourth breakfast option.

(l) Classify the instant breakfast according to the definitions of food terms on page 236.

(m) List common reasons for skipping breakfast. Provide a healthy food choice to counter these reasons.

Synthesis

(n) How does your typical breakfast compare with the three options you studied here? What changes could you make to ensure a good start to your day?

✔ Check Your Understanding

1. Create a table of food terms and their definitions. Give one example (not mentioned in the student text) for each term.

2. Describe the similarities and differences between
   (a) a functional food and a nutraceutical
   (b) a dietary supplement and a meal replacement
   (c) a fortified food and a GEF
   (d) an organic food and a natural food

3. Compare and contrast the sources and actions of the two types of dietary fibre.

4. Devise 10 "true or false" questions to test your classmates' knowledge of the role and importance of dietary fibre.

5. Classify each food group as containing primarily soluble or insoluble fibre.

rice	legumes	vegetables
fruits	cereals	nuts

CASE STUDY

Highly Processed versus Natural Foods

Much of our Western diet is composed of refined or processed foods. Consider how much white flour, white sugar, white rice, processed oil, and margarine we consume each day. This development is relatively new. For millennia, flour was produced by grinding grains between large stones. The final product, 100% stone-ground whole-wheat flour, contained everything that was in the grain.

Grains are the seeds of grasses. As such, they are nutrient storehouses. Of the 44 essential nutrients that are naturally obtained from foods, only four are missing from wheat: vitamins A, B_{12}, and C, and the mineral iodine. Most of the 40 essential nutrients in grains are contained in the **bran** and the **germ** of the wheat kernel (**Figure 10**). The **endosperm** is the starchy middle layer.

With the invention of bleaching and high-speed milling in the late 19th century, white bread and other products made from white flour and sugars became mainstays in the Western diet. As a result, certain vitamin B deficiency diseases became so prevalent that health officials urged the milling industry to keep some whole grain in the flour. There was, however, a lucrative market for animal feed that contained bran and germ. Instead of keeping some whole grain in the flour, the milling industry decided to "enrich" or fortify the long-lasting white flour by adding back some of the lost nutrients. This practice continues today (**Figure 11**).

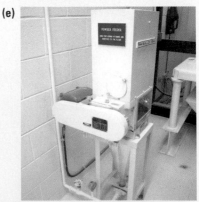

Figure 11 Flour milling in Canada **(a)** wheat intake **(b)** cleaning and tempering **(c)** the milling process **(d)** flours **(e)** flour treatment **(f)** animal feed by-products (e.g. bran flakes)

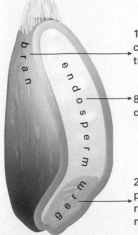
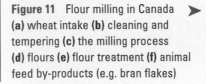

15% of the wheat kernel by mass; contains B vitamins, phytochemicals, trace minerals, and fibre

83% by mass; contains protein, carbohydrate, fat, and water

2.5% by mass; contains vitamin E, protein, fibre, potassium, iron, folic acid, riboflavin, magnesium, zinc, thiamine, niacin, and essential fatty acids

Figure 10 Cross-section of a grain of wheat

In the milling process (**Figure 11(c)**), the bran, germ, and endosperm are separated. The grain is heated to 200°C—a temperature that can kill healthful enzymes. If the flour is overexposed to air during heating, oils in the grain may become rancid. Today, whole-grain flour is made by adding back the germ and bran after grinding and separating the grain. White flour consists of ground-up endosperm, used in a variety of forms: bleached or unbleached, enriched or non-enriched. All-purpose, bread, cake, and pastry flours are some examples of white flour.

Further processing occurs as white flour is used to produce consumer products (**Figure 12**). Dough conditioners are added to bread, along with other ingredients to improve rise and prevent sticking. Chemical preservatives allow bread to be shipped long distances and to

DID **YOU** KNOW?

War and Fibre in Denmark
During the Second World War, flour refining was stopped in Denmark. Studies later related this action to a marked decline in cancer, heart disease, diabetes, kidney trouble, high blood pressure, and a drop in death rate.

remain on the shelf for many days without spoiling. Cold breakfast cereals and puffed grains require an extrusion process that uses high temperatures and high pressures. This process can further destroy nutrients, including the synthetic vitamins that are added to replace the vitamins that are destroyed by refining and milling. Such mass-produced, highly processed, and refined breads and baked goods have become the norm in our society.

Despite all the negatives, there are some practical reasons for refining grains. Bran and germ interfere with the bread-making qualities of flour. Fibre can actually reduce the nutritional value of foods by binding with proteins and reducing their effectiveness. Wheat bran contains phytic acid, which reduces the effectiveness of calcium. During the Second World War, when flour refining was less common, an epidemic of rickets (resulting from deficiencies in vitamin D and calcium) affected half of the children in the city of Dublin, Ireland. As well, the high fat concentration in the germ shortens the shelf life of whole grains. The oils oxidize easily, and a rancid taste can develop at about the same rate that milk sours.

Technology's answer has been to apply faster, hotter, and more aggressive processing. Consumers demand and receive a pure-looking product that will not spoil quickly. Today, most refined cereal products are fortified with B vitamins and iron to compensate for the nutrients that are lost during processing.

(a) List the nutrients that are lost when a wheat kernel is refined.

(b) Compare the nutritive content of white bread with the nutritive content of whole-grain bread, using the data in **Figure 12**.

(c) Use a flow chart to trace the processing of flour from kernel to bread slice.

(d) List the advantages and disadvantages of flour refining.

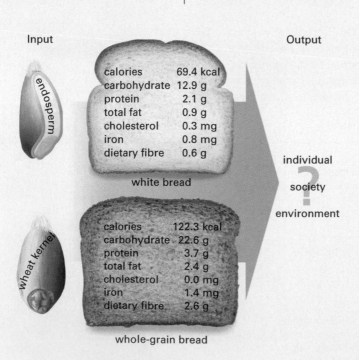

Input

endosperm

calories	69.4 kcal
carbohydrate	12.9 g
protein	2.1 g
total fat	0.9 g
cholesterol	0.3 mg
iron	0.8 mg
dietary fibre	0.6 g

white bread

wheat kernel

calories	122.3 kcal
carbohydrate	22.6 g
protein	3.7 g
total fat	2.4 g
cholesterol	0.0 mg
iron	1.4 mg
dietary fibre	2.6 g

whole-grain bread

Output

individual

? society

environment

Figure 12 Is all bread the same?

Explore *an* Issue

Food Refining

Food refining has considerable advantages for both manufacturers and retailers. Refined products have longer shelf lives and more uniform composition, taste, and appearance—qualities that consumers have come to expect (**Figure 13**). Food refining has advantages for the nutraceutical industry as well, because many people now augment their diets with nutritional supplements.

Food refining also has disadvantages, however. It removes valuable nutrients, including dietary fibre. The resulting product is unbalanced because only some nutrients are restored during the enrichment process. In communities where the basic diet is still natural and unrefined, the incidence of certain conditions, such as cancer and diabetes, is much lower or nonexistent compared with the incidence in our society. The costs for treating these conditions are high. Finally, refining involves chemical processes (such as bleaching) that have environmental as well as health implications.

Statement: The use of refined flour in food processing should be restricted to 50% of the total flour used.

Decision-Making Skills

○ Define the Issue
● Research
● Defend a Decision
● Identify Alternatives
● Analyze the Issue
● Evaluate

1. As a class, identify various stakeholders (such as nutritionists and manufacturers) for the issue.

2. Your group will select or be assigned to represent one stakeholder's position. Search for information in newspapers and periodicals, and on the Internet.

 www.science.nelson.com

3. Prepare an argument to support your stakeholder's position.

4. Use audiovisual aids to defend your stakeholder's position to the class.

5. Complete a cost–benefit analysis as different aspects of the issue are presented (see **Appendix A1**).

6. Attempt to reach a class consensus on the statement. Could you reach a consensus? Explain why or why not.

7. Write a paragraph that represents your personal opinion on the issue. Would you change bread types? Why or why not?

sugar cane

Figure 13 What are the advantages and disadvantages of refining food?

SUMMARY

- Research and development of space products has resulted in new forms of consumer foods.
- Food can be broadly categorized as natural versus modified or fortified, and organically grown versus chemically assisted.
- GEFs are one class of novel foods, regulated by Canada's Food and Drugs Act.
- Functional foods and nutraceuticals are products that provide health benefits beyond their nutritional value.
- NHPs are taken in dosage form to maintain or improve health or to prevent or treat diseases.
- The use of dietary supplements is recommended only in certain situations. Doses above the DRI may be toxic.
- Customized food products, such as meal replacements, are formulated to provide essential nutrients.
- Energy bars are becoming a popular alternative to chocolate in the North American diet.

- Dietary fibre can be soluble (pectin) or insoluble (cellulose). Fibre regulates our digestive system, preventing many diseases and disorders.
- Most of the essential nutrients in a wheat kernel are found in the germ and bran. Endosperm contains starch.
- There are both costs and benefits to our consumption of highly processed or refined foods.

Key Terms

organic food

fortified food

novel food

functional food

nutraceutical

natural health product (NHP)

dietary supplement

meal replacement

bran

germ

endosperm

ASSESSMENT

Understanding Concepts

1. Rick prepares himself a garlic, tomato, and broccoli stir fry. After he eats his stir fry, he has strawberry yogurt and tea. Identify the functional foods in Rick's meal, and specify the possible health benefits he receives.

2. Explain how "junk foods"—foods with little or no nutritional value—can be classified as functional foods.

3. Summarize the role and importance of dietary fibre.

4. List the principal nutrients that are found in wheat bran, germ, and endosperm. Use your list to rank the nutritive value in each of these three components of grain.

5. Which four essential nutrients are missing in the wheat kernel? Give one good food source of each missing nutrient.

6. Why is food refined? Describe the process of flour refining. What alternatives are available to the consumer?

7. Arrange all the Key Terms into a concept map, showing the interrelationships among the terms.

Applying Inquiry Skills

8. The food energy requirement for astronauts is determined by the National Research Council formula for basal energy expenditure (BEE). For women, BEE $= 655 + (9.6 \times W) + (1.8 \times H) - (4.7 \times A)$, where $W =$ weight in kg, $H =$ height in cm, and $A =$ age in years. For men, BEE $= 66 + (13.7 \times W) + (5 \times H) - (6.8 \times A)$. Calculate what your food energy requirement in space would be, using this formula.

9. Suppose that you have a family history of colon cancer. Compile a list of dietary suggestions (dos and don'ts) that you can follow.

 www.science.nelson.com

10. What's in a sports drink? Interpret the label shown in **Figure 14**. Use Internet resources to define each active ingredient, based on the food definitions in this topic. Describe each advertised benefit.

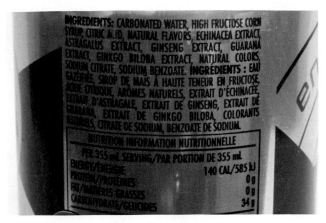

Figure 14

Making Connections

11. Read the article about food in space, found on the Nelson Web site. Then answer the following questions.

(a) Describe a beverage package, giving reasons for each modification.
(b) What is the Safe Haven food system? Why is this system necessary on the International Space Station?
(c) List five examples for each space food category.
    (i) NF   (ii) T   (iii) IM   (iv) R

12. Should nutraceuticals be registered as foods under Canada's Food and Drugs Act? Research this issue. Prepare a pros and cons table, and write a paragraph that summarizes your opinion.

13. Design a poster that promotes the health benefits of fibre. Use the slogan "A bran muffin a day keeps the doctor away."

14. Many people augment a balanced diet with vitamin pills and mineral supplements. What advice would you give them?

15. Suppose that you see two loaves of bread on the supermarket shelf. Both loaves are in brown wrappers, and both are described using healthy sounding words, such as "multigrain" and "cracked wheat." How would you decide which loaf to buy?

16. Under what circumstances would you use a meal replacement? Explain, using an example.

17. Use a diagram to describe how sugar is refined. What are the costs and benefits of consuming white sugar, to society and to the individual?

18. Many people strongly believe that all genetically engineered foods should be clearly labelled so that consumers can choose whether or not to buy them. Research the issue of labelling GEFs. What are the advantages and disadvantages of labelling? When your research is complete, write a letter to the editor of your local newspaper, outlining your position on this issue.

Reflecting

19. Eating is a big production, both for society and the individual. Food is expensive to produce, transport, and deliver. Food takes time to buy and prepare. As the world population increases, the land base for food production decreases. For decades, it has been technologically possible to nourish humanity with a "food pill" (**Figure 15**), yet we have not done so. Why not? How important is the act of eating to you?

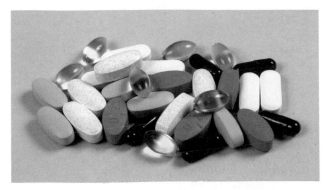

Figure 15

In Balance:
ENERGY
USE

Peter finishes the training run exhausted and out of breath. He knows that if he is going to make the dragon-boat team, he must be in shape. With his pack-a-day smoking habit and 18 kg of excess weight, becoming fit will be a struggle.

(a) Aside from its effect on physical fitness, tobacco addiction increases the risk factors for several health conditions. Name three health conditions associated with tobacco.

(b) What health conditions are associated with excess weight?

First, Peter goes to his family physician for a thorough checkup. Although he doesn't need a doctor to tell him that he is overweight and needs to quit smoking, he wants advice on lifestyle changes that will benefit him long after the dragon-boat races are over.

(c) Why should a weight-loss regime begin with a doctor's examination?

(d) What are some of the tests and procedures that Peter's doctor might suggest?

As Peter waits in the examining room, he notices the photos in **Figure 1**.

(e) Based on the photos, why should Peter quit smoking?

(f) Peter has been unsuccessful in previous attempts to quit smoking. What advice can you give him?

Aside from dragon-boat racing, Peter lives a sedentary life. He drives his car to and from work, and he spends his leisure time at home playing computer games. He knows that he lacks the knowledge and motivation to design his own fitness program. He selects a fitness centre (**Figure 2**) near his home that has a full range of equipment and employs both a nutrition counsellor and a personal trainer.

(g) Evaluate Peter's decision to join a fitness centre. What are the advantages and disadvantages of this approach?

(h) Why do you think Peter is interested in lifestyle changes rather than just a diet?

How would you rate your level of general health? What steps would you take if you wanted to improve your general health and well-being?

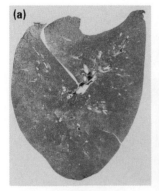
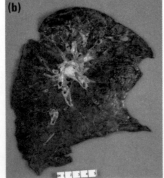

Figure 1 **(a)** A nonsmoker's lung **(b)** A smoker's lung

Figure 2 A one-stop fitness centre

Peter is a fast-food junkie. Several times a week, he eats breakfast at McDonald's (**Figure 3**), lunch at Dairy Queen, and dinner at KFC. In this activity, you will use the nutritional information on each company's Web site to calculate the energy value (in calories) of each meal, and obtain a daily total.

 www.science.nelson.com

(a) Create a table to calculate the food energy content of the following meals:

McDonald's breakfast
orange juice
sausage McMuffin
coffee with cream and sugar

Dairy Queen lunch
double cheeseburger
super fries
small chocolate shake
medium chocolate sundae

KFC dinner
2 pieces of original chicken recipe (59-g drumstick; 161-g breast)
potato wedges (102 g)
coleslaw (130 g)
apple pie slice (108 g)

(b) What is Peter's total food energy intake for these three meals? How does it compare with a suggested daily total of 11 300 kJ or 2700 kcal?

(c) Assess Peter's food choices using Canada's Food Guide. Which nutrients are in excess? Which nutrients are deficient?

(d) Based on these three meals alone, what advice do you have for Peter?

Figure 3 What is the energy value of this meal?

Food Energy

The human body burns food as fuel to provide energy. In Canada, energy is measured in joules (J), an SI unit named after British scientist James Joule (1818–1889). Food energy, however, is commonly measured in calories. One calorie is the amount of energy required to raise the temperature of one gram of water one degree Celsius (**Figure 4**). Food energy is often given in kilocalories or Calories (1000 calories): One kilocalorie (or one Calorie), is equal to 4.18 kJ. For example, the average daily energy requirement for an adult female can be expressed as 2200 kcal, 2200 Cal, or 9200 kJ.

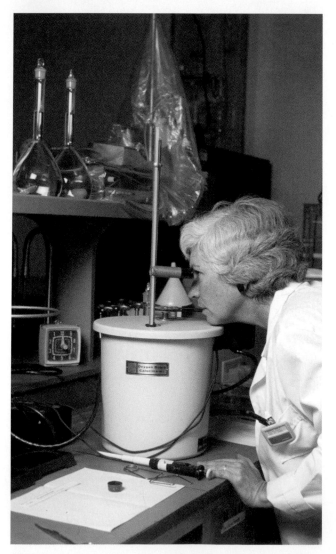

Figure 4 Energy measurements are obtained by burning food in a calorimeter.

Table 1 Energy Provided by Food

Component of food	Energy provided (kJ/g)	Energy provided (kcal/g)
carbohydrates	17	4
proteins	17	4
fats	38	9
alcohol	29	7
vitamins and minerals	0	0

Each component of food provides a predictable amount of energy in calorimeter tests (**Table 1**). In practice, our bodies use each component differently and at different rates.

Energy Balance

About half of our daily food intake is used to maintain the body at a constant temperature. The **basal metabolic rate (BMR)** is the energy required to maintain the body at rest: that is, awake but engaging in no physical activity. The BMR for an adult male ranges from 6688 kJ to 7524 kJ (1600–1800 kcal/day). The BMR for an adult female ranges from 5016 kJ to 6270 kJ (1200–1500 kcal/day).

Several factors affect BMR. Four of these factors are given below.

- Body composition: Lean tissue is metabolically more active than fat tissue.
- Age: BMR drops about 2% per decade after the age of 20 years.
- Gender: Female BMR is usually 10% lower than male BMR due to a higher percentage of body fat at similar body weight.
- Energy intake: As the body consumes less energy, it performs more efficiently (**Figure 5**).

Metabolism is the sum of all the chemical reactions that occur within the body cells. A chemical messenger that is produced in the thyroid gland (located in the neck) regulates the rate at which the body converts food energy into other forms of energy. As the release of the chemical messenger increases, metabolism

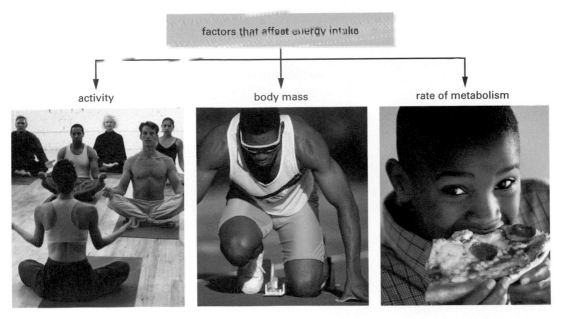

factors that affect energy intake

activity — body mass — rate of metabolism

Figure 5 Energy needs vary.

increases. Part of the energy from metabolism is converted into heat energy to warm the body. A person with a low metabolic rate uses food energy very efficiently. Little food energy is converted into heat, and therefore less energy escapes from the body. Instead, the food energy is converted into fat—the energy storage compound. A person with a high metabolic rate converts a large part of the food energy into heat. Consequently, less food energy is converted into fat and the person remains relatively thin.

The balance between energy input and energy output is finely tuned. To maintain balance, the energy in the food that is consumed should equal the energy output. The energy output is used for growth, exercise, and normal metabolic reactions (**Figure 6**). If food intake is increased or energy output is decreased, an imbalance occurs. The body gains mass as excess energy is converted into fat.

Table 2 lists the amount of energy that is required daily by humans of varying ages and lifestyles.

energy input (food)

energy output

activity

repair of damaged cells

maintenance of body temperature

excess energy stored as fat

Figure 6 Energy output must equal energy input in a balanced system. Unused energy is stored as fat.

D3: In Balance: Energy Use

Table 2 Daily Energy Requirements

Description	Energy requirement (kJ per day)	Energy requirement (kcal per day)
newborn	2 000	480
child (2–3 years old)	6 000	1440
teenage girl	9 500	2270
teenage boy	12 000	2870
office worker	11 000	2630
manual worker	15 000	3590

Estimating Body Fat

For males, the recommended body fat content is 15% to 18% of total body weight. For females, it is 20% to 25% of total body weight. With age, fat percentages rise in both males and females, reaching 30% to 40% of total body weight. The presence of excess body fat has been linked to cardiovascular disease, diabetes, high blood pressure, cancer, arthritis, gall bladder disease, certain reproductive disorders, and psychosocial difficulties. Body fat percentages can be determined in several ways:

- the caliper test, which measures skin-fold thickness (the thickness of the skin) at various locations on the body
- underwater weighing techniques
- an electrolipograph, which measures the movement of electrical impulses through body tissue

Height and weight measurements can be used to categorize body size. The **body mass index (BMI)** is calculated by dividing an individual's mass, in kilograms, by the square of his or her height, in metres. Adults of normal weight have a BMI of 18.5 to 24.9. A BMI of 27 indicates excess weight. Because the BMI does not distinguish between weight due to muscle and weight due to fat, it is not a foolproof way to define obesity. In general, however, as the BMI increases, so do health risks.

Almost one-third of adult Canadians are obese, according to the definitions in **Figure 7**.

Activity and Energy

For a person to maintain body weight, the intake of food energy must equal the BMR plus the energy expended during activities. When resting, the body

may need 20% fewer calories per day than when doing hard physical work or exercising strenuously. The rate at which stored energy is used during exercise depends on the intensity of the exercise and on body size. Higher-intensity activities, such as running, result in greater energy expenditures than lower-intensity activities such as walking (**Table 3**). The following Sample Problem shows how to use this information.

Sample Problem

How much energy does a 75-kg person require to sleep all day? The energy factor for sleeping is 4.1 kJ/kg/h. The total energy required can be calculated by multiplying the energy factor by the body mass, in kilograms, by the amount of time spent on an activity.

Solution

Given Information

energy factor = 4.1 kJ/kg/h
body mass = 75 kg
time = 24 h

energy required = energy factor × body mass × time
= 4.1 kJ/kg/h × 75 kg × 24 h
energy required = 7380 kJ

The energy required is 7380 kJ.

Definition of Obesity: Body fat content >25% (males) or >30% (females) total body weight, BMI >30

Figure 7 The definition of obesity in Canada

Weight loss requires a negative energy balance, which means that the total energy entering the body must be less than the total energy being used by the body. A negative energy balance may be achieved by eating less or exercising more, or by a combination of the two.

Weight gain requires a positive energy balance. The total energy entering the body must be greater than the total energy being used by the body. One kilogram of fat has the energy value of 32 200 kJ, or 7700 kcal.

Table 3 Energy Factors for Various Activities

Type of activity	Energy factor (kJ/kg/h)	Type of activity	Energy factor (kJ/kg/h)
sleeping	4.1	walking (6.4 km/h)	20.6
sitting	5.2	badminton	21.5
writing	6.0	cycling (15.3 km/h)	25.8
standing	6.3	hiking, fast dancing	27.0
singing	7.1	tennis, downhill skiing	36.2
keyboarding, card playing	9.0	climbing stairs, running (8.8 km/h)	37.5
washing the car, cooking	10.5	cycling (20.9 km/h)	40.5
playing piano	11.2	cross-country skiing	42.0
walking (3.2 km/h)	11.6	swimming crawl (45.7 m/min)	49.1
bowling	13.6	handball	49.5
cycling (13 km/h)	15.8	running (12.9 km/h)	62.0
walking (4.8 km/h)	16.2	competitive cross-country skiing	73.6

D3.2 Activity NO MORE COUCH POTATOES! >

A 1998–99 National Population Health Survey by Health Canada provided the following statistics:

- In Canada, 58% of youth, aged 12 to 19, were not physically active in the three months before the survey. There were significantly more inactive females (64%) than males (52%) (**Figure 8**).
- As many as 84% of youth may not be active enough to meet the guidelines for optimum growth and development.
- Youth in higher-income families are most likely to be physically active (56% versus 33%–43% for other income levels).

- The proportion of physically active people decreases with age. 55% of Canadians face increased risk of chronic disease and premature death as a result of physically inactive lifestyles.

In these statistics, the term "physically active" means using more than 12.56 kJ of energy per kilogram of body weight per day. International guidelines for youth recommend 25 kJ/kg/day to 34 kJ/kg/day—a much higher level of activity.

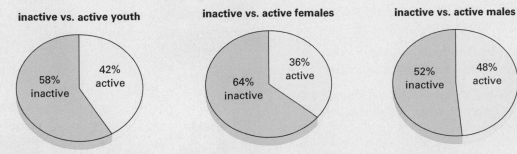

inactive vs. active youth 58% inactive 42% active

inactive vs. active females 64% inactive 36% active

inactive vs. active males 52% inactive 48% active

Figure 8 Physical activity in Canadian youth

Find *Canada's Physical Activity Guide to Healthy Active Living* and its accompanying handbook on the Nelson Web site. Study the handbook, and answer the following questions.

 GO | www.science.nelson.com

(a) List the benefits of regular physical activity.

(b) List the health risks of inactivity.

(c) What is a reasonable goal for daily physical activity? Do you meet this goal?

(d) After moderate exercise for 40 min, Peter felt warm and noticed that his breathing rate increased. What types of activities would likely result in these effects?

(e) Design a 20-point matching question that categorizes activities as Endurance, Strength, or Flexibility.

(f) How much energy would you have to expend each day to meet the Canadian definition of "physically active"? Are you physically active?

(g) Set goals for incorporating more physical activity into your daily life. Read the case histories and the activity suggestions for ideas.

(h) Take the Physical Activity Readiness Questionnaire (PAR-Q), found in the handbook. How did you rate?

(i) Create a one-week calendar to track your physical activity. Devise and follow a plan to increase your activity level. Write a reflective paragraph about the benefits you have observed, and any implications these benefits may have for you in future.

(j) Calculate your class average.

D3.3 Activity | MONITORING CARDIOVASCULAR FUNCTION

In this activity, you will determine your resting pulse and listen to your heart at rest and after exercise.

1. While sitting still, place your index and middle fingers near your wrist, as shown in **Figure 9**. The pulse you feel is blood rushing through the brachial artery in your arm.

(a) Count the number of heartbeats in 15 s. Calculate your heart rate as beats per minute.

2. Place a stethoscope (**Figure 10**) to your own chest, and listen for your heartbeat.

(b) Record what you heard.

3. After 1 min of moderate exercise (e.g., walking on the spot), listen for your heartbeat again using the stethoscope.

(c) Using the chest diagram provided, draw where you heard the clearest heartbeat.

(d) Did the sound of your heartbeat change after exercise? Describe what differences you heard.

(e) Explain why those differences occurred.

 Do not perform this activity if you are not allowed to participate in physical education classes.

Use rubbing alcohol to disinfect the earpieces of the stethoscope before and after use.

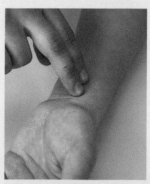

Figure 9 Arteries near the surface of the skin allow you to take your pulse.

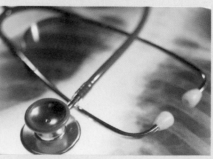

Figure 10 A stethoscope magnifies sounds within the body.

Cardiovascular Function

No larger than the size of your fist and with a mass of about 300 g, the heart beats about 72 times/min from the beginning of life until death (**Figure 11**). During an average lifetime, the heart pumps enough blood to fill two large ocean tankers.

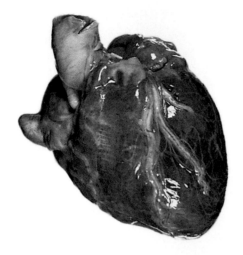

Figure 11   Mammalian heart showing atria and ventricles

Every minute, 5 L of blood cycles from the heart to the lungs, picks up oxygen, and returns to the heart. Then, the heart pumps the oxygen-rich blood and nutrients to the tissues of the body. The circulatory system plays a central role in providing the oxygen that the body's cells require. This oxygen is used to produce energy for a variety of processes including building new materials, such as proteins, and repairing tissues.

The human heart consists of two pumps separated by a wall of muscle. The pump on the right powers the pulmonary (lung) circuit. The pump on the left powers the systemic circuit (**Figure 12**). Each pump consists of a thin-walled **atrium** and a thick-walled **ventricle**. The atria receive blood from veins and pump it into the ventricles; the more muscular ventricles then pump the blood to distant tissues. When the heart muscles contract, the valves of the heart prevent blood from flowing back into the ventricles (**Figure 13**).

The familiar *lubb-dubb* heartbeat is caused by the closing of the heart values. When the atria (the upper chambers) are relaxed, they begin to fill with blood. This relaxation is called **diastole**. As the atria push blood into the ventricles (the lower chambers), they contract, pushing blood into the arteries. This contraction is known as **systole**. The increase in pressure during systole forces one heart valve shut, causing the *lubb* sound. As the ventricles relax, blood flows into them. The decrease in pressure causes a second heart valve to close with a *dubb* sound, preventing blood from flowing back from the arteries into the ventricles.

Every time the heart beats, blood surges through the arteries. This increase in pressure causes the arteries to stretch and increase in diameter. Where the arteries are near the surface of the body, the increase in diameter can be felt as the **pulse**.

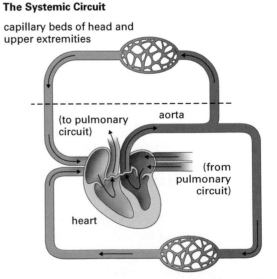

Figure 12   The pulmonary and systemic circuits of the circulatory system: The blood vessels carrying oxygenated blood are shown in red. The blood vessels carrying deoxygenated blood are shown in blue.

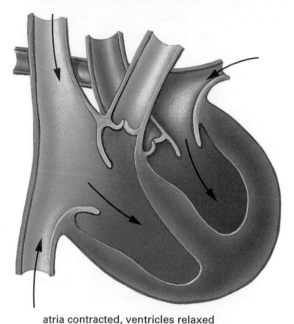

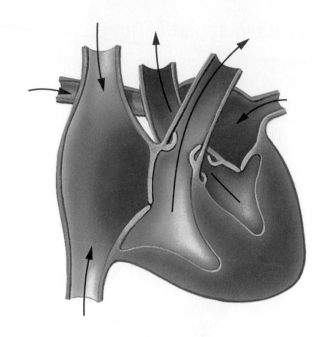

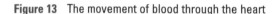

atria contracted, ventricles relaxed

atria relaxed, ventricles contracted

Figure 13 The movement of blood through the heart

Blood pressure is the force of the blood on the walls of the arteries. It can be measured with an instrument called a **sphygmomanometer**. A cuff with an air bladder is wrapped around the arm, and the air bladder is inflated with a pump. This action cuts off blood flow to the major arteries of the arm. A stethoscope is used to listen for the sound of blood entering the artery as air is gradually released from the cuff (**Figure 14**). The pressure on the gauge of the sphygmomanometer at which the sound is first heard is called the systolic blood pressure. Normal systolic blood pressure for a young adult is about 120 mm Hg (millimetres of mercury, a unit of pressure). The cuff is then deflated even more until the sound disappears—a result of blood flowing into the artery as the ventricles fill. At this point, the pressure on the gauge is called the diastolic blood pressure. Normal diastolic blood pressure for a young adult is about 80 mm Hg. The normal blood pressure for a young adult is reported as 120/80 ("120 over 80").

Many factors can raise or lower blood pressure from its normal range. Low blood pressure reduces the body's capacity to transport blood around the body. High blood pressure, called **hypertension**, can weaken an artery, which might result in the artery rupturing. Hypertension is associated with heart disease, stroke, and kidney failure.

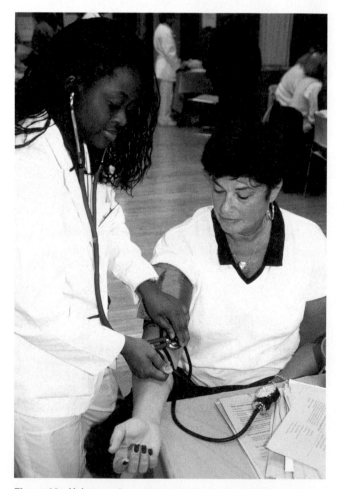

Figure 14 Using a sphygmomanometer and a stethoscope to measure blood pressure

There is overwhelming scientific evidence that establishes the relationship between exercise and cardiovascular health. The more physically active you are, the lower is your risk of developing a cardiovascular problem, such as atherosclerosis, coronary heart disease, or hypertension. Physical fitness does not guarantee that you will not develop any cardiovascular problems, but it significantly reduces your risk.

Personal fitness trainers need to understand the structure and function of body systems to determine the overall fitness of an individual and to plan an appropriate program (**Figure 15**). They use blood pressure and heart rate, along with other measures, such as endurance, strength, flexibility, body composition (the ratio of fat to bone to muscle), and recovery time.

Fitness trainers are particularly interested in aerobic fitness, which is the ability of the heart, lungs, and bloodstream to supply oxygen to the cells of the body (especially the muscle cells) during physical activity. Fitness trainers are also interested in how quickly the body returns to normal conditions after the stress of physical activity. The speed of recovery is an indication of the body's ability to maintain **homeostasis**, or balance.

In this investigation, you will use simple exercises to determine how your body responds to physical activity. You will note changes in blood pressure and

Inquiry Skills

○ Questioning	● Planning	● Analyzing
○ Hypothesizing	● Conducting	● Evaluating
● Predicting	● Recording	● Communicating

pulse rate that indicate your body's response. As well, you will compare the responses of smokers and nonsmokers to norms for your age group. The results of this investigation may give you a preliminary indication of your level of physical fitness.

Question
How are blood pressure and pulse rate affected during and after exercise?

Prediction
With a partner, discuss how blood pressure and pulse rate are affected during and after exercise.
(a) Predict how blood pressure and pulse rate are affected during and after exercise.

Experimental Design
(b) Design a controlled experiment to test your Prediction. In your design, include
- descriptions of the independent, dependent, and controlled variables
- a step-by-step description of the procedure
- a list of safety precautions
- a table to record your observations

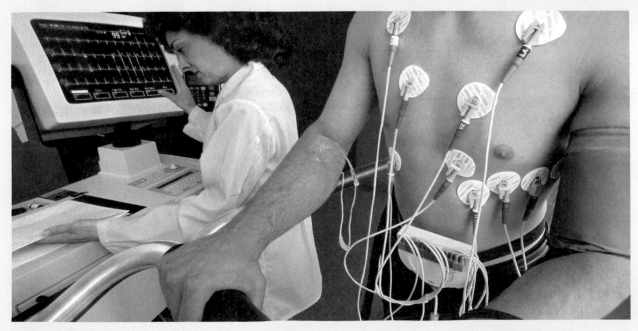

Figure 15 Some personal fitness assessment centres use technology to determine an individual's level of physical fitness.

Materials

stopwatch, or a watch with a second hand
sphygmomanometer
stethoscope

 Do not perform this investigation if you are not allowed to participate in physical education classes.

Procedure

1. Submit your Procedure, safety precautions, and observation table to your teacher for approval.

2. Carry out your Procedure.

3. Write a report. (See **Appendix A7** for the proper format.) In your report, be sure to include ways in which you could improve your Experimental Design.

Analysis

(c) On the same grid, plot your results for both your blood pressure and pulse rate. Determine your recovery time for each value. (*Hint:* Use two different vertical axes. Plot blood pressure on the left vertical axis and pulse rate on the right vertical axis.)

(d) Calculate the average recovery times of smokers and nonsmokers in your class.

How does your recovery time compare with these average recovery times? Explain, with reference to the group you belong to.

(e) Answer the Question based on your Analysis.

Evaluation

(f) Evaluate your Prediction.

(g) Describe any problems or difficulties you experienced while carrying out your Procedure. What could or should you have done differently?

Synthesis

(h) Give reasons for the pulse and blood-pressure changes observed in the nonsmoking group and the smoking group.

(i) Use the evidence obtained in this investigation to explain how the body maintains homeostasis.

(j) Explain how recovery time indicates level of physical fitness.

(k) Research the average resting pulse rate and blood pressure for your age and gender. How do your pulse rate and blood pressure compare with these values? What reasons can you suggest for any differences?

(l) If you repeated this investigation, what new variables would you study? Write a brief description of the new procedure.

✓ Check Your Understanding

1. After a workout, Arwen consumes a sports drink that contains 540 kJ of energy. How many kilocalories does the drink contain?

2. What is the basal metabolic rate? Describe factors that affect the BMR. Calculate your BMR by following links on the Nelson Web site.

 www.science.nelson.com

3. Estimate your daily energy requirements using the data in **Table 3** (on p. 253).

4. Write a summary paragraph using the terms *energy input, energy output, energy balance, weight loss,* and *weight gain*.

5. Define "body mass index." Calculate your BMI. Why is BMI not a foolproof method for assessing weight?

6. (a) Most people cannot work intensively for a long time. A well-trained cross-country skier, however, can operate at close to peak performance for 3 h or more! Using **Table 3** (on p. 253), calculate the total amount of energy that is used by a skier during a 3-h period of competitive cross-country skiing. Assume that the skier has a mass of 50 kg.

   (b) How long would you have to bowl to use the same amount of energy as the competitive cross-country skier in (a)?

7. Describe two instruments that are used to monitor cardiovascular function. How are these instruments similar? How are they different?

8. What is blood pressure? How is it determined?

Society & the Environment

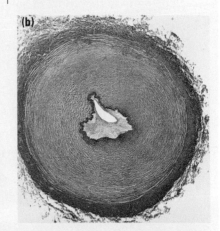

Heart-Smart Strategies

Heart disease is the leading cause of death in Canadians over the age of 65, and the second-most prevalent cause of death in the 45 to 64 age range. Blockage of blood flow through the heart arteries is usually caused by **atherosclerosis**. As fat molecules in the blood form larger and larger blockages, they slowly close off the opening of a blood vessel. Calcium and other minerals are deposited on top of the fat, forming plaque. The buildup of plaque in a coronary artery can narrow the artery (**Figure 16**), which causes a decrease in the supply of oxygen and other nutrients to the muscle tissues of the heart. If the supply is cut off, the tissues die and a heart attack,

or **myocardial infarction (MI)**, results. The common symptoms of an MI include sharp chest pain, pain in the neck and arms, shortness of breath, and nausea.

Some risk factors for heart disease—such as age, gender, genes, and diabetes—are uncontrollable. Other risk factors—such as smoking, hypertension, cholesterol, physical inactivity, excess weight, and stress—are controllable (**Figure 17**).

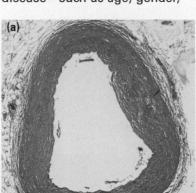

Figure 16 (a) A cross-section of a normal artery (b) A cross-section of an artery from a person with atherosclerosis: Plaque deposits have narrowed the passageway.

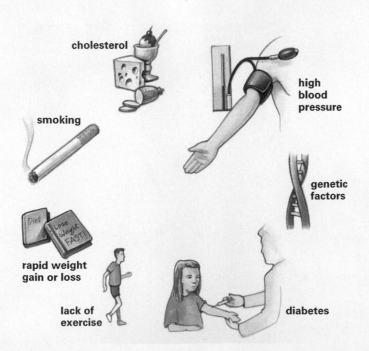

Figure 17 Stressors on a healthy heart: Usually, more than one factor contributes to the development of a cardiovascular problem.

(a) Draw a sequence of annotated diagrams illustrating plaque buildup in an artery.

(b) One cause of an MI is the obstruction of blood flow by plaque in a coronary artery. Describe another possible cause.

(c) Interview a heart attack survivor to obtain a description of her or his symptoms. Compare your description with the descriptions obtained by other class members. Speculate on reasons for differences.

(d) Form a hypothesis on how each controllable risk factor contributes to atherosclerosis.

D3.5 Activity | A HEART-SMART DIET

There is now a wealth of consumer information about meal planning and preparation for healthy hearts (**Figure 18**). A heart-smart diet is one that consists of

- reduced fat intake
- reduced salt intake
- lower caloric intake
- increased fibre intake

 GO | www.science.nelson.com

(a) Salt has not been discussed in this topic. Speculate on the effect of salt on cardio-vascular function.

(b) Compile a list of 10 substitutions in a heart-smart diet. For example, use 1% or skim milk instead of whole or 2% milk or cream.

(c) Construct a one-day heart-smart menu plan to provide nutrients and caloric intake for a moderately active adult male.

(d) Find three recipes that follow the guidelines for a heart-smart diet.

(e) Prepare one of these recipes at home. Report on the feedback you receive from those who ate it.

(f) In addition to smart eating habits, what else can you do to promote a healthy heart?

DID **YOU** KNOW?

Fat Teens
In North America, 80% of adolescents (13–18 years old) exceed the dietary recommendations for total and saturated fat.

Figure 18 Healthy eating promotes healthy hearts.

Responsibility for Heart Disease

A cigarette smoker has two to three times the risk of having a heart attack, compared with a nonsmoker. If a smoker also has high blood pressure and high cholesterol levels, then his or her chances of having a heart attack can be increased by up to eight times! Even light smokers have an increased risk of heart disease, with women having a relatively higher risk than men. A recent study shows that just half an hour of secondhand smoke can impair normal blood flow to the heart.

Inhaling tobacco smoke causes several immediate responses in the heart and blood vessels:

- Within 1 min after a person starts to smoke, the heart rate begins to rise. During the first 10 min of smoking, the heart rate may increase by as much as 30%.
- Nicotine raises blood pressure, causing the blood vessels to constrict, forcing the heart to work harder to deliver oxygen to the rest of the body.
- Smoking tends to increase blood cholesterol levels, which contributes to the buildup of fatty deposits in the arteries.
- Smoking raises the levels of fibrinogen (a protein that causes blood to clot) and platelets (also involved in the formation of blood clots), which make the blood stickier.
- Carbon monoxide in cigarette smoke attaches itself to the hemoglobin in red blood cells much more easily than oxygen does, reducing the amount of oxygen that is available to tissues.

All of these responses increase a smoker's risk of developing various forms of atherosclerosis. As atherosclerosis progresses, blood flow is restricted in narrowed arteries and the blood is more likely to form a clot. The sudden blockage of an artery with a clot may lead to a fatal heart attack or stroke (brain cell damage).

Many people, including a significant number of doctors, feel that smokers should assume their fair share of the costs associated with the diagnosis and treatment of their coronary heart disease. Since Canada has a system of public healthcare, however, smokers do not have to pay these costs.

Decision-Making Skills

- ● Define the Issue
- ● Research
- ● Defend a Decision
- ○ Identify Alternatives
- ● Analyze the Issue
- ● Evaluate

Statement: Smokers should assume some share of the costs for the diagnosis and treatment of coronary heart disease.

1. Research the correlation between heart disease and smoking, using links on the Nelson Web site.

 GO www.science.nelson.com

2. In a class discussion, consider the following questions to help you decide on the statement. Add more questions, as appropriate.
   - Is there adequate and valid scientific evidence to establish, with certainty, the relationship between smoking and heart disease?
   - Can doctors be certain that smoking has contributed to an individual's heart disease?
   - Why should smokers be singled out and treated differently than other people (e.g., overeaters), who may also incur additional costs to the healthcare system because of their lifestyle choices? What are some other diseases or conditions that may be caused by lifestyle choices? Should people with these diseases or conditions be required to contribute to the cost of their treatment?
   - How would you assign a percentage to each contributing risk factor for heart disease?
   - Is it fair that taxpayers must pay for the diagnosis and treatment of diseases that individuals can prevent? Should the taxes that smokers pay when they buy cigarettes be considered their share of the healthcare costs? Should tobacco companies pay some of the costs of diagnosis and treatment, since they make the cigarettes?

3. Set up a cost–benefit table to complete during the class discussion (see **Appendix A1**).

4. After you have weighed all the arguments, state and justify your decision in the form of a letter to your provincial Ministry of Health.

SUMMARY

- Lifestyle factors (such as exercise, diet, and smoking) can promote or impede optimum body function.
- In Canada, energy is measured in joules. Food energy is commonly expressed in calories (1 kcal = 4.18 kJ). Different nutrients provide different amounts of energy when metabolized: carbohydrates provide 17 kJ/g (4 kcal/g); proteins provide 17 kJ/g (4 kcal/g); and fats provide 38 kJ/g (9 kcal/g).
- The BMR is the minimum amount of energy that a resting person requires to maintain life processes. The BMR is affected by a number of factors.
- Food intake must provide enough energy for growth, exercise, and normal metabolic functions. Energy balance occurs when intake equals expenditure. Excess food energy is converted into fat at a rate of 32 200 kJ/kg (7700 kcal/kg).
- Several methods can be used to determine body fat percentages. The most common method is the BMI calculation. A BMI range of 18.5 to 24 is considered healthy for adults. A BMI of 27 is considered overweight. A BMI over 30 is considered obese. *CAUTION:* The BMI does not distinguish between muscle mass and fat mass.
- Most Canadian youth are physically inactive and consequently face increased risk of chronic disease and premature death.

- Cardiovascular function can be monitored using pulse and blood pressure measurements. A sphygmomanometer measures pressure differences as blood flows through the heart atria and ventricles. Normal adult blood pressure is 120 (systole) over 80 (diastole).
- Atherosclerosis (the formation of plaque obstructions in blood vessels) is the most common cause of MI, or heart attack. Risk factors for cardiovascular diseases may be uncontrollable (such as age, gender, genes, and diabetes) or controllable (such as smoking, hypertension, cholesterol, physical inactivity, excess weight, and stress.)
- To maintain a healthy heart, reduce your intake of fats, salt, and calories, and increase your intake of dietary fibre.

Key Terms

basal metabolic rate (BMR)	pulse
body mass index (BMI)	sphygmomanometer
atrium	hypertension
ventricle	homeostasis
diastole	atherosclerosis
systole	myocardial infarction (MI)

ASSESSMENT

Understanding Concepts

1. List factors that affect energy output.

2. Is it possible for two people who are equally active to maintain the same body mass yet eat different amounts of food? Explain your answer.

3. Define "physically active," using both Canadian and international standards. Use **Table 3** (on p. 253) to illustrate activities, and their duration, that would satisfy the requirements of each standard.

4. Kevin wants to lose 4 kg. How many kilojoules of energy does this mass represent? Express your answer in both kilojoules and kilocalories.

5. How does exercise affect your heart rate? your blood pressure? Provide an explanation for any change.

Applying Inquiry Skills

6. Refer to **Table 3** on page 253.
   (a) Calculate the amount of energy that is consumed by a 75-kg person while sitting for 5 h. How much energy is consumed by the same person while sitting and using a computer keyboard for 5 h?
   (b) Calculate the amount of energy that is required by a 55-kg person while standing for 5 h. How much more energy is required if the person sings while standing?
   (c) How much energy would you use during 25 min of continuous swimming? Show your work.
   (d) List the activities you participate in on a typical day. Estimate how much time you spend at each activity, and then calculate your energy demand for one day.

7. Three students measured their heart rates to test their bodies' responses to exercise. **Table 4** gives their results. Answer the following questions, and explain your thinking.
   (a) Which student is in the best physical condition?
   (b) What factors could account for the results of student 3?
   (c) Improve the design of the data table.

Table 4   Heart Rate Observations

Stage	Student		
	1	2	3
resting heart rate	68	76	71
rate after 1 min of exercise	74	80	74
rate after 5 min of exercise	85	94	80
rate 1 min after stopping	83	92	78
rate 3 min after stopping	79	88	75
rate 5 min after stopping	74	86	72

8. Follow links on the Nelson Web site to check the most recent survey of the Physical Activity Monitor by the Canadian Fitness and Lifestyle Research Institute. List the 10 most popular physical activities for youth in your province. Design a survey to determine the top 10 activities in your community. Account for differences in your provincial data.

 www.science.nelson.com

Making Connections

9. The Canadian population is facing an energy balance paradox. We are gaining weight while claiming that we are eating less and being more active. Your teacher will provide you with an article from the National Institute of Nutrition. Write a critique of this article.

10. Use information on the Nelson Web site to compare various methods of calculating body fat. Describe each method, and list its advantages and disadvantages.

 www.science.nelson.com

11. Some alcoholics may be obese, yet their dietary intake is poor. Explain this discrepancy.

12. As a person ages, the number of body cells steadily decreases and energy needs decline. If you were planning an older adult's diet, which foods would you emphasize, and why? Which foods would you de-emphasize, and why? Use the modified pyramid available on the Nelson Web site.

 www.science.nelson.com

13. Propose a course of action, from a political and/or economic perspective, to encourage people to eat less fast food. Identify the stakeholders and their positions.

14. Should smoking be allowed in bars and restaurants? Explain your answer. What is the current legislation in your province for smoking in public places? What is your personal stance on this legislation? Justify your position.

15. Currently, Canadians consume 38% of their daily calories from fat. Suggest ways to reduce fat in the diet.

16. Review the statistics compiled by the National Population Health Survey (p. 253). Suggest reasons for the data listed in each bullet.

17. Design a pamphlet that illustrates the relationship between smoking and heart disease. Consider distributing it to schools and community centres in your area.

Reflecting

18. Although fast-food companies are now developing and promoting "healthy menu choices," many nutritionists attribute North American health problems to fast-food consumption. Do you agree or disagree? Support your opinion using specific examples. How will your new awareness of this issue affect your dietary choices?

D4 Read *the* Label: FOOD ADDITIVES

Maeve stood in the soup aisle at the supermarket, dazzled by the display in front of her. On her grandmother's shopping list was "soup," but Maeve had no other information about the kind of soup her grandmother wanted (**Figure 1**). Maeve knew that her grandmother had diabetes and a heart condition, so it seemed to Maeve that her grandmother needed a soup that was "low"—low calorie, low sugar, low salt, and low taste.

Figure 1 Soup selection

(a) Are Maeve's conclusions correct? Be more precise about the dietary needs of an elderly, diabetic heart patient.

Maeve pulled out several dehydrated soup packages and studied the labels. She recognized the first few ingredients, but the vast majority resembled the chemicals on the labels of reagent bottles used in chemistry experiments (**Figure 2**).

INGREDIENTS: PASTA, DEHYDRATED VEGETABLES (TOMATOES, CORN, ONIONS, PARSLEY, BEETS), MODIFIED POTATO STARCH, SUGAR, SALT, HYDROGENATED SOYBEAN/ COTTONSEED OIL, MONOSODIUM GLUTAMATE, HYDROLYZED SOY PROTEIN, CORN SYRUP SOLIDS, COLOUR, CITRIC ACID, SPICE, SILICON DIOXIDE, DISODIUM GUANYLATE, DISODIUM INOSINATE AND SULPHITES. MAY CONTAIN TRACES OF MILK INGREDIENTS.

Figure 2 Ingredients in instant tomato pasta soup

(b) What are the general functions of the chemicals in foods?

(c) What factors do you consider when choosing a soup?

Next, Maeve moved to the baking area. Instead of sugar, her grandmother used artificial sweeteners in many recipes. What a bewildering array of sweeteners there was to choose from (**Figure 3**)! Maeve worried about the health risks that her grandmother was taking by eating synthetic sugar. After all, products deemed safe today could possibly be associated with a cancer risk in mice tomorrow.

Figure 3 Sugar substitutes

(d) Cyclamates are banned in the United States, yet permitted for use as tabletop sweeteners in Canada. Suggest reasons for this discrepancy.

(e) In 1977, the Canadian government banned saccharin as a food additive when the artificial sweetener was linked with bladder cancer in rats. The amount of saccharin that the rats consumed was the equivalent of a human drinking 800 cans of diet drink per day. Justify the government's decision.

(f) Definitive tests on food additives often involve animal testing. Explain your personal opinion about this practice.

How concerned are you about the number and types of additives in the food you consume? How important are food additives to your lifestyle?

D4.1 Activity | CHEMICAL SOUP

A typical instant soup package may contain the ingredients shown in **Figure 2** (on p. 264) In this activity, you will identify each food additive, and state its purpose in the soup.

1. List all the food additives given in **Figure 2** (on p. 264).
(a) What criteria did you use to determine whether the ingredient is a food additive?

2. Create a table to record each food additive and its purpose.

3. Complete your table using Internet databases on the Nelson Web site.

GO www.science.nelson.com

(b) Choose one of the food additives in your table. Find three other non-soup products in which the additive is used. How would each product be different if the additive was not used?

(c) Why can a soup made from the first six ingredients not be dehydrated, packaged, and sold to the consumer? Why are the other ingredients considered to be necessary?

D4.2 Activity | A FOOD ADDITIVE IN ACTION

When foods combine with the oxygen in air, a chemical reaction occurs. This reaction is called oxidation. It may result in a change in the food's colour, texture, flavour, and/or nutritional value. To limit or prevent the oxidation of food, anti-oxidants are added during processing. In this activity, you will test a common food additive that is used to prevent oxidation (**Figure 4**).

Figure 4 Setup for preventing oxidation

Materials
apple
knife
concentrated lemon juice
2 beakers or glasses
paper towel

1. Cut the apple into at least nine pieces.

2. Roll one-third of the apple pieces in lemon juice, and drain off the excess.

3. Roll one-third of the apple pieces in water, and drain off the excess.

4. Leave one-third of the apple pieces uncoated, as the control group.

5. Leave all the apple pieces undisturbed on a paper towel for about 30 min.
(a) Record your observations.
(b) Analyze your observations. Propose reasons for differences among the three groups of apple pieces.
(c) Suggest one other substance in your kitchen that would have the same effect as the lemon juice.
(d) What chemical is used in the food industry to prevent oxidation of cut fruit pieces?

GO www.science.nelson.com

The Classification of Food Additives

Humans have added substances to foods for thousands of years in order to preserve or improve the taste. Today, food additives allow consumers to enjoy a variety of safe, tasty, and convenient foods year-round, without having to shop daily. Health Canada defines a food additive as any substance that, when added to food, becomes part of the food or alters the characteristics of the food. Condiments (such as sugar, salt, and pepper) are considered to be ingredients, not food additives. **Non-nutritive food additives** do not contribute to the nutritive value of foods and are not foods themselves. An example is potassium nitrite. This salt is added to cured meat and poultry products as a preservative agent. It is responsible for the pink or red colour of many preserved meats, such as bacon and hot dogs. Foods that are treated with such preservatives take longer to spoil.

In Canada, the use of food additives is regulated by the Food and Drugs Act. Food additives may be classified broadly (**Figure 5**) or according to use (**Table 1**).

Table 1 Classification of Non-Nutritive Food Additives According to Use

Purpose or use	Examples of products
Product consistency: Emulsifiers, stabilizers, thickeners, and leaveners give products a consistent texture. Anti-caking agents help substances, such as salt, flow freely. Other chemicals help to modify the acidity and alkalinity of foods.	baked goods, cake mixes, salad dressings, ice cream, processed cheeses, table salt, chocolate
Food preservation: Preservatives retard product spoilage caused by mould, bacteria, fungi or yeast, or by exposure to air. They extend the shelf life, or "keeping quality," of food.	breads, cured meats, fats, oils, cheeses, crackers, potato chips, cake mixes, soft drinks, frozen and dried fruits
Taste and appearance: Natural and synthetic flavours enhance the taste of foods. Natural and synthetic colours enhance the appearance of certain foods to meet consumer expectations.	soft drinks, soups, candies, baked goods, jams, yogurts, cheeses

DID **YOU** KNOW?

Food Additives Add Up!
It is estimated that an individual consumes about 65 kg of food additives each year.

Food Additives

Incidental or Indirect
Pesticides, dioxin, asbestos, antibiotics, trace metals, hydrocarbons, microbial toxins

Intentional or Direct
Identified on product label

Manufacturers assure that amounts present are so insignificant as to be safe.

Figure 5 A broad classification of food additives

Profile of a Non-Nutritive Food Additive: Caffeine

Caffeine is considered to be the world's most popular drug. Some surveys show that over 50% of North Americans begin their day with a cup of coffee, a well-known source of caffeine (**Figure 6**). The caffeine in coffee, tea, and cocoa is naturally present. Caffeine can be extracted from the seeds or leaves of these plants and added to other consumer products, such as soft drinks and headache and cold remedies.

Figure 6 Is caffeine the world's most popular drug?

Consider the following facts about caffeine:

- Caffeine is a mild stimulant. It activates the central nervous system, stimulates the digestive tract, speeds up metabolism, increases urine output, temporarily raises blood pressure, and elevates the brain levels of serotonin (a neurotransmitter that affects mood).
- In high doses, caffeine can elevate blood sugar and cause rapid heartbeat, irritability, insomnia, and anxiety.
- There has been some evidence associating caffeine with heart disease, certain cancers, infertility, birth defects, and osteoporosis.
- Caffeine is used to treat migraine headaches. It increases the potency of analgesics (such as Aspirin) and can relieve asthma by widening the breathing passages.
- The body cells absorb caffeine within 15 min to 45 min of consumption. On average, caffeine has a half-life of about 3 h. (In other words, within 3 h, 100 mg is reduced to 50 mg).
- Smokers remove caffeine from their blood twice as fast as nonsmokers. Smokers tend to drink more coffee than nonsmokers.

- To enhance performance, many athletes consume a cup of coffee or the equivalent amount of caffeine from a supplement or other food source (about 85 mg) 1 h before an endurance exercise. Larger amounts of caffeine appear to be counterproductive. The International Olympic Committee (IOC) has banned caffeine above a urine level of 12 µg/mL (the equivalent of four large cups of coffee).
- Current evidence suggests that a daily intake of up to 450 mg of caffeine (four large cups of coffee) poses no threat to a healthy adult, although there is a wide range of sensitivity.
- Regular drinkers develop a tolerance to caffeine. Many people become addicted to caffeine. Withdrawal symptoms include headaches, irritability, sleepiness, and lethargy.
- Because caffeine crosses the placenta and is transferred into breast milk, it is not recommended for pregnant or breast-feeding women. People who experience irregular heartbeats or palpitations are advised to reduce or eliminate caffeine.

D4.3 Activity TRACKING CAFFEINE CONSUMPTION

Where do you fall on the caffeine scale?

1. Use **Table 2** to help you monitor your daily caffeine intake over three days. Copy the table, and complete it with specific data found in the table called "Caffeine Content of Food and Drugs" on the Nelson Web site.

 www.science.nelson.com

2. Answer the following three questions. They may help you decide whether you should change your caffeine-drinking habits.
   (a) What is your average daily caffeine intake?

(b) Considering the effects of caffeine, do you wish to decrease your daily intake of caffeine? Formulate an action plan. Consider limiting caffeinated drinks by choosing another drink on occasion, or switching to only decaffeinated drinks.

(c) In the future, could caffeinated drinks be cast in the same unsavoury light as tobacco? Take an interactive caffeine quiz on the Nelson Web site to discover more about the effects of coffee and tea.

 www.science.nelson.com

Table 2 Sample Observations

Source of caffeine	Amount of caffeine per serving (mg)	Number of servings	Total (amount per serving × number of servings)
coffee, brewed, 227 g	135		
coffee, decaffeinated, 227 g	5		
tea, 227 g	50		
cola, 280-mL can	35		

D4.4 Investigation | THE BODY'S RESPONSE TO CAFFEINE

A pulmonary function test measures the amount of air that is taken into the lungs with a deep breath, and the speed at which the air is expelled. Respirometers (**Figure 7**) and spirometers are used in pulmonary function tests to monitor respiratory conditions. Obstructive lung diseases (such as asthma, emphysema, and chronic bronchitis) cause a decrease in the air flow, due to a narrowing or blockage of the airways. Restrictive lung diseases (such as pulmonary fibrosis) cause a decrease in the amount of air that is inhaled, due to a decrease in the elasticity or amount of lung tissue.

The volume of a normal breath and your maximum lung volume can be used to indicate your health. **Figure 8** shows the various relationships between lung volumes and breathing depths. The terms that are used in **Figure 8** are defined below.

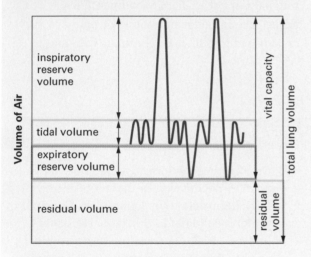

Figure 8   Lung volumes and breathing depths

Definitions of Terms

inspiratory reserve volume: the amount of air that can be forcibly inhaled after a normal inhalation

tidal volume: the amount of air that is inhaled and exhaled in a normal breath

expiratory reserve volume: the amount of air that can be forcibly exhaled after a normal exhalation

vital capacity: the amount of air that can be exhaled

residual volume: the air that remains in the lungs and respiratory tract after exhalation (approximately 20%)

total lung volume: vital capacity plus residual volume

Inquiry Skills

○ Questioning   ○ Planning   ● Analyzing
○ Hypothesizing   ● Conducting   ● Evaluating
● Predicting   ● Recording   ● Communicating

Figure 7   Measuring lung capacity

In this investigation, you will measure lung volumes that correspond to different depths of breathing. You will then repeat these measurements after consuming a caffeinated drink, to determine the effect of this common food additive on your body.

Question

What effect does caffeine consumption have on your normal and maximum breathing volumes?

Prediction

(a) Predict the effect of caffeine consumption on your normal and maximum breathing volumes.

Materials

spirometer with disposable mouthpieces
nose plug (optional)
250-mL caffeinated beverage

 NEVER inhale through the spirometer mouthpiece.

Do NOT share mouthpieces.

Label one end of the mouthpiece "mouth." Always exhale into this end of the mouthpiece.

Procedure

1. Set the spirometer gauge to zero. Place a new, unused mouthpiece in the spirometer.

2. Relax and allow yourself to get into a regular, calm breathing pattern. Then, AFTER inhaling normally, put the mouthpiece in your mouth, hold your nose closed, and exhale normally through your mouth.

(b) Read the gauge on the spirometer. Record the value as your tidal volume in a data table.

3. Reset the spirometer gauge to zero. Inhale and then exhale normally. AFTER exhaling normally, put the mouthpiece in your mouth and forcibly exhale all of your remaining air.

(c) Record this value as your expiratory reserve volume in your data table.

4. Repeat step 3, but this time take a deep breath and then exhale fully, forcing the maximum volume of air from your lungs.

(d) Record this value as your vital capacity in your data table.

(e) Use the relationships shown in **Figure 7** (on p. 268) to calculate your inspiratory reserve volume. Record this value in your data table.

(f) Record data from at least two other students in your data table.

5. Repeat steps 1 to 4, 60 min after consuming 250 mL of a caffeinated drink approved by your teacher.

Analysis

(g) Answer the Question.

(h) How do your lung volumes compare with the lung volumes of your classmates?

(i) How might body size, gender, or health account for any differences?

Evaluation

(j) Evaluate your Prediction.

(k) Describe any problems or difficulties you experienced while carrying out the Procedure. What could or should you have done differently?

Synthesis

(l) People who are going to have a pulmonary function test are advised to avoid cola, chocolate, and other agents that contain caffeine for 6 h before the test. Explain why.

(m) Hypothesize on the effects of caffeine on heart rate and blood pressure. Design and conduct an investigation to test your hypothesis.

(n) Design an investigation that would allow you to determine the effect of physical activity on lung capacity.

(o) In this investigation, you studied the effects of caffeine on lung capacity and breathing rates. Suggest other factors that may influence lung capacity and breathing rates.

(p) Bronchial asthma is characterized by a reversible narrowing of the breathing passages. How might this condition affect your expiratory reserve volume? Give reasons for your answer.

(q) Research suggests that caffeine improves airway function by a modest amount in asthmatic patients for up to 4 h. Use the Internet to find evidence from two recent experiments.

 www.science.nelson.com

✔ Check Your Understanding

1. What is a non-nutritive food additive? What is a nutritive food additive? Give two examples of each.

2. Describe two ways in which food additives are categorized.

3. For what purposes are non-nutritive food additives used in baked goods?

4. Is lemon juice a nutritive or non-nutritive food additive, as you tested it in D4.2 Activity: A Food Additive in Action?

5. Classify each non-nutritive food additive according to its use.

   caffeine   potassium nitrite
   cyclamate   baking powder

6. Create a table to summarize what you have learned about caffeine. Divide your table into three columns, with the following headings: Positive, Negative, Neutral.

7. Describe two different types of lung disease.

The Costs and Benefits of Non-Nutritive Food Additives

Eating a turkey sandwich on whole-wheat bread, with potato chips and a soft drink, sounds pretty good. Does eating nitrate, sodium stearyl lactylate, monocalcium phosphate, and aspartame have the same appeal? Probably not, but these are only some of the additives that are commonly found in sandwich meat, bread, and almost every other type of processed food.

We know a lot about the benefits of food additives. What about the negatives? Officially, food additives may not be used to conceal damage or spoilage,

to deceive consumers, or to reduce the nutrient content of a product. As well, they may not be used in excess of the technical amounts needed to perform their functions. Despite all the safety testing, however, there are documented relationships between additives and human health, as summarized in **Table 3**.

(a) Review and list the benefits of using non-nutritive food additives.

(b) What are the most common health risks associated with non-nutritive food additives?

(c) Present the information in **Table 3** in the form of a concept map. Use the heading "Health Risks of Non-Nutritive Food Additives."

(d) What steps can you take to decrease the quantity of non-nutritive food additives you consume?

DID **YOU** KNOW?

Poisons in Our Food
Harmful additives that were used in the past as colour or flavour enhancers included poisonous copper sulfate to colour pickles, alum to whiten bread, and indigo to colour tea.

Table 3 Relationships between Additives and Human Health

Type of non-nutritive food additive	Effect on human health
artificial food colours	allergies, asthma, hypersensitivity, some cancers
artificial flavours	allergic or behavioural reactions
artificial sweeteners (aspartame, acesulfame K, and cyclamate)	behavioural problems, allergies, hyperactivity, possibly cancers
preservatives (such as BHA, BHT, and EDTA)	allergic reactions, hyperactivity, some cancers, possible liver and central nervous system toxicity
nitrites and nitrates	metabolize into nitrosamines, which can cause cancers
sulfites (sulfur dioxide and metabisulfites)	allergic and asthmatic reactions
monosodium glutamate (commonly known as MSG)	common allergic and behavioural reactions, including headaches, dizziness, chest pains, depression, and mood swings; also a possible neurotoxin

CS

The average Canadian consumes a larger amount of soft drinks than water.

1. Answer the following questions, using information from the Nelson Web site.

 www.science.nelson.com

(a) What food ingredients are in soft drinks?
(b) List the typical non-nutritive food additives in a can of cola, and describe the purpose of each.
(c) Outline the nutritional impact of soft drinks.
(d) Outline the health impact of soft drinks.
(e) Compare the nutritional and health impacts of regular and diet soft drinks.
(f) A typical soft drink contains 630 kJ (150 kcal) of food energy. If you drink two cans of soft drinks daily, how many days would it take you to gain an extra kilogram? Based on this number, how much weight would you gain in one year? (Assume that you are already consuming enough food to maintain your weight.)

(g) What can you conclude about soft drink consumption?
(h) Debate the following statement: "Soft drink vending machines should be banned in schools."

2. The new generation of soft drinks uses guarana as a source of caffeine. Products like Guru, Speedster Fruit Punch, Pro Circuit Thermo Charge Fruit Punch, and Raw Extreme Thermogenic Fruit Punch are marketed as energy drinks. Use links from the Nelson Web site to answer the following questions.
(a) Compare the caffeine content of these guarana-containing products with the caffeine content of a can of cola.
(b) Why are guarana drinks not regulated by Health Canada?

 www.science.nelson.com

Explore *an* Issue

Food Additive Safety

Like many scientific developments, food additives are a controversial issue. Research supports the relationships listed in **Table 3** (on p. 270) but the link is not as direct as in other relationships. Does cooking in aluminum pots predispose an individual to Alzheimer's disease? What is the relationship between food additives and attention deficit and hyperactivity disorder (ADHD)? Will the sugar substitute that is deemed "safe" today be safe tomorrow?

1. Choose one additive that has been linked to health problems.

2. Search for information about the additive in newspapers and periodicals, and on CD-ROMs and the Internet.

 www.science.nelson.com

Decision-Making Skills

● Define the Issue ○ Identify Alternatives
● Research ● Analyze the Issue
● Defend a Decision ○ Evaluate

3. Express the additive–health relationship in the form of a question.

4. Identify the issue, and explain why it is controversial.

5. Complete a cost–benefit analysis of the additive, based on the information from your research (see **Appendix A1**).

6. Identify various foods that contain the additive.

7. Prepare a 1-min newscast, commercial, or radio advertisement that reflects your opinion on the issue.

SUMMARY

- Most processed, packaged food products that are sold today contain additives.
- Food additives may be classified as direct (intentional) or indirect (incidental), or nutritive or non-nutritive. They may also be classified according to their use.
- Non-nutritive food additives are used to maintain product consistency, to preserve the food's palatability and/or wholesomeness, to enhance taste and appearance, and to prolong shelf life.
- Caffeine is a mildly addictive stimulant that is widely added to food products. There are risks and benefits to the use of caffeine. Ingesting a small amount of caffeine may improve lung function by widening the breathing passages.
- The consumption of non-nutritive food additives has been linked to health problems, such as cancer, allergies, asthma, hyperactivity, headaches, and other neurological conditions.
- Soft drinks present many health risks, because of what they contain and what they replace in the diet.

Key Term

non-nutritive food additive

ASSESSMENT

Understanding Concepts

1. Classify each additive as direct or indirect:

soil bacteria	caffeine	dye
lead	MSG	potassium nitrite
dioxin	antibiotics	vitamin D

2. Yeast is a single-celled organism that is used to make wines ferment and breads rise. Classify this additive based on the information in **Figure 5** and **Table 1** (both on p. 266).

3. Under what conditions is the use of food additives forbidden?

4. List the major health risks that are associated with food additives.

5. Describe how caffeine affects body functions.

Applying Inquiry Skills

6. Design and conduct a survey to determine daily soft drink consumption in your school. Summarize your results in a 30-s radio announcement. In your announcement, include information about the health risks associated with soft drink consumption.

7. Maeve noticed that she got a headache after drinking three cups of artificially sweetened coffee in an hour. She hypothesized that the aspartame was responsible.
   (a) Evaluate her hypothesis.
   (b) Design an experiment to test her hypothesis.

8. A research group studied a group of elite cyclists and a group of high-school students to determine whether caffeine provided any clear advantage. Each group pedalled at 80% maximum capacity for as long as possible. **Table 4** shows the average amount of time that each group was able to pedal after drinking decaffeinated coffee and after drinking caffeinated coffee.

Table 4 Observations

Group	Average cycling time (min)	
	Decaffeinated coffee (250 mL)	Caffeinated coffee (250 mL, 340 mg caffeine)
elite athletes	82	123
students	41	42

   (a) Identify the issue that was studied by the research group.
   (b) Identify the control for the study.
   (c) Identify the independent and dependent variables.
   (d) What conclusions can you draw from the data?
   (e) Neither group was told which coffee contained caffeine. Why?
   (f) The description of the study does not indicate how much time passed between each exercise test. Explain why it is important to know this factor.

9. The average vital capacity for young adult males is 4600 mL of air. Compared to this figure, use the terms "higher" or "lower" to predict the vital capacity of each of the following people:
   (a) a young adult female
   (b) an asthmatic male
   (c) an athletic male
   (d) an obese female
   (e) a young adult male after drinking 135 mg of caffeine

Making Connections

10. Use Internet sources to complete **Table 5**. List three examples for each purpose or use. Record any reported side effects for each example.

Table 5 Food Additives

Purpose or use	Food additive	
	Example	Side effects
gives or retains food colour		
preserves food		
artificial sweetener		
flavour enhancer		
maintains food texture		

11. It is difficult to find a list of banned food additives. It is much easier to find lists of permitted food additives. Suggest why lists of permitted additives are more readily available.

12. Peter is 18 kg overweight. He drinks about six cups of coffee and smokes a pack of cigarettes daily. Speculate on his lung capacity, heart rate, and blood pressure. What health risks does he face? Suggest lifestyle changes to reduce these risks.

13. Learn more about artificial sweeteners from the article on the Nelson Web site. Compare the four major groups of sweeteners to sugar, in terms of their sweetness, caloric content, advantages of use, and associated risks.

14. In Canada, 20% of children between the ages of 1 and 2 years old already consume soft drinks. What dangers do you see in this practice?

15. Caffeine is a diuretic. Define the term "diuretic." Suggest several effects that excessive caffeine consumption might have on body function.

16. Is there any evidence to suggest that food additives cause attention deficit hyperactivity disorder? Using Internet search engines, define this disorder, summarize possible causes, and present results from recent studies.

17. Choose a specific career related to food—product development, testing, packaging, or marketing. Collect information on the educational background, aptitudes, required skills, typical tasks, and salary range of the chosen career.

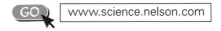

Reflecting

18. What is the price of progress? Most of the food we buy has been "processed," and processing means additives. How confident are you that the food you eat is safe? What is your philosophy of food selection?

Weighty Issues:
FAD DIETS *and* EATING DISORDERS

Five students in Ms. Fex's science class looked nervously at the next question in their assignment: "Calculate and interpret your BMI using the information in **Figure 1**." Calculating was easy. Interpreting, however, would force them to confront issues at the core of who they were and how they felt about themselves.

Kiyo was into calculations. He had used formulas for years to determine the balance of protein supplements and steroids that sustained his trim, sculpted form. A BMI of 32 was testament to his ability to achieve a goal. He was all muscle and no fat. He laughed at the idea of being in the obese category.

(a) Is Kiyo obese?

(b) Protein is a major nutrient. How can too much of a good thing be bad?

(c) List what you know about the dangers of steroid use.

At the other end of the BMI scale, Tami looked astounded at her BMI calculation of 17. How could it be, when she knew that she was fat? She appeared fat in the mirror. She felt fat. Tami imagined herself gaining weight just by looking at food. The mere thought of eating nauseated her.

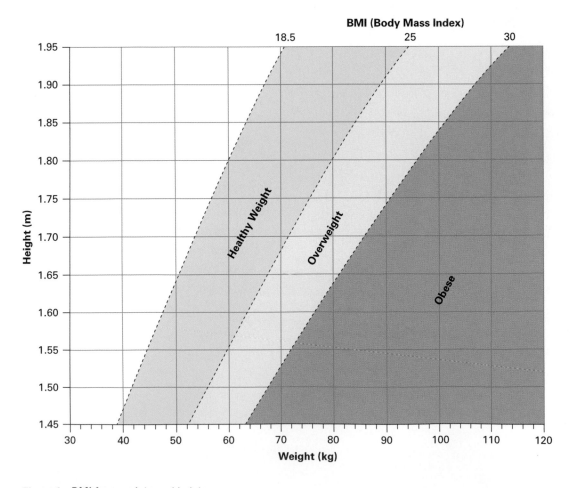

Figure 1 BMI from weight and height

(d) Speculate on Tami's eating disorder. List what you know about its causes and effects.

Cam studied his BMI calculation of 38 and wondered if he could fudge the number a little. But what was the point? He was grossly obese and had been for years. His parents were obese, as were his brothers and sisters. He didn't think he ate any more than his classmates. Even when his doctor prescribed sensible weight-loss regimes, they didn't seem to make a difference. The kilos kept piling on.

(e) Is obesity genetically or environmentally determined?

(f) Put yourself in Cam's shoes. Write a reflective paragraph about how it would feel to be extremely obese in our society.

At 23, Caitlin's BMI was in the average range. What the number did not reflect was the fact that her weight had fluctuated 40 kg in the past year. At this point, she was midway into the cycle. She had struggled with bulimia since a bullying incident, and trouble at home did not help. When the pressures became too much, it was hard to resist the binge-and-purge cycle. Caitlin was aware of the health risks, however, and was determined to succeed.

(g) List what you know about bulimia—its causes and effects.

Meredith's BMI of 25 indicated borderline overweight, where she has been all her life. Although her bubbly personality hid her weight insecurities, she felt like an ox beside her size-six friends. Even one clothes size smaller would be an improvement. To this end, Meredith tried every fad diet going. For a while, each diet seemed to work. But the "rules" were so strict that eventually she slipped back into her old eating habits and the weight returned.

(h) In general, how successful is dieting?

(i) Describe some of the fad diets and weight-loss regimes on the market today.

(j) Interview a friend or family member who is following a fad diet or weight-loss regime. Which foods are permitted? Which foods are forbidden? How successful is the diet perceived to be?

(k) How do you feel about dieting? Describe your own approach to weight management.

(l) Write a cautionary paragraph about using BMI as a health index. (**Figure 2** may give you some ideas.)

Figure 2 Who has the ideal BMI?

Is dieting the answer to all of our weight problems? Are the new fad diets effective and safe? What's the most appropriate solution to our weight problems?

Science & Technology

Overnutrition

Overnutrition is the long-term consumption of excess nutrients. In North America, overnutrition is caused by the consumption of excess proteins, carbohydrates, fats, and minerals (salt). The health risks of high nutrient intake are summarized in **Table 1**.

The consumption of excess nutrients also leads to excess energy intake, which can cause serious health conditions. Some examples are hypertension, high blood cholesterol, heart disease, stroke, insulin resistance (glucose intolerance), diabetes, gallstones, gout, osteoarthritis, sleep apnea, cancers (endometrial, colon, breast, and prostate), menstrual irregularities, infertility, irregular ovulation, urinary stress incontinence, uric acid kidney stones, and psychological disorders (depression, eating disorders, distorted body image, and low self-esteem).

The most obvious result of overnutrition is obesity, a health condition that affects a growing number of Canadians. Obesity is a disease of complex, multiple causes, which lead to an energy imbalance and to the accumulation of large amounts of body fat. Obesity is measured most often as excessive weight for a given height, and it is defined as a BMI over 30. Obesity can be confirmed using measurements such as waist circumference (**Table 2**) and waist–hip ratio. Both measurements are good predictors of the health risks of excess weight.

Table 2 The Relationship Between Waist Circumference and Obesity-Related Complications

| Gender | Risk of obesity-associated metabolic complications | |
	Increased	Substantially increased
males	>94 cm	>102 cm
females	>80 cm	>88 cm

DID **YOU** KNOW?

More Fat, Not More Fat Cells
The number of fat cells in your body does not change after puberty. As your body stores more fat, each fat cell simply gets bigger.

Table 1 Health Risks Associated With a High Intake of Certain Nutrients

Nutrient	Health risks
proteins	Excess proteins cause extra metabolic stress to be placed on the liver and kidneys.
	They may trigger allergies.
	They may lead to dehydration due to excessive urine output.
	They may also lead to loss of calcium, resulting in osteoporosis or the formation of kidney stones.
carbohydrates	Excess carbohydrates can increase the level of blood fats, which is a risk factor for artery and heart diseases.
salt (sodium)	The average North American daily sodium intake is 20 times higher than the recommended 2400 mg.
	Excess salt intake is associated with high blood pressure (cardiac disease and stroke), stomach cancer, cataracts, and osteoporosis.
	Overweight people tend to retain sodium and are more sensitive to its effects.
fats (saturated fats and cholesterol)	Saturated fats raise low-density lipoprotein (LDL) cholesterol levels, directly implicated in the formation of arterial plaques.
	Blood cholesterol levels are more directly affected by the amount of saturated fats consumed than by the amount of cholesterol consumed.
	Hydrogenated or trans fats act like saturated fats by raising LDL and lowering HDL cholesterol levels.

A simple imbalance between energy input and expenditure is one cause of weight gain leading to obesity. As **Figure 3** shows, however, many other causes may also be involved.

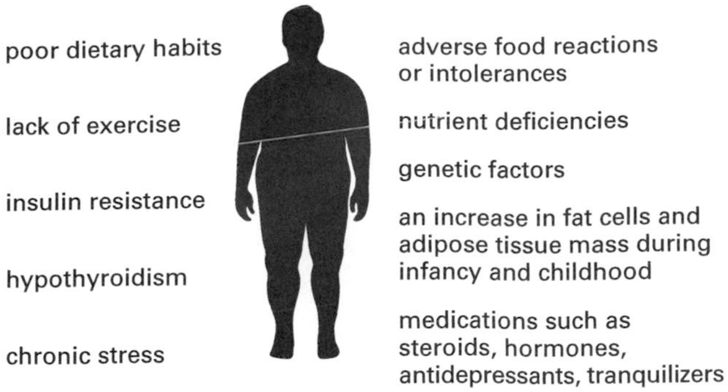

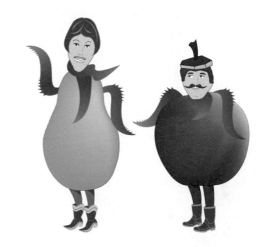

poor dietary habits

lack of exercise

insulin resistance

hypothyroidism

chronic stress

adverse food reactions or intolerances

nutrient deficiencies

genetic factors

an increase in fat cells and adipose tissue mass during infancy and childhood

medications such as steroids, hormones, antidepressants, tranquilizers

Figure 3 Multiple causes of obesity

Fat Facts

Adipose (fat) tissue (**Figure 4**) is an essential structure in the human body. It is found mainly beneath the skin (subcutaneous fat) and on top of the kidneys. Adipose tissue consists of specialized connective tissue that stores fat in the form of triglycerides: molecules that contain three fatty acids. Adipose tissue has three functions: heat insulation, cushioning, and most importantly, a source of energy. Any food beyond what the body needs for its current energy demands is converted to fat and stored in adipose tissue. Because fat is stored with very little water, it is a highly efficient energy source. Recall that more energy can be derived per gram of fat (38 kJ/g or 9 kcal/g) than per gram of carbohydrate (17 kJ/g or 4 kcal/g) or protein (17 kJ/g or 4 kcal/g). The average woman, with 20% body fat, has about one month's worth of energy stored as fat.

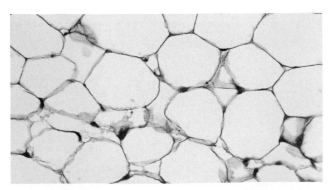

Figure 4 Most body cells have small vacuoles. Adipose cells are adapted to store high-energy fat compounds by having larger vacuoles.

The presence of estrogen and testosterone results in distinctive fat distribution patterns (**Figure 5**). An adult female tends to carry fat in her breasts, hips, waist, and buttocks, producing a "pear" shape. An adult male tends to carry body fat in his chest, abdomen, and buttocks, producing an "apple" shape. In general, females show greater lower-body fat distribution and males show more upper-body fat distribution.

Figure 5 Gender differences in fat distribution

Gender is not the only factor that determines fat distribution patterns. Genetics also plays a role, as evidenced by looking at the similarity in fat distribution within same-sex family members. Another factor is age. As people get older, their body fat distribution may change. For example, after menopause, women tend to accumulate more upper-body or abdominal fat. Extreme weight gain and weight cycling ("yo-yo dieting") may also increase upper-body fat. Like simple waist measurements, upper-body fat distribution can be linked to the health risks listed on page 000. Waist–hip ratio is a good way to determine upper-body fat distribution. You can calculate your waist–hip ratio by measuring the circumference of your waist and dividing it by the circumference of your hips. Women are at risk if this ratio exceeds 0.85. Men are at risk if this ratio exceeds 0.95.

Fat controls appetite through hormonal feedback mechanisms with the hypothalamus. The hypothalamus is an area in the brain that houses the body's hunger and satiety centres. Once considered inert, adipose tissue is now thought to act as a chemical factory that pumps out hormones called **adipokines**. When fat is present in normal amounts, fat cells produce a beneficial adipokine that increases the body's sensitivity to insulin. High levels of

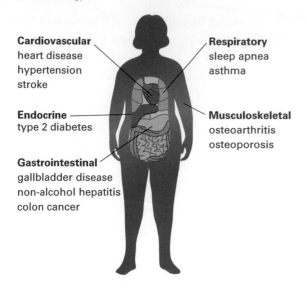

Figure 6 Adipose tissue is associated with obesity-related health problems.

insulin cause fat retention. When excess fat accumulates, fat cells secrete other adipokines that trigger diseases such as atherosclerosis, diabetes, and osteoarthritis (**Figure 6**). For this reason, obese people have multiple health problems. These health problems can improve once the weight is lost.

Weight-Loss Strategies

New research shows that, for overweight people, even a modest weight loss of 10% to 15% can reduce the risk of many of the diseases and conditions listed in **Figure 6**.

There are many popular, but ineffective, approaches to losing weight. Diet pills contain chemicals that suppress the appetite or raise the metabolic rate. Many medications that advertise rapid weight loss without requiring a change in diet or activity level do not advertise the dangers of using them—hypertension, stroke, dehydration, and poor nutrient absorption. For example, ephedrine, found in many popular weight control products, is associated with all of these health risks. Some weight-loss regimes claim that certain foods, such as grapefruit, burn fat. These regimes are not based on scientific fact, and limiting food choice leads to a monotonous, unbalanced diet. Meal replacements control calories by replacing regular meals and snacks with low-calorie beverages or prepackaged foods. Success requires using these expensive products indefinitely. Very-low-calorie (<4180 kJ/day or <1000 kcal/day) diets or liquid "fasts" promote rapid weight loss, but most

of the weight that is lost is either water or muscle. Because muscle loss slows down metabolism, most people gain back the weight after stopping these diets.

In extreme cases, some people turn to weight-loss surgeries. Bariatric surgery (stomach stapling) involves closing off the stomach, leaving only a small pouch about the size of a thumb for food. This procedure reduces the amount of food that can be consumed at one time. Gastric bypass surgery, the most common procedure, goes one step further. Surgeons not only shrink the stomach, but also reroute digestive matter from the stomach directly into the small intestine. The digestive matter bypasses the duodenum, where most absorption occurs, thereby decreasing the number of calories absorbed. There is a 1% death rate for bariatric and bypass surgeries. As well, up to 20% of patients need additional surgery to mend complications, such as abdominal hernias. Liposuction, another surgical procedure, removes unwanted fat from certain body areas. Liposuction is a cosmetic procedure, however, so it does not address underlying problems. Risks of liposuction include infection, fat or blood clots, excessive fluid loss or accumulation, damage to vital organs, and even death.

About 95% of people who diet regain the weight they lost because the diet they used ignored or understated the need to change eating and exercise behaviours permanently. Reducing food intake while increasing energy expenditure ensures long-term weight control. A weight loss of 0.5 kg per week brings the best results. Rapid weight loss impairs cardiac function, body temperature regulation, and muscle mass and endurance. It also increases the likelihood of regaining weight. Yo-yo cycles of dieting (**Figure 7**) are harmful to both psychological and physical health.

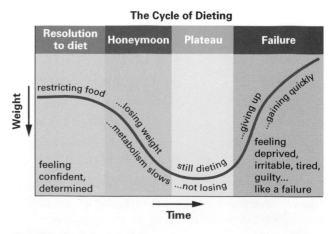

Figure 7 The cycle of dieting

It is estimated that 70% of Canadian women and 35% of Canadian men are dieting at any given time. Several diets are available today, popularized by media stars and public figures. In this activity, you will assess four of these diets. Two of the most popular diets are summarized in **Figure 8**.

(a) Evaluate the Atkins and Zone diets based on what you have learned in this unit. What do their strengths and weaknesses appear to be? Use links on the Nelson Web site to research expert opinions on each diet.

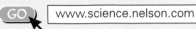

(b) Research two other popular diets. Summarize your findings under the headings "Claim" and "Reality."

GO www.science.nelson.com

(c) Choose any popular diet. Plan one day's menu, following the rules of this diet. Using the food composition table found on the Nelson Web site, gather information about the calories, proteins, carbohydrates, and fats provided by your menu. Assess the adequacy of your menu, using Canada's Food Guide and DRI information.

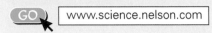

(d) In the introduction to this topic, Meredith is struggling to control her weight. What advice would you give her?

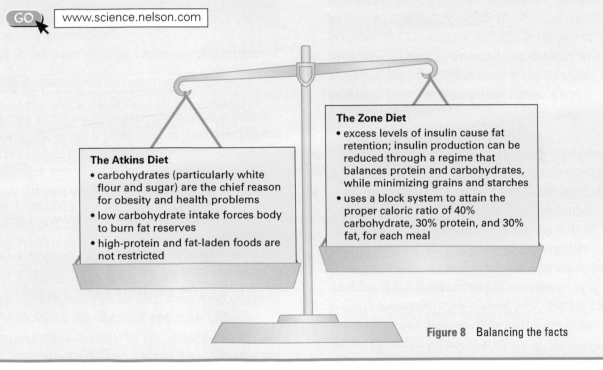

The Atkins Diet
- carbohydrates (particularly white flour and sugar) are the chief reason for obesity and health problems
- low carbohydrate intake forces body to burn fat reserves
- high-protein and fat-laden foods are not restricted

The Zone Diet
- excess levels of insulin cause fat retention; insulin production can be reduced through a regime that balances protein and carbohydrates, while minimizing grains and starches
- uses a block system to attain the proper caloric ratio of 40% carbohydrate, 30% protein, and 30% fat, for each meal

Figure 8 Balancing the facts

Eating Disorders

Eating disorders are health conditions that are characterized by a preoccupation with weight, resulting in severe disturbances in eating behaviour. Four examples are given in **Table 3** on the next page.

Eating disorders are complex. There are many contributing factors, such as

- age: onset usually between the ages of 14 and 25

- gender: female:male ratio of 9:1
- genetics: some links suspected
- personality traits: feelings of worthlessness, low self-esteem, depression, pressure to achieve for others and not for oneself
- dieting: the most common feature of all sufferers
- traumatic events: physical, sexual, or emotional abuse, bullying at school, death or illness of a family member

The first step toward treatment is recognition of the disorder. The Canadian Mental Health Association recommends medical treatment and psychotherapy, including family counselling.

Although different eating disorders have different causes and symptoms, they share many serious medical and psychological complications:

- noticeable weight loss or gain
- hyperactivity
- loss of hair and/or growth of fine body hair
- excessive constipation
- menstrual irregularities
- swollen glands

- tooth loss/decay
- severe dehydration
- risk of heart irregularities
- possible risk of emphysema

DID **YOU** KNOW?

The Prevalence of Eating Disorders

Approximately 3% of women will be affected by eating disorders in their lifetime. About 0.5% to 4% of women will develop anorexia nervosa, and about 1% to 4% will develop bulimia. Binge eating disorder affects about 2% of the population.

Table 3 Description of Eating Disorders

Eating disorder	Description
anorexia nervosa	• intense and irrational fear of body fat and weight gain, even when emaciated • disturbance in an individual's perception of his or her body weight, size, or shape • refusal to maintain a minimal normal weight (85%) for height and age • for women, loss of three consecutive menstrual periods
bulimia	• lack of control over eating behaviour, although weight may be normal • recurrent episodes of binge eating (minimum average of two binge eating episodes per week for at least three months) • regular self-induced vomiting, strict fasting, use of laxatives or diuretics, and excessive exercise
binge eating disorder (BED)	• binge eating without the use of compensatory weight control behaviours • food consumption that is frequent, rapid, often secretive, and in large volumes • found in about one-fifth of obese persons
pica	• craving for non-food items, most commonly dirt, clay, chalk, paint chips, cornstarch, baking soda, coffee grounds, cigarette ashes, rust, and plastics • usually found in pregnant women, people who have diets that are deficient in minerals, and people who have psychiatric disturbances or certain ethnic customs • harmless unless substances are toxic or contaminated, and then may be fatal

✓ Check Your Understanding

1. Describe three indicators or measurements that are used to assess weight-related health risks.

2. List 20 diseases and health conditions that are associated with excess weight. Rank these diseases and conditions from most serious to least serious.

3. What is the function of adipose tissue?

4. What are adipokines? Describe how they can act in both beneficial and harmful ways.

5. Create a table that lists the advantages and disadvantages of each weight-loss strategy mentioned in this topic.

6. Why is it good advice to lose only 0.5 kg per week if weight control is necessary?

7. Compare and contrast anorexia and bulimia.

CASE STUDY

The Effect of Alcohol Input on Body Function

Even though alcohol is not considered to be a fad diet or a food additive, it is the most common non-food item consumed worldwide. Unlike food, alcohol is metabolized without digestion and used very quickly by the body. About 10% of the alcohol that is consumed is expelled via breathing and urine. About 20% is absorbed directly across the walls of an empty stomach, reaching the brain within 1 min. A further 20% is broken down by enzyme action in the stomach. The remaining 50% is rapidly absorbed into the blood from the small intestine.

Although alcohol affects every organ in the body, it affects the liver the most. Liver cells are normally fuelled by fatty acids. When alcohol is present, liver cells must first metabolize the alcohol. This effect causes fatty acids to build up in the liver, making the liver less efficient at performing its regular tasks. Because the liver can metabolize only 14 mL of alcohol per hour (**Figure 9**), excess alcohol circulates around the body until it is metabolized. As a result, the health effects of alcohol consumption are widespread (**Table 4**).

Figure 9 One standard drink contains 14 mL of ethanol. Moderate alcohol use is considered to be one drink per day for women and one to two drinks per day for men.

(a) Considering the energy content of alcohol, why are many alcoholics malnourished?

(b) Alcohol consumption has been linked to low testosterone production in men. What are some possible long-term consequences of this effect?

(c) Can alcohol be consumed sensibly? Explain your answer using information presented here.

(d) What effect does exposure to alcohol in commercials and films have on youth drinking patterns?

(e) Debate the following statement: "By increasing taxes on alcohol, governments can lower alcohol consumption."

Table 4 Health Effects of Alcohol Consumption

Disease or condition	Effect of alcohol
arthritis	increases risk of arthritis
cancer	increases risk of cancer in the mouth, throat, breast, esophagus, liver, pancreas, and rectum
fetal alcohol syndrome	causes physical and behavioural abnormalities in the fetus
heart disease	raises blood pressure, blood lipids, and the risk of stroke and heart disease in heavy drinkers
	may lower the risk of heart disease in light to moderate drinkers
kidney disease	enlarges the kidneys, alters hormone functions, and increases the risk of kidney failure
liver disease	causes fatty liver, alcoholic hepatitis, and cirrhosis
malnutrition	increases the risk of protein–energy malnutrition through reduced protein synthesis and impaired absorption of calcium, iron, phosphorus, zinc, and several vitamins
nervous disorders	impairs balance and memory; implicated in dementias
psychological disturbances	causes insomnia, depression, and anxiety

D5.2 *Activity* | MAPPING NUTRITION >

The Food and Agriculture Organization of the United Nations (FAO) tracks food availability at national, regional, and global levels. It uses a measure called **dietary energy supply (DES)** to estimate the average daily food energy that is available per person per day. DES includes the food that countries produce or import for human consumption. DES does not indicate what people actually eat, nor does it reflect uneven distribution of supplies within countries. At the top of the list is Denmark, with 15 800 kJ (3780 kcal) available per person per day. Somalia has just 6600 kJ (1580 kcal) available per person per day. Canada's DES is estimated to be 13 000 kJ (3100 kcal) per person per day. If the world's food supply was redistributed according to need, the world's population could be fed with 11 400 kJ (2720 kcal) per person per day.

The map in **Figure 10** illustrates the food energy gap between the world's richest and poorest countries. **Figure 11** illustrates the significant differences in the types of foods that make up a daily diet in different parts of the world.

(a) Copy and complete the table. List five countries in each category.

DES >2000 kcal/day	DES 2000–2600 kcal/day	DES <2600 kcal/day

(b) What can you conclude after studying this map?

Mapping Nutrition and Malnutrition, Dietary Energy Supply (1994–1996)

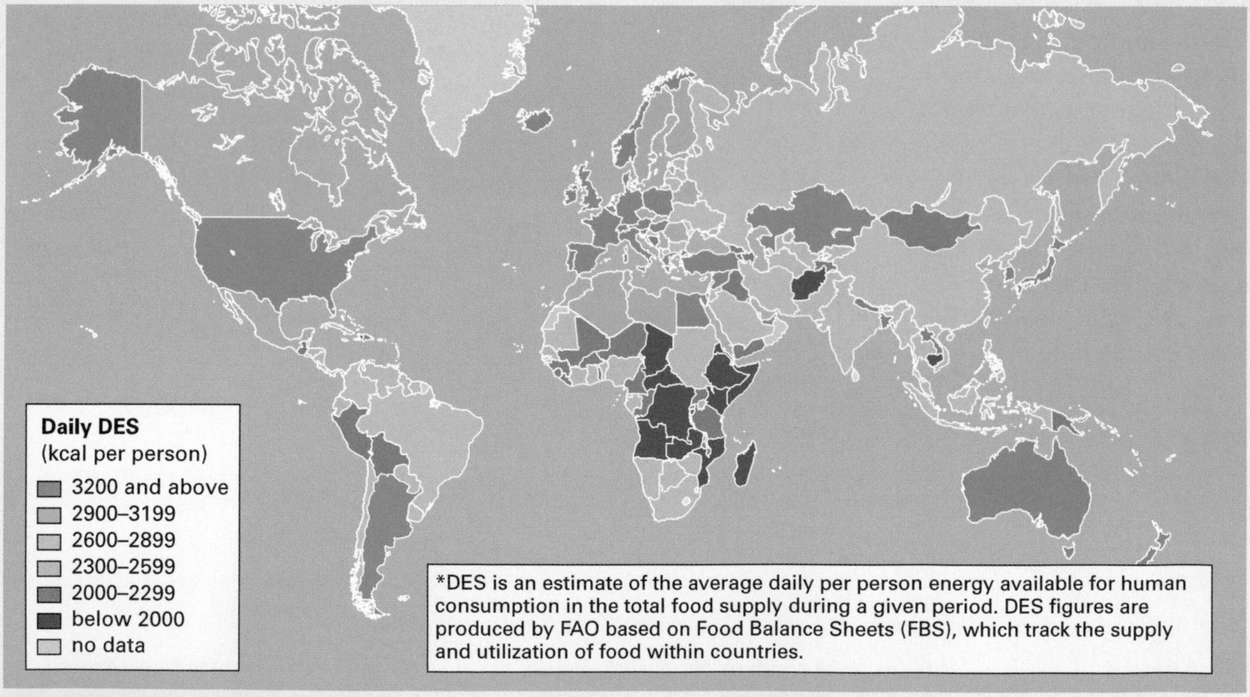

Daily DES
(kcal per person)
- ■ 3200 and above
- □ 2900–3199
- □ 2600–2899
- □ 2300–2599
- ■ 2000–2299
- ■ below 2000
- □ no data

*DES is an estimate of the average daily per person energy available for human consumption in the total food supply during a given period. DES figures are produced by FAO based on Food Balance Sheets (FBS), which track the supply and utilization of food within countries.

While DES does not indicate food consumption, it does identify: those countries in which people are more likely to have enough to eat (represented by shades of green ■ ■ □); those in which the daily DES is marginal (yellow □); and those in which hunger and malnutrition are likely to be widespread (orange ■). Those countries that face the most severe food supply shortages, with average daily DES below 2000 kilocalories per person per day, are coloured in red (■).

Figure 10 Mapping nutrition and malnutrition

There are large differences in the daily diets around the world. **Figure 11** compares the average DES of industrialized countries, Asia, and Sub-Saharan Africa. The pie chart shows energy consumption: total DES average (inner circle); the share of carbohydrates, fats, and proteins (middle circle); and the share of food groups (outer circle).

(c) Compare the average DES for each region with the estimated DES if the world's food supply was distributed evenly.

(d) For each region, estimate the percent intake of carbohydrates, fats, and proteins. Analyze your estimates according to the dietary reference intakes (DRIs) in topic D1.

(e) Create a hypothesis that might explain the incidence of heart disease and obesity in each of the three geographic regions.

(f) For each region, estimate the percent intake of each food group. Analyze your estimates.

(g) Speculate on the incidence of intestinal tract cancers in each of the three geographic regions.

(h) Serious health problems are seen in countries where 75% of the calories come from cereals and tubers. Can you suggest why?

(i) According to the UN, the average minimum daily caloric requirement is 9800 kJ (2350 kcal) per person per day. Using food composition tables, plan a day's menu that provides this amount of food energy.

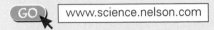 GO www.science.nelson.com

(j) Many people around the world experience famine and hunger. What roles could science, technology, society, and individuals play in alleviating this situation?

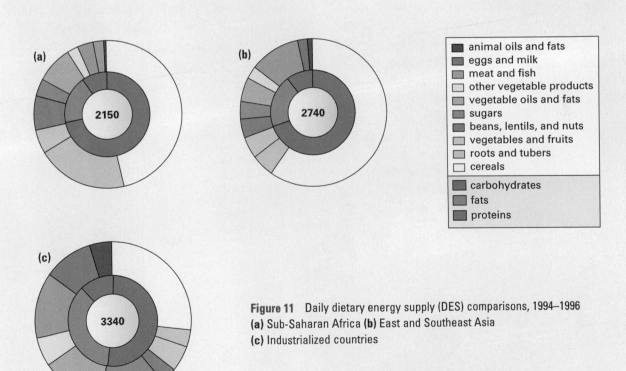

Figure 11 Daily dietary energy supply (DES) comparisons, 1994–1996
(a) Sub-Saharan Africa **(b)** East and Southeast Asia
(c) Industrialized countries

Legend:
- animal oils and fats
- eggs and milk
- meat and fish
- other vegetable products
- vegetable oils and fats
- sugars
- beans, lentils, and nuts
- vegetables and fruits
- roots and tubers
- cereals

- carbohydrates
- fats
- proteins

D5.3 Activity | OBESITY

Approximately 46% of Canadian adults are overweight or obese, and Canada has one of the world's worst rates of childhood obesity (**Figure 12**). One-third of Canadians are at increased risk for disability, disease, and premature death due to obesity. According to 1997 statistics, obesity costs the Canadian healthcare system more than $1.8 billion a year, with indirect costs likely doubling this estimate.

Using articles from the Nelson Web site, answer the following questions.

 GO www.science.nelson.com

(a) Compile a list of statistics that supports the claim that obesity is becoming a global epidemic.

(b) Compile a list of statistics for obesity in Canada.

(c) The national average of obesity in Canada is 14.9%. Study the map in **Figure 13**. Suggest reasons why obesity is common across such widely different regions of Canada. What factors could the regions with significantly lower obesity incidence have in common?

(d) Report on obesity in the province where you live. Compare the rate of obesity from 1995 to 2001 with the rate in two other Canadian provinces. Speculate on reasons for the differences.

(e) What are the top three direct costs of treating obesity? What are some indirect costs?

(f) Some medical sources list obesity as the number one health problem in North America today. Do you agree or disagree? Explain.

Figure 12 Obesity rates have reached epidemic proportions in Canada.

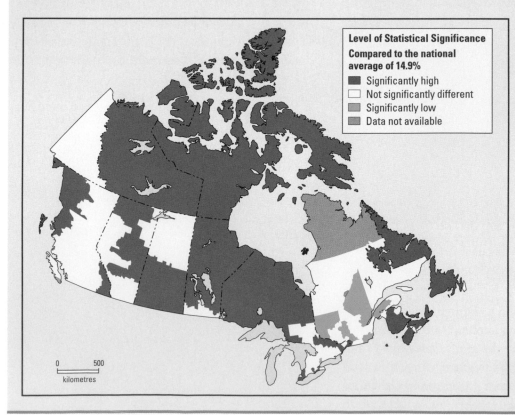

Level of Statistical Significance
Compared to the national average of 14.9%

■ Significantly high
□ Not significantly different
■ Significantly low
■ Data not available

0   500
kilometres

Figure 13 Body mass index (BMI); proportion of the population, aged 20 to 64, classified as obese (BMI 30+)

Childhood Obesity

Why are so many Canadian children obese? The prevalence of childhood obesity in Canada increased from 2% in 1981 to between 10% and 15% in 1996. The problem appears to be less pronounced in the western provinces and more pronounced in the eastern provinces, with obesity increasing faster among boys than among girls. Canadian childhood obesity rates are double the rates in some European countries and similar to the rates in the United States.

Obesity increases the risk of other health conditions for Canadian children. Chronic diseases such as type 2 diabetes and hypertension—once thought to be adult afflictions—now affect many youth. Studies confirm that obese children are likely to become overweight adults. As well, obese children may suffer teasing and harassment by other children, or be treated differently by teachers and other adults, according to Health Canada.

Between 1990 and 1998, the proportion of children who ate fruits and vegetables daily, or exercised outside school hours, decreased steadily. During this time, priorities in the school system changed, resulting in less emphasis on physical education. Whereas competitive sports programs are thriving, there are fewer grassroots sports. Children are driven to school instead of walking or cycling, often for safety reasons. The popularity of fast foods, video and computer games, and mall activities has spawned a generation of couch potatoes. Inactivity plus excess food consumption equals obesity.

Statement: To prevent childhood obesity, daily physical education classes should be compulsory.

1. Translate the information in **Figure 14** into sentence form.

Decision-Making Skills

○ Define the Issue   ● Identify Alternatives
● Research   ● Analyze the Issue
● Defend a Decision   ○ Evaluate

2. In your group, research the issue, using information on the Nelson Web site.

 www.science.nelson.com

3. Write a list of points and counterpoints.

4. Reach a decision in your group.

5. Prepare to defend your group's position in a class debate (see **Appendix A7**).

6. Submit your reasoned personal opinion on the issue in paragraph form.

7. Respond to the following statement in paragraph form: "Children are obese because of unlimited access to good-tasting, high-fat, nutritionally bankrupt foods."

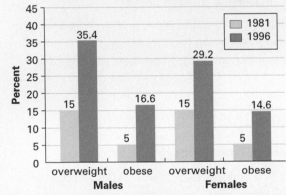

Prevalance of Overweight and Obese Children Aged 7–13 Years in Canada, 1981 and 1996

Source: Tremblay MS, Willms DJ. Secular trends in the body mass index of Canadian children. CMAJ [serial online] 2000 Nov 28 [cited 2001 Nov 28]; 163(11):[9 screens]. Available from: URL: http://www.cma/cmaj/vol-163/issue-11/1429.htm

Figure 14 Can this trend be reversed?

SUMMARY

- Overnutrition is the excess consumption of nutrients (fats, carbohydrates, proteins, and salt) and calories. Excessive weight is directly linked to diseases or high-risk health conditions.
- Health risks can be related to a BMI >30, a waist circumference >94 cm for males or >80 cm for females, and a waist–hip ratio >0.95 for males or >0.85 for females.
- Adipose tissue provides heat insulation, cushioning, and an efficient source of energy for the body. Fat cells produce hormones called adipokines that act in both beneficial and harmful ways.
- Fat distribution patterns are determined by sex hormones, genetics, age, food intake, weight fluctuations, and general health. Upper-body fat distribution is associated with the development of health risks.
- Weight loss may be accomplished through medical procedures, such as surgeries and liposuction. Consumer weight loss strategies include diet pills, fad diets that promote certain ingredients or combinations, meal replacement products, and liquid fasts (intakes of <4180 kJ or <1000 kcal per day).
- Long-term weight control is best achieved through reducing food intake while increasing energy expenditure. Most diets are ineffective.

An estimated 95% of dieters regain all the weight they lose, and then some.
- Anorexia is characterized by weight below what is considered normal and an intense fear of weight gain. Bulimia is characterized by strict fasting, excessive exercising, an intense fear of weight gain, and episodes of dieting and bingeing. Food is purged from the body by vomiting, laxatives, or diuretics. All eating disorders have serious medical and psychological complications.
- Alcohol consumption affects every organ of the body, with the greatest damage done to the liver.
- Countries can be rated according to their dietary energy supply (DES). DES and human health are not directly related.
- Obesity rates have reached epidemic proportions in Canada, with great costs to both individuals and society. Between 10% and 15% of Canadian children are obese, with the number steadily growing. Childhood obesity is linked to food consumption patterns, lack of physical activity, and lifestyle.

Key Terms

overnutrition

adipokine

dietary energy supply (DES)

ASSESSMENT

Understanding Concepts

1. Draw a concept map that includes five diseases or conditions that can be caused by overnutrition, as well as the excess nutrients that are associated with these diseases or conditions.

2. Jesse automatically shakes salt over all his food before tasting it. What advice can you give him?

3. Give evidence that refutes the following statement: "If fat people pushed themselves away from the table, their problem would be solved."

4. What is the relationship between fat distribution patterns and the health risks that are associated with excess weight?

5. Describe how fat tissue contributes to several eating conditions related to obesity.

6. Explain why eating disorders have as much to do with mental state as they do with food.

7. Is obesity an eating disorder? Give reasons for your answer.

Applying Inquiry Skills

8. There are many fad diets on the market. List ways in which you can evaluate a weight loss program.

9. Extremes in body mass—both overweight and underweight—can be linked to industrialization.

Analyze the data in **Figure 15**, and describe the trend. Suggest reasons for this trend.

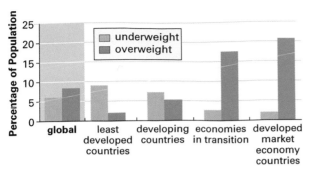

Figure 15 The relationship between weight and industrialization (WHO)

10. **Table 5** appeared in a recent issue of the *International Journal of Obesity*.

Table 5 Rates of Canadian Children (Ages 7–13) at Risk of Being Overweight or Obese by Adulthood (Age 18), 1981 and 1996

	Males		Females	
	1981	1996	1981	1996
Likely to be overweight by age 18	11%	33%	13%	27%
Likely to be obese by age 18	2%	10%	2%	9%

(a) Interpret the data in sentence form.

(b) Relate the data to gender fat distribution patterns. Propose reasons for discrepancies.

(c) What is the relevance of overweight children and teens becoming obese adults?

(d) Devise an action plan to decrease obesity rates.

11. **Figure 16** illustrates trends in daily fruit and vegetable consumption by Canadian children, from 1990 to 1998.

(a) Propose reasons for gender differences.

(b) Design, conduct, and evaluate a similar survey for your school population.

Making Connections

12. What causes overnutrition? What can be done about it?

13. Diabetes affects 1.5 million Canadians. It is the third-largest killer in Canada. Describe diabetes and its relationship to overnutrition. How can you decrease your risk of developing diabetes?

14. Your 13-year-old cousin has a BMI of 32 and a 0.98 waist–hip ratio. Assess his health risks. Propose some specific strategies that he and his family can use to ensure a healthier future.

15. In North America, 40% of women continually yo-yo diet. Describe some of the dangers that are associated with this type of dieting.

16. Compile a list of healthy eating "dos and don'ts" for weight management.

17. You suspect that your friend has an eating disorder. What can you do to help your friend?

18. Do media pressures to be thin cause eating disorders? Organize your thoughts using a pros/cons table. Express your opinion in a short paragraph.

19. Write and perform a skit about a doctor discussing the health dangers of alcohol consumption with a patient.

Reflecting

20. Current research suggests that when teens finish growing, they reach a stable weight range known as their *set point*. Although your set point may fluctuate 2 kg to 5 kg, your body sustains it if you eat when hungry, stop eating when full, and exercise moderately. Reconcile this physiological fact with the obsessive need to diet in our society. In your opinion, how difficult is it to be healthy today?

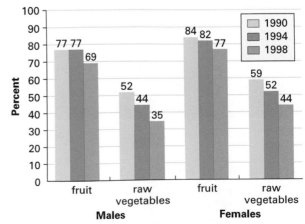

Source: King AJC, Boyce WF, King MA. Trends in the Health of Canadian Youth. Ottawa: Health Canada; 1999

Figure 16 Trends for Canadian children in Grade 6 who ate fruits and vegetables daily, 1990–1998

TASK: The Effect of Food Intake on Body Function

How does food intake affect the way that *your* body functions (**Figure 1**)? Are you like a truck running on empty or a finely tuned racing car fuelled on high-octane energy? Create a food and fitness diary in the form of a video journal, photo journal, brochure, or portfolio.

1. Record everything you eat or drink for three days, using the format in **Table 1** below.

(a) Analyze your dietary record using Canada's Food Guide. In which food groups is your intake sufficient? In which food groups is it deficient?

(b) Analyze your dietary record according to DRIs. Which macronutrients are in excess? Which are deficient?

(c) Look at your intake of fruits and vegetables. Speculate on the vitamin and mineral content of your diet. Which nutrients appear to be lacking, and why?

(d) Evaluate the fibre content of your diet.

(e) How would you describe the balance between natural foods and refined foods in your diet? How would you describe the balance between fast foods and foods made from scratch?

Figure 1 The performance of these Olympic athletes is affected by food intake.

Table 1 Dietary Record

Time of day	Food or drink	Amount	Calories (kcal)	Proteins (g)	Carbohydrates (g)	Fibre (g)	Fats (g)	Saturated fats (g)

2. Keep a three-day activity log. Divide your activities into the following six levels: Sleeping, Very light, Light, Moderate, Vigorous, Maximum effort. (See *Canada's Physical Activity Guide to Healthy Active Living*.)

(f) Estimate your BMR.

(g) Use the information in **Table 3** on page 253 to estimate the energy factor for each level of activity. Calculate your total energy expenditure from your activities each day.

(h) Compare your energy expenditure with your energy intake. Are you in positive, negative, or equal energy balance?

3. Consider the importance of additives in your diet.

(i) List any nutritive food additives you consume, and explain why you consume them.

(j) How much caffeine do you consume each day? How would you assess your consumption of other non-nutritive food additives?

4. Consider the physiological data that you collected about yourself during the activities and investigations in this unit.

(k) Record your average heart rate before (resting), during, and after exercise.

(l) Record your blood pressure before (resting), during, and after exercise.

(m) Record your lung capacity before (resting), during, and after exercise.

5. Collate personal data related to your weight and health.

(n) Calculate your BMI. Record your waist circumference and your waist–hip ratio.

(o) Use these data to assess any health risks associated with your weight.

6. Review your results of D0.1 Activity: How's Your Body Image? in the unit introduction.

(p) Write a paragraph summarizing your perception of your body, and the importance you place on these feelings.

7. Formulate an action plan, based on what you have learned in this unit.

(q) Set goals to maintain or improve your health.

(r) Compose 10 guidelines to follow, in order to achieve these goals.

SUMMARY

Throughout this unit, you have had opportunities to

- demonstrate an understanding of food components and their effects on body functions
- make inferences about the impact of eating patterns on body functions, based on an analysis of data from laboratory investigations and from print and electronic sources
- explain how personal and societal factors affect eating behaviours, and evaluate the social and economic impact of the use of non-nutritive food additives

Copy the following graphic organizer into your notebook, and use it to help you summarize your understanding of the key concepts in each of the four major topics. Add the key concepts related to the topic that you chose for your Unit Task.

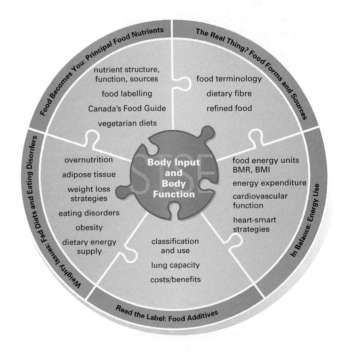

Unit D Review

Understanding Concepts

1. **(a)** List the advantages of obtaining daily nutrients from a balanced diet rather than from dietary supplements.
   (b) Describe some circumstances in which dietary supplements are recommended.

2. Explain why even a modest weight loss of 10% to 15% can substantially reduce the health risks associated with obesity.

3. What are the costs and benefits of non-nutritive food additives?

4. Why is dietary fibre considered to be an essential part of our daily food intake?

5. What effects does exercise have on body functions?

6. List the four features of a heart-smart diet.

7. Compare and contrast the effects of caffeine and alcohol on body functions.

Applying Inquiry Skills

8. How much energy would a 75-kg male use in one day if he slept for 12 h, stood for 5 h, used a computer keyboard for 3 h, biked for 30 min, walked for 1.5 h, and sat for 2 h? If his food intake provided 10 870 kJ (2600 kcal), would he be in a positive or negative energy balance? Show your work.

9. New research suggests that people on diets show signs of diminished brain function. Create a hypothesis that might explain this effect. Design an experiment to test your hypothesis.

10. Cut out the nutritional labels from the boxes of any two breakfast cereals. Calculate the cost per gram, and compare essential nutrients, including fibre. Which cereal would you choose, and why?

11. **Table 1** shows the food energy that is contained in equal volumes of various dairy products. Different research groups proposed different explanations after examining the data.

    Group 1: All milk has the same energy value.

    Group 2: The greater the mass of milk is, the greater its energy value is.

    Group 3: The greater the fat content is, the greater the energy value is.

Group 4: The energy value of different types of milk cannot be determined by looking at the volume used.

Table 1 Dairy Products and Their Food Energy

Milk product	Mass (g) per 250 mL	Food energy (kJ) per 250 mL
whipping cream	252	3640
whole milk	257	660
2% milk	258	540
skim milk	258	380
buttermilk	258	430
evaporated milk	356	1490

   (a) Which of these explanations is/are reasonable?
   (b) If someone was concerned about excessive energy intake, which dairy products would you recommend avoiding? Explain why.

12. A recent study concluded the following:

    - Heavy coffee drinkers generally smoke more, drink more alcohol, and eat more fatty foods than people who do not drink coffee.

    - Decaffeinated coffee drinkers are more likely than other coffee drinkers to take care of themselves. They tend to take more vitamins, exercise more regularly, and eat more cruciferous vegetables, such as broccoli. As well, they are more likely to use seat belts when they drive.
    (a) Design a survey to collect similar data in your community.
    (b) Conduct your survey, and interpret the data.

Making Connections

13. Study the functional food guide pyramid in **Figure 1**. Using information on the Nelson Web site, list five functional foods that are associated with each benefit.

    - improvement in heart health
    - reduced risk of cancer
    - antioxidant

 www.science.nelson.com

Figure 1 A functional food guide pyramid

14. Potato chips and French fries are now advertised as "cholesterol-free."
    (a) Explain why this advertising is misleading. Present three viewpoints: the manufacturer's, a nutritionist's, and a consumer's.
    (b) Clip a food advertisement from a newspaper or magazine. Analyze the advertisement for accuracy and effectiveness.

15. To what extent should the government be allowed to control the substances we consume? Explain your position, using specific examples.

16. Our society is obsessed with thinness and dieting, yet obesity rates are rising alarmingly. Explain this paradox using key concepts you have learned in the unit.

17. You are concerned about the lack of variety in your aunt's diet. Use the information in **Figure 2** to help you persuade her to alter her eating habits. Present your ideas in a short position paper. Include one day's menu, which reflects the dietary changes you propose.

18. The diet industry in North America earns a profit of about $40 billion per year, yet 95% of people who diet fail to reach their goals. What are the societal implications of these statistics?

19. Provide information to support or refute the following comment: "The current obesity pandemic reflects the profound changes to our society over the past 20 to 30 years. These changes have created an environment that promotes a sedentary lifestyle and the consumption of a high-fat, energy-dense diet."

20. Write four paragraphs about the following statement: "As countries work to feed their people, the message must be 'eat healthy food, not just more food.'"

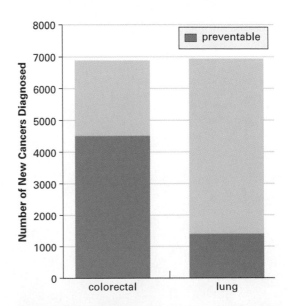

Figure 2 The number of colon, rectal, and lung cancers, potentially preventable by eating fruits and vegetables, and by regular exercise, Ontario 2000

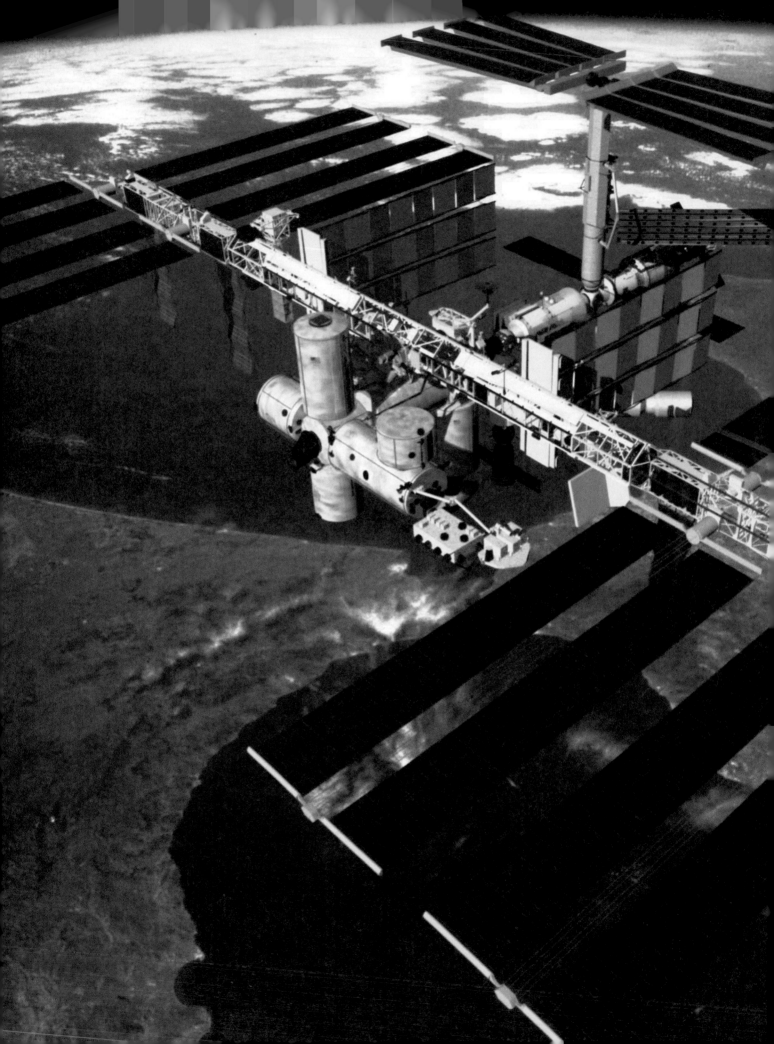

Science

and

SPACE

The pace of activity is both brisk and deliberate as half a dozen experiments are readied on board the International Space Station (ISS). Switches must be thrown, compartments must be sealed, and electronic sensors need to be double-checked before tiny, self-contained laboratories will spring into action. The experiments will take advantage of a condition that can be duplicated for much less than a minute on Earth—*microgravity*. The results of the experiments will not only help unlock mysteries related to human physiology, fluid dynamics, and the growth of crystals, but they will also lead to the development of a host of spinoff materials and technologies on Earth. The applications are endless: unique treatments for human diseases, a variety of new products, and novel technologies that have not yet been imagined. The knowledge gained as a result of living and working in space may answer some of the most fundamental questions related to life processes—questions that have puzzled scientists for years—and may perhaps enable us to establish permanent settlements on the Moon and Mars, and possibly beyond.

(a) What is microgravity?

(b) When astronauts are shown on board a space shuttle or the ISS, why do they appear to be floating?

We all become intimately acquainted with gravity very early in life. We first master the feat of rolling over, we learn to sit up, and eventually we are able to stand. Each learned skill is an act of defiance against this fundamental force of nature. Toddlers taking their first few cautious steps soon discover that an inability to cope with gravity leads to a frustrating but luckily short tumble to the ground. The constant downward tug provided by our planet has helped shape the human form and the form of every other living organism on Earth.

(c) Suggest some tasks that would be more difficult and others that would be easier to accomplish if the force of gravity were stronger than it currently is. What if gravity were much weaker?

(d) How do you think the human form would be different if gravity on Earth were much stronger than it is? What if gravity were much weaker? Suggest how other organisms might be different if the pull of gravity were weaker or stronger.

From obvious applications such as satellite television and weather forecasting to less obvious spinoffs such as CAT scans and cancer treatments, space technology touches nearly every aspect of our lives. Some spinoffs have appeared in response to the potential risks associated with microgravity; other spinoffs have taken advantage of microgravity's unique conditions.

As pervasive as space technology is, it has all come about in only three generations. Robert Goddard (**Figure 1**), an American, launched the first liquid-fuelled rocket on March 16, 1926. It managed to reach a height of 13 m on a flight that lasted just under 3.0 s. Within a decade, Goddard's rockets were reaching altitudes of over 1500 m and speeds in excess of 800 km/h. Goddard went on to design multistage rockets that ultimately took people into space.

Figure 1 As early as 1920, Robert Goddard had proposed a method of launching a small rocket that could reach the Moon. He suggested that the rocket carry an explosive charge so that he could witness its arrival through a telescope on Earth. Shown here is Goddard with his first liquid-fuelled rocket.

In the 1930s, German scientists and engineers started developing their army's rocket program under the leadership of Wernher von Braun. In 1942, they successfully launched the V-2 rocket: a ballistic missile capable of delivering a 750-kg warhead at a speed of 5600 km/h over a range of 400 km. V-2 rockets terrorized England, beginning in September 1944, but they were used too late in World War II to affect its outcome. Fearing that the allied forces would learn Germany's secrets, Hitler ordered the execution of the German rocket scientists and engineers.

Fortunately, 120 of them escaped by surrendering to American forces. They were later sent to the United States along with a number of V-2 rockets. Under the leadership of von Braun, they were responsible for originating the American space program (**Figure 2**). In 1949, a V-2 rocket was used to boost an American-built missile to an unprecedented height of nearly 400 km, reaching a speed of almost 9000 km/h.

Figure 2 Wernher von Braun and his engineers developed the Saturn 5 rocket, which was used during the Apollo missions. Shown here is the *Apollo 11* launch.

In the meantime, the U.S.S.R. was busy with its own rocket program. Using the principles developed by Konstantin Tsiolkovsky (**Figure 3**), considered the father of "cosmonautics," the Russians surprised the world in October 1957 with the launch of the first satellite, *Sputnik 1*. Within a month, *Sputnik 2* carried the first living organism into space: Laika, a dog, orbited Earth every 90 min, paving the way for manned space

Figure 3 Konstantin Tsiolkovsky helped the U.S.S.R. become the first country to put a satellite in orbit and to put a man in Earth orbit. With the launch of *Sputnik 1* in 1957, the race for space had begun.

flight. In April 1961, cosmonaut Yuri Gagarin was the first human to orbit Earth. His single passage around the planet lasted 108 min at an altitude of 300 km. Ten months later, the Americans followed with the successful flight of John Glenn, who made three orbits over a 5-h period. Recognizing that there was a strategic advantage for a country to have the ability to go into space, the National Aeronautics and Space Administration (NASA) was created.

The Mercury missions, which took Glenn into orbit, were followed by the Gemini missions, which focused on flying, manoeuvring, rendezvousing, and docking with other spacecraft. These skills were necessary for the later Apollo missions, which ultimately landed two men on the Moon and returned them safely to Earth (**Figure 4**).

Figure 4 In 1960, recognizing the importance of establishing a presence in space, American President John F. Kennedy challenged NASA to land a man on the Moon and return him safely to Earth before the end of the decade. NASA accomplished this on July 20, 1969, when Neil Armstrong and Buzz Aldrin were the first people to set foot on the Moon. Michael Collins, the third *Apollo 11* astronaut, was assigned to remain on board the lunar orbiter while his colleagues made history on the surface below.

After six successful Moon landings, NASA turned its attention back to Earth orbit with the space shuttle flights. Between 1981 and 2003, when the space shuttle *Columbia* broke up during reentry, 112 missions took place. The 25th mission, in January 1986, also resulted in tragedy when the space shuttle *Challenger* exploded 72 s after launch, killing all seven crew members.

Since its inception in 1989, the Canadian Space Agency (CSA) has worked in conjunction with NASA, the European Space Agency, and other space agencies by contributing several technological innovations and by launching important satellites. The Canadarm, Canada's most significant contribution to the space shuttle program, has proved to be a valuable tool for manipulating orbiting objects and for constructing the ISS.

Although the ISS can house scientists for extended periods of time, past experiences in space have demonstrated that the human body does not respond favourably to microgravity. While the relatively short duration of a space shuttle mission poses no long-term ill effects, some astronauts have lived for months on orbiting laboratories such as the American *Skylab* (**Figure 5**) and the Russian *Mir*. Lessons learned from these long exposures to microgravity have taught us that serious physiological changes take place in a number of body systems, changes that could jeopardize the health of the astronauts and the mission itself. Solutions are essential if we are to maintain a presence in space and travel to distant destinations. Fortunately, research is providing some of these solutions; it is also leading to important treatments for a variety of medical conditions that affect people on Earth.

Figure 5 Launched in 1973, *Skylab* orbited Earth 16 times each day and remained in space for six years.

(e) Speculate on the physiological effects associated with living in a microgravity environment.

(f) Suggest how artificial gravity can be produced in space.

For humans to survive in space, a number of environmental elements, such as atmosphere, pressure, and temperature, must be carefully controlled. Space suits must protect astronauts from the vacuum of space and dangerous radiation (**Figure 6**). In addition, adequate supplies of air, water, and food are required. Maintaining livable conditions inside a spacecraft or an orbiting platform presents scientists and engineers with special challenges. Maintaining a livable environment and providing adequate supplies for extended missions, such as a mission to Mars, which will take six months, becomes daunting.

Figure 6 Once out of the space shuttle or space station, astronauts must be protected.

Although the environmental conditions of space threaten human life, they are well suited to a variety of scientific investigations. Gravity affects many processes; scientists on board orbiting spacecraft can study these processes in the absence of gravity. In particular, the behaviour of fluids, which is largely controlled by gravity, has become the subject of intense study. The growth of protein crystals in a microgravity environment is also being studied because of its promising applications in medicine.

(g) Why do bubbles rise to the top of a pot of boiling water? How might boiling happen in microgravity?

With information being relayed around the planet at the speed of light, Earth has never been so accessible to so many people. Some satellites provide us with views of weather patterns and land formations; others peer outward to the depths of the universe, helping to increase our understanding of the cosmos.

As new technologies are developed to satisfy the needs of the space program, many find applications on Earth. There are numerous products, such as electronics, building materials, and fabrics, that were first used in space but are now found in most homes.

(h) List some ways that satellite technology is commonly used.

(i) Identify any products that you think could have their origin in the space program.

In this unit, you will learn what makes up a microgravity environment and how microgravity allows scientists to study a wide variety of properties and processes. You will also learn how microgravity poses serious health risks for people who live in space for extended periods of time and how these people cope with the risks to help us establish a permanent presence in space. In an investigation, you will simulate the physiological effects of microgravity on humans. In activities, you will grow crystals and learn how their growth can be optimized in space. You will also study the behaviour of fluids and discover the role of surface tension in microgravity. Finally, you will consider the promises and risks that lie ahead as humans continue to push the frontiers of space science.

Questions to Think About

As you explore the topics in this unit, keep the following questions in mind:

- How is microgravity achieved on Earth and in Earth orbit?
- What risks are faced by people who venture into space?

- How is microgravity uniquely suited to manufacturing certain products and carrying out certain processes?
- Is pursuing a presence in space worthwhile when the benefits are weighed against the risks?
- What does the future hold for humankind in space?

Unit Task Introduction

There are many challenges that need to be overcome before a manned mission to Mars can take place. In the Unit Task, you will have the opportunity to explore the logistics of planning such a mission. You will use your understanding of the various challenges—medical, technological, and physiological—and the inquiry and communication skills you have developed to present your recommendations on an aspect of the mission that interests you. Read the description and requirements on pages 358 to 359 before you start the unit topics, so that you can prepare for the Unit Task as you progress through the unit.

You open your eyes one morning and discover that the two friends who shared your room for the night seem to be oddly placed from your perspective. One friend is sleeping on the ceiling directly above you, and the other is sleeping on the wall to your left. As you become more awake, you realize that you do not really feel like you are even lying down. What you do feel are several straps across your body holding you somewhat tightly against the mattress.

Your arms are raised in front of you. One of your hands is nearly touching your face, but you do not seem to be making any effort to keep it there. You are convinced that you must be dreaming. You decide to get out of bed, but you have no sense that "up" is necessarily away from your mattress. In fact, you have no sense of "up" whatsoever. Finally, you remember what is going on. You and your astronaut colleagues have shared quarters for the scheduled sleep period, and now you must rely solely on visual cues to manoeuvre your way around these quarters and around the entire ISS. Your sense of balance has abandoned you entirely. You are on board an orbiting platform of science and technology, where there is no sense of "up" or "down" (**Figure 1**).

(a) In this imaginary situation, why do you not have a sense of "up" or "down"? Why do you need visual cues to make sense of your surroundings?

In photographs and video clips of astronauts inside a space shuttle or an orbiting platform, such as the ISS, they appear to be floating. Many people refer to this condition as "weightlessness" or being in an environment of "zero g." Not only do the astronauts not seem to be anchored in any way, but other objects also move around the cabin, apparently free of any gravitational effects.

(b) Is there no gravitational force affecting the astronauts? Is the gravitational force so weak that it is insignificant? Is there some other explanation? If so, how is this observation explained?

(c) What other effects of this environment might you find disconcerting?

(d) Are there experiences you could have on Earth that would produce sensations similar to the "weightlessness" described here? Explain.

Before you can appreciate the challenges of living in space, as well as the potential rewards it may offer, you need to understand what gravity is, how it operates, and why it seems to be nonexistent for orbiting astronauts and satellites. Can "weightlessness" be duplicated on Earth? If so, why do we not normally experience it?

(a)

(b)

Figure 1 **(a)** Living in orbit can be very disorienting.

(b) Eating in orbit can also be challenging.

Science & Technology

Gravity and Microgravity

There are four fundamental forces of nature: electromagnetic force, strong nuclear force, weak nuclear force, and gravity. The electromagnetic force (which includes both electric and magnetic forces) is responsible for holding electrons close to their positively charged home nuclei. The strong nuclear force binds protons and neutrons tightly together within atomic nuclei. The weak nuclear force is responsible for interactions between elementary particles, called quarks, that make up protons and neutrons. This force is associated with radioactive decay.

Gravity is by far the weakest fundamental force of nature. Gravity is also distinguished from the other three forces by being the only one that never repels. Unlike a pair of identical magnetic poles that push each other away, the force of gravity always works to attract two objects. Gravity also extends infinitely far. The gravitational force that Earth exerts not only holds the Moon in its orbit and keeps you firmly anchored on the ground, but also extends its influence on every other object. In fact, so do you and anything else that is composed of matter. You exert a gravitational influence on every other bit of matter everywhere within the entire universe.

In 1687, Sir Isaac Newton supplied the first model for gravity (**Figure 2**). In what is arguably the most important scientific literary work of all time, the *Principia*, Newton not only laid the foundations for all motions (the study of mechanics) but for gravity as well. Although Newton was not able to estimate how strong the force of gravity is, he correctly identified the two factors that determine gravity's strength and explained how they do this. The unit of force—the newton (N)—was named in his honour. If you hold an average-sized apple in the palm of your hand, you feel a force of approximately 1 N as Earth pulls it against your hand.

The strength of the force of gravitational attraction between two objects is dependent on both the masses of the objects and their separation distance. For the first factor, the force is directly proportional

to the product of the masses of the objects. This is written as the mathematical expression

$$F_G \propto m_1 m_2$$

where F_G is the force of gravitational attraction (measured in newtons), m_1 and m_2 are the masses of the two objects (measured in kilograms), and the symbol $\propto$ reads as "is proportional to" or "varies as."

For example, if Earth were twice as massive as it is (all other things being equal), it would exert twice as much gravitational force on you as it currently does. If Earth were three times as massive, it would exert three times the force. If both you and Earth had double your present masses, the force of gravitational attraction pulling you toward Earth and Earth toward you would be four times ($2 \times 2 = 4$) what it presently is.

Figure 2 Sir Isaac Newton (1642–1727) had formulated most of his ideas by the age of 25. In addition to making significant contributions to the study of mechanics, Newton contributed to optics and the associated study of light and is credited with the invention of calculus. He lived to the age of 85, which in itself was an accomplishment in the 18th century.

The second factor that is used to determine the strength of the gravitational force is the distance between the two objects. This is measured as the distance between the two centres. However, the relationship is not a linear one. The force of gravitational attraction between two objects varies inversely as the square of the distance, d (measured in metres), between their centres. So the greater the separation distance of the two objects, the more weakly they attract each other. This is written as the mathematical expression

$$F_G \propto \frac{1}{d^2}$$

From this expression, you can see that the force of attraction falls off very quickly with increased distance between the centres of the two objects. If the distance between them is doubled, the force is only one-quarter as strong $\left(\frac{1}{2^2} = \frac{1}{4}\right)$. Move the two objects three times as far apart, and the force becomes only one-ninth as strong $\left(\frac{1}{3^2} = \frac{1}{9}\right)$ (**Figure 3**).

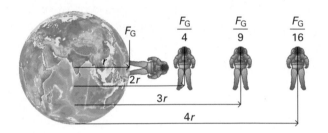

Figure 3 The force of gravitational attraction between two objects is inversely proportional to the square of the distance between their centres.

The combined expression provided by Newton is

$$F_G \propto \frac{m_1 m_1}{d^2}$$

Because this is an expression of proportion rather than an equation, Newton could not directly calculate the strength of the gravitational force between two objects. Nevertheless, he was able to gain significant insight into the motions of planets, moons, and all other celestial objects because gravity is the sole force that dictates these motions.

Of course, an equation is often more useful than an expression of proportion. All that was needed to change Newton's expression into an equation was a proportionality constant. In 1798, an English physicist named Henry Cavendish verified the propor-

tionality constant that Newton had suggested more than a century earlier. The proportionality, called **Newton's law of universal gravitation**, became the equation that is widely used today:

$$F_G = G \frac{m_1 m_2}{d^2}$$

where G, the universal gravitational constant, has a value of 6.67×10^{-11} N·m²/kg². This is a tiny number—it would take a very large amount of mass provided by one or both objects (or a very small separation distance) to result in a sizable gravitational force of attraction between them. Thus, gravity is a very weak force. After all, you are able to overcome the force of gravity exerted upon you by the entire planet when you climb out of bed every morning.

The size of the universal gravitational constant has tremendous importance in relation to the evolution of the universe. If the value had been slightly greater, making gravity a little stronger, the universe might never have been able to expand beyond a small size and would have collapsed in on itself in a relatively short time. If the value had been a little weaker, matter that was present before the universe had structure would never have come together by mutual gravitation. Planets, stars, and galaxies would never have formed, and life could not have begun.

Sample Problem

A brick with a mass of 1.0 kg is sitting on Earth's surface. Earth's mass is 5.98×10^{24} kg and its radius is 6.38×10^6 m; calculate the force of gravitational attraction between Earth and the brick.

Solution

Given Information

$G = 6.67 \times 10^{-11} \dfrac{\text{N•m}^2}{\text{kg}^2}$

$m_1 = 5.98 \times 10^{24}$ kg

$m_2 = 1.0$ kg

$d = 6.38 \times 10^6$ m

$F_G = ?$

$F_G = G \dfrac{m_1 m_2}{d^2}$

$\quad = 6.67 \times 10^{-11} \dfrac{\text{N•m}^2}{\text{kg}^2} \dfrac{(5.98 \times 10^{24}\,\text{kg})(1.0\,\text{kg})}{(6.38 \times 10^6\,\text{m})^2}$

$F_G = 9.8$ N

The magnitude of the force of gravity that is exerted by Earth on the brick (and by the brick on Earth) is 9.8 N.

(Note in the sample problem that the small distance from Earth's surface to the middle of the brick can be ignored because it is insignificant when compared to the radius of Earth.) This is an important result because it can be used to calculate the force of gravity acting on all objects at Earth's surface. For example, if a force of 9.8 N acts on a 1.0-kg object, then the force acting on a 2.0-kg object is 2(9.8 N), or 19.6 N. Thus, the strength of the gravitational force acting on every 1.0 kg of matter at Earth's surface is 9.8 N. Scientists refer to this quantity as the **gravitational field strength** at Earth's surface, symbolized by $g = 9.8$ N/kg. Every object is surrounded by its own **gravitational force field**; the strength of this field is determined by the mass of the object and the distance from the object.

The force of gravity you experience at the surface of Earth is commonly referred to as your **weight**. Most weight scales (household scales or supermarket scales) are calibrated in kilograms, which is a measure of mass not weight. If an object were placed on a scale on the surface of the Moon, it would measure about one-sixth as much as it does on Earth. The object has the same mass (the quantity of matter) regardless of its location, but its weight is dictated by the strength of the gravitational field it sits in. A scale that has been calibrated on Earth in a gravitational field of 9.8 N/kg would provide a different reading if used on the Moon.

Imagine Earth's gravitational field as an unbreakable soap bubble surrounding Earth. If the soap bubble is inflated, so that it moves farther from Earth's surface, its wall will grow thinner. Similarly, the gravitational field strength becomes weaker with increased distance. The more the soap bubble is inflated, the thinner the soap film becomes. It never gets so thin, however, that the soap bubble breaks. Similarly, gravity extends indefinitely, or infinitely far. Now imagine that other soap bubbles represent the gravitational fields of the Sun, the Moon, and other planets in our solar system. Imagine how they merge together and continually change, in complex combinations, as the planets revolve around the Sun. If you put yourself anywhere within this "gravitational foam," you would feel the combined effects of the gravitational fields of all of these celestial objects, constantly tugging you in ever-changing directions and with ever-changing forces. Expand your imaginary solar system to the gravitational fields of distant stars, and even other galaxies, all contributing to the overall gravitational force that you are subjected to—a very dense "gravitational froth." Of course, you are never really aware of any gravitational field except Earth's because of Earth's close proximity and large mass.

The gravitational influences of the Sun and the Moon certainly do not go unnoticed. The two bodies produce a combined gravitational effect on the world's oceans, causing the tides (**Figure 4**). While the Moon is primarily responsible for the tides, the greatest tidal bulges (spring tides) are created when the Sun, the Moon, and Earth are aligned. When the Sun and the Moon are at right angles to Earth, the tides are at their minimum (neap tides). The alignment of these three bodies, as well as local geography, causes the tides to reach different heights at different locations. Some of the world's most dramatic tides are recorded in Nova Scotia, in the Bay of Fundy (**Figure 5**).

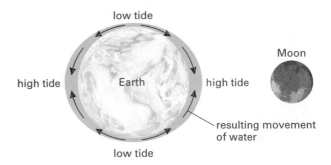

Figure 4 This polar view of Earth shows high tides on the sides of Earth that are in line with the Moon. The other sides of Earth, perpendicular to this line, experience low tides. (Water levels are exaggerated.)

Figure 5 Low tide along the coast of the Bay of Fundy

E1.1 Activity | OUR COSMIC NEIGHBOURS

Use **Table 1** to answer the following questions:

(a) Explain why the gravitational field strength of the Sun is so much greater than the gravitational field strength of any of the planets (**Figure 6**).

Figure 6 The planets of our solar system reveal a stunning variety of sizes, colours, and compositions.

(b) Neptune is over 17 times as massive as Earth, yet its surface gravitational field strength is only slightly greater than Earth's. Suggest a reason why.

(c) Jupiter's radius is only 20% larger than Saturn's, but its gravitational field strength is nearly two and a half times that of Saturn. Why?

(d) If we eventually colonize another planet, Mars would be the most likely choice. Describe how you think you might feel on the Martian surface. Suggest a few ways that your life would be different, from a gravitation point of view.

(e) From the data, make at least two other observations that might seem odd until fully considered in light of universal gravitation.

(f) If you weigh 600 N on Earth's surface, what are your maximum and minimum weights standing on the surfaces of other planets in our solar system?

Table 1 Physical Data on Solar System Objects

Object	Mass (kg)	Radius (m)	Gravitational field strength, g (N/kg)
Sun	1.99×10^{30}	6.96×10^{8}	274.0
Mercury	3.28×10^{23}	2.44×10^{6}	3.7
Venus	4.83×10^{24}	6.05×10^{6}	8.8
Earth	5.98×10^{24}	6.38×10^{6}	9.8
Mars	6.37×10^{23}	3.40×10^{6}	3.7
Jupiter	1.90×10^{27}	7.15×10^{7}	24.8
Saturn	5.67×10^{26}	6.03×10^{7}	10.4
Uranus	8.80×10^{25}	2.56×10^{7}	9.0
Neptune	1.03×10^{26}	2.48×10^{7}	11.2
Pluto	1.25×10^{22}	1.20×10^{6}	0.6
Moon	7.35×10^{22}	1.74×10^{6}	1.6

DID **YOU** KNOW?

Variation of *g*

The gravitational field strength at the surface of Earth varies between 9.78 N/kg at the equator and 9.83 N/kg at the poles because of the difference in distances from these two locations to the centre of the planet. Earth is somewhat flattened at the poles, a characteristic left over from its formation and its continuous spin.

From Newton's law of universal gravitation, we know that we can never escape the gravitational influence of Earth, or any other object. Why, then, do astronauts appear to be weightless or immune to the effects of gravity?

A space shuttle orbits Earth at an altitude of approximately 400 km. When you compare this altitude with the distance from the centre of Earth to Earth's surface, approximately 6400 km, an orbiting space shuttle is barely off the ground. In fact, the strength of the gravitational field at the position of the space shuttle is nearly 90% of its value at the surface of Earth. Therefore, astronauts and everything else on board the space shuttle weigh 90% of what they weigh on Earth.

Unlocking this puzzle lies in understanding what it means to be "in orbit." Have you ever ridden on an amusement park ride that lifts you high into the air and then suddenly releases you, resulting in a "free fall" straight down (**Figure 7**)? If so, you may have briefly experienced something close to the feeling that orbiting astronauts experience.

Figure 7 Many amusement park rides offer a sense of "free fall."

Imagine the unfortunate experience of standing inside an elevator when the supporting cable suddenly snaps. The elevator and its contents begin to fall, pulled downward by the force of gravity. Suppose you were holding something in your hand, and you let go of it when the elevator fell. Would the object fall to the elevator floor? Would it "fall" upward toward the ceiling? Would it stay just in front of your hand where you let go of it? The answer lies in Newton's law of universal gravitation and Newton's second law of motion. According to **Newton's second law of motion**, when an object experiences a force, it accelerates in the direction of the force. The acceleration of the object varies directly with the force and inversely with the mass of the object. This means that a large force acting on a given object results in a greater acceleration than a smaller force acting on the same object would. This also means that the larger the mass the force acts upon, the smaller the object's acceleration.

How can these laws be applied to the falling elevator? The elevator and all of its contents are falling with the same acceleration. Thus, the object you released from your hand appears to be "floating" in front of you. You and the object are both falling with the same acceleration, so the object is not moving relative to you. Earth pulls more massive objects with greater forces, but because they have greater masses, their accelerations are identical to the accelerations of less massive objects. Everything falls with the same acceleration! Just as Earth's gravitational field strength is 9.8 N/kg at Earth's surface, the acceleration due to gravity at Earth's surface is 9.8 m/s^2—for everything.

Even though this result is universally accepted, it is contrary to our everyday experience. Obviously, if a feather and a brick are dropped side by side, the brick reaches the ground much sooner than the feather. Why? The air resistance acting on the feather is much greater than the air resistance acting on the brick, and this results in the different drop times. If you release a brick and a feather together in a falling elevator, they remain side by side for the entire descent and in exactly the same positions from which you released them. Of course, this assumes that the elevator itself has no air resistance acting to slow its descent. While the effects of air resistance are often ignored when considering objects in free fall, scientists who study free fall cannot ignore them.

What if you happen to be standing on a bathroom scale in the falling elevator? You would find the scale reading exactly zero during the fall. Since both you and the bathroom scale are falling at the same rate, you are no longer exerting any force on the scale. Therefore, the scale registers no weight. The floor of the elevator no longer supports the scale, and the scale no longer supports you. You have achieved the feeling of **weightlessness** because you are falling with the acceleration due to gravity (9.8 m/s^2). However, it is important to remember that you are still well within Earth's gravitational field, and, therefore, you are not truly weightless, just apparently so.

To explain the apparent weightlessness of being in orbit, Newton imagined firing cannonballs horizontally with increasing speeds. If a cannonball is fired with relatively low speed, it will travel a short distance horizontally as it is falling to the ground. If the cannonball's muzzle velocity is increased, it will travel a greater distance before reaching the ground. If Earth was flat, the cannonball would travel a horizontal distance dependent on the speed with which it was fired. But Earth's surface is curved.

Now imagine firing a cannonball with a sufficiently large initial speed so that as it is falling to the ground, the surface of Earth curves away from beneath it at the same rate. The cannonball continually falls but never reaches Earth's surface. The cannonball has achieved **orbit** (**Figure 8**).

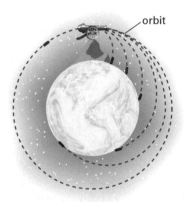
orbit

Figure 8 If an object is projected horizontally with sufficient speed, it will assume an orbit around Earth.

Put yourself in the place of the cannonball, and think about how you would feel as you moved in a circular orbit around Earth. You would experience the sensation of falling, the same feeling you would have on the elevator. There would be no end to the fall, however, no "bottom" of the elevator shaft. Being in orbit is identical to perpetually falling. The motion is both forward and downward. You are falling downward, and, at the same time, you are moving uniformly around the circular path.

Even though astronauts are well within Earth's gravitational field and therefore have weight, they appear to be weightless because they are continuously falling. This condition is often referred to as microgravity, which is perhaps an inappropriate term in light of what you have learned about gravity and orbits. **Microgravity** means that the effects of gravity have been minimized by orbital motion. It is the minimization of these gravitational effects that poses special challenges but also offers unique opportunities.

E1.2 Activity GRAVITY AND ELEVATORS

In this activity, you will distinguish apparent weight from actual weight.

Materials
500-g mass
spring scale

1. Stand inside a stationary elevator and suspend the mass from the spring scale. Note the reading on the scale.

2. As the elevator moves up and down, observe how the reading on the spring scale changes.
   (a) When the apparent weight of the object differs from its actual weight, how is the elevator moving?
   (b) Why does the apparent weight differ from the actual weight only briefly?

E1.3 Activity MEASURING GRAVITY   >

Air force pilots often experience gravitational forces that put substantial strains on their bodies. These forces are known as *g*-forces, and they can make a pilot feel heavier or lighter than normal, depending on how the airplane is manoeuvring. If the plane is in level flight at a constant speed, the pilot will feel absolutely normal. Once the plane accelerates, the sensation will change.

If accelerating downward with an acceleration equal to the acceleration of gravity (in free fall), the pilot will have the sensation of being weightless, the same feeling that an astronaut has in a microgravity environment. If accelerating upward, the pilot will feel heavier than normal. You can think of this as a "macrogravity" environment.

In this activity, you will use a device called an accelerometer (**Figure 9**) to measure the force of gravity under normal conditions and under conditions that mimic microgravity and macrogravity. A video camera that can replay action in slow motion would be an asset. Take a reading of the g-force indicated on the accelerometer in each step.

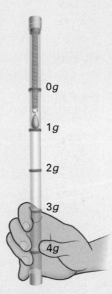

Figure 9 A typical vertical accelerometer for student use

Materials
accelerometer
video camera (optional)
cushion

1. Hold the accelerometer as high in the air as you can, and let it fall to the ground. You will need to cushion its fall in a suitable way.

2. Lift the accelerometer upward, attempting to maintain a constant speed.

3. Move the accelerometer downward with a constant speed.

4. Move the accelerometer so that it indicates a constant 2.0g force and a constant 3.0g force.

   (a) What did you discover about the relationship between the motion of the accelerometer and the g-force it registers?

   (b) Describe how you moved the accelerometer to achieve these g-forces.

   (c) Is it possible to produce negative g-forces? Describe how you would have to move the accelerometer to do this.

✓ Check Your Understanding

1. (a) What factors affect the strength of the gravitational force that two objects exert on one another?
   (b) How does each factor affect the force?

2. For each situation, determine the new value of the gravitational field strength at Earth's surface.
   (a) Earth's mass and radius are both doubled.
   (b) Earth is three times as massive and has twice its present radius.
   (c) Earth's mass is halved, and its radius is increased by a factor of 3.

3. If you had only half your present mass, how much more massive would Earth have to be in order to exert four times the gravitational force on you as it currently does? Assume that Earth's size does not change.

4. Define each of the following terms: weight, gravitational field, gravity, microgravity, weightlessness, orbit.

5. Describe the sensation of being in orbit. Explain how you could duplicate this sensation on Earth.

6. Think about Newton's model of firing a cannonball with enough speed to get it into orbit. Would the speed need to be greater or less if the cannonball was fired from a greater height? Explain your answer. (*Hint:* Compare the speeds of the planets in their orbits around the Sun.)

7. (a) Sometimes the relative size of a number is masked by writing it in scientific notation. Express the value of G, 6.67×10^{-11} N•m^2/kg^2, as a decimal number.
   (b) Describe why objects must be so massive in order to attract one another gravitationally with any significant force.

8. Are the terms "zero g" and "weightless" appropriate when describing orbiting objects? Explain your answer.

Society & the Environment

Microgravity

The term "microgravity" is used to refer to conditions in which gravitational effects have been minimized, where objects are in free fall. There are a number of methods that can be used to achieve these conditions.

Drop Towers

Facilities called **drop towers**, in which the air is removed, are similar to a free-falling elevator. Many drop towers are holes in the ground, such as mine shafts, although some are erected above ground (**Figure 10**). The deepest drop tower currently in operation is located in Japan. It uses a mine shaft that is nearly 500 m deep. Canisters are dropped from a variety of heights in the drop towers. As the canisters fall, the enclosed experiments are performed under microgravity conditions. (The canisters land in a cushioned area.)

Figure 10 Some drop towers can provide microgravity conditions for up to 10 s.

Aircraft

A specially outfitted jumbo jet is taken on a flight that is like a roller coaster ride through the sky. As the jet climbs over the top of a peak in its flight, apparent weightlessness is experienced on board. The flight usually lasts 2 h to 3 h, and many periods of microgravity (each lasting approximately 25 s) are experienced. Passengers who have experienced the unnerving sensations on board NASA's KC-135 jumbo jet often refer to the plane as the "vomit comet" (**Figure 11**).

Figure 11 Weightlessness inside NASA's "vomit comet"

Sounding Rockets

A powerful sounding rocket that carries a payload soars to suborbital heights (**Figure 12**). The rocket achieves a maximum height across a curved trajectory. Once the rocket's fuel is spent, the only force acting on it is gravity, so from that time forward the rocket is in free fall. As the rocket continues to climb to its maximum height and subsequently falls to the ground, it achieves microgravity conditions.

Figure 12 A Black Brant sounding rocket on its way to a suborbital flight. In nautical terms, "to sound" means to take measurements of the depth of water. Although not flying in water, sounding rockets are designed to take measurements.

Orbiting Platforms

Experiments can be performed in the microgravity conditions on orbiting platforms such as the Russian *Mir* and American *Skylab* (which are no longer in orbit), the space shuttle, and the ISS (**Figure 13**). Since these platforms have permanent microgravity conditions, they can be used for experiments that need to be conducted over extended periods of time.

Figure 13 The ISS orbiting Earth

Is Microgravity Research Worth the Environmental Consequences?

There are several methods for achieving microgravity conditions, and some of these methods do not involve going into orbit. Although this type of research is important, it is not without some environmental consequences. For example, the KC-135 aircraft is used primarily to help acclimatize astronauts to the apparent weightlessness they will experience when they go into orbit, but there are several concerns related to its continued use.

Statement: The environmental consequences of achieving microgravity using aircraft are minimal compared with the benefits of the research.

1. In your group, research the issue. Search for information in newspapers and periodicals, and on CD-ROMs and the Internet.

 www.science.nelson.com

2. Identify individuals, organizations, and government agencies that have addressed the issue.

3. Identify the perspectives of opposing positions, and arrange these perspectives in a suitable graphic organizer.

Decision-Making Skills

- Define the Issue
- Identify Alternatives
- Research
- Analyze the Issue
- Defend a Decision
- Evaluate

4. Role play either a NASA representative, who has been asked to address a group of local citizens who are upset about the environmental consequences of the KC-135, or a member of the citizens' group.
   - As the NASA representative, you must provide arguments that continued use of the KC-135 aircraft is vital to the space program.
   - As a member of the citizens' group, you must demonstrate that the environmental consequences of the aircraft cannot be justified.

   Prepare a speech (not exceeding 500 words) that presents your position. You may use the arguments in **Table 2** as a starting point for your speech.

5. Present your speech, and defend your group's position in a class discussion.

6. How did your group reach a decision about which position to defend?

Table 2 Arguments on Achieving Microgravity Using Aircraft

Proponents' claims	Opponents' claims
The quantity of fuel used by the KC-135 is such a tiny fraction of the general fuel consumption that it is insignificant by comparison.	The KC-135 produces a considerable amount of air pollution as a result of the large quantity of jet fuel it consumes.
For health and safety reasons, astronauts must be exposed to apparent weightlessness before venturing into space.	The KC-135 consumes a large quantity of valuable jet fuel on every flight. The expense and use of this valuable resource is not warranted.

SUMMARY

- The concept of gravity was first proposed by Sir Isaac Newton in 1687. Newton described gravity as a force of attraction that all masses exert on one another.
- The force of gravity exerted by two objects on each other varies directly with the product of their masses and inversely as the square of the distance between their centres. This relationship is summarized in Newton's law of universal gravitation:

$$F_G = G\frac{m_1 m_2}{d^2}$$

where the universal gravitational constant, G, equals 6.67×10^{-11} N•m²/kg².
- Gravity is one of four fundamental forces of nature. It is unique because it only ever attracts two objects. It has an infinite reach, and in relative terms, it is by far the weakest of the fundamental forces.
- The strength of the gravitational field, g, that surrounds an object depends on the object's mass and size. The average value for the gravitational field at Earth's surface is 9.8 N/kg.
- An object's weight is defined as the force of gravity that is exerted upon the object. It depends on the object's mass and the strength of the gravitational field in which the object is located.

- Even though Earth's gravitational field has the greatest effects on objects at Earth's surface, the Moon also influences Earth: the Moon is primarily responsible for the tides.
- An object in orbit experiences microgravity as a result of being in constant free fall. At Earth's surface, this situation is like falling with an acceleration of 9.8 m/s². In the absence of air resistance, all objects fall with this acceleration at Earth's surface.
- Objects in orbit appear to be weightless because they are falling, as is everything around them.
- Microgravity is a perpetual condition for orbiting objects, but it can be duplicated for short periods of time on or near Earth's surface in drop towers, specially outfitted aircraft, and on board sounding rockets.

Key Terms

gravity	Newton's second law
Newton's law of	of motion
universal gravitation	weightlessness
gravitational field	orbit
strength	microgravity
gravitational force field	*g*-force
weight	drop tower

ASSESSMENT

Understanding Concepts

1. **(a)** Describe the difference between your normal weight and your apparent weight.
   (b) Under what conditions are your normal weight and your apparent weight equal? When would they be different?

2. Using examples, differentiate between the terms "gravitational field strength" and "gravitational force strength."

3. Describe some ways that life would be different on a planet with much greater or much less gravity than on Earth.

4. **(a)** List some ways that gravity works for us by making tasks easier to accomplish.

(b) List some tasks that would be easier if gravity were stronger.

(c) List some tasks that would be easier if gravity were weaker.

5. The gravitational field strength on Mars is 3.7 N/kg. If you were to drop an object from just above the Martian surface, at what rate would the object fall?

6. The force of gravity that Earth exerts on you (your weight) can be calculated using the formula $F_G = mg$, where m is your mass (in kilograms) and g is 9.8 N/kg. The force of gravity can also be calculated using the formula

$$F_G = G\frac{m_1 m_2}{d^2}.$$

Knowing that Earth's radius is 6.38×10^6 m, calculate Earth's mass.

Applying Inquiry Skills

7. The height of a drop tower depends on the time required for the drops. The distance d, in metres, that an object will free fall from rest can be calculated using the equation

$$d = v_i t + \frac{1}{2} at^2$$

where v_i is the initial speed (0 m/s), a is the acceleration due to gravity (9.8 m/s²), and t is the time, in seconds, of the fall. After substituting 0 m/s for v_i and 9.8 m/s² for a, this equation reduces to $d = 4.9t^2$.

(a) Calculate the height of a drop tower for falls of 1.0 s, 2.0 s, 3.0 s, up to 10.0 s. Record your results in a table.

(b) Plot a graph of drop tower height (y-axis) against drop time (x-axis).

(c) If the cost of erecting a drop tower is dependent on its height, what are the cost implications of building drop towers to achieve greater drop times?

8. The speed of an object in orbit depends entirely on its altitude above Earth's surface.

(a) Using Newton's cannonball analogy for explaining orbital motion, describe why an object's speed and altitude are related.

(b) Explain why an object's mass does not need to be considered.

9. Design an experiment to test the idea that two objects of different masses fall at the same rate. Assume that you cannot eliminate air resistance.

10. When you stand on a scale on Earth, the scale registers the force of gravity exerted upon you by Earth (your weight). Calculate the weight of a 60-kg person on the surface of each planet listed in **Table 3**.

Table 3 Comparison of Gravitational Field Strengths

Planet	Gravitational field strength (N/kg)
Earth	9.8
Mars	3.7
Jupiter	24.8
Pluto	0.58

Making Connections

11. Astrologers believe that the positions of the planets at the time of birth influence a person's life. If the influence is gravitational, how would the influence of a distant planet compare with the influence of a nearby object?

(a) Calculate the gravitational force that Mars ($m_{Mars} = 6.4 \times 10^{23}$ kg) would exert on a 4.0-kg baby at Mars' closest approach ($d = 7.8 \times 10^{10}$ m).

(b) What mass would need to be placed 1.0 m away from the baby to have the same gravitational effect?

(c) What would you say to an astrologer who claims that the positions of the planets at the time of birth influence a person's life?

12. In a 1970s Hollywood disaster film, several people were shown pressed against the ceiling of an elevator as it plummeted toward the ground.

(a) Explain the "bad science" depicted.

(b) Under what conditions could a person possibly come off the floor during such a descent?

13. The CSA is investigating a number of areas in which microgravity plays a central role, such as fluid physics, glass manufacturing, and crystal growth. Choose one area, and summarize the research that is currently being conducted as well as the possible applications of this research.

 www.science.nelson.com

14. Research and compare the use of drop towers and aircraft as methods for achieving microgravity conditions. In your comparison, consider the following questions.

(a) What are the design features of each method?

(b) How is microgravity achieved?

(c) How long can microgravity be maintained?

(d) What can each method be used for?

 www.science.nelson.com

15. List six careers that are directly related to current microgravity research, plus six secondary careers.

 www.science.nelson.com

Living *in* Space:
SPECIAL
CHALLENGES

The mission to date had taken its toll on the crew. Upon leaving Earth four months ago on the first manned mission to Mars, there was initial jubilation and excitement. The crew had been well trained and thoroughly conditioned for the challenges that lay ahead, not only for their arrival at the planet but, perhaps more importantly, for the trip itself.

As expected, the crew experienced a certain degree of disorientation, head and chest congestion, and stomach upset during the first few days. These symptoms passed, however, more quickly for some than for others. The crew took great delight in moving about the ship in weightlessness, and some invented demonstrations and games to entertain the others.

The views from the portholes had been magnificent as the ship left Earth's orbit and swung around the Moon. As the days passed, Earth receded from view, and all they could see were star fields. Sensing day from night became more difficult: The crew's circadian (daily) rhythms largely deserted them. Some crew members became restless and found it difficult to sleep. Others found routine jobs arduous to complete and complained of a lack of concentration.

(a) Most people sleep at night and are awake during the day. This is considered a circadian rhythm because it is an activity cycle based on a 24-h period. ("Circadian" is from two Latin words: *circa*, which means "about," and *dies*, which means "day.") Provide some other examples of circadian rhythms that are common to most people.

The daily radio communications with loved ones were always welcomed, even though they were taped. The vast distance meant a delay of about half an hour between question and answer, and this delay was getting longer as the ship ventured farther from Earth. It was difficult not to be able to help family members cope with emergencies, to celebrate birthdays and anniversaries, and to hold children and spouses. The crew missed home-cooked meals, as well. As much as mission control had attempted to supply nutritious and inviting meals, the meals were becoming routine. Talk often centred around favourite foods they would devour when they got home. This would have to wait for nearly two years, however.

The crew continued with the required daily regimen of exercise to maintain as much muscle mass and bone strength as possible. The mission doctor monitored blood chemistry, urine composition, and bone density very closely and prescribed supplements as required. While some of the medical effects of microgravity were well understood, others were not.

At one point, a crew member became ill with a virus that had unknowingly been acquired before launch. Subsequently, the entire crew came down with symptoms as the infection spread throughout the ship. Fortunately, the toilet continued to function properly.

Although the ventilation and water recycling systems were operating perfectly, the living quarters were feeling more confining (**Figure 1**). All would have welcomed the opportunity to stretch their legs and move about with greater freedom. Once on Mars, they would still be confined to their space suits and small living quarters.

Figure 1 Cramped living quarters

Preparations for the Mars landing would begin in earnest soon. The crew wondered what gravity would feel like again, having been without it for so long. Even though Mars' gravity is less than half of Earth's, there was some uncertainty over how difficult standing and moving about would be. Everyone would certainly need to be careful once they arrived; a broken leg could jeopardize the entire mission.

There seemed to be little doubt that the housing facilities and supplies had successfully arrived months before and that everything was in good working order. Would Mars harbour surprises, however, that had not been foreseen by mission control or spotted by the robotic rovers that had preceded this mission? The answer was only 10 weeks away.

Will a manned mission to Mars be possible someday? What are the medical effects of space flight? Are the benefits of space exploration worth the costs?

(b) This scenario suggests a number of challenges that could be encountered on a manned mission to Mars. What other challenges can you think of? Suggest possible consequences of each challenge.

(c) In what ways would a manned mission to Mars be similar to the early colonization of North America by European and British settlers? In what ways would it be different?

(d) Have similar challenges been encountered by astronauts on space shuttles or on orbiting platforms such as *Mir, Skylab*, and the ISS? How have astronauts coped?

(e) From this scenario, identify challenges that result specifically from microgravity conditions. Suggest how microgravity is responsible for each challenge.

E2.1 Activity   PACKING FOR A MISSION TO MARS

A manned mission to Mars will take approximately 2.5 years, including 190 days of travel, one way. Normally, space agencies send robots for missions of this duration. As long as sufficient fuel is on board and solar cell arrays can get enough sunlight to keep the computers and other systems operating, little else needs to accompany the spacecraft. However, when a human crew sets out on such an extended mission, everything changes. Meticulous planning will be essential.

Preceding the manned mission, it is likely that at least two unmanned spacecraft will arrive on Mars (**Figure 2**), carrying with them housing facilities, vehicles, a return spacecraft, and all the essentials the crew will need while on the planet's surface and for the trip home.

In this activity, you will identify the supplies required for a crew of seven on a return mission to Mars and estimate quantities of the supplies you will need.

(a) Essentials: Air and water can largely be recycled, but a sufficient quantity of food will need to be transported with the crew. What types of food will be best to take along? Suggest a typical daily menu, and then estimate what quantity of each food item will be required.

(b) Extras: List other items that you think would need to accompany the crew on such a mission. Provide reasons for your choices.

(c) Personal Items: If you were selected as a crew member for the mission and you are allowed to bring 20 kg of personal items, suggest what you would bring along, and provide reasons for your choices.

Figure 2 An artist's depiction of a landing site on Mars

Science & Technology

Medical Effects of Space Flight

Space is not very hospitable. When astronauts venture outside Earth's atmosphere, they leave behind its natural protection. The atmosphere is not very thick (**Figure 3**), yet it acts as a barrier to lethal radiation and charged particles that are emitted from the Sun. The atmosphere also prevents meteors—some travelling at tens of kilometres per second—from reaching Earth's surface. If you have ever witnessed a meteor streaking across the night sky, you will know why some people mistakenly call meteors "shooting stars."

Figure 3 If Earth were the size of an apple, the atmosphere (shown in blue) would be as thin as the apple's peel.

Aside from the occasional molecule drifting toward its nearest gravitational attractor, space is very nearly a perfect vacuum. In other words, there is a total lack of any kind of gas pressure. On Earth, gas pressure allows you to breathe. As your diaphragm moves up and down, small differences in air pressure are created inside and outside your chest cavity, drawing in air and expelling it. If you were to venture outside a spacecraft without a protective suit, air would be immediately expelled from your lungs. Dissolved gases in your tissues and blood would not be able to stay in solution, so your skin would inflate like a balloon and rupture as the gases escaped.

Temperature is related to the average speed of the particles in a substance, but space is a vacuum and is devoid of particles. Strictly speaking, then, space has no temperature. Heat cannot move through space by either conduction or convection because both of these methods of heat transfer require particles. However, heat can be radiated. Just as you can feel the radiant heat from the Sun, objects in space absorb and radiate heat, resulting in a change in temperature. Outside a spaceship, an astronaut's space suit can reach a temperature of 120°C when exposed to the Sun but plummet to −160°C when shaded from the Sun.

The Sun is a source of potentially lethal electrically charged particles, which bombard Earth at very high speeds. Earth's magnetic field protects us by deflecting most of these particles past the planet and steering some toward the magnetic poles, where they interact with atmospheric molecules. The results are the beautiful displays of aurora borealis and aurora australis, commonly known as the northern and southern lights. The Sun is also a source of ultraviolet radiation, much of which is absorbed by ozone in the upper atmosphere. Occasionally, a solar eruption sends a burst of charged particles and radiation toward Earth (**Figure 4**); some of these particles travel with speeds that are sufficient to pass through a fully suited astronaut or the hull of a spaceship. Human exposure to such radiation is linked to cancer, sterility, and central nervous system damage. Delicate electronic equipment can also be damaged or destroyed.

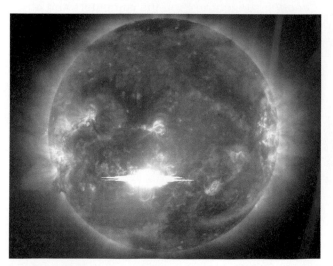

Figure 4 Eruptions on the Sun directed at Earth can threaten the health of astronauts.

DID **YOU** KNOW?

Radiation in Space
During a trip to Mars, an astronaut would be exposed to an amount of radiation equivalent to approximately 30 000 chest X-rays!

While the hull of a spaceship offers some protection, astronauts are exposed to higher-than-normal levels of radiation. To work outside a spaceship, an astronaut needs a protective space suit that is constructed to the very highest standards (**Figure 5**).

Figure 5 An astronaut's suit is made up of about 12 layers. Liquid circulates through the inner layers to stabilize body temperature. A pressure bladder allows the astronaut to operate under normal atmospheric pressure, and the outer layers serve as insulation from heat and cold and as a shield against fast-moving particles. Pictured is a Russian space suit.

For a long space flight, one of the most daunting challenges will be coping with extended microgravity conditions. If astronauts continue to live and work in space, the effects of microgravity need to be well understood and controlled, if not altogether eliminated. The physiological and psychological effects of microgravity are many and varied, and they are a central focus of research for scientists involved in space programs.

Before we ventured into space, some scientists made dire predictions about the effects of microgravity. Some suggested that the heart would race uncontrollably; others thought that it might not beat at all. There was a concern that astronauts might become helplessly depressed or absolutely exhilarated, making them unable to perform necessary functions. Some scientists thought that swallowing would become difficult, thinking would be impaired, and sleeping would be either unavoidable or impossible.

Before exposing humans to microgravity conditions, a number of animals were launched into space. In 1957, the Soviet *Sputnik 2* carried a dog, Laika, on the first orbital flight by a living test subject (**Figure 6**). In subsequent launches, mice, rats, cats, and monkeys were all sent into space to set the stage for human space flights. In experiments since then, many other species—such as snails, spiders, fruit flies, worms, fish, frogs, and tortoises—have been studied.

Figure 6 Laika was the first living organism to be launched into space. While *Sputnik 2* was in orbit for 162 days, the Russians believe that Laika lived for only 2 days.

DID **YOU** KNOW?

The First Astronaut
Before John Glenn's flight in 1962, a chimpanzee named Enos spent three hours in microgravity during a test flight. This was to ensure that the equipment was functioning properly and that exposure to microgravity could be tolerated by primates.

Space Sickness

Space sickness, also known as "space adaptation syndrome," affects nearly half of the people who venture into orbit. The symptoms are dizziness, disorientation, and nausea, not unlike being seasick on a rocking ship. Generally, symptoms last only a few hours to a few days. The cause seems to stem from a response of the **vestibular system** of the inner ear to microgravity.

While the mechanism is not entirely understood, scientists do know that our sense of balance comes, in part, from the **semicircular canals** and the **otolith organs**, which are located next to the cochlea and together make up the inner ear (**Figure 7**).

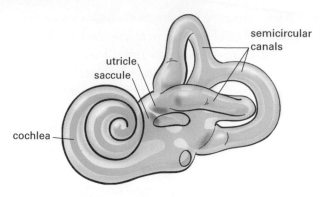

Figure 7 The inner ear consists of the cochlea, the semicircular canals, and the otolith organs (the utricle and the saccule). Imagine the corner of a room with the two walls and ceiling lying in three planes, all perpendicular to each other. The semicircular canals are arranged like this.

The three semicircular canals are hollow structures filled with fluid and lined with tiny nerve hairs. The fluid is held down within these structures in a normal gravity environment. When your head rotates in any direction, the fluid moves within the semicircular canals and washes across the nerve hairs. This in turn triggers impulses that are interpreted by your brain to mean movement and the orientation of your head. In a microgravity environment, the fluid sloshes about haphazardly within the semicircular canals, resulting in random impulses being sent to the brain. The brain interprets them to mean that the head is moving about. Meanwhile, the sensory input from the eyes tells the brain that the head is stationary. Some scientists believe that these conflicting signals are responsible for the symptoms of dizziness and nausea that so many astronauts experience. The symptoms eventually pass once the brain is able to resolve the confusion.

The structure of the two otolith organs is similar to the structure of the semicircular canals. Tiny nerve hairs stand upright within the otolith organs. Microscopic crystals, suspended in a jellylike membrane, surround the hairs. When your head accelerates, the crystals within the membrane move against the nerve hairs, which send signals to your brain indicating the motion. In a microgravity environment, the proper functioning of the otolith organs is compromised.

Inner ear infections can impair the function of the otolith organs and the semicircular canals, resulting in symptoms that are similar to those of space sickness, particularly dizziness and nausea. A lack of stimulation of touch sensors in the skin and gravity sensors in the joints can intensify the symptoms.

Microgravity can be simulated for only short intervals on Earth, which is currently a maximum of around 30 s. Therefore, astronauts get acquainted with the effects of space sickness during brief exposures on board specially outfitted jumbo jets—vomit comets—that take them through a series of parabolic flight paths (**Figure 8**).

Figure 8 During a parabolic flight path, the jet climbs at a 45° angle and then dives at the same angle. The result is a zero-gravity environment that lasts 25 s to 30 s.

Space Anemia

When the human body is exposed to microgravity, a number of changes take place that ultimately lead to potentially dangerous changes in blood chemistry. Because body mass is 70% water, the distribution of body fluids is largely dictated by gravity. When subjected to microgravity, body fluids migrate from the lower extremities to the upper torso and head. Some astronauts report symptoms that are similar to chest and nasal congestion. Astronauts' faces tend to become puffy (**Figure 9**), and their legs grow thinner.

Receptors in the upper body sense the excess fluid, and the body responds by suppressing thirst and by increasing elimination through urination. A perceived excess blood volume is countered by a reduction in red blood cell production. The production of energy is related to the availability of oxygen, which binds with red blood cells that circulate

Figure 9 The upward movement of body fluid causes the face to appear puffy (right).

throughout the body. With a decreased blood volume and fewer red blood cells, the transport of oxygen is reduced, leading to **anemia**. Within one or two days in a microgravity environment, an astronaut's total blood volume may decrease by as much as 20%. Provided that the astronaut remains in a microgravity environment, where it is easier for the heart to pump blood to the upper extremities without a gravitational pull downward, decreased blood volume is not a problem. However, when the astronaut returns to a normal Earth gravity, blood begins to pool in the legs and feet once again. Because the heart cannot provide sufficient oxygen to the cells, the symptoms of anemia become apparent. These include a lack of energy, a drop in blood pressure, and heightened respiratory and heart rates. The symptoms are similar to those faced by someone who has recently donated blood. Heavy activity is not recommended until the blood volume returns to normal, generally within a few days.

Bone Deterioration

Your bones are always adapting to various stresses that you put on them. Bone tissue is constantly being destroyed by osteoclast cells, and new bone tissue is constantly being constructed by osteoblast cells. As the muscles exert new forces on the bones, the bones are reshaped by the osteoclast and osteoblast cells to support the new forces. In a microgravity environment, the lack of forces on the bones causes the bone-building process to slow while the bone-destroying process seems to be maintained. The resulting **bone demineralization** causes calcium to leach from the bones. This not only weakens the skeletal structure, but may also cause

astronauts to develop kidney stones. Excess calcium is filtered from the blood by the kidneys and can precipitate, forming small, jagged stones. If these stones enter the urethra, the pain is excruciating. A medical emergency like this would seriously threaten any space mission.

Over a million Canadians suffer from bone loss, called osteoporosis (**Figure 10**). Although more common in postmenopausal women, most people eventually acquire it to some degree. Research into osteoporosis that is currently being conducted in space may lead to better treatments on Earth.

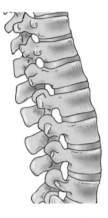
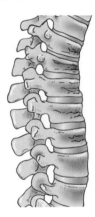

Figure 10 The spine on the left is normal; the spine on the right has osteoporosis.

Bone loss has been measured at 1% to 2% for each month of exposure to microgravity, with some astronauts losing as much as 20% of bone mass in the hips and lower extremities over a six-month period. This is not terribly problematic as long as the astronaut remains in the microgravity environment. Upon returning to a more normal gravity, however, weakened bones are subject to fracture. Imagine how a Mars mission would be jeopardized by an astronaut breaking a leg or a hip upon arriving at the planet after months of exposure to microgravity. Unless effective treatments are developed, missions lasting two or three years could cause an intolerable loss of bone mass.

DID **YOU** KNOW?

Osteo-Archeology
When bones are put under stress, they bend according to the forces they are subjected to. If bones are put under persistent stress, they acquire permanent changes in their shapes. Based on these changes, archeologists can often suggest whether a person had a life of hard labour.

Muscle Changes

Just as bones deteriorate when they are not subjected to constant stress, so does muscle tissue. With nearly every muscular movement you make, from standing to lifting to walking, you are constantly using your muscles to overcome the force of gravity.

When a muscle is immobilized or used less, it **atrophies**, or wastes away. For example, have you ever seen an arm or leg after it has been in a cast for an extended period of time? Compared with the size of the corresponding limb, there is an obvious difference due to inactivity of the muscles during the healing process. Muscle atrophy is a significant concern for astronauts. Reduced muscle mass means reduced strength and stamina. Although the effects appear to be totally reversible upon returning to a normal gravity environment, the ability of a weakened astronaut to pilot a shuttle during reentry could be compromised.

Even the heart muscle is affected by space flight. As fluid first begins to shift headward, the heart grows larger to cope with the increased blood volume. However, the heart does return to normal once the body has eliminated the excess fluid.

An astronaut's spine typically grows 2 cm to 5 cm in length because the disks between the vertebrae expand in the absence of gravity. This growth causes acute back pain for many astronauts as their muscles adjust to the new conditions.

> ### DID **YOU** KNOW?
>
> **Growing in Your Sleep**
> When you are sleeping, the disks in your back relax and your spine lengthens. You are always your tallest when you first wake up in the morning, by about one centimetre.

From 2001 to 2002, a collaborative study on the effects of microgravity was conducted by the European Space Agency, the French space agency (Centre national d'études spatiale, CNES), and the National Space Development Agency of Japan. Researchers discovered that some effects of microgravity, particularly those related to fluid shift from the lower body upward, can be simulated by bed rest in a head-down inclined position. They found that a gradient of 6° is optimal for simulating the desired effects.

In the study, 28 subject volunteers spent three months in the declined position (**Figure 11**), taking their meals and tending to personal hygiene with the help of a specially designed bathroom and shower facility. Their free time was occupied with reading, watching television, and talking with friends and relatives on the telephone. No personal visits were allowed.

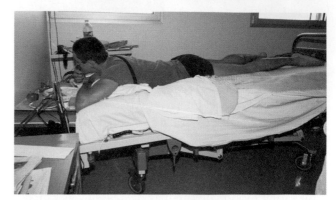

Figure 11   The effects of body fluid shift in microgravity are simulated by extended bed rest in a declined position.

The volunteers were split into three groups:

- a control group, which remained in bed
- a second group, which remained in bed but exercised three times a week to counteract muscle loss due to inactivity
- a third group, which remained in bed but received treatment for the resulting bone deterioration

Some of the results were apparent almost immediately, and some took longer to show up. Researchers hope that the results will help determine why we lose muscle mass during inactivity and what mechanism causes bones to lose calcium when not subjected to load-bearing forces. The results will be important for astronauts who spend extended periods of time in space and for millions of bedridden patients who suffer some of the same symptoms.

Other Effects

Most of the effects of sustained exposure to microgravity were identified during early flights into space in the 1960s. There are now proposals for future manned missions to the Moon and for the establishment of a permanent colony there. Plans for astronauts to travel to Mars have also received important endorsements from both the scientific community and the United States government. These bolder ventures, of much longer durations, will present new challenges.

It is difficult to predict the consequences of the psychological stress that a crew may endure from the tedium of a long flight in closed quarters, perhaps for months on end. If astronauts develop anxiety and depression, how will these conditions be treated? Studies indicate that the prolonged stress associated with space flights weakens the immune system, leaving astronauts less able to ward off infections. Because healing processes are impaired, bone fractures and other injuries that happen during a space flight may take much longer than normal to heal.

Crew members may become ill or develop serious medical problems during a long flight. Medical emergencies, such as heart attacks or severe trauma, will need immediate response. Should crew members have the necessary training and equipment to deal with any medical situation?

Another concern is possible exposure to toxins or allergens that get released into the living and working quarters, perhaps by a malfunctioning ventilation or water recycling system. Will the crew have the necessary tools and expertise to make the repairs as quickly as possible? There may also be unpredictable effects of a long space flight. Surprises are nothing new to space exploration.

Unfortunately, the history of space exploration is not without some disturbing disasters. A cabin fire killed three *Apollo 1* astronauts in 1967 while still on the launch pad. In the same year, a Soviet *Soyuz 1* capsule's parachute failed to open, killing one cosmonaut. In 1971, a *Soyuz 2* capsule lost cabin pressure during reentry, killing three. The space shuttle *Challenger* exploded shortly after liftoff in 1986, killing seven astronauts, and the space shuttle *Columbia* burned up during reentry in 2003, killing its crew of seven. There are many others, including test pilots and ground crew, who have died in the pursuit of space exploration. While a tragedy often resets the agenda of a country's space program, progress continues. No doubt, there will continue to be a human cost to these ventures.

Artificial Gravity

Since most of the medical effects of space flight stem from extended exposure to microgravity, being able to simulate gravity, particularly on long-duration missions, seems like a good idea. If a strong enough force were exerted upward against the soles of an astronaut's feet to result in an upward acceleration of 9.8 m/s², the astronaut, in microgravity, would have the sensation of standing in normal gravity. Just as an upward-accelerating elevator makes you feel heavier in normal gravity, an upward acceleration could make an astronaut feel normal in microgravity.

Imagine that you are riding a roller coaster at a constant speed along a horizontal section of track. When the car you are riding in suddenly enters a vertical loop, you are pushed against your seat and suddenly feel heavier. The sensation stems from your inertia, a concept addressed in Newton's first law of motion. According to **Newton's first law of motion**, stationary objects remain at rest and moving objects keep moving at a constant speed in a straight line until a force is applied. Objects with greater mass have more inertia, since larger forces are required to accelerate them.

You experience the effects of inertia all the time. If you are a passenger in a stopped car and the car is hit from behind, your head seems to jerk backward as the car accelerates forward. This sensation results from your body moving forward and your head tending to stay behind. Similarly, when a car turns a corner, you feel as though you are pushed to the outside of the curve when, in fact, your inertia would have you travel in a straight line. The sensation of being pushed up against the car door by some mysterious force when turning a corner is actually the result of the door pushing against you, preventing you from continuing along a straight-line path.

Consider the roller coaster example again. When you are moving along the horizontal section of track, your inertia would have you continue along this path. When your car reaches the vertical loop, your seat exerts an upward force against you, overcoming your inertia. At any point in the vertical loop, your inertia could send you off along a tangent to the circle. (Think about how a stone at the end of a string, whirling around in a circle, flies off along a straight line perpendicular to the string if the string breaks.) In order to keep you moving in a circle on the roller coaster track, the seat must push you continuously toward the centre of the circle, always perpendicular to the direction your inertia would have you move. Even though you may feel as if you are being pushed outward against your seat, the seat is actually pushing you inward. The outward force you sense when moving in a circular motion does not actually exist. It is really an inward force, called the **centripetal force**, that keeps you moving in a circular path.

E2.2 Investigation MEASURING PHYSIOLOGICAL CHANGES IN SIMULATED MICROGRAVITY CONDITIONS

In this investigation, you will measure some of the physiological responses of your body to an upward shift of fluids caused by being placed in a head-down position, tilted at 6°.

Several stations will be set up in your classroom. Each station will be equipped with a complete set of measuring devices and a data table for recording all the measurements over the duration of the investigation. One person in your group will be the test subject, and another person will be the control (sitting) subject. At least two people will need to take and record the measurements.

You will measure the following physiological responses for both the test and control subjects: systolic and diastolic blood pressure, heart rate, respiration rate, body temperature, neck circumference, and lower leg circumference.

Take the measurements at 5-min intervals over a 30-min time period. Because all measurements cannot be taken simultaneously, they must be spread out over a period of time. Be sure to take the measurements for the same response at the same time within each 5-min interval. Monitor both the control subject and test subject for each physiological response.

 If you have a medical condition such as asthma, a seizure disorder, a cardiovascular problem, or a neurological disorder, you should not be a test subject. Instead, you can be a control subject, or you can take or record the measurements.

If you are a test subject and you feel unwell at any time during the investigation (e.g., you have a headache, dizziness, or shortness of breath), you should discontinue immediately, assume a horizontal position, and have a classmate inform your teacher.

Questions

(i) What physiological responses are caused by a shift of fluid from the lower extremities to the upper torso and head?

(ii) Is there a relationship between length of exposure and the extent of the physiological responses?

Inquiry Skills

○ Questioning	○ Planning	● Analyzing
○ Hypothesizing	● Conducting	● Evaluating
● Predicting	● Recording	○ Communicating

Predictions

(a) Predict what change, if any, you expect for each physiological response you test.

(b) Predict how the exposure time will affect the extent of each physiological response.

Materials

flat surface for test subject (large enough to support a person comfortably and able to be tilted 6°)
comfortable chair for control subject
sphygmomanometer
stethoscope
forehead thermometer tape
cloth or plastic tape measure (or string)
stopwatch

Procedure

Part 1: Systolic and Diastolic Blood Pressure and Heart Rate

1. Using sphygmomanometer, measure and record each subject's systolic and diastolic blood pressure (see **Appendix A4**). If only a single sphygmomanometer is available at each station, the control and test subjects will have to be monitored one after the other. The test subject should be monitored first, when the experiment begins; the control subject can be monitored after sitting for several minutes.

 Do not restrict the flow of blood any longer than one minute.

Follow the instructions provided with the sphygmomanometer.

Take only one reading in a 5-min interval.

2. The sphygmomanometer may measure heart rate as well. If not, heart rate can be measured by first finding the subject's pulse at the radial artery in the wrist. Monitor and record the heart rate when you take each blood pressure reading.

Part 2: Respiration Rate

3. Measure and record each subject's respiration rate by counting the number of breaths the subject takes in 1 min. This measurement should be taken during the last minute of each 5-min interval.

Part 3: Body Temperature

4. Place the forehead thermometer tape on the subject's forehead, and leave it in place for the duration of the experiment (**Figure 12**). Observe and record the subject's temperature at the end of each 5-min interval.

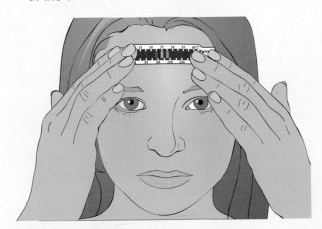

Figure 12 Forehead thermometer tape

Part 4: Neck Circumference

5. Using the tape measure, measure and record the circumference of each subject's neck. Be sure to place the tape measure at the same location on the neck for every measurement. You can use a string if a tape measure is not available.

Part 5: Leg Circumference

6. Using the tape measure, measure and record the circumference of each subject's lower leg at the largest expanse of the calf muscle.

Analysis

(c) Analyze the data you collected, noting which readings changed over time and how they changed for both the test subject and control subject. Compare the data for the test subject and control subject.

(d) Answer the Questions.

(e) Identify which physiological responses were influenced by the test subjects' declined position.

(f) Identify the responses that were time-dependent in each position. Show these correlations.

Evaluation

(g) To what extent did your results support your Predictions?

(h) In your opinion, are your results valid? Do you think your results reliably reflect what you would observe in a microgravity environment? Explain.

(i) What changes would you make to the design of this investigation to improve the quality of your results?

Synthesis

(j) Suggest some medical applications on Earth for the knowledge gained from this type of investigation.

The idea of using centripetal force to create **artificial gravity** has long been considered the solution to overcoming the effects of microgravity. This could be achieved in a number of ways. If the entire spaceship were rotated while in flight, centripetal forces that could simulate gravity would be created. Even if a section of the spaceship—a revolving ring perhaps—were rotating at the proper rate, a normal gravity environment could be replicated. An astronaut, standing on the inside of the ring, would have a sense that "up" was toward the centre of the ring and "down" was radially outward (**Figure 13**).

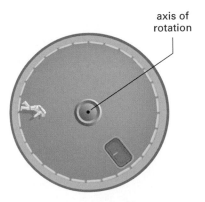

Figure 13 An astronaut walking in simulated gravity inside a rotating spaceship

The rate of rotation and the radius of the ring would determine how much centripetal force is exerted. For this to be a practical way of simulating gravity, the rotating ring would need to be very large. Otherwise, the amount of force acting along the length of the astronaut's body would vary, and the beneficial effects would be greatly diminished.

Another way to take advantage of centripetal force would be to have a large mass on the end of a tether line attached to a spaceship and to rotate the mass and spaceship end around end. This would be similar to having two objects tied together by a string and throwing them so that they spun around a common central point (called the centre of mass). A spaceship could be designed with two pods attached to one another by a long column; astronauts could travel from pod to pod through the column. The whole spaceship could be rotated to simulate gravity in each pod, and a microgravity environment would exist at the centre of the column.

For particularly long flights, a spaceship could be taken through a series of accelerations and decelerations along its flight path. While speeding up, "down" would seem to be toward the rear of the ship. When decelerating, "down" would seem to be in the direction of travel. These sensations would be similar to what you experience in a car that is accelerating and decelerating. If propulsion systems could accelerate a spaceship to 10% of the speed of light, which is orders of magnitude above what is currently possible, accelerating at a rate equivalent to normal gravity (9.8 m/s^2), the ship would reach full speed in about 3.5 days. A full cycle of speeding up and slowing down would occur approximately once a week.

Overcoming the medical effects of microgravity by centripetal force or other forces might not require full Earth gravity. Only a fraction of the 9.8 N/kg might provide sufficient benefits. This might mean that simpler spaceship designs would be possible.

Large and complex spaceships would be enormously expensive and would require unprecedented engineering to design and construct. At least in the near future, space programs will likely continue to use more conventional spaceships, which are small and somewhat cramped. Astronauts may have to rely on rigorous exercise programs, diet, and drugs to deal with the medical effects of microgravity. The experiences of astronauts who have spent long periods of time on *Mir* and *Skylab* have taught scientists much about the effects of microgravity. Similar experiences on the ISS should help to provide ways to overcome these effects.

E2.3 Activity   SIMULATING GRAVITY   >

Astronauts could walk about on the inside of a rotating ring, with the centripetal force acting inward toward the centre of the rotation. The centripetal force would be supplied by the force of the floor acting upward on the bottoms of the astronauts' feet.

Consider the forces that act on an object as it moves in a circle that describes a vertical plane (**Figure 14**). At the top of the circle, the downward centripetal force is supplied partly by gravity and partly by the tension in the string. At the

bottom of the circle, the upward-acting tension in the string must be great enough to overcome gravity and provide the centripetal force that pulls the object toward the centre of the circle.

As such, the tension in the string is always greatest when the object is at the bottom of the circle and least when the object is at the top. In microgravity, the tension would be the same at all locations.

In this activity, you will simulate gravity by tying an object to the end of a string and whirling it around in a circle. The string will supply the centripetal force that acts on the object, preventing the object from flying off on a line tangent to the circle, as its inertia would have it do. With a little practice, you will figure out the speed you need to rotate the object to keep it barely moving in a vertical circle. The minimum speed will depend on the length of the string, and this is the speed that a revolving ring of that radius would

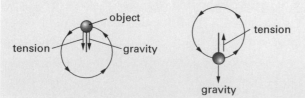

Figure 14 The forces of tension and gravity act on an object moving in a vertical circle. At all places in the circle, gravity acts downward and tension acts toward the centre of the circle.

need to move to simulate normal Earth gravity. At the minimum speed, the force acting to keep the object moving in a circle is supplied entirely by gravity because the tension in the string has become effectively zero.

Materials

eye protection
piece of string approximately 1.5 m long, with marks indicating 20 cm, 40 cm, 60 cm, 80 cm, 100 cm, and 120 cm
washer with mass of approximately 20 g

 Wear eye protection.
Make sure that the work area is clear and that the string can be safely rotated.

Procedure

1. Tie the washer to one end of the string. Check to make sure that the washer is properly secured.

2. Put on eye protection. Practise whirling the string around in a circle that describes a vertical plane, with a speed that just barely keeps the washer moving in the circle. Have one member of your group stand at a safe distance out of the plane of the circle and measure the time to complete 10 rotations using each length of string (from 20 cm to 120 cm).

(a) Determine and record the period of rotation for each length of string.

Analysis

(b) Plot a graph of radius of rotation (along the x-axis) against period of rotation (along the y-axis).

(c) Describe the shape of the graph.

Synthesis

(d) Apply your results to the revolving pods on a spaceship that is designed to simulate gravity. How is the rotation rate of the revolving pods dependent on the radius of rotation?

(e) Think about the physiological effects of a body's inertia during an acceleration. Suggest reasons for having an astronaut in a horizontal position during a launch.

(f) A pail of water can be swung in a vertical circle without the water falling out, even when the pail is upside down at the top of the circle. Explain why the water stays in the pail.

(g) A centrifuge is an instrument that separates materials with different densities by rapidly spinning them around a central pivot point. Describe how a centrifuge works. Use the principle of inertia in your description.

✓ Check Your Understanding

1. Have you ever experienced symptoms similar to those associated with space sickness as a result of unconventional movements? If so, describe the circumstances.

2. What is the connection between calcium loss and the production of kidney stones?

3. List the medical effects of exposure to microgravity, and provide a brief description of each.

4. Suggest how some of the medical effects of microgravity could be minimized.

5. By explaining the physical principles involved, describe how a rotating platform can be used to simulate gravity.

6. Aside from the physiological effects associated with microgravity, what other health risks are astronauts exposed to inside orbiting spacecraft?

7. What special challenges related to the crew's health are likely to be encountered during a manned mission to Mars that would last nearly three years in total?

Society & the Environment

Coping with Microgravity: A Plan of Action

The challenges of living in space for extended periods of time are daunting. Ongoing research, being conducted worldwide, is not only contributing some solutions to the challenges, but is also providing new treatments for common medical conditions on Earth. **Table 1** summarizes some of these applications of space research.

Table 1 Applications of Space Research on Earth

Area of research	Possible applications
space adaptation of nervous system	A greater understanding of neural pathways may lead to treatments for a variety of nervous disorders.
cartilage cells	The culturing of cartilage cells in space holds great promise for the treatment of bone diseases.
muscle atrophy	A combination of exercise (**Figure 15**) and growth hormone has been found to help in the treatment of age-related muscle wasting and the development of rehabilitation techniques. 
bone demineralization	Research being conducted on the loss of calcium from bone during space flights may help scientists develop treatments for common bone diseases, such as osteoporosis. There have already been benefits in designing and evaluating artificial joints.

Figure 15
Exercising in space

E2.4 Activity   RESEARCH IN SPACE: BENEFITS ON EARTH

In this activity, you will learn more about research that is being conducted by organizations such as NASA, the CSA, the European Space Agency, and the National Space Development Agency of Japan. For example, NASA's Office of Biological and Physical Research (OBPR) conducts fundamental research to learn more about the challenges of living in space and how these challenges can be met through further research and new technologies. Its mandate includes identifying applications of space research that can enrich the lives of people on Earth.

Visit the Web sites of OBPR, the CSA, and other space agencies to find recently published research. Look for studies that deal specifically with the medical challenges of living in space.

You may wish to focus on one of the physical or psychological challenges presented in this topic or another challenge that interests you.

GO www.science.nelson.com

(a) Share your findings in a group. Combine your ideas to develop a comprehensive strategy for dealing with the medical challenges of living in space. As a group, identify applications that space research has had or may have for people living on Earth.

(b) How reliable were your sources of information?

(c) How current was the research you found?

(d) Did you find conflicting results in any of the research?

Exploration or Contamination?

Immediately after the *Apollo 11* return capsule splashed down, the astronauts climbed into biological isolation garments (**Figure 16**), which were designed to minimize contamination by microorganisms the astronauts might have acquired while on the Moon. They spent 21 days in an isolation chamber, where their medical condition was closely scrutinized. Physicians were not studying the effects of microgravity on the astronauts; rather, they were looking for symptoms of disease caused by alien germs. Although scientists were nearly certain that there had never been life on the Moon, they thought it wise to take precautions and keep the astronauts isolated for 21 days. Today, astronauts are not exposed to any sources of possible contamination, at least not until they return to the Moon or go to Mars.

Figure 16 A biological isolation garment

Space scientists are currently designing manned missions to return to the Moon and, more ambitiously, to travel to Mars. In early 2004, scientists concluded that Mars once had considerable quantities of liquid water on its surface. Water is the single most important ingredient for life to exist.

Decision-Making Skills

- Define the Issue
- Identify Alternatives
- Research
- Analyze the Issue
- Defend a Decision
- Evaluate

Did Mars once have living organisms in its seas or on its land surfaces? Do dormant microorganisms still exist on Mars? Is there a risk to humans who visit Mars if they are exposed to these microorganisms? No doubt such questions will be seriously considered before people venture to Mars.

However, astronauts will be taking pieces of Earth with them to Mars. Plants, soil, air, and water will all need to be transported with the astronauts so that they can establish a presence on the planet. Microorganisms will undoubtedly tag along with these basic necessities. Is there a danger that we will contaminate another planet, something we have taken great precautions against happening to Earth?

Statement: The benefits of space exploration justify the risk of introducing microorganisms to other planets.

1. In your group, research the issue. Search for information in newspapers and periodicals, and on CD-ROMS and the Internet.

 www.science.nelson.com

2. Identify individuals, organizations, and government agencies that have addressed the issue.

3. Identify the perspectives of opposing positions, and arrange these perspectives in a suitable graphic organizer.

4. Write a short position paper (no more than 500 words), summarizing your group's position.

5. Role play the situation in a town hall meeting. Prepare to defend your group's position in the meeting.

6. How did your group reach a decision about which position to defend? After your meeting, did you think of anything you could have done differently? Explain.

SUMMARY

- Earth's atmosphere and magnetic field protect us from radiation and charged particles that are released by the Sun. Astronauts have greater exposure to solar radiation and charged particles.
- Space is nearly a perfect vacuum, where the concept of temperature has no meaning. Temperature extremes occur, however, when radiant heat is absorbed or emitted.
- The lack of atmospheric pressure in space means that astronauts need extensive life-support systems.
- Microgravity conditions during space flights are responsible for numerous medical effects experienced by astronauts.
- The symptoms of space sickness include dizziness and nausea caused by conflicting sensory input from the eyes and inner ear.
- An upward shift of body fluids causes swelling of the face and upper torso. Reacting to this, the body eliminates water; this leads to more concentrated blood. Red blood cell production is reduced, and anemia can result.
- Microgravity leads to a loss of calcium from the bones, resulting in a weakened skeletal structure and the possible development of kidney stones.

- Muscles atrophy and bones deteriorate in microgravity, resulting in a weakened state upon return to normal gravity. Rigorous exercise programs can minimize these effects.
- Other effects of microgravity include psychological stress, which has been linked to a weakened immune system.
- The effects of a shift of body fluids in space can be simulated on Earth and measured.
- Producing artificial gravity through centripetal acceleration may alleviate many of the medical effects of space flight.
- Research into the medical effects of microgravity continues to be a major focus of space programs worldwide. The research is aimed at solving problems associated with space flight, but it has spin-off benefits for people on Earth.

Key Terms

space sickness
vestibular system
semicircular canals
otolith organs
anemia
bone demineralization

atrophy
Newton's first law
   of motion
centripetal force
artificial gravity

ASSESSMENT

Understanding Concepts

1. Using **Figure 17** as a guide, identify some of the medical effects of microgravity. Describe how microgravity contributes to each effect.

2. Exercise programs on Earth often use gravity as a force to work against. Suggest how exercise programs in space would be different.

3. Speculate on how the vestibular system of the inner ear would respond to partial gravity and to intense gravity. Provide reasons for your answers.

4. Explain why you could make the symptoms of space sickness less severe by simply closing your eyes.

5. Which of the medical effects of microgravity could pose the greatest threat on a mission that lasted many months? Provide a reason for your answer.

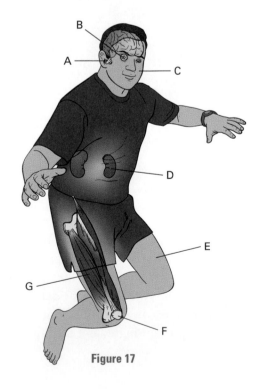

Figure 17

6. Provide two examples that show how your own inertia can be beneficial, and two other examples that show how your inertia can be harmful.

7. Simulating gravity through centripetal forces may eliminate many of the medical effects of microgravity. What are the challenges of simulating gravity on a space mission?

Applying Inquiry Skills

8. Describe how you could use a penny, a playing card, and a tabletop to demonstrate the law of inertia (Newton's first law of motion) for an object that is at rest and for an object that is moving.

9. An object is attached to the end of an elastic cord and whirled around in a vertical circle at a constant speed.
   (a) What changes in the length of the cord would you expect to see when the object is at various locations in the circle? With the permission of your teacher, test your prediction.
   (b) Provide an explanation for what you predicted and/or observed.
   (c) Repeat the experiment with the object travelling in a horizontal plane. What differences do you notice? Explain.

10. Design an experiment to test the effect of microgravity on the development of kidney stones. You have been given access to astronauts on board the ISS to help with your research. Outline your experimental procedure, including the controls that would need to be in place.

11. You are conducting an experiment to test the effect of elevating the feet on the circumference of the lower legs over a period of time while lying horizontally.
   (a) Create a graph with leg circumference on the y-axis and time on the x-axis. Draw the shape of the graph you would expect for this experiment.
   (b) Draw another graph showing what you would expect if neck circumference was measured against time for the same subject.

12. To some extent, you grow taller when you assume a horizontal position while sleeping. Design an experiment to test the hypothesis that the difference in your bedtime height and your waking height is related to the amount of sleep you get.

Outline the procedure you would use. With your teacher's permission, try your experiment.

Making Connections

13. The G-suit was developed to counteract the negative effects of extreme accelerations experienced by pilots (**Figure 18**). Research this Canadian invention. In a short report, summarize how the G-suit was developed and what principles it applies to allow pilots to withstand extreme g-forces.

 www.science.nelson.com

Figure 18

14. Research the development of the space suit. Summarize its protective features, and describe one modern spinoff.

 www.science.nelson.com

15. Visit the Web site of the CSA to research how astronauts perform routine functions, such as eating, sleeping, and attending to personal hygiene. Choose one function, and prepare a brief report on how it is handled.

 www.science.nelson.com

16. Much medical research is being conducted on Earth focusing on some of the same questions that scientists conducting space-based research are trying to answer. Do you think the extra cost associated with conducting medical research in space is justified? Provide arguments on both sides of the issue.

Reflecting

17. Comment on the ethical implications of sending living organisms into space as test subjects. Would you support sending some species but not others? In what ways, if any, do you think ethical standards are different today than they were in the 1960s when the first animal test subjects were used?

Working *in* Space: POTENTIAL REWARDS

Imagine sitting at a desk in a crowded gymnasium, surrounded by a hundred or more students: Your final exam is about to begin. You feel well prepared, but you know there will be mathematical questions about Newton's universal law of gravitation. Even though math has never been your favourite subject, you have practised questions like this and feel confident that you can answer them.

You have extra pens and pencils and, of course, your calculator. You press the button to power up your calculator. There is no response. The screen is blank! As a feeling of panic begins to set in, you realize that this situation could have been avoided. Had your calculator been solar powered instead of battery operated, light would now be coaxing electrons from the solar cells and supplying the much-needed electricity.

Solar cells were invented in the 1950s to power satellites. Now, however, they are found in many applications on Earth. Silicon semiconductor crystals supply the solar power, based on the interaction of electrons with individual atoms within a crystalline framework. These crystals are also at the heart of all types of computing devices.

Scientists have long understood that knowledge of nature at a molecular level is the key to understanding macroscopic processes. Your studies in science have taught you much about what the world is like at the molecular level. You already have a sense of how molecules are put together and how they can be broken apart and reassembled.

Imagine that you are a single molecule of water.

(a) What would you look like?

(b) What holds you together as a molecule? Can you be broken apart? If so, how?

(c) You are seldom alone but usually in the company of others exactly like you. To what extent are you attracted to one another? What is the source of this attraction?

(d) When grouped with other water molecules in a small droplet, why do you take on a nearly spherical shape?

(e) Describe how you would behave differently in microgravity. Provide a reason for each suggestion.

(f) Give some examples of where you have been. Use your imagination.

A central focus for space scientists is the investigation of materials and processes at the molecular level. In orbit, the effects of gravity can be eliminated entirely, effects so strong they often mask how molecules and other particles behave and interact. In particular, combustion, boiling, crystal formation (**Figure 1**), and the behaviour of fluids are all significantly different in microgravity.

Figure 1
Crystals inside a rock cavity

(g) Name some substances you are familiar with that have crystalline structures, and describe the shape of their crystals in each case.

(h) You have probably noticed sugar crystals forming in jam or honey after their jars have been sitting for some time. Suggest the mechanism that causes crystals to begin forming.

The differences present special challenges for some processes and opportunities for others. How do crystals grow? How do fluids behave in microgravity, compared to on Earth? Are there any benefits to society to research fluid behaviour in space?

Science & Technology

Crystals and Fluid Behaviour

Space scientists studying how crystals grow and how fluids behave in a microgravity environment have contributed to medicine and other sciences and technology on Earth.

Crystals

In many substances, such as salt and sugar grains, the particles are arranged in an ordered way, called a crystalline composition. You may have inspected salt and sugar grains more closely, perhaps under a microscope, and discovered that they have unique three-dimensional shapes.

Some crystals are composed of a single type of atom, but this alone does not dictate the substance's characteristic shape and properties—how it will behave on its own and how it will interact with other substances under a variety of conditions. Structure is also important. For example, graphite and diamond are both composed entirely of carbon atoms, but, because of their structures, they have very different properties.

In diamond (**Figure 2(a)**), each carbon atom is tightly bound to its neighbours above, below, and to the sides. This arrangement makes diamond the hardest natural substance, ideal for cutting, drilling, and polishing almost anything else. Diamond is also highly prized for its optical qualities: its ability to refract and reflect light. When cut into a gemstone shape, much of the light entering the diamond becomes internally reflected and exits through the top faces, giving the stone its brilliance.

In graphite (**Figure 2(b)**), the carbon atoms are arranged in thin two-dimensional sheets, with their bonds between atoms to each side but not between atoms above and below. These thin sheets are easily separated from one another. When graphite is ground into a powder, mixed with clay, and formed into thin rods, we call it pencil lead, even though it contains no lead.

Many compounds also have crystalline structures. Compounds are pure substances that are composed of two or more types of atoms. Salt (sodium chloride), for example, is a compound that is composed of the elements sodium and chlorine. The atoms are stacked together in a uniform way, providing the crystal with its characteristic cubic shape (**Figure 3(a)**). Quartz, composed of silicon and oxygen, forms a six-sided column capped on the ends by hexagonal pyramids (**Figure 3(b)**).

Figure 3 **(a)** Salt crystals **(b)** Quartz crystals

Quartz crystals are used in a wide variety of common instruments. When weak electric currents are applied to a thin slice of a quartz crystal, the crystal vibrates very quickly and with a constant frequency. This property makes quartz ideal for use in time-keeping devices such as watches. In the early days of radio, this property was used to help transform weak radio signals into sound in a crystal radio

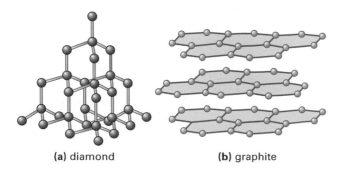

(a) diamond **(b) graphite**

Figure 2 Although diamond **(a)** and graphite **(b)** are composed entirely of carbon atoms, their unique crystalline structures give them very different properties.

ear piece. Quartz crystals are exceptionally transparent, making them ideal for optical applications, as well. When melted and reformed into long, thin strands, quartz is transformed into optical fibres, capable of transmitting digital light signals over great distances (**Figure 4**).

Figure 4
Fibre optics are commonly used to carry cable television signals and telephone conversations, as well as signals in a variety of other electronic equipment.

Solar calculators use a thin slice of silicon crystal to which impurities have been added. When light falls on the crystal, electrons are released and a small electric current is produced. The resulting voltage is sufficient to align other crystals suspended in a liquid. These crystals partially block light that enters the calculator display from above, producing the dark patches that form numbers and letters on the screen. **Liquid crystal displays** (LCDs) have many applications. Significant currents are possible in large arrays of solar cells, making them vital to satellites, space platforms, and power sources on Earth (**Figure 5**).

Why do crystals grow in specific shapes? Consider snowflakes. Snowflakes can be composed of a single ice crystal or several ice crystals that have become attached to each other. Ice crystals are composed of water molecules, which are made up of two hydrogen atoms and one oxygen atom (**Figure 6**).

During **crystallization**, which is the formation of crystals, molecules come together and pack themselves into a specific arrangement dictated by the electron structure of the individual atoms. In a water molecule, for example, both hydrogen atoms are tightly bound to the oxygen atom by strong covalent bonds, the result of shared electrons between atoms.

Figure 5   Large arrays of solar cells in a centralized location can provide power to other locations.

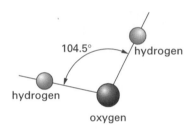

Figure 6   A water molecule has the shape of an open V, with the oxygen atom at the apex and the hydrogen atoms at the tips.

As water molecules come together during crystallization, they are attracted to each other by much weaker hydrogen bonds. Each hydrogen atom of one molecule is attracted to an oxygen atom of another molecule. As the water molecules continue to congregate, they become arranged in a hexagonal (six-sided) shape (**Figure 7**). This uniform structure, called a **crystal lattice**, is formed like you would stack identical chairs.

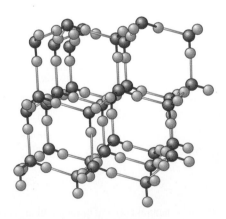

Figure 7   Water molecules are arranged in an ice crystal that takes on a hexagonal shape.

Figure 8 Snowflakes form in a variety of beautiful shapes, all with six arms growing outward from a central hexagonal ice crystal.

The individual molecules, like chairs, "fit" on top of each other with a particular orientation. The resulting "stack" of molecules takes on a form dictated by the shape of the individual molecules.

As the crystal continues to grow, with additional water molecules attaching themselves to the original seed crystal, the points of the hexagon grow more quickly than the sides. This growth pattern results in the six arms of a snowflake growing out from the central ice crystal, forming a complex and beautifully symmetric shape (**Figure 8**).

The original seed crystal, or **nucleation site**, is most often a grain of dust in the air. The dust serves as a landing pad—water molecules accumulate on it. If you melt a sample of fresh, clean snow, you will find that the meltwater is not entirely pure. It may contain a surprising number of small granules of dust and dirt. Some of these granules were the original seeds upon which the snowflake grew; others were suspended in the air and incorporated by the falling snowflakes. Snowflakes continue to accumulate molecules of water as they fall through moisture-laden air on their way to the ground. Thus, the final size and shape of a snowflake are determined by several factors, including the humidity and temperature of the air.

For crystals to grow, there must be a high concentration of molecules in a solution. A solution is a homogeneous mixture of a solute and a solvent. The amount of solute that can be dissolved depends on the temperature of the solvent. For example, if you dissolved sugar (the solute) in a volume of water (the solvent) at a particular temperature, you would find that you could only dissolve a certain amount of sugar. You would reach maximum solubility, and the solution would be **saturated**. If you added more sugar and stirred the solution, the sugar crystals would simply settle to the bottom. If you heated the solution, however, you would increase the solubility and more sugar would dissolve.

If you cool a saturated solution, lowering the solubility, crystals will form in the solution and fall to the bottom of the container. Alternatively, if you allow water to evaporate from the solution, you will increase the concentration of the solution and possibly force crystals from the solution. Thus, for a crystal to begin forming, the concentration of a solution must be above the saturation point. Otherwise, the molecules of solute will stay dissolved. When a solution has more solute dissolved in it than it would normally have at a given temperature, it is said to be **supersaturated**. The solution has exceeded its normal solubility. When a seed crystal is dropped into a supersaturated solution it provides surfaces upon which solute molecules can congregate. The seed crystal may grow very rapidly.

While some crystals can be grown to a large size, these crystals are likely not perfect. Upon close inspection, crystals generally have flaws: one or more of their faces may be incomplete, or corners may be broken. On an even smaller scale, there may be internal flaws that are not easily visible.

Scientists use **X-ray crystallography** to see the molecular configuration of crystals. During X-ray crystallography, thin beams of X-rays are fired through crystals. These beams are scattered by the atoms, producing characteristic patterns on photographic film. The patterns that are formed depend on the arrangement of the atoms in the crystal. Once the patterns are understood, so is the molecular structure of the crystal.

E3.1 Activity | SEEDING A SUPERSATURATED SOLUTION

In a supersaturated solution, the process of crystallization can proceed with surprising speed. In this activity, you will make a supersaturated solution of sodium thiosulfate. You will then drop a single crystal into the solution, to act as a nucleation site. You will observe the crystal growing as identical molecules come out of solution and adhere to it.

Materials
eye protection
25 g sodium thiosulfate
test tube
water
250-mL beaker
hot plate
glass rod

 Wear eye protection.

Take appropriate precautions when working near the hot-water bath.

Procedure

1. Wearing eye protection, fill a clean test tube approximately three-quarters full of granular sodium thiosulfate. Add 2 or 3 drops of water to the test tube.

2. Prepare a hot-water bath by placing a beaker of water on the hot plate. Heat the water bath to near boiling.

3. Put the test tube in the hot-water bath. Stir the solution with a clean glass rod until the sodium thiosulfate has completely dissolved. At this temperature, the solution is unsaturated.

4. Remove the test tube from the hot-water bath, and allow it to cool slowly to room temperature. During the cooling process, the solution will pass from unsaturated to saturated to supersaturated. If the solution begins to crystallize, put the test tube back into the hot-water bath until the solid has fully dissolved, and then cool the solution to room temperature again.

5. Holding the test tube in your hand, drop a single crystal of sodium thiosulfate into the supersaturated solution. Observe the test tube until the entire solution has crystallized.

(a) Record your observations. Describe how rapidly the crystallization process proceeded in the supersaturated solution. Describe any changes in temperature you noticed as crystallization took place.

6. Reheat the test tube to return the crystals to a solution. Dispose of the solution according to your teacher's instructions.

Analysis

(b) When the solution was seeded and quickly crystallized, there was a noticeable quantity of heat released. Knowing that an input of energy is required to break chemical bonds, explain why heat is released during crystallization.

Synthesis

(c) How is your observation in (b) similar to the change in ambient air temperature during a snowfall?

E3.2 Activity | GROWING ALUM CRYSTALS   >

Potassium aluminum sulfate, $KAl(SO_4)_2$, is commonly known as alum. Alum crystals have an octahedral (eight-sided) shape. Large alum crystals can be grown with some care and patience (**Figure 9**).

In this activity, you will prepare a saturated solution of alum in water and allow the water to slowly evaporate, forcing alum crystals to grow. You will then select a seed crystal, place it in another saturated solution, and allow it to continue to grow. As the solvent slowly evaporates,

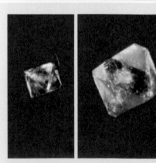

Figure 9 Alum crystals

more alum will be forced from the supersaturated solution and will adhere to the crystal.

To grow an alum crystal of optimum purity and uniformity, you must be extremely careful not to contaminate your solution. Use clean glassware, and avoid introducing anything into the solution that could act as a nucleation site.

Materials
eye protection
2 clean 250-mL beakers
200 mL water
30 g potassium aluminum sulfate (alum)
thermometer
glass rod
two 15-cm lengths of fine thread
mineral oil or cooking oil
hot plate
paper towel (free of lint)
elastic band
hand lens or magnifying glass
razor blade or scalpel (optional)
forceps
low-power microscope

 Alum is non-toxic, but a solution of alum can irritate your eyes. Wear eye protection when working with the alum solution.

When using the scalpel, cut the crystal away from your fingers.

Procedure

1. Fill one 250-mL beaker with water. Wearing eye protection, heat the water to 60°C. Add the alum, stirring until it is completely dissolved. Let the mixture stand for a few minutes until it appears clear. There may be some residue on the bottom of the beaker.

2. Using the glass rod, decant the solution into a second beaker. Do not allow any residue to be transferred. Your teacher will demonstrate the proper technique for decanting (**Figure 10**).

3. Tie a thread to the middle of the glass rod. Lay the rod across the top of the beaker, with one end of the thread suspended in the solution to a depth of no more than 1.5 cm. Using your fingers, apply oil to the thread that remains above the surface of the solution to prevent the formation of crystals on this part of the thread.

4. Place a clean paper towel across the top of the beaker and secure it with an elastic band. You will have to cut a hole in the paper towel for the glass rod. Allow the beaker to sit undisturbed and away from any heat sources for approximately one week. After a few days, you should observe alum crystals growing on the submerged thread or forming on the bottom of the beaker.

5. Remove the thread and the best seed crystal you can find, either on the thread or at the bottom of the beaker. For the best results, choose a crystal that has an octahedral shape and smooth faces. You may find a hand lens or magnifying glass helpful for choosing the best crystal.

6. Using the hot plate, heat the solution to 60°C to redissolve the remaining crystals. Allow the solution to cool completely.

7. Carefully tie a piece of thread around the seed crystal. You might find this easier to do if you carefully notch the side of the crystal with a razor blade or scalpel. Hold the crystal with forceps on a cutting board, and carefully cut a notch in the side.

8. Suspend the crystal in the cooled solution as before. Secure a paper towel on top of the beaker.

Figure 10 When decanting your solution into the clean beaker, pour the solution slowly down the glass rod. Avoid transferring any sediment into the clean beaker.

9. Carefully observe the crystal when it first enters the solution. If the solution is not saturated, your seed crystal will start to dissolve. If you see any indication that your seed crystal is dissolving, remove it immediately. You will need to resaturate the solution by heating it, dissolving more alum, decanting the solution, and cooling it.

10. Leave the beaker undisturbed as before for approximately one week, observing it each day to see how the crystal is growing.

11. Once your alum crystal has reached a reasonable size (about 1 cm across), remove it from the beaker. Carefully observe its structure under a hand lens or a low-power microscope.

Analysis

(a) Several factors affect the growth of alum crystals. For each situation below, describe the likely effect.

(i) The solution that was used to grow the seed crystal was not decanted.

(ii) The solution that was used to grow the seed crystal was not saturated.

(iii) There were fluctuations in the temperature of the solution in which the final crystal was growing.

(iv) The beaker was left uncovered.

(v) The beaker was sealed airtight.

(vi) The beaker was exposed to direct sunlight.

(vii) The seed crystal was irregular in shape.

(b) Describe how you think the size and quality of your crystal would likely have been different if you had grown your crystal in microgravity.

Evaluation

(c) Consider what may have been responsible for any imperfections you notice on the faces. What could you have done differently to minimize these imperfections?

Protein Crystals

Researchers use X-ray crystallography to discover the molecular structure of very complex substances, such as protein crystals (**Figure 11**). Protein crystals have intrigued many scientists because their structures hold the answers to key questions about biological systems.

Proteins are large, complex organic molecules that are essential to life. There are thousands of proteins in the human body:

- Enzymes are proteins that help chemical reactions proceed; enzymes facilitate the breakdown of large molecules and the manufacture of other molecules that are essential in cellular functions.
- Proteins transport materials across membranes and throughout the body. For example, the blood protein hemoglobin transports oxygen from the lungs to all cells.

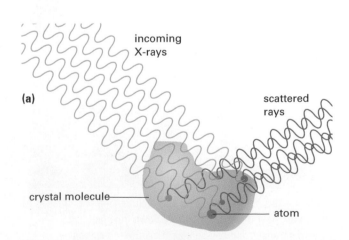

(a)

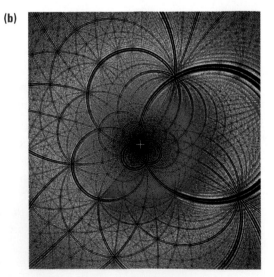

(b)

Figure 11 **(a)** An X-ray is scattered by a crystal and leaves an impression on a photographic film. **(b)** The X-ray diffraction pattern of a protein crystal is shown.

- Proteins are responsible for building and repairing DNA.
- Insulin is a protein hormone that regulates blood sugar.
- Antibodies are defensive proteins that combat viruses and bacteria.
- Tendons, ligaments, and hair are all made of structural proteins.

Scientists understand the structure of only about 1% of proteins. An increased understanding will lead to better diagnoses and medical treatments.

Protein crystals are somewhat different from the hard, rocklike crystals you have been learning about in this topic. Because protein crystals have a high water content, they are often described as "soft" crystals. They are typically very small (0.2 mm to 0.5 mm), fragile, and difficult to manipulate (**Figure 12**).

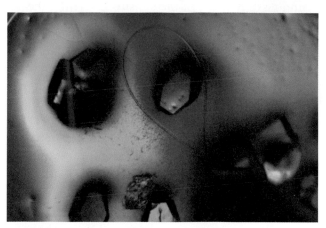

Figure 12   Protein crystals

Crystals need to be grown slowly to have exceptional structure and purity. This allows the molecules to accumulate one by one onto the seed crystal and not interfere with each other as they align with the molecules that are already within the crystal lattice. Scientists have developed the following process for growing protein crystals at an optimal rate:

1. A solution of protein in a solvent is prepared.
2. The solvent escapes very slowly by diffusion, with molecules migrating from an area of relatively high concentration to an area of lower concentration. This creates a more concentrated and ultimately supersaturated protein solution. Protein molecules begin to move together and nucleate in the supersaturated solution.
3. As more solvent is drawn out of the solution, the protein crystal grows larger.

While the process seems simple in theory, it is difficult in practice. As protein molecules come out of solution and adhere to the seed crystal, the remaining solution becomes less concentrated and therefore less dense. The solution that is adjacent to the crystal begins to rise. This creates an upward convection current, which disturbs the protein molecules. The protein molecules may not adhere to the crystal with the proper orientation, creating a disordered crystal lattice.

Another challenge to growing protein crystals is **sedimentation**. For example, in E3.2 Activity: Growing Alum Crystals, you observed that alum crystals formed on the bottom of the beaker. As crystals form, they become heavier than the surrounding solution and sink to the bottom. As they accumulate as sediment, they become attached and grow into one another. Only single, uniform crystals can be mapped using X-ray crystallography.

Scientists realized that these challenges would be solved if gravity were eliminated. After all, gravity is responsible for creating convection currents and sedimentation. Without gravity, protein molecules would be able to adhere to one another more uniformly and produce crystals with superior internal structure. This has been put to the test on space shuttle missions and the ISS, and crystals of unsurpassed size and quality have been grown (**Figure 13**).

Figure 13   Protein crystals that are grown in microgravity (left) are larger and better quality than Earth-grown crystals (right). From these crystals, scientists are able learn more about protein structure, which helps them develop more efficient medications.

X-ray crystallography on these improved crystals has already yielded some important results. Scientists now have a better understanding of the structure of hemoglobin and insulin. Understanding the structure of hemoglobin offers potential for the treatment of sickle cell anemia, a genetic disorder that results from small structural differences in the hemoglobin.

Understanding the structure of insulin may lead to superior quality injectable insulin for diabetics.

Scientists in the semiconductor industry are also excited about the potential rewards of growing crystals in space. Devices such as microchips, video cameras, and radiation detectors use thin slices of crystals composed of silicon and germanium (semiconductors). Typically, the two materials are heated to beyond melting point, mixed into a solution, and then allowed to cool and crystallize.

On Earth, the ability to produce pure semiconductor crystals is jeopardized by the difference in the densities of these two materials. Germanium is about three times as dense as silicon and tends to sink to the bottom of the container. In addition, when the forming crystal comes in contact with the sides of the container, small imperfections result. The walls of the container put pressure on the crystal and nudge molecules slightly out of alignment.

In microgravity, the density difference has no effect on uniform mixing, and crystals grow without touching the walls of their container. By studying crystals grown in microgravity, scientists have learned how to grow superior crystals on Earth. This knowledge has led to better quality crystals for the semiconductor industry.

Fluid Behaviour

Liquids and gases are both considered fluids because they have the ability to flow. A gas completely fills its container, however, while a liquid takes the shape of its container to a level determined by its volume. These definitions apply to fluids on Earth; gases and liquids behave quite differently in microgravity.

Living in a gravity environment, you expect things to behave in predictable ways, and we have developed a variety of technological devices that depend on gravity to operate properly:

- The flow of blood through your body and fluids through pneumatic and hydraulic systems are governed by these properties.
- Fluids transporting thermal energy (heat) from one location to another drive the operation of heating and cooling systems.
- The generation of much of our electricity requires thermal energy to be transported as high-pressure water vapour from a boiler to a turbine/generator unit and then condensed back into liquid water.

- The operation of vehicles is dependent on numerous fluid systems, including brakes, fuel, coolant, and air conditioning.
- Plumbing systems are based entirely on the movement of fluids.

Since fluids play a central role in a variety of applications on Earth and in space, scientists and engineers need to understand how they behave.

What are some of the complications that microgravity could present to fluid behaviour? Imagine trying to take a shower or drink from a glass. How would a fire burn, and how would you put one out? Consider how fluids would behave when heated or cooled and how they would mix, if at all.

As a fluid is heated on Earth, the warmer particles move farther apart, making the fluid above the heat source less dense than the cooler fluid surrounding it. Because of the density difference, the warm fluid rises, and cooler fluid moves in to replace it. This process is called **buoyancy-driven convection**, and it is responsible for a wide variety of phenomena: weather patterns, ocean currents, and the movement of the continental plates of Earth's crust.

In a microgravity environment, convection currents do not form because fluids do not separate as a result of differences in density. This makes for some engaging observations and interesting challenges. **Figure 14** shows a candle flame burning in regular gravity and another in microgravity. In regular gravity, candle wax melts, evaporates, and combusts as it combines with the oxygen in the air. The heat of the

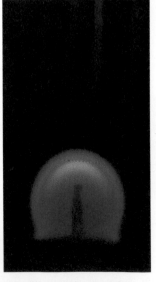

Figure 14 A candle flame burns very differently in normal gravity (left) than in microgravity (right).

flame drives air upward, and cooler air moves in from below. The convection currents surrounding the candle flame give it its characteristic elongated shape. In microgravity, the candle flame takes on a very different appearance. Without convection, the flame burns more dimly and as a spherical shell surrounding the wick. There are no convection forces either elongating the flame or supplying fresh air to help support the combustion.

Surface Tension

While convection in fluids is certainly driven by gravity, another important property of fluids, surface tension, is independent of this force. **Surface tension** is what allows water to bead on a freshly polished car after a rain shower; it is also what allows insects to scurry across the surface of a pond without getting wet (**Figure 15**). Droplets of water dripping from a faucet are spherical in shape because of surface tension. The surface of water seems to have an elastic membrane that is not easily penetrated.

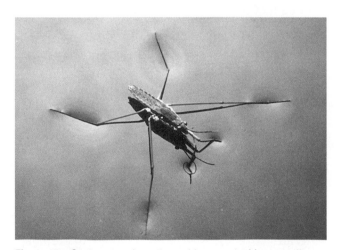

Figure 15 Surface tension allows this water strider to walk on the surface of the water.

The surface tension of water is a result of its chemical makeup. Recall that water molecules are attracted to one another through hydrogen bonding. At the centre of a droplet of water, the water molecules are attracted to all of their surrounding neighbours. At the edge of the droplet, the molecules are attracted to others closer to the centre and to the sides. The water molecules pull on each other, forming a sphere with the least amount of surface area. A droplet hanging from a faucet is somewhat elongated because gravity deforms it. As it falls, its spherical shape is apparent. A bead of water on a polished car has a domed appearance, because the individual molecules pull the surface of the droplet upward through mutual attraction (**Figure 16**).

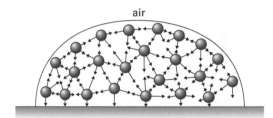

Figure 16 The forces attracting water molecules create surface tension and pull a water droplet into a bead on a flat surface.

Is it possible to weaken these attracting forces and reduce surface tension? This can be accomplished in two ways. The first way is to add heat. Heating a liquid weakens the bonds between the molecules, thus reducing the surface tension. The second way to reduce surface tension is to use a surfactant. A **surfactant** is a material that dissolves in water but does not bind as tightly with the water molecules as they bind with each other. With the attractive forces across the surface weakened, the surface tension is reduced. Detergents are surfactants that help water dislodge particles of dirt from fabrics.

E3.3 Activity MAKING AND BREAKING SURFACE TENSION >

In this activity, you will observe how surface tension can support a variety of objects and how it can be reduced by adding a surfactant and by heating.

Materials
glass petri dish
water
sewing needle
tweezers

hand lens or dissecting microscope
liquid dish soap
finely ground pepper
liquid food colouring
hot plate
eye protection
cooking oil
ground cinnamon

Procedure

Part 1: Floating Needle

1. Fill a clean petri dish with water so that the level of the water is just below the rim.

2. Hold the sewing needle with the tweezers. Gently lower the needle onto the surface of the water.

3. Using a hand lens or a dissecting microscope, observe the surface of the water all around the needle.

(a) Describe the appearance of the surface of the water around the needle. Record your observations.

4. Add 1 or 2 drops of liquid dish soap a distance from the needle.

(b) Describe what happened when the soap reached the needle. Record your observations, along with an explanation for what you observed.

Part 2: Sink or Swim?

5. Fill a clean petri dish with water so that the level of the water is just below the rim.

6. Shake some pepper onto the surface, making sure that it is evenly distributed.

7. Add a drop of liquid dish soap to the centre of the beaker, and observe what happens.

(c) Record your observations, along with an explanation for what you observed.

Part 3: Surface Tension Current Flows

8. Fill a clean petri dish with water so that the level of the water is just below the rim. Allow the water to settle completely in the petri dish.

9. From a height of about 5 mm, place a drop of food colouring on the surface of the water. Before the food colouring can disperse very far, touch the food colouring with a toothpick dipped in liquid dish soap.

(d) Record your observations, along with an explanation for what you observed.

Part 4: Surface Tension and Temperature

 Use a glass petri dish that can be heated on a hot plate.

Wear eye protection, and do not overheat the oil.

Take care when removing the hot petri dish from the hot plate.

10. Fill a glass petri dish with cooking oil to a depth of between 1 mm and 2 mm.

11. Wearing eye protection, sprinkle ground cinnamon onto the surface of the oil, and begin heating it on a hot plate. It is important to have a very thin layer of oil so that convection currents cannot form. Any movement of the cinnamon grains will be due to changes in surface tension.

(e) Record your observations, along with an explanation for what you observed.

As demonstrated in E3.3 Activity: Making and Breaking Surface Tension, surface tension is weakened by adding a surfactant or by heating. A change in surface tension can cause a fluid to flow. The turbulence you observe in a pot of boiling water results primarily from convection currents, although turbulence across the surface of the water is also created by changes in surface tension. In a gravity environment, surface tension flows are usually masked by the more powerful convection flows. In a microgravity environment, convection flows do not occur, so surface tension flows predominate.

The process of boiling particularly interests scientists. Water undergoes a change of state when it reaches a sufficiently high temperature. In the liquid state, attractive forces are strong enough to keep the water molecules close to one another. As the temperature increases, the more rapid movement of the water molecules makes it increasingly difficult for them to stay close together. At the boiling point, the molecules have sufficient thermal energy to move far apart from one another, thus entering the gaseous state. As a pot of water on a hot stove begins to boil, small bubbles of water vapour immediately rise as a result of their low density.

In microgravity, where density is of no consequence, the process of boiling is quite different. If a heating element is placed in water, a water vapour bubble forms. The bubble does not move, however, because there is no convection due to density differences. The bubble remains where it formed, growing larger as liquid water vaporizes at its edges (**Figure 17**). With no convection, the hot element is isolated. Cooler water does not wash over the element, which quickly leads to the element overheating and burning out.

Combustion

Combustion is a process that is largely driven by convection. As a fire burns, the fuel must be supplied with oxygen. The hot combustion products rise from the flames because of their greater buoyancy. Fresh air is pulled into the partial vacuum that is created.

If astronauts were faced with a fire on board a spaceship, the flames would need to be extinguished quickly and with the appropriate equipment. Combustion, like the behaviour of fluids, is very different in microgravity. The combustibility of materials is different, and flames smoulder and spread in odd ways. Therefore, conventional fire-fighting methods would be ineffective.

Figure 17 Boiling in microgravity is very different from boiling in normal gravity.

A fluids and combustion facility on the ISS will be dedicated to researching these two processes. Among the expected payoffs of this facility are improved combustion processes that will reduce airborne pollutants, the development of more efficient heating, cooling, and ventilation systems, and improvements in propulsion and power systems.

✔ Check Your Understanding

1. When an ice crystal melts with the addition of heat, are the covalent bonds or the hydrogen bonds broken? Explain.

2. Why do crystals form within a supersaturated solution rather than within an unsaturated solution?

3. Why is a clean beaker necessary for growing good crystals?

4. What advantages does microgravity offer for growing superior crystals?

5. How is a picture provided by a dental or bone X-ray different from the picture of a crystal provided by X-ray crystallography?

6. Define the terms "buoyancy-driven convection" and "surface tension."

7. (a) The shape of a stationary droplet of water at the end of an eyedropper is slightly different on Earth than it is in microgravity. Describe the difference, and provide a reason for the difference.

   (b) What could you do to a droplet of water on Earth so that it would assume the same shape as a droplet in microgravity?

8. (a) If you looked at the beads of two liquids on a polished surface, how could you tell which liquid has greater surface tension?

   (b) What does the shape of a liquid bead tell you about the chemistry of the molecules of the liquid?

9. Describe how a surfactant weakens surface tension.

10. Explain why combustion is a concern to space scientists.

11. Describe how the process of boiling is altered in microgravity.

12. (a) How would the operation of a kitchen kettle be compromised in microgravity?

   (b) Describe how you could alter its design and have it operate properly.

Society & the Environment

Fluid Systems

If we are to establish a permanent presence in space, technological devices that depend on the properties of fluids will have to be redesigned. Many fluid systems on Earth use gravity as a driving force for moving gases and liquids from one location to another. Very often, buoyancy and convection drive this motion. In a microgravity or macrogravity environment, fluids behave quite differently. As scientists continue to learn about boiling, convection flows, surface tension flows, and combustion, they will be able to design better models for weather patterning, improved processes for industries such as oil refining, and superior drugs that rely on the body's circulatory system for delivery. Superior flame design, which has already led to improved fire safety for spaceships and orbiting space platforms, will help reduce polluting emissions from a variety of combustion devices.

E3.4 Activity | DESIGN CHALLENGE: REDESIGNING FLUID SYSTEMS

Your interaction with fluids and fluid systems is more extensive than you probably realize. Because you are always operating within Earth's gravitational field, however, you expect that liquids will always run downhill and hot air will always rise. Because there is no "up" or "down" in microgravity, fluids behave very differently.

In this activity, you will be a member of a team which will compete in a design challenge with another team.

1. With your team and your opposing team, identify a common device that relies on fluids (**Figure 18**).

Figure 18 The operation of many simple devices depends on the properties of fluids in a gravity environment.

2. Working separately, each team will suggest how the device uses the properties of fluids to function and describe how the device would operate differently in microgravity.

3. Working separately, each team will develop a design for a device that would accomplish the same task in microgravity, including details about how it would operate.

4. Have members of the other teams serve as judges for this challenge and decide which team has suggested the superior design.

Use the following example as a model.

The Device: A conventional oven

The Problem: A conventional oven uses an electrical element to heat air in a cavity. Food is placed in the oven for a period of time until it is cooked. As air close to the element is heated, it becomes less dense and rises. Cooler air moves to the element, where it gains thermal energy. The hot air in contact with the food transfers some of its heat, becomes less buoyant, and sinks, only to be replaced by hotter air. In a microgravity environment, buoyancy- and convection-driven flows do not occur. The air beside the element would grow hotter, but the oven would not be efficient at transferring heat to the food.

Solution 1: Electrical fans within the oven could circulate hot air within the cooking space, thereby transferring heat from the element to the food.

Solution 2: A flexible heating element, embedded in a conducting sheet, could be wrapped around the food. Cooking by this method would rely entirely on conduction.

Space Research and Combustion

Combustion is an essential process in our technological world. We depend on it for energy production, transportation, and other industrial processes. Combustion, however, is also the cause of many of our environmental problems, such as air pollution, global warming, and acid rain (**Figure 19**). Each year, fires destroy countless homes and forests and kill thousands of people.

(a)

(b)

Figure 19 **(a)** Combustion is the source of much pollution. **(b)** Acid rain is responsible for the damage to this sculpture.

In Units B and C, you learned that the management of gaseous waste is a critical environmental concern. Since the process of combustion is based on the properties of fluids, better knowledge of fluid behaviour may lead to improved management of gaseous waste. Fluids are also a primary concern of space scientists, as they attempt to solve problems related to fluid behaviour in microgravity. As scientists learn more about fluid behaviour from experiments conducted in microgravity, they may find solutions to gaseous waste management problems on Earth.

Decision-Making Skills

- Define the Issue
- Identify Alternatives
- Research
- Analyze the Issue
- Defend a Decision
- Evaluate

Statement: Space research in fluid behaviour should continue so that we may apply the benefits on Earth, especially any benefits related to combustion.

1. In your group, research the issue and arrive at a consensus on whether or not you agree with the statement. Search for information in newspapers and periodicals, and on CD-ROMs and the Internet. Specifically, search for studies related to fluid behaviour in space and applications of these studies on Earth. Also search for information about a recent or current experiment related to combustion.

 www.science.nelson.com

2. Identify individuals, organizations, and government agencies that have addressed the issue.

3. Identify the perspectives of opposing positions, and arrange these perspectives in a suitable graphic organizer.

4. Prepare a brief report (no more than 300 words) that includes an outline of the procedure for the combustion experiment, a summary of the experimental results, and an overview of how the results could be applied on Earth.

5. Defend your group's position in a class discussion.

6. How did your group reach a decision about which position to defend?

SUMMARY

- The atoms (or molecules) in a crystal are arranged in a highly ordered fashion, called a crystal lattice. The shape of the lattice is determined by the properties of the individual particles.
- Because of their unique properties, crystals are used in a variety of technological devices.
- Impurities and imperfections are common in crystals, but they are minimized when crystals are grown in microgravity, where buoyancy effects and sedimentation are eliminated.
- Crystallization starts at a nucleation site, with the crystals growing larger as particles adhere to the surfaces of the seed crystal.
- The concentration of a solution determines whether it is unsaturated, saturated, or supersaturated. Supersaturated solutions have more solute dissolved than their solubility would normally allow. Crystals form in supersaturated solutions.
- X-ray crystallography is an important technique for studying the internal structure of crystals.
- Protein crystals can be grown with far superior quality in microgravity.
- Knowledge of protein structure has important benefits for medicine.

- Fluids (gases and liquids) behave very differently in microgravity, where buoyancy and convection are eliminated.
- Surface tension is created by attractive forces among the molecules; it acts as an invisible film across the surface of a liquid.
- Surface tension is reduced by adding a surfactant or by increasing temperature.
- Temperature-induced surface tension flows predominate in microgravity.
- The behaviour of fluids in microgravity poses challenges in the design and operation of fluid systems in spaceships, but greater understanding of fluid behaviour will result in practical applications on Earth and in space.

Key Terms

liquid crystal displays	X-ray crystallography
crystallization	sedimentation
crystal lattice	buoyancy-driven
nucleation site	convection
saturated	surface tension
supersaturated	surfactant

ASSESSMENT

Understanding Concepts

1. Some crystals are very hard, while others are quite brittle. Provide a reason for this difference.

2. Explain what determines a crystal's shape.

3. Are the hydrogen bonds between water molecules stronger in the liquid state or the solid state? Provide evidence to support your answer.

4. Explain why crystals tend to have fewer imperfections if they are grown slowly.

5. Explain why crystals with few imperfections and sufficient size are required for X-ray crystallography.

6. List three potential benefits of growing crystals in microgravity.

7. If Earth had a more intense gravitational field, how would fluid flow be affected? Provide some specific examples.

8. Crystals can form in a solution by cooling the solution or by extracting solvent by diffusion. Describe how each method promotes crystallization.

9. (a) Using several examples, explain why boiling is an important process in homes and industries.

   (b) What special challenges does microgravity present for the process of boiling?

10. Describe why heating a liquid generally reduces its surface tension.

11. Under what conditions would a candle flame take on a different appearance inside an elevator? Suggest what the new shape would be, and explain why.

12. How would a bead of water on a polished or waxy surface be affected if a material that had the opposite effect of a surfactant was added (**Figure 20**)?

Figure 20

13. Using the Key Terms listed on page 340, create a concept map for this topic. Indicate the connections between the related terms.

Applying Inquiry Skills

14. Suppose you are writing instructions for elementary school students who will be growing crystals.
    (a) List the suggestions you would include so that their crystals will be large and have the best quality possible.
    (b) Which part(s) of the process are the students likely to find the most difficult?

15. Outline an experimental procedure for each task below. Be sure to build in proper controls.
    (a) Compare the surface tensions of a variety of liquids.
    (b) Test the effectiveness of various materials as surfactants.
    (c) Determine the relationship between the temperature of a liquid and its surface tension.

16. Suppose you are conducting a crystal-growing experiment on board the ISS. During the early phases of the experiment, you discover that your crystals are not growing uniformly. Describe what you might do to salvage the experiment.

Making Connections

17. (a) Why is knowledge of fluid behaviour essential for meteorologists?
    (b) What other occupations rely on this type of knowledge?

18. Water droplets form nearly spherical shapes on Earth (**Figure 21**). If scientists learn how to control surface tension, what commercial and industrial applications that use small droplets might be enhanced?

Figure 21

19. One of the first commercial products made in space was a tiny glass microsphere with a diameter of only 10 μm (smaller than the width of a human hair); see **Figure 22**. Microspheres have a variety of applications. For example, they are used to calibrate optical instruments, where tiny distances must be very precise. They are also used to deliver radiation to tumour sites in the body. This technique was first approved in Canada in 1991 and is now being used at 14 sites in the United States to treat patients with liver cancer. The glass spheres are made by allowing molten glass to cool and harden. Growing such perfect spheres with consistently uniform size proved difficult on Earth, however. Explain why, and describe how perfect spheres can be grown in space.

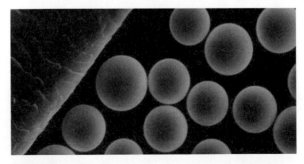

Figure 22

Reflecting

20. Go back to the questions in the topic introduction, and review the answers you wrote from a water molecule's perspective. How has your mental picture of a molecule changed after studying this topic?

E4 Space Technology: BENEFITS and SPINOFFS

You awake in the morning to the day's weather forecast on your clock radio. As you are getting ready for school, you turn on the television to check the sports highlights from the night before. You glance at the morning newspaper, which features the latest discovery by the Hubble Space Telescope. Flipping the pages, you read about a happy ending for a crew who was rescued at sea as a result of their emergency beacon being detected from their foundering ship. Just before you leave for school, you decide to check your e-mail, hoping that you received a message from a friend you met while vacationing. On your way to school, you get a call on your cell phone and make plans for the weekend. Even though you have been awake for only an hour, satellite technology has already touched your life in several ways (**Figure 1**).

Figure 1 **(a)** The Hubble Space Telescope **(b)** Image taken by the Hubble Space Telescope **(c)** Bell ExpressVu's Nimiq 1

(a) Based on this scenario, identify six ways that satellite technology plays a role in your life.

(b) Satellite dishes are becoming more popular as a way to receive television programming. Why can receiving dishes always point in the same direction to receive signals even though Earth is constantly rotating?

(c) You may have seen some of the earliest home satellite dishes that measured several metres in diameter—much larger than those in use today. What does the reduced size of today's satellite dishes tell you about how this technology has changed since it was first introduced?

Some argue that the human and monetary costs of the space program are not justified by the benefits it provides. Others feel that many important benefits have come directly from the space program and other less obvious but equally important benefits have come from technological spinoffs. However you feel, it is undeniable that our society is becoming increasingly dependent on technology related to the space program.

(d) Identify some common items you use daily or a service you might use from time to time that you think could have roots in the space program. Explain the connections.

(e) Where do you stand on the issue of costs versus benefits of the space program? Give reasons for your answer.

(f) What occupations do you think are connected directly and indirectly with satellites? Make a list, and show the connection in each case.

(g) What other applications of satellites or the space program in general are you familiar with that have not been mentioned in this scenario?

What are some of the spinoffs of space technology? What is the function of different satellites orbiting Earth? What are Canada's contributions to space exploration?

Space Technology

The development of the space program has required many technological innovations. From the first small, unguided rockets to modern spacecraft and orbiting platforms, the space program has required increasingly sophisticated propulsion and guidance systems, life support systems, and imaging and communications devices. Because of the challenges associated with launching objects from Earth into space, these systems and devices have become smaller, more lightweight, and highly integrated. Many of them have resulted in useful spinoffs for life on Earth. Every day, you use many products that have their roots in the space program, and you rely on the information received and relayed by the hundreds of satellites that orbit above Earth.

Technological Spinoffs

Highly advanced digital cameras, first developed for satellite studies of Earth's atmosphere, have become incorporated into a number of important devices. At the heart of the modern digital camera is charge-coupled device (CCD) technology.

> ### DID **YOU** KNOW?
>
> **Invention of CCDs**
> CCDs were invented by Canadian Willard S. Boyle in 1969, when he was working at Bell Research Laboratories in the United States.

CCDs consist of tiny, light-sensitive cells, or pixels, that produce small electric currents when struck by light. The amount of electricity produced by an individual pixel is proportional to the intensity of the light striking it. A signal processor collects the electric currents produced by an array of millions of pixels and produces a highly refined digital image. Supersensitive CCD devices, developed for use on the Hubble Space Telescope, have been incorporated into medical-imaging devices that allow doctors to visualize tissues more clearly than X-rays do. For example, the devices can pinpoint suspected cancerous regions, so biopsies can be performed with tiny needles instead of by invasive surgery.

The images that satellite cameras capture often require processing to provide greater detail and to help scientists interpret what they are seeing. This is accomplished using digital imaging software, which was originally developed to enhance pictures taken by Apollo astronauts on the Moon. Digital imaging software has led to magnetic resonance imaging (MRI) and computerized axial tomography (CAT scan) technologies (**Figure 2**), which produce superior quality images for medical diagnoses.

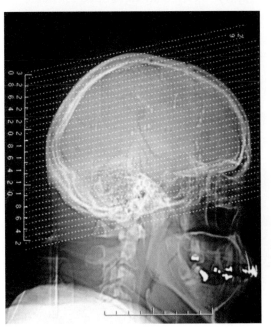

Figure 2 CAT scan of a human head

Atherosclerosis, a common circulatory system disease, is caused when fatty materials are deposited along the walls of arteries. The fatty materials thicken, harden, and may eventually block the arteries. Conventional treatments are heart bypass surgery and angioplasty. During heart bypass surgery, the surgeon uses a graft vein from another site in the body to bypass the blocked arteries. During angioplasty, the surgeon threads a small balloon through an artery to the blockage by means of a catheter; the balloon is then inflated to expand the artery and restore proper blood flow. Lasers that were originally developed for studying Earth's ozone layer are now being used as an alternative to these two treatments.

Laser light, carried by fibre optic bundles that have been directed within a catheter to the blockage, burns away the plaque buildup on the arterial walls. Another set of optical fibres illuminates the site and returns video pictures so that the surgeon can monitor the progress of the procedure. The laser used in this procedure is unique in that it operates at a much lower temperature than conventional lasers do. The high temperatures of conventional lasers would not be tolerated by the delicate tissue that lines the coronary arteries.

An alternative treatment for esophageal cancer and some types of lung cancer uses light-emitting diodes (LEDs) in conjunction with photosensitive drugs (**Figure 3**). This treatment, called photodynamic therapy, was originally developed for plant experiments on space shuttles. Photodynamic therapy kills cancerous cells but leaves adjacent tissue untouched. Scientists are exploring its use to promote the healing of injuries sustained on long space flights, when the human immune system is weakened.

Figure 3 Cancer-treating drugs are injected intravenously and then stimulated into action by tiny LEDs focused on the tumour.

NASA has developed a tiny device that can monitor several of an astronaut's body functions, such as body temperature and blood pressure, and then transmit the data for analysis. On Earth, this device, which is small enough to be swallowed, can provide information about a patient's gastrointestinal activity, the health of an unborn baby, and the body functions of a high-performance athlete.

While performing fluid research with an optical device developed at NASA, researchers realized that the technology could be useful for detecting the early stages of cataract development, which is a fogging of the eye's lens. The device was adapted and is now used to diagnose a number of degenerative eye diseases in a painless and noninvasive procedure.

A number of challenges associated with launching and landing spaceships safely have been investigated by NASA. These investigations have subsequently led to a variety of safety systems that are now in widespread use worldwide. Research planes, deliberately flying into intense weather systems, were repeatedly struck by lightning and subjected to high winds to measure the effects on the plane's performance. As a result of this research, lightning protection systems were developed, as well as early warning radar devices that can predict dangerous wind patterns ahead of a plane.

In wet conditions, a plane can hydroplane when landing or taking off. NASA found that cutting small grooves into the runway surface and channelling water into the grooves and off the runway surface greatly improved the performance of the tires. The same technology is now applied on highways, walkways, and ramps where wet surfaces are hazardous.

Microelectromechanical systems are tiny sensors (some as small as a hair) originally developed as accelerometers to measure the *g*-forces experienced by astronauts. The same technology is now in widespread use in airbag control devices, pacemakers, and a number of household appliances.

The fabric developed for space suits has also found applications on Earth. Made of fibreglass and coated with Teflon, the fabric is lightweight, fire-resistant, and very strong. The fabric is used as a roofing material in some shopping malls and sports facilities, such as Vancouver's BC Place stadium (**Figure 4**). The fabric allows some light to penetrate while reflecting the Sun's heat, thereby reducing lighting and air-conditioning costs.

Figure 4 The roof on Vancouver's BC Place is made from 4 ha of the same fabric used for astronauts' space suits.

Virtual reality (VR) devices, first developed by NASA, are able to generate a combination of three-dimensional images and realistic sounds to create a virtual environment for the user (**Figure 5**). A VR device, equipped with the necessary instruments, can allow a surgeon who is working in one location to perform an operation on a patient in another location. Virtual reality technology could prove invaluable to a technician diagnosing an equipment problem on board a spacecraft, an architect touring a virtual building, or an officer investigating a crime scene from a remote location.

Figure 5 Virtual reality technology is not just entertainment. More and more companies are using this technology to simulate processes before implementing them.

Many everyday devices were first engineered to meet the needs of the space program:

- Smoke detectors were developed for use on *Skylab*, NASA's first orbiting space platform.
- One of the objectives of the Apollo missions to the Moon in the 1960s and 1970s was to return rock samples to Earth. This presented the challenge of inventing a lightweight, battery-powered device that could drill holes in the Moon's surface. Today, there are a variety of cordless, rechargeable power tools that were initially developed to meet this need.
- Water filters were first introduced during the Apollo program to sterilize the astronauts' drinking water.
- Scratch-resistant lenses and lenses with coatings that filter out harmful radiation were first developed for the space program to protect sensitive imaging devices and the astronauts' eyes.
- Every product you purchase is labelled with a bar code, a series of vertical black and white lines that can be scanned and read by a laser mechanism. Bar-code technology was initially developed for NASA to keep track of the countless parts that are used in launch vehicles. The same technology is now used worldwide to identify products, maintain inventories, and track shipments.

Satellites

Objects that orbit much larger bodies are considered to be **satellites**. For example, Earth is a satellite of the Sun, and the Moon is a satellite of Earth. There are currently well over 2000 artificial satellites in Earth orbit, placed there by over 20 countries. Add in other objects that we have placed in space, including debris from launches and satellites that are no longer operational, and the number exceeds 25 000 (**Figure 6**).

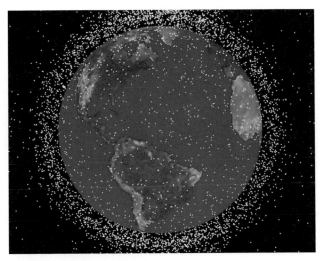

Figure 6 Orbiting space debris is a constant threat to satellites. A collision with even a tiny particle, travelling with a relative speed of thousands of kilometres per hour, could have devastating consequences. The Space Surveillance Network tracks all orbiting objects that are the size of a baseball and larger. This amounts to nearly 8000 objects, with 93% of them being space debris and non-operational satellites. (artist's depiction)

All artificial satellites share several common design features: a power source, a computer system, a grapple fixture, and guidance controls.

- A power source is required to run the instrumentation and relay data back to Earth or to other satellites. Satellites generally use solar cells, which convert sunlight directly into electricity. Depending on the satellite's power requirements, the body of the satellite is covered with solar cells, or larger solar array panels are used. If the satellite is not constantly in direct sunlight, rechargeable batteries are used. Some satellites have been powered by small nuclear reactors, but this power source has inherent dangers associated with the satellite falling back to Earth or being destroyed during launch and scattering radioactive debris on the ground below.
- A satellite's computer controls and monitors all onboard systems, relaying information back to

Earth and receiving commands when adjustments need to be made. Antennas of various shapes and sizes send and receive this information.

- Many satellites are equipped with a grapple fixture. If a satellite is launched from a space shuttle, the Canadarm attaches itself to the grapple fixture when launching it or when retrieving it for repairs.
- Satellites must maintain a very stable flight path in orbit, because any wobbling could ruin images and distort transmissions. Attitude controls prevent wobbling. The satellite's instruments must constantly point in the proper direction, and its solar panels must be at the proper angle to the Sun. Attitude is maintained by spinning either the entire satellite or a gyroscope on the satellite. The spinning allows the satellite to move along a smooth orbital path, just as a bicycle is stabilized when its wheels are turning.

From time to time, a satellite's orbit must be adjusted. This is particularly important when a satellite is in a low-Earth orbit (350-km to 1500-km altitude), where many communications satellites orbit. Here, occasional random collisions with stray atmospheric particles create a small amount of frictional drag. This reduces the satellite's speed slightly, causing it to lose altitude. If left uncorrected, the satellite's orbit will continue to decay and it will crash to Earth. Thrusters are used to push the satellite back into its proper orbital position. Thrusters are also used on spacecraft travelling to the Moon and planets whenever the speed and direction need to be changed. When satellites are launched from a space shuttle or rocket, thrusters nudge them into their proper orbits.

Thrusters use the principle of action and reaction forces as first proposed by Newton. **Newton's third law of motion** states that for every action, there is an equal and opposite reaction. In other words, forces always occur in pairs, and the two forces in any pair are equal in strength and opposite in direction. The force of gravity acts between two objects, one pulling on the other. You exert as much gravity upward on the entire planet as Earth exerts downward on you. Similarly, if you and a friend stood facing each other on ice skates and you exerted a force on your friend directly away from you, not only would your friend move away from you but you would also move away from your friend. The "action" force you exerted would cause your friend to accelerate in one direction. The "reaction" force exerted upon you would

cause you to accelerate in the opposite direction. Combining these observations with Newton's second law, we can see that an object with a larger mass has a smaller acceleration. The forces have equal magnitude but they may be acting on different masses.

A thruster consists of a nozzle from which a compressed gas can be expelled. When the gas is released, the force pushing it outward is matched by an equal force that is exerted in the opposite direction by the gas pushing on the satellite. The satellite accelerates away from the escaping gas. If the satellite needs to be manoeuvred to the right, for example, the thruster expels gas to the left.

A satellite's orbit depends on its mission. Many communications satellites are placed in a **geosynchronous orbit**, in which they orbit Earth at the same rate as the planet spins on its axis (**Figure 7(a)**). Because the satellite's orbit is synchronized with the rotation of Earth, the receiving antenna (satellite dish) can remain in a fixed position once it is pointed at the satellite. A satellite's altitude is directly related to its orbital period (the time to complete a single orbit). For a satellite to remain above a fixed position, the geosynchronous orbit above the equator must have the fixed altitude of 36 000 km. With hundreds of television, weather, and communications satellites currently in this orbit, it is becoming increasingly crowded.

Other satellites are placed in **asynchronous orbits**, which typically have much lower altitudes and orbit Earth in or near the plane of the equator (**Figure 7(b)**). An asynchronous orbit allows a satellite to peer down at a particular position on Earth at different times each day and to survey an entire latitudinal slice of Earth.

Satellites in **polar orbits** cross near the poles with each pass. In this way, they can view different slices of Earth's surface with each orbit, as Earth rotates beneath them (**Figure 7(c)**), and thus survey the entire planet within a few orbital passes.

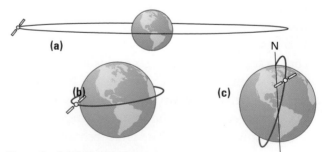

Figure 7 **(a)** A geosynchronous orbit **(b)** An asynchronous orbit **(c)** A polar orbit

Looking Inward

Most satellites focus their instruments toward Earth, performing an amazing variety of functions. The purposes of several inward-looking satellites are summarized in **Table 1**.

Table 1 Satellites That Look Toward Earth

Atmospheric Studies

By studying the ionosphere, scientists have learned more about the formation of the northern and southern lights. They also hope to better understand how damaging radiation affects the performance of all satellites. With the launch of Alouette in 1962, Canada became the first country to study the ionosphere. More recently, in 1996, NASA launched Polar, a satellite in a low polar orbit that has the same purpose.

Communications

By moving electronic information around Earth at the speed of light, television and radio broadcasts, long distance phone calls, and fax transmissions are made possible.

Some communications satellites send and receive information from Earth's surface, and others send signals to another satellite. In 1972, Canada launched the world's first domestic communications satellite in geosynchronous orbit, Anik 1. Now in its sixth generation, Anik F satellites provide television broadcasts and services to businesses that transmit information electronically (**Figure 8**).

Figure 8 The Anik F series of satellites will provide various communications applications—such as tele-medicine, tele-learning, e-commerce, and high-speed Internet—for many years.

Reconnaissance

Used primarily for military purposes, reconnaissance satellites monitor troop and equipment movements from space. Radio signals can be intercepted, and information can be transmitted around the globe instantly.

Search and Rescue

Emergency radio beacons, which are standard equipment on aircraft and ships, are detected by these satellites. Since 1982, the Cospas-Sarsat search-and-rescue satellite system has been in use. Using a near-polar orbit, with Earth rotating beneath, the satellites are able to monitor the entire planet for distress beacons.

Weather

Geosynchronous satellites as well as other satellites that are in polar orbits continually monitor cloud patterns, ocean temperatures, snow thickness, the movement of ice fields, and water vapour levels in the air (**Figure 9**).

Figure 9 This satellite image shows a hurricane approaching the eastern seaboard.

Global Positioning System (GPS)

A minimum of 24 Navstar satellites are positioned in circular orbits at an altitude of approximately 20 000 km. To determine the location of a GPS receiver, signals are sent, at the speed of light, from at least three of the satellites. The position of each satellite at any given time is known to high precision, so the time taken to receive a signal can be used to determine the distance from the satellite to the receiver. The GPS receiver coordinates the signals and pinpoints its location (**Figure 10**).

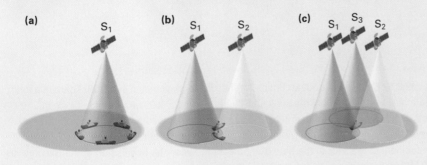

(a) S_1 **(b)** S_1 S_2 **(c)** S_1 S_3 S_2

Figure 10 GPS satellites are used to determine the location of an object, such as a boat. **(a)** Using only one satellite, the boat's location is known to be somewhere along the circumference of a circle. **(b)** Using two satellites simultaneously, the location is found to be at one of two intersection locations. **(c)** Using three satellites simultaneously, the intersection of the three circles is the exact location of the boat.

Among Canada's most notable contributions to space science is remote sensing technology. Many satellites are equipped with a variety of imaging devices that use emitted and reflected radiation across a broad spectrum. These devices detect such things as crop damage, pollution emissions, and mineral deposits. In 1995, the CSA launched RADARSAT-1, a remote sensing satellite that uses synthetic aperture radar (SAR) technology developed in Canada.

In SAR technology, microwave frequency signals are bounced off a target. The time delay between sending a signal and detecting its echo provides the distance to the target. By directing radar signals across the entire surface of a large target, details of its surface features can be mapped. The resolution of the details depends on how large the receiver is. (The resolution of an image refers to the smallest object size that can be seen.) Just as the resolution of a telescope is determined by the size of its objective lens or mirror (called the aperture), the resolution of a radar image is determined by the size of the receiver antenna. The key to SAR technology is having a small receiver move across a large distance while receiving the radar echoes, and processing the data as if they had come from a very large receiving antenna. In this way, a synthetic aperture is created, which is capable of producing highly detailed images. RADARSAT-1 can provide images that cover areas as large as 250 000 km^2 with resolutions of 100 m, and images that cover areas

as small as 2500 m^2 with resolutions of 8 m. Because clouds are invisible to radar, images are not distorted by atmospheric conditions. In addition, images can be obtained day or night, since this system uses radio waves, not visible light (**Figure 11**). RADARSAT-2, which is scheduled for launch in 2005, will carry the most advanced SAR technology to date.

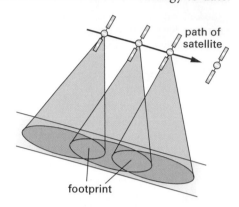

Figure 11 As the satellite moves along its path, radar "snapshots" are taken of the ground below. The overlapping footprints are processed to produce a high-resolution image.

Satellite images are purchased for a variety of applications. Oil spills at sea can be detected and monitored (**Figure 12**). Damage from volcanoes, hurricanes, and earthquakes can be inspected. Governments can survey the encroachment of deserts on populated areas, the production of greenhouse gases, the extent of flooding, and the amount of snow and ice cover.

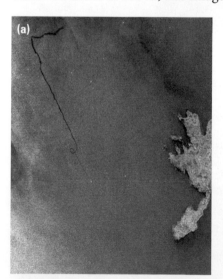  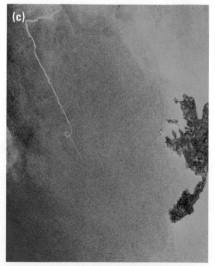

Figure 12 **(a)** An image taken off the Estonian coast by ENVISAT (European Space Agency Earth-observation satellite). There is a long, clear oil slick. A vessel can clearly be detected at the southern end of the slick shortly after doing a 360° turnaround. **(b)** An image taken the following day by RADARSAT-1. The oil slick has not drifted too much, and you can see the weathering effects on the slick. You can also see that the vessel continued to release oil as it entered the Gulf of Riga. **(c)** A composite of the ENVISAT and RADARSAT-1 images. You can see the actual drift and development of the slick in the time that passed between the acquisition of the two images. The slicks highlighted in blue are from the RADARSAT-1 image, and the slicks highlighted in light green are from the ENVISAT image.

In 1962, Canada launched its first satellite, Alouette, into orbit. Since then, Canada has launched several series of satellites, designed to perform a variety of functions (**Figure 13**). Satellites reach orbit by a number of launching platforms and carry instruments that are designed to meet the specific needs of the missions. In this activity, you will research one of the Canadian satellites listed in **Table 2**. Then you will summarize your findings in a written or oral report, a slide show, or another creative presentation of your choice.

Your research should focus on the following topics:

(a) Launching platform: How was the satellite placed into orbit?
(b) Orbit: What type of orbit did (or does) the satellite follow?
(c) Mission: What was the purpose of the satellite? Was the purpose of the satellite fulfilled?

(d) Structural details: What are the design features of the satellite? Provide details about its size, mass, instrument package, and other important features.
(e) Status: Is the satellite currently in service? If not, how long was it operational, and did it exceed its expected useful lifetime? If so, how long is it expected to continue to perform?
(f) Cost: What was the cost of the satellite, and how was it financed?

Table 2 Canadian Satellite Series

Satellite series	Year of launch
Alouette	1962
Anik A	1972
Anik B	1978
Anik C	1982
Anik D	1982
Anik E	1990
Anik F	2000
ISIS	1969
Hermes	1976
RADARSAT-1	1995
MSat	1996
Nimiq	1999
SciSat	2003

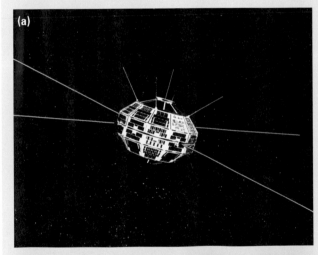

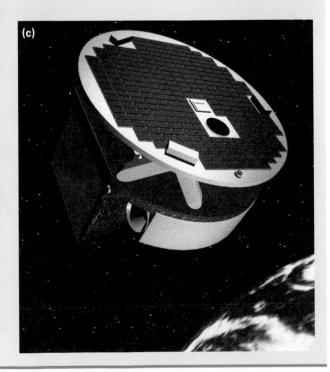

Figure 13 **(a)** Alouette **(b)** RADARSAT-1 **(c)** SciSat

Looking Outward

While many satellites look toward Earth, others have been designed to focus their instruments away from the planet and survey both nearby and distant celestial objects. The purposes of some outward-looking satellites are summarized in **Table 3**.

Table 3 Satellites That Look Away from Earth

Hubble Space Telescope (HST)

The HST was launched from the cargo bay of the space shuttle *Discovery* in 1990. It orbits 600 km above Earth, well above the atmosphere. Being above the atmosphere is desirable because the atmosphere significantly degrades the quality of telescopic images. Relative movements of atmospheric layers at different temperatures can cause an image to shimmer, much like what you would see if you looked through the air directly above a candle flame (**Figure 14**).

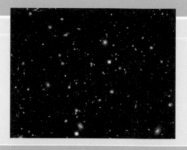

Figure 14 The HST has provided astronomers with unprecedented images.

MOST (Microvariability and Oscillations of Stars)

This Canadian satellite has been called the "Humble Space Telescope." Compared with the $2 billion HST, MOST is considered a bargain at $10 million. MOST is 100% Canadian, created with contributions from various institutions across the country (**Figure 15**). The satellite collects light from stars and from objects around other stars billions of light-years away.

Figure 15 The first Canadian satellite in a new breed called microsatellites, MOST is the size of a suitcase and has a mass of only 50 kg. Launched in 2003, MOST maintains a polar orbit at an altitude of 800 km.

COBE (Cosmic Background Explorer) and WMAP (Wilkinson Microwave Anisotropy Probe)

Both COBE (launched in 1992) and WMAP (launched in 2001) surveyed the sky for cosmic microwave background radiation, a remnant echo of the big bang. COBE data revealed tiny fluctuations in temperature at various points in the sky (**Figure 16**, top). According to COBE data, the universe has cooled to about 3° above absolute zero since the big bang. The WMAP mission, carrying more sensitive instruments, provided higher resolution pictures of the very early universe (**Figure 16**, bottom), leading scientists to establish the age of the universe at 13.7 billion years.

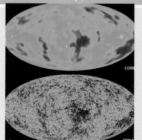

Figure 16 Scientists concluded that the variations in temperature are evidence of the early distribution of matter in the universe. Their findings have been used to refine theories about the formation of galaxies, star clusters, and regions completely void of matter.

Chandra X-ray Observatory

Launched in 1999, Chandra was the largest satellite to be carried aloft by a space shuttle. Chandra orbits at a distance that is 200 times more remote than the orbit of the HST. It peers into high-energy regions of space, studying areas of star formation, nebulas, supernovas, and black holes (**Figure 17**).

Figure 17 Chandra's precisely shaped mirrors allow scientists to "see" in the X-ray portion of the electromagnetic spectrum and thus discern features with unprecedented detail.

SOHO (Solar and Heliospheric Observatory)

SOHO is part of a joint mission by NASA and the European Space Agency. Launched in 1995, SOHO studies the Sun (**Figure 18**) and the solar wind, a stream of charged particles emitted from the Sun. Many of these particles hit Earth. When these particles interact with our upper atmosphere, they cause the northern and southern lights. After a particularly large outburst from the Sun, the solar wind becomes particularly strong and can affect radio transmissions worldwide, as well as the operation of satellites.

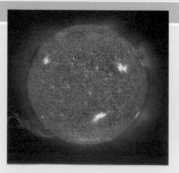

Figure 18 SOHO studies the Sun's extensive atmosphere and turbulent interior.

Space Probes

Some space vehicles explore the solar system and beyond. Although space probes do not meet the definition of a satellite, they have the same features: a power source, a computer system (including an instrument package and a communications system), and guidance controls. As space probes have become increasingly sophisticated, scientists have made amazing discoveries about the universe. **Table 4** describes some of the notable space probes.

As scientists use satellites and space probes to learn more about Earth and the universe, many new questions arise. There are numerous proposals for new instruments and space vehicles designed to answer these questions. Information about missions that are currently underway and others that are planned or under study is readily available on the Internet.

Space probes such as *Pioneer* and *Voyager* have given scientists a far better understanding of other planets by flying relatively close to them. However, landing on a distant planet and sampling its atmosphere and terrain can yield even more spectacular results. Robotic spacecraft have successfully landed on Venus and Mars, and with an announcement early in 2004, NASA is committed to an even more ambitious proposal: landing humans on Mars.

To prepare for such a mission, much needs to be known. In early 2004, two rovers landed on Mars to begin sampling rocks, soil, and atmosphere. While there is no known liquid water on Mars today, one of the objectives of the mission was to search for evidence of water having been on the surface of Mars in the past. Scientists concluded, based on the evidence collected, that Mars once had considerable quantities of water on its surface. This evidence

Table 4 Space Probes

Pioneer 10 and *Pioneer 11*

The mission objective of *Pioneer 10*, launched in 1972, was to reach Jupiter and take the first close-up photographs of the solar system's largest planet. The following year, *Pioneer 11* was launched; it proceeded to Jupiter and then to Saturn. Both spacecraft continued to journey outward through the solar system, gathering information about the solar wind and cosmic rays. *Pioneer 11* lost radio contact with Earth in 1995, but *Pioneer 10* continued to send signals until 2003, 31 years after its launch.

When these spacecraft were designed and launched, researchers expected that they would continue to travel in silence well beyond the solar system. For this reason, both spacecraft have plaques, or "calling cards," in case they are ever intercepted by an extraterrestrial civilization (**Figure 19**).

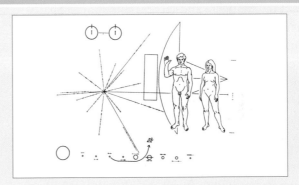

Figure 19 These "calling cards," which picture a man and a woman and provide the location of Earth within the Milky Way Galaxy, were intended to provide information about humans and the place of origin of the spacecraft.

Voyager 1 and *Voyager 2*

Launched in 1977, the mission of these twin spacecraft was to survey the gas giant planets of the outer solar system. As they approached Jupiter, they used its gravitational pull to accelerate to incredible speeds and to be hurled toward Saturn and beyond. Both spacecraft flew by Jupiter and Saturn, making numerous discoveries about these giant planets and their moons. *Voyager 2* continued on to Uranus and Neptune, and is the only probe to visit these remote planets to date.

After they completed their primary missions in 1989, the two spacecraft then took on a new role, an interstellar mission. Both spacecraft continue on their journeys, which will eventually take them out of the solar system and away from the Sun's influence into interstellar space. They have enough electrical power and thruster fuel to operate until the year 2020. Eventually their inertia will take them past other stars as they wander through the Milky Way Galaxy.

Voyager 1 and *Voyager 2* carry gold-plated disks, which are recordings of voices and sounds of nature from around the world (**Figure 20**).

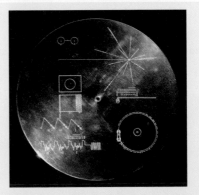

Figure 20 "The Sounds of Earth" feature music and sounds from nature, as well as 116 encoded pictures and voice greetings in 55 different languages.

means that Mars may have once had conditions suitable for sustaining life.

Scientists predict that 10 to 15 years of preparation will be required before a manned mission could set out for Mars. The journey would likely take between six and eight months, and astronauts would remain on the planet for about one year before returning. Once there, astronauts would be faced with numerous survival challenges, such as frigid temperatures, a poisonous atmosphere, and ultraviolet radiation levels hundreds of times the levels experienced on Earth.

The Canadarm

Among Canada's many contributions to space technology, perhaps none is more recognized than the Shuttle Remote Manipulator System (SRMS), or **Canadarm**. From the time that space shuttles were first conceived, scientists have recognized that the Canadarm is vital to the success of a variety of missions.

The Canadarm was designed and constructed by a team of engineers and technicians at Spar Space Systems Robotics (now MD Robotics), based in Brampton, Ontario. The Canadarm cost $108 million to design and build. Originally proposed to launch, manoeuvre, and recover satellites, the Canadarm has also been indispensable in helping to construct the ISS. It has also been used in several unscheduled exercises:

- deploying a faulty antenna on a satellite
- dislodging ice from a waste-water vent
- helping a satellite achieve its orbit after it had failed to do so itself

The Canadarm made its debut in space on the space shuttle *Columbia* in 1981. In exchange for the Canadarm, Canada has joined NASA on several missions, and four more Canadarms have been purchased for use on other space shuttles.

The Canadarm cannot support its own weight on Earth; it was designed to work in space. However,

it still has considerable strength. Newton's first law of motion provides an explanation: An orbiting object may have no apparent weight, but it nevertheless possesses inertia. For the Canadarm to grapple and manoeuvre a satellite of several tonnes, it must be able to overcome the vehicle's considerable inertia by slightly altering its course. To capture a satellite, the space shuttle first matches the satellite's speed so that there is no relative motion between the two objects. The Canadarm then reaches for the satellite and firmly grasps its grapple fixture. To do this, the Canadarm's booms and joints must be made of materials that are both lightweight for launch economy and sufficiently strong to manoeuvre massive payloads.

The Canadarm has proved itself to be an engineering triumph. With a mass of 410 kg and a length of 15.2 m, it is modelled after a human arm. The manipulator has a shoulder joint, upper arm, elbow, lower arm, wrist joint, and hand. The shoulder joint can move both up and down (pitch) and sideways (yaw). The elbow is able to provide pitch only; the wrist provides pitch, yaw, and roll (rotation). Equipped with lights and closed-circuit television cameras along its length, astronauts can closely monitor its movements as they direct it with two hand controllers situated inside the orbiter.

A second generation of arm, Canadarm2, is affixed to the ISS. Capable of walking itself end over end across the skeleton of the ISS, it is used to lift modules and attach them to the ISS, as well as to service the exterior surfaces. A rail system that is secured to the ISS also allows the Canadarm2 to travel from place to place with greater speed. Since the Canadarm2 has even more dexterity than its predecessor, it can handle a payload as massive as an entire space shuttle. In addition, it is equipped with a far more sophisticated vision system and an innovative touch sensor system, which together allow astronauts to manipulate objects with pinpoint precision (**Figure 21**).

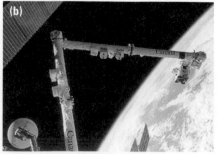

Figure 21
(a) The Canadarm
(b) The Canadarm2

Like other space technologies, the Canadarm has spawned a number of spinoffs. For example, remote manipulators have been engineered to service nuclear-power generating stations and pipe lines that lie on the ocean floor. Similar devices have also been developed to inspect and clean sites that house toxic wastes.

E4.2 Activity | DESIGNING AND BUILDING A ROBOTIC ARM

In this activity, your class will design, build, and test models of the Canadarm, complete with the booms, joints, and a hand. Your class will be divided into groups, and each group will design and build its own model. Within each group, individuals or smaller groups will be responsible for the following tasks:

- identifying what materials you will use to construct your model
- designing and building the various components of your model
- overseeing how the various components will be assembled to complete your model
- testing and modifying the design

Suggestions are provided to help you select appropriate materials, but you are not limited to these suggestions. The complexity of your model depends on the time you have available to complete it and the expertise of your group. You may wish to have your model manually manipulated or operated by small electric motors or a pulley system.

Your model will need to move from a neutral position into a position from which it can grasp an object with a mass of no more than 500 g, lift the object, and move the object to another location using all of its joints.

As you construct each component of your model, you will need to test its integrity and operation and modify its design as you see fit. Be careful to choose materials that will allow your model to operate well within the parameters of the task it must perform. Before assembling your model, you should test each component again.

See **Figure 22** for a schematic of the design of the Canadarm.

Suggested Materials

Joints
Consider using hinges, gears, pulleys, or screw-top lids that allow for movement. Freedom of movement is an essential component of the design.

- The shoulder joint consists of two mechanisms that allow the arm to provide pitch and yaw.
- The elbow joint provides pitch only.
- The wrist joint is capable of pitch, yaw, and roll and therefore requires three mechanisms to handle these movements.

Booms
Consider using tubes of cardboard, aluminum, wood, fibreglass, or plastic. Strength is the most important factor for the booms.

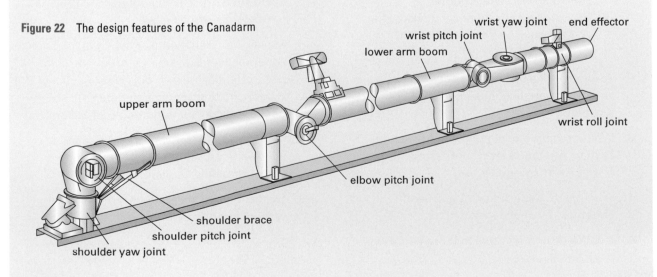

Figure 22 The design features of the Canadarm

- The booms (upper and lower arms) provide the manipulator with its reach.
- The booms must be able to link the joints.

Wiring Harness

If your model is activated by motors, you will need to deliver electricity to the motors. If your model uses a system of pulleys, you will need to suspend cords along the length of the robotic arm. Simplicity of design is an important consideration for the wiring harness.

- Wires or cords will need to be suspended along the booms and across the joints, but not interfere with their movements.

End Effector

This is the manipulator's hand. It must be able to grasp an object and hold the object securely. Consider using a clamping device or a wrapping mechanism, similar to the original design.

Control System

The operation of the manipulator is remote-controlled. If your model is simple, with the various joints manipulated by hand, a control system is not required. If your model incorporates motors or pulleys for movement, these should be controlled from beyond the shoulder joint.

Evaluation

(a) Evaluate your model and the models built by other groups. Identify which model provided the best performance for each of the components: joints, booms, wiring harness, end effector, and control system.

(b) Describe how the tests you performed to evaluate the designs of the various components would have been different if you had been testing these components in a microgravity environment.

(c) Describe the characteristics of the materials that are required for a robotic arm to operate in the unique environmental conditions of space.

(d) Evaluate the design and construction process itself. Comment on the teamwork within your group. Suggest improvements you could make to the division of responsibility for completing the device and performing the required tasks.

✓ Check Your Understanding

1. (a) What are the advantages of digital cameras that use CCD technology over conventional film cameras?
   (b) Name some other optical devices that you think could benefit from CCD technology.

2. Aside from its use in surgical procedures, what other applications does fibre optics technology have?

3. What are some advantages of MRI and CAT scan technologies over more conventional X-rays as imaging devices?

4. How has transportation safety been enhanced by space research?

5. List the design features that are common to all satellites.

6. What type(s) of orbits would require satellites to have batteries as well as solar panels to meet their electrical needs? Provide a reason for your answer.

7. Explain, with an example, why the following statement is false: "All the action–reaction pairs of forces on two objects are equal in magnitude but opposite in direction, so neither object can undergo acceleration."

8. In what way is the action of an inflated balloon upon release analogous to a rocket thruster? Explain.

9. Suggest an application of remote sensing technology not mentioned in the topic.

Society & the Environment

Weighing the Costs and Benefits of Space Exploration

Many people have argued that the costs of the space program are unjustified. The costs, in terms of dollars and loss of lives, are staggering. Could the many spinoff technologies have been developed on Earth? Should pressing problems on Earth receive greater attention and money before venturing into space to seek answers to questions that have seemingly few direct benefits for humans?

Other people argue that the benefits outweigh the costs. Has the information supplied and relayed by satellites provided us with instant worldwide communication and increased safety in travel? Are the breakthroughs in medical services and microelectronics beneficial? People regularly choose to become involved in a variety of dangerous professions, accepting the associated risks with the conviction that their work is important. Perhaps we are simply driven to explore the unknown and to seek answers to questions without the need for immediate rewards.

Explore *an* Issue

Are the Costs of the Space Program Worth the Money?

The costs and benefits of the space program have been debated at length by experts and the general public.

Statement: The costs associated with the space program are justified by the benefits.

1. In your group, research the issue. Search for information in newspapers and periodicals, and on CD-ROMs and the Internet.

    www.science.nelson.com

2. Identify individuals, organizations, and government agencies that have addressed the issue.

3. Identify the perspectives of opposing positions, and arrange these perspectives in a suit-

Decision-Making Skills

- Define a Issue
- Identify Alternatives
- Research
- Analyze the Issue
- Defend the Decision
- Evaluate

able graphic organizer. **Table 5** will help you get started.

4. As a group, choose a position. Defend your group's position in a class debate (see **Appendix A7**).

5. How did your group reach a decision about which position to defend?

6. Which side won the debate? Why do you think this side won?

Table 5 Opposing Claims of the Space Program

Proponents' claims	Opponents' claims
When compared with annual federal spending, space programs account for a small fraction of the total.	NASA's annual budget is billions, and the CSA's annual budget is hundreds of millions of taxpayer dollars.
The space program provides employment opportunities for millions of people.	The inevitable loss of human life and the risks of living in space prove that human space flight is too dangerous.
Medical technologies and a host of other spinoff technologies have had proven benefits for us all.	Products that have their roots in the space program could have been developed on Earth at far less cost.

SUMMARY

- The benefits of satellite technology and spinoffs of the space program are numerous and varied.
- Technological spinoffs of the space program can be found in many areas such as medicine, communications, household products, travel safety, and electronics.
- All satellites, regardless of their specific functions, have common design components.
- Satellites have a variety of purposes, such as communications, scientific study, search and rescue, remote sensing, reconnaissance, and weather monitoring and forecasting.
- Canada has been a leader in satellite technology, making significant contributions to space programs worldwide. Among the most celebrated achievements of the Canadian space program is the Canadarm, a device essential to the success of space shuttle missions and the construction of the ISS.
- Space probes have ventured beyond Earth orbit, with successful landings on the Moon, Venus, and Mars. Others have flown past Jupiter, Saturn, Neptune, and Uranus, providing scientists with information about these distant worlds.
- The benefits of the space program have not been achieved without considerable costs in terms of money and loss of life.

Key Terms

satellite

Newton's third law
   of motion

geosynchronous orbit

asynchronous orbit

polar orbit

Canadarm

ASSESSMENT

Understanding Concepts

1. Provide two examples, other than those in this text, that illustrate how Newton's third law of motion applies to space travel.

2. What are the advantages of having exploratory satellites above Earth's atmosphere?

3. List three advances in medicine and medical procedures that are directly related to the space program.

4. Fire protection suits are used when firefighters are extremely close to intense heat sources (**Figure 23**). What features would these suits have in common with the space suits that are worn by astronauts?

Figure 23

5. List the types of satellites that are currently in use, according to their purposes.

6. Copy and complete **Table 6**. There may be more than one type of satellite for an orbit.

Table 6

Orbit	Type of satellite
geosynchronous	
polar	
asynchronous	

7. Compare Earth-orbiting satellites and space probes destined for other planets. How would their designs be similar, and how would they be different? Suggest reasons for your answers.

8. Canada's MOST satellite is an example of a microsatellite, a type that is becoming more popular. Describe the advantages of microsatellites over more conventional satellites.

9. In August 2004, NASA launched the space probe *Messenger* to study the planet Mercury. Explain why launching a probe to go into orbit around Mercury is like trying to stop suddenly while running downhill.

Applying Inquiry Skills

10. At one end of a sheet of paper, draw a semicircle of radius 3.2 cm to represent one hemisphere of Earth (radius 6400 km). Using this scale, draw and label the orbital positions of
    (a) a space shuttle (altitude 400 km)
    (b) the HST (altitude 600 km)
    (c) a remote sensing satellite (altitude 750 km)
    (d) a GPS satellite (altitude 20 000 km)
    (e) a geosynchronous communications satellite (altitude 36 000 km)

11. Draw a circle that represents Earth, with its rotational axis situated vertically on your paper. Add the shapes of common satellite orbits, including the type(s) of satellite in each orbit.

12. Draw a circle of radius 1.6 cm to represent Earth (radius 6400 km).
    (a) How many geosynchronous satellites, orbiting at an altitude of 36 000 km, would be required to relay a signal completely around the planet. Assume that the signal follows a "line of sight" path?
    (b) Repeat (a) using communications satellites orbiting at an altitude of 800 km.

Making Connections

13. MD Robotics, the manufacturers of the Canadarm and Canadarm2, are world leaders in robotics, but their work is not restricted to space applications. Visit the MD Robotics Web site and read about applications that are used exclusively on Earth. Choose one application that is a result of space research. Prepare a short oral presentation about this application to share with the class.

 www.science.nelson.com

14. (a) In what ways are weather satellites directly responsible for saving lives? Provide some examples.
    (b) What other types of satellites can help save lives?

15. Identify and research a satellite that is currently in the planning stage. Provide brief details about its design and mission objectives.

 www.science.nelson.com

16. Research the Apollo missions to the Moon. Prepare a short report to explain why the skills associated with manoeuvring, rendezvousing, and docking spacecraft were essential.

 www.science.nelson.com

17. List 10 occupations that are connected in some way with the space program. Provide the educational background or set of skills that you expect are required for each occupation.

 www.science.nelson.com

18. Launched in 2004, the *Rosetta* probe is destined to orbit and land on a comet at the conclusion of a 10-year journey (**Figure 24**). Describe some of the special challenges that would be unique to such a mission.

Figure 24

TASK: Mission to Mars

In this Unit Task, you will consider the logistics of a manned mission to Mars using what you have learned about the risks and benefits associated with living and working in space (**Figure 1**).

Figure 1 Astronauts will have to contend with a less than hospitable planet when they arrive at Mars.

Because of the relative motions of Earth and Mars, there are launch windows that open approximately every 26 months. Using conventional propulsion systems, the journey to Mars will take approximately six to eight months, but the return trip will have to wait for over a year before the planets are suitably aligned again. The entire mission will likely last approximately 2.5 years. While in transit, astronauts will be subjected to microgravity; during their stay on Mars, the gravitational field strength they will encounter is 3.7 N/kg.

The atmosphere of Mars is very different from that of Earth (**Table 1**). The thin Martian atmosphere is devoid of ozone, so ultraviolet radiation is much more intense than on Earth. In addition, Mars has virtually no magnetic field, so charged particles, mostly from the Sun, are not deflected around the planet or funnelled to the poles as they are on Earth. Of some comfort to the astronauts, Mars turns on its axis in just under 25 h. This means that the duration of day and night will seem like home, although little else will.

Your task is to choose one challenge associated with a manned mission to Mars and to recommend solutions to this challenge. Three suggestions are provided, but you may choose any challenge that interests you. Consult your teacher before making your final choice.

Suggestions

- What are the physiological and psychological risks associated with flights to and from Mars? How could they be minimized? Consider what knowledge has been gained through space science.
- How will the challenge of surviving the Martian environment be met? Consider power, shelter, air, water, and food, and how you could acquire these basic needs. Could satellite technology help?
- What design features would be appropriate for space suits, shelter, and transportation on the

Table 1 Comparison of Atmospheres

Parameter	Earth	Mars
average temperature	14°C	−63°C
average atmospheric pressure	101.3 kPa	0.6 kPa (0.6% of Earth's)
atmospheric composition	78% nitrogen 21% oxygen 1% carbon dioxide, argon, and other gases	95.3% carbon dioxide 2.7% nitrogen 1.6% argon 0.1% oxygen

Martian surface? Consider the properties of the materials required and how they might function in the Martian environment.

 www.science.nelson.com

Analysis

(a) Identify the specific environmental conditions that result in the problems your challenge presents.

(b) Are there existing solutions to these problems? If so, how can these solutions be implemented? If not, what technologies may provide solutions?

Evaluation

(c) How confident are you that the challenge you chose can be successfully overcome? Provide reasons for your answer.

(d) Did anyone else consider this challenge? If so, what were the solutions?

(e) When the solutions are considered against the inherent risks, would you be willing to accept the uncertainty and become a member of the mission? Provide reasons for your answer.

SUMMARY

Throughout this unit, you have had opportunities to

- study the environmental conditions of space, especially microgravity
- learn why microgravity poses serious health risks and how these health risks can be overcome
- learn how microgravity offers conditions that are suitable for a number of manufacturing processes and scientific investigations
- discover how space research has had benefits for us on Earth and for those who choose to live on

orbiting space platforms and who may choose to live on other worlds in the future
- identify applications and spinoffs of satellite technology

Copy the following graphic organizer into your notebook, and use it to help you summarize your understanding of the key concepts in each of the four major topics. Add the key concepts related to the topic that you chose for your Unit Task.

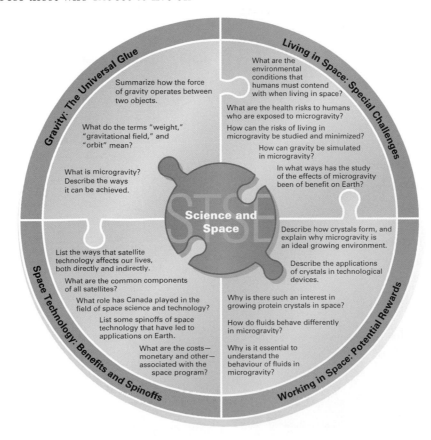

Unit E Review

Understanding Concepts

1. Explain how microgravity can be achieved in a normal gravity environment and how normal gravity can be achieved in a microgravity environment.

2. An object's weight on Earth, in newtons, is calculated by multiplying its mass, m, measured in kilograms, by the gravitational field strength, $g = 9.8$ N/kg. The gravitational field strength on the surface of the Moon is 1.6 N/kg.
   (a) Calculate the weight of a fully equipped astronaut with a mass of 100 kg on the lunar surface.
   (b) Calculate the astronaut's weight if both the mass and the diameter of the Moon were three times greater.
   (c) If you dropped an object from just above the Moon's surface, at what rate would it accelerate to the surface?

3. Consider the sensation you have when riding in an elevator.
   (a) Describe how heavy you seem (compared with your normal weight) when the elevator is stationary, accelerating upward, accelerating downward, moving upward at a constant speed, and moving downward at a constant speed.
   (b) How would the elevator have to be moving for you to feel weightless?

4. Describe how living things on Earth are naturally protected from a variety of dangers that would be encountered on the Moon, where there is no atmosphere and no magnetic field.

5. Astronauts often simulate space missions under water before leaving Earth (**Figure 1**). In these simulations, they are outfitted in space suits and work on submerged models of satellites. What purpose does this type of training serve?

Figure 1

6. An untethered astronaut is stranded some distance from her spaceship; she has a non-operational but detachable jetpack. Describe how she could return safely to the spaceship. Discuss the principle(s) that you applied in your answer.

7. (a) List some of the challenges related to operating a fluid system in a microgravity environment.
   (b) Describe how a fluid system might operate by taking advantage of microgravity.

8. (a) What precautions should you take to ensure the growth of high-quality crystals?
   (b) How does microgravity aid crystal growth?

9. List six medical benefits related to space science.

10. List six household products that have their roots in the space program.

11. If you were designing a satellite to survey the entire surface of Mars, what type of orbit around Mars would be most suitable? Provide a reason for your answer.

12. If you were designing a satellite to relay information from a lunar base back to Earth, what type of orbit around the Moon would you choose? Provide a reason for your answer.

Applying Inquiry Skills

13. **Table 1** lists the gravitational field strength at the surface of five hypothetical planets, using Earth as a reference. Identify any entries in the last column that appear to be incorrect, and correct them.

Table 1

Planet	Radius	Mass	Gravitational field strength
Earth	1.0	1.0	1.0
A	2.0	2.0	0.5
B	2.0	4.0	2.0
C	0.5	2.0	4.0
D	0.5	0.5	2.0
E	4.0	2.0	1.0

Making Connections

14. The images in **Figure 2**, taken by RADARSAT-1, document the Ohio River flood in 1997. The false-coloured image was created by merging the three black and white images. By assigning a colour to each subscene and then merging all three, the impact of the flooding on the surrounding land cover and the progression of the flood are clearly identified.
    (a) Explain how images like this might lead to improved flood predictions.
    (b) What other benefits do images such as these have for society?

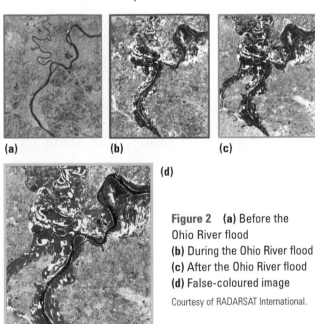

(a)   (b)   (c)

(d)

Figure 2   (a) Before the Ohio River flood
(b) During the Ohio River flood
(c) After the Ohio River flood
(d) False-coloured image

Courtesy of RADARSAT International.

15. Imagine you are an engineer designing items for use in space. Describe the features required by the materials you would use to design
    (a) spaceship hulls
    (b) space suits
    (c) space helmets

16. A number of scientists are investigating the design of a "space elevator" as an alternative method of placing satellites in orbit and launching other spacecraft (**Figure 3**). Research the space elevator, and comment on its feasibility.

 www.science.nelson.com

17. The vast majority of Canadian satellites are used for communications. In fact, Canada has no weather satellites of its own. Suggest a reason why we have so many communications satellites.

18. In March 2004, the robotic rovers *Spirit* and *Opportunity* discovered conclusive evidence that Mars was once a very wet planet.
    (a) With this evidence firmly established, what other questions could be investigated on follow-up missions?
    (b) How does this evidence lend itself to manned missions to Mars?

19. What do you think are the most compelling arguments for and against continued research to establish a permanent human presence in space. Provide reasons for your choices.

20. GPS technology has recently been incorporated into automobiles. Suggest other applications where this technology would prove to be useful.

21. Tele-medicine, a relatively new application of satellite technology, allows a surgeon to use a robot to operate on a person in one location while manipulating the robot from another location entirely. Suggest the advantages inherent in this technology, and provide some scenarios where this might be useful.

Extension

22. Some of the medical problems associated with living in microgravity may be solved using biofeedback techniques, which would allow astronauts to control, to some extent, some of their bodies' autonomic functions. For example, through concentration, it is possible to influence heart rate and blood pressure. Research biofeedback techniques, and prepare a short summary of their perceived advantages over conventional treatments for combating the effects of microgravity.

 www.science.nelson.com

Figure 3

Appendices

CONTENTS

A1 Decision Making

Modern life is filled with environmental and social issues that have scientific and technological dimensions. An issue is defined as a problem that has at least two possible solutions rather than a single answer. There can be many positions, generally determined by the values that an individual or a society holds, on a single issue. Which solution is "best" is a matter of opinion; ideally, the solution that is put into practice is the one that is most appropriate for society as a whole.

The common elements of the decision-making process are outlined in the graphic below.

Even though the sequence is presented as linear, you may go through several cycles before deciding you are ready to defend a decision.

Process Description

The first step in understanding an issue is to explain why it is an issue, describe the problems associated with the issue, and identify the individuals or groups, called stakeholders, involved in the issue. You could brainstorm the following questions to research the issue: Who? What? Where? When? Why? How? Develop background information on the issue by clarifying facts and concepts, and identifying relevant attributes, features, or characteristics of the problem.

Examine the issue and think of as many alternative solutions as you can. At this point, it does not matter if the solutions seem unrealistic. To analyze the alternatives, you should examine the issue from a variety of perspectives. Stakeholders may bring different viewpoints to an issue and these may influence their position on the issue. Brainstorm or hypothesize how various stakeholders would feel about your alternatives.

Formulate a research question that helps to limit, narrow, or define the issue. Then develop a plan to find reliable and relevant sources of information. Outline the stages of your information search: gathering, sorting, evaluating, selecting, and integrating relevant information. You may consider using a flow chart, concept map, or other graphic organizer to outline the stages of your information search. Gather information from many sources, including newspapers, magazines, scientific journals, the Internet, and the library.

> **Defining the issue** → **Identifying alternatives/positions** → **Researching the issue**

Example: Genetically Modified Foods

Genetically modified foods (GMFs) are foods that have been altered by the insertion of genes from a different species. Crops can be genetically modified to grow quickly, to be resistant to diseases and pests, or to be efficient at absorbing nutrients from the soil.

There is growing public debate about GMFs. Have they been tested enough to assure us that there will be no long-term effects from eating these foods? What will be the impact of genetically engineered species on natural species?

The issue is the overall safety of foods produced from genetically engineered organisms. In this debate, there are two positions: you either support genetic engineering in agriculture or you do not support it. **Table 1**, on page 366, lists the potential groups or stakeholders who may be positively or negatively affected by the issue. Develop your knowledge of the background information on the issue by clarifying facts and identifying features.

One possible solution for people concerned about GMFs is to ban their production. Since farmers who grow GMFs would lose income, it might be necessary to offer subsidies to these farmers.

Think about how various stakeholders might feel about the alternatives. What would be the perspective of a consumer? a local politician? a farmer? a geneticist? an economist? a nutritionist? **Table 2**, on page 366, lists the possible perspectives on an issue.

Remember that one person could have more than one perspective, or two people looking at an issue from the same perspective might disagree. For example, geneticists might disagree about the impact of genetically engineered species on natural species.

A possible research question: What are the advantages and disadvantages of genetically modified foods?

There are five steps that must be completed to effectively analyze the issue:

1. Establish criteria for determining the relevance and significance of the data you have gathered.

2. Evaluate the sources of information.

3. Identify and determine what assumptions have been made. Challenge unsupported evidence.

4. Determine any relationships associated with the issue.

5. Evaluate the alternative solutions, possibly by conducting a cost–benefit analysis.

After analyzing your information, you can answer your research question and take an informed position on the issue. You should be able to defend your solution in an appropriate format—debate, class discussion, speech, position paper, multimedia presentation (such as a computer slide show), brochure, poster, or video.

Your position on the issue must be justified using supporting information that you have researched. You should be able to defend your position to people with different perspectives. Ask yourself the following questions:

- Do I have supporting evidence from a variety of sources?
- Can I state my position clearly?
- Can I show why this issue is relevant and important to society?
- Do I have solid arguments (with solid evidence) supporting my position?
- Have I considered arguments against my position, and identified their faults?
- Have I analyzed the strong and weak points of each perspective?

The final phase of decision making includes evaluating the decision itself and the process used to reach the decision. After you have made a decision, carefully examine the thinking that led to your decision.

Some questions to guide your evaluation:

- What was my initial perspective on the issue? How has my perspective changed since I first began to explore the issue?
- How did we make our decision? What process did we use? What steps did we follow?
- In what ways does our decision resolve the issue?
- What are the likely short- and long-term effects of the decision?
- To what extent am I satisfied with the final decision?
- What reasons would I give to explain our decision?
- If we had to make this decision again, what would I do differently?

Analyzing the issue

Defending the decision

Evaluating the process

The relationships related to the issue include the following: GMF has arisen from the need to produce more and better food for the world's population. A consequence may be that consumers will refuse to buy GM products, thereby increasing the demand for traditionally produced food and increasing prices accordingly. Another consequence is that public funds are being spent to support research in genetically modified food crops.

Table 3, on page 367, shows a cost–benefit analysis of producing GMFs.

By reviewing the research and performing a cost–benefit analysis on the information, we conclude that the benefits of using GMFs are greater than the risks. The production of GMFs will solve an immediate problem of world hunger by producing more food faster, by producing food with a higher nutritional content, and by reducing the need for chemical use in food production. The use of GMFs provides an immediate solution to world hunger, which we consider to be a major benefit for their production. There are, however, calculated risks involved in full-scale GMF production. We may produce new organisms whose long-term effects on an ecosystem cannot be known ahead of time. However, our evidence indicates that the probability of serious damage is minimal when compared with the overall benefits that GMFs will bring to society.

This issue came to my attention through the many newspaper articles I had read that warned of a growing danger to people and the environment with the production and sale of GMFs. After researching the issue, I found that the vast majority of recent scientific reports conclude that, while there are some long-term unknowns, the production and consumption of GMFs are as safe as those of non-GMFs. In fact, some studies indicate that the production of some organically grown foods could be even more dangerous. While every effort was made to obtain the most current, scientific information on GMFs and their effects on humans, other species, and the environment, the number and quality of studies focusing on the long-term environmental impact of GMFs is relatively low. These studies need to be carried out. By examining such research, we may be able to make better-informed decisions regarding the use of these foods.

Table 1 Stakeholders in the Genetically Modified Food Debate

Stakeholders	Viewpoint
scientists	GMFs may end world hunger.
farmers	GM crops require less pesticides and herbicides.
doctors	GMFs can be created to solve health problems. For example, children whose major diet staple is rice often have a vitamin A deficiency. Rice can be genetically engineered to produce vitamin A.
environmentalists	Genes from GM crops may spread to create superweeds and superbugs.
politicians	GMFs can end world hunger.
health critics	Genetic alterations may produce substances that are poisonous or that trigger allergies and disease.

Table 2 Perspectives on an Issue

Perspective	Focus of the perspective
cultural	customs and practices of a particular group
ecological	interactions among organisms and their natural habitat
economic	the production, distribution, and consumption of wealth
educational	the effects on learning
emotional	feelings and emotions
environmental	the effects on physical surroundings
esthetic	artistic, tasteful, beautiful
ethical/moral	what is good/bad, right/wrong
legal	the rights and responsibilities of individuals and groups
political	the effects on the aims of a political group or party
scientific	logical or research information based
social	the effects on human relationships, the community, or society
spiritual	the effects on personal beliefs
technological	machines and industrial processes

A Cost–Benefit Analysis Model

Cost–benefit analysis is a tool used to organize and analyze information gathered in research. A thorough analysis of the costs and benefits associated with each alternative solution can help you decide on the best alternative.

- Research as many aspects of the proposal as possible. Look at it from different perspectives.
- Collect as much evidence as you can, including reasonable projections of likely outcomes if the proposal is adopted.
- Classify each potential result as being either a benefit or a cost.
- Quantify the size of the potential benefit or cost (perhaps as a dollar figure, as a number of lives affected, or on a scale of 1 to 5).
- Estimate the probability (percentage) of that event occurring.

- By multiplying the size of a benefit (or cost) by the probability of its happening, you can calculate a probability value for each potential result.
- Total the probability values of all the potential costs and all the potential benefits.
- Compare the sums to help you decide whether to accept the proposed action.

Table 3 shows a cost–benefit analysis of the issue. Note that there could be other possible results. Although you should try to be objective in your assessment, the beliefs of the person making the cost–benefit analysis will have an effect on the final sums. The possible outcomes considered for analysis, the assessment of the relative importance of a cost or benefit, and the probability of the cost or benefit actually arising will vary according to who does the analysis. For example, would you agree completely with the values placed in the "Costs" and "Benefits" columns of the analysis in **Table 3**?

Table 3 Cost–Benefit Analysis of Producing Foods from Genetically Modified Organisms

| Possible result | Costs | | | Possible result | Benefits | | |
	Cost of result (scale of 1 to 5)	Probability of result occurring (%)	Cost × probability		Benefit of result (scale of 1 to 5)	Probability of result occurring (%)	Benefit × probability
GMFs increase human health risks.	very serious 5	research is inconclusive (50%)	250	Food supplies increase and food becomes cheaper.	great 5	very likely (90%)	450
GM crops are more competitive and eliminate natural species.	serious 4	likely (80%)	320	GMFs have higher nutritional value than their natural counterparts.	great 5	likely (75%)	375
GM species negatively affect other species in the food chain.	serious 4	somewhat likely (60%)	240	GM crops require less chemical fertilizers.	high 4	somewhat likely (60%)	240
Total cost value			**810**	**Total benefit value**			**1065**

A2 Scientific Inquiry

Planning an Investigation

In our attempts to further our understanding of the natural world, we encounter questions, mysteries, or events that are not easily explained. We can use controlled experiments or observational studies to help us look for answers or explanations. The methods used in scientific inquiry depend, to a large degree, on the purpose of the inquiry.

Controlled Experiments

Controlled experiments are performed when the purpose of the inquiry is to create or test a scientific concept. In a controlled experiment, an independent variable is purposefully and steadily changed to determine its effect on a second, dependent variable. All other variables are controlled or kept constant.

The common components for controlled experiments are outlined in the flow chart below. *Even though the sequence is presented as linear, there are normally many cycles through the steps during an actual experiment.*

Process Description

Choose a topic that interests you. Determine whether you are going to carry out a given procedure or develop a new experimental design. Indicate your decision in a statement of the purpose.

Your Question forms the basis for your investigation. Controlled experiments are about relationships, so the Question could be about the effects on variable A when variable B is changed. The Question could be about what causes the change in variable A. In this case, you might speculate about possible variables and determine which variable causes the change.

A hypothesis is a tentative explanation. You must be able to test your hypothesis, which can range in certainty from an educated guess to a concept that is widely accepted in the scientific community. A prediction is based on a hypothesis or a more established scientific explanation, such as a theory. In the prediction, you state what outcome you expect from your experiment.

The design of a controlled experiment identifies how you plan to manipulate the independent variable, measure the response of the dependent variable, and control all the other variables.

Stating the purpose → **Asking the question** → **Hypothesizing/ predicting** → **Designing the investigation**

Example: Diffusion and Osmosis

The purpose of this investigation is to examine the conditions under which water moves into and out of cells.

Under what conditions does water move into and out of cells?

If a model cell is placed in a hypotonic solution (having lower concentrations of solute than the cell), water will move into the cell. If a cell is placed in a hypertonic solution (having higher concentrations of solute than the cell), water will move out of the cell.

Three model cells are constructed from dialysis tubing. Two are filled with distilled water and one with a starch suspension. One of the cells with distilled water is placed in a beaker of starch suspension. The other two cells are placed in beakers of distilled water. Iodine is added to the distilled water in the beakers. (Iodine is used as an indicator to detect the presence of starch.) The mass of each cell is recorded and other observations are made at the beginning and after 10 min and 20 min.

Table 1 Observations of Model Cells

Model cell	Initial mass (g)	Mass after 10 min (g)	Mass after 20 min (g)	Other observations
cell A—dialysis tube with distilled water in beaker of distilled water				
cell B—dialysis tube with starch suspension in beaker of distilled water				
cell C—dialysis tube with distilled water in beaker of starch suspension				

There are many ways to gather and record observations during an investigation. It is helpful to plan ahead and think about what data you will need and how best to record them. This helps to clarify your thinking about the Question posed at the beginning, the variables, the number of trials, the procedure, and your skills. It will also help you organize your evidence for easier analysis later.

After thoroughly analyzing your observations, you may have sufficient and appropriate evidence to answer the Question posed at the beginning of the investigation.

At this stage of the investigation, you will evaluate the processes that you followed to plan and perform the investigation. Evaluating the processes includes reviewing the design and the procedure. You will also evaluate the outcome of the investigation, which involves assessing the evidence—whether it supports the hypothesis or not—and the hypothesis itself.

In preparing your report, your aim should be to describe your design and procedure accurately, and to report your observations accurately and honestly.

> **Gathering, recording, and organizing observations** → **Analyzing the observations** → **Evaluating the evidence and the hypothesis** → **Reporting on the investigation**

The measurements and observations will be recorded in a table like **Table 1**.

The results will be analyzed to determine if there were any changes in mass and if there were any other observable changes. Changes in mass and/or colour should enable us to determine what is happening with the cells.

To evaluate this investigation, we have to ask ourselves several questions. Is our model cell an appropriate model? Do the results allow us to determine how water moves into and out of cells? Does the evidence gathered support our hypothesis? Are there possible sources of error that may invalidate the evidence?

For the format of a typical lab report, see **Appendix A7**.

Observational Studies

Often the purpose of inquiry is simply to study a natural phenomenon with the intention of gaining scientifically significant information to answer a question. Observational studies involve observing a subject or phenomenon in an unobtrusive or unstructured manner, often with no specific hypothesis. A hypothesis to describe or explain the observations may, however, be generated after repeated observations, and modified as new information is collected over time.

The flow chart below summarizes the stages and processes of scientific inquiry through observational studies. *Even though the sequence is presented as linear, there are normally many cycles through the steps during an actual study.*

Process Description

| Choose a topic that interests you. Determine whether you are going to replicate or revise a previous study, or create a new one. Indicate your decision in a statement of the purpose. | In planning an observational study, it is important to pose a general question about the natural world. You may or may not follow the Question with the creation of a hypothesis. | A hypothesis is a tentative explanation. In an observational study, a hypothesis can be formed after observations have been made and information gathered on a topic. A hypothesis may be created in the analysis. | The design of an observational study describes how you will make observations relevant to the Question. |

Stating the purpose → **Asking the question** → **Hypothesizing/ predicting** → **Designing the investigation**

Example: Local Vegetation

| The purpose of our investigation is to conduct an inventory of the plants in our local area to determine the most common trees and to determine if the vegetation in our local area is typical of that found in the boreal forest biome. | What are the most common species of trees in our local region? Is the vegetation in our region representative of the vegetation in the boreal forest biome? | There is considerable variation in the vegetation found throughout any biome. However, one would expect that certain species would be more common than others and would be found throughout the biome. Since we are geographically located in what is defined as the boreal forest biome, we would expect that the most common trees in this area would be those that define the vegetation of the boreal forest (i.e., spruce, fir, and pine). | We will conduct an inventory of trees in 10 sample areas of our local region. Each sample area will be 10 000 m^2 (100 m $\times$ 100 m). All species of trees will be identified (using the common and scientific names) and counted in each sample area. The sample areas will be selected by placing a scaled grid over a map of the region and then randomly selecting 10 cells of the grid. |

Table 2 Inventory of Trees in Sample Areas of Local Region

Tree species (common and scientific name)	Sample area										Total
	1	2	3	4	5	6	7	8	9	10	

There are many ways to gather and record observations during an investigation. During your observational study, you should quantify your observations where possible. All observations should be objective and unambiguous. Consider ways to organize your information for easier analysis.

After thoroughly analyzing your observations, you may have sufficient and appropriate evidence to answer the Question posed at the beginning of the investigation. You may also have enough observations and information to form a hypothesis.

At this stage of the investigation, you will evaluate the processes used to plan and perform the investigation. Evaluating the processes includes evaluating the materials, the design, the procedure, and your skills. The results of most such investigations will suggest further studies, perhaps correlational studies or controlled experiments to explore tentative hypotheses you may have developed.

In preparing your report, your aim should be to describe your design and procedure accurately, and to report your observations accurately and honestly.

Gathering, recording, and organizing observations

Analyzing the observations

Evaluating the evidence and the hypothesis

Reporting on the investigation

The data will be recorded in a table like **Table 2**.

The data from the table will be plotted on a bar graph to show the frequency distribution of the various species. This will make it easier to identify the most common species.

In the evaluation of this investigation, we must first decide whether our sample areas collectively represent the forested areas of our local region. We can then compare the frequencies of the different species in the local area with the frequencies of those species in the typical boreal forest. The results of this investigation might lead us to speculate about the reasons (such as climate, topography, and soil) for any differences in vegetation between our local area and the typical boreal forest.

For the format of a typical lab report, see **Appendix A7**.

Correlational Studies

When the purpose of scientific inquiry is to test a suspected relationship (hypothesis) between two different variables, but a controlled experiment is not possible, a correlational inquiry is conducted. In a correlational study, the investigator tries to determine whether one variable is affecting another without purposefully changing or controlling any of the variables. Instead, variables are allowed to change naturally. It is often difficult to isolate cause and effect in correlational studies. A correlational inquiry requires very large sample numbers and many replications to increase the certainty of the results.

The flow chart below outlines the steps that are important in designing a correlational study. The investigator can conduct the study without doing experiments or fieldwork, for example, by using

Process Description

Choose a topic that interests you. Determine whether you are going to replicate or revise a previous study, or create a new one. Indicate your decision in a statement of the purpose.

In planning a correlational study, it is important to pose a question about a possible statistical relationship between variable A and variable B.

A hypothesis is a tentative explanation. In a correlational study, a hypothesis can range in certainty from an educated guess to a concept that is widely accepted in the scientific community.

The design of a correlational study identifies how you will gather data on the variables under study and also identifies the potential source. There are two possible sources—observations made by the investigator and existing data.

```
( Stating the     ) → ( Asking the     ) → ( Hypothesizing/ ) → ( Designing the   )
(   purpose        )   (   question      )   (  predicting     )   ( investigation  )
```

Example: Colourblindness in Males and Females

The purpose of this investigation is to determine if there is a statistical relationship between the sex of an individual and colourblindness.

Is there a greater percentage of males than females who are colourblind?

Red–green colour blindness is a sex-linked recessive disorder. In a large sample, the incidence of colourblindness among males will be significantly higher than the incidence among females.

An equal number (200 each) of males and females in the school will be surveyed for colourblindness. The data will be recorded in a table and the percentage of colourblind individuals will be calculated. The actual, or observed, percentage will be compared to the percentage we would expect if there were no relationship between the two variables.

databases prepared by other researchers to find relationships between two or more variables. The investigator can also make his or her own observations and measurements through fieldwork, interviews, and surveys.

Even though the sequence is presented as linear, there are normally many cycles through the steps during the actual study.

Table 3 Individual Colourblind Test Results

Participant #	Colour plate #	Identified correctly (Y/N)
1	1	
	2	
	3	
	4	
2	1	
	2	
	3	
	4	

There are many ways to gather and record observations during your investigation. It is helpful to plan ahead and think about what data you will need and how best to record them. This is an important step because it helps to clarify your thinking about the question posed at the beginning, the variables, the number of trials, the procedure, and so on. It will also help you organize your information for easier analysis later.

After thoroughly analyzing your observations, you may have sufficient and appropriate evidence to enable you to answer the question posed at the beginning of the investigation.

At this stage of the investigation, you will evaluate the processes that you followed to plan and perform the investigation. Evaluating the processes includes reviewing the design and the procedure. You will also evaluate the outcome of the investigation, which involves assessing the evidence—whether it supports the hypothesis or not—and the hypothesis itself. The results of your investigation may be used to create new related studies.

In preparing your report, your objectives should be to describe your design and procedure accurately, and to report your observations accurately and honestly.

Gathering, recording, and organizing observations → **Analyzing the observations** → **Evaluating the evidence and the hypothesis** → **Reporting on the investigation**

Individual and group results will be recorded in tables like **Tables 3** and **4**.

Once we have totalled the number of individuals who are colourblind, we will calculate a percentage for each sex. If there was no relationship between the sex of the individual and the incidence of colourblindness, we would expect an equal percentage of males and females to be colourblind.

Was the sample size adequate? If the survey was completed on 10 other samples of this size, what is the likelihood that the results would be different? Do the survey results indicate that the incidence of colourblindness is significantly higher among males than females or can any difference be attributed to random variation in the sample?

For the format of a typical lab report, see **Appendix A7**.

Table 4 Percentage of Colourblind and Normal by Sex

	Colourblind	Normal
Male		
Female		

A3 Technological Problem Solving

There is a difference between science and technology. The goal of science is to understand the natural world. The goal of technological problem solving is to develop or revise a product or a process in response to a human need. The product or process must fulfill its function but, in contrast with scientific problem solving, it is not essential to understand why or how it works. Technological solutions are evaluated based on such criteria as simplicity, reliability, efficiency, cost, and ecological and political ramifications.

Even though the sequence presented in the graphic below is linear, there are normally many cycles through the steps in any problem-solving attempt.

Process Description

This process involves recognizing and identifying the need for a technological solution. You need to state clearly the question(s) that you want to investigate to solve the problem and the criteria you will use as guidelines and to evaluate your solution. In any design, some criteria may be more important than others. For example, if a tool measures accurately and is economical, but is not safe, then it is clearly unacceptable.

Use your prior knowledge, experience, and creativity to propose possible solutions.

During brainstorming, the goal is to generate many ideas without judging them. They can be evaluated and accepted or rejected later.

To visualize the possible solutions, it is helpful to draw sketches. Sketches are often better than verbal descriptions in communicating an idea.

Planning is the heart of the entire process. Your plan will outline your processes, identify potential sources of information and materials, define your resource parameters, and establish evaluation criteria.

Seven types of resources are generally used in developing technological solutions to problems—people, information, materials, tools, energy, capital, and time.

Defining the problem ➤ Identifying possible solutions ➤ Planning

Example: Optical Instruments

For example: What is the location of the site to be observed (i.e., is it on land or under water)? How big (long) must the instrument be? What are the limits on the cost of construction materials? Will we need a light source? How much money do we have available?

In this case, you are asked to design and construct an optical instrument to meet the following criteria:

- a total reach of 1 m
- able to reach around two 45° turns and a 90° turn (as illustrated in **Figure 1**)
- incorporates a light source at the far viewing end
- moveable mirrors and/or lenses
- costs $50 or less
- reusable
- no negative impact on the viewing area

In any design, some criteria may be more important than others. For example, if a design is the right size, allows adequate observation, and can be reused easily but is likely to damage the observation area, then it is clearly unacceptable.

See sketches of two possible designs in **Figure 2**.

Design 1 shows a series of short sections joined together by pin hinges. The sections can be manoeuvred by strings running through the loops at the top of each section.

Design 2 shows a flexible bar, similar to a vertical blind bar, with suspended mirrors that can be moved along the bar. The angle of the mirrors can be controlled by strings that are run through loops on the bar.

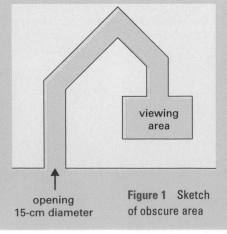

viewing area

opening
15-cm diameter

Figure 1 Sketch of obscure area

People: The human resources required to solve this problem include you and your partner.
Information: You are already very familiar with mirrors. You will need to fully understand the law of reflection and be able to calculate angles of incidence and reflection.
Materials: As well as the limitations imposed by your proposed solution, cost, availability, and time, you are restricted to materials that can be obtained in school or at home. Materials to consider include mirrors, lenses, glue, wire, light bulb, wood or other casing material, and so on.
Tools: Your proposed design could require the use of common hand tools such as a saw, pliers, shears, and glue guns, but your design should not require any specialized tools or machines.
Energy: The only energy requirement for this problem is a source of electrical energy for the light.
Capital: The capital resources must be minimal, otherwise it may be more efficient to purchase a commercial model. Limit your design to a cost of $50 or less.
Time: You should be able to construct your optical instrument within 60 min (not including designing and testing).

The solution will be evaluated on how well it meets the design criteria established earlier.

In this phase, you will construct and test your prototype using trial and error. Try to change only one variable at a time. Use failures to inform the decisions you make before your next trial. You may also complete a cost–benefit analysis on the prototype.

To help you decide on the best solution, you can rate each potential solution on each of the design criteria using a five-point rating scale, with 1 being poor, 2 fair, 3 good, 4 very good, and 5 excellent. You can then compare your proposed solutions by totalling the scores.

Once you have made the choice among the possible solutions, you need to produce and test a prototype. While making the prototype, you may need to experiment with the characteristics of different components. A model, on a smaller scale, might help you decide whether the product will be functional. The test of your prototype should answer three basic questions:

- Does the prototype solve the problem?
- Does it satisfy the design criteria?
- Are there any unanticipated problems with the design?

If these questions cannot be answered satisfactorily, you may have to modify the design or select another potential solution.

Table 1 Design Analysis

Criterion	Design 1	Design 2
reach	4	3
navigate turns	4	3
light source	4	4
movable mirrors/ lenses	4	3
cost	5	4
reusability	5	3
impact on viewing area	1	4
Total score	**27**	**24**

In presenting your solution, you will communicate your solution, identify potential applications, and put your solution to use.

Once the prototype has been produced and tested, the best presentation of the solution is a demonstration of its use—a test under actual conditions. This demonstration can also serve as a further test of the design. Any feedback should be considered for future redesign. Remember that no solution should be considered the absolute final solution.

Evaluation is not restricted to the final step. However, it is important to evaluate the final product using the criteria established earlier, and to evaluate the processes used while arriving at the solution. Consider the following questions:

- To what degree does the final product meet the design criteria?
- Did you have to make any compromises in the design? If so, are there ways to minimize the effects of the compromises?
- Did you exceed any of the resource parameters?
- Are there other possible solutions that deserve future consideration?
- How did your group work as a team?

Constructing/ testing solutions

Presenting the preferred solution

Evaluating the solution and process

Table 1 illustrates the ratings for two different telescope designs. Note that although Design 1 came out with the highest rating, one factor (impact on viewing area) suggests we should go with Design 2. This is what is referred to as a trade-off. We have to compromise on other criteria such as reusability in order to ensure that the instrument does not damage or interfere with the viewing area. By reviewing or evaluating product and processes to this point, we may be able to modify Design 2 to optimize its performance on the other criteria.

The optical device was presented to the class through a demonstration and a video.

The class was given an opportunity to provide feedback by filling out a survey questionnaire. The designers conducted a self and peer evaluation of the design and construction processes and produced a report.

(a) Design 1

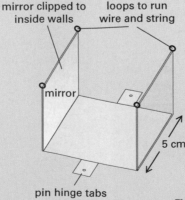

mirror clipped to inside walls
loops to run wire and string
mirror
5 cm
pin hinge tabs

(b) Design 2

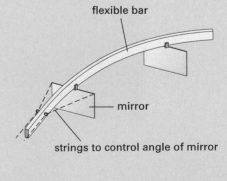

flexible bar
mirror
strings to control angle of mirror

Figure 2

A4 Scientific Investigation Skills

The Stethoscope and Sphygmomanometer

Medical personnel often have to rely on external observations in an attempt to determine what is going on inside the human body. These observations are noninvasive procedures and are very important in helping medical personnel decide what further tests are required to diagnose health problems. Two of the most common instruments used to make these observations are the stethoscope (**Figure 1**) and the sphygmomanometer (**Figure 2**).

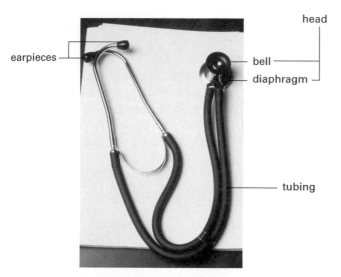

Figure 1 The stethoscope

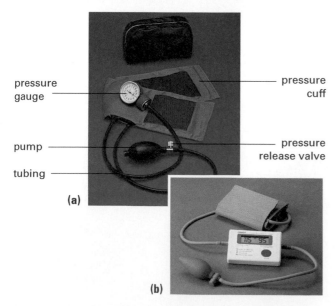

Figure 2 Two of the many types of sphygmomanometer: **(a)** analog display and **(b)** digital display

Using the Stethoscope

The stethoscope is used to listen to sounds inside the body. These sounds are generated by the heart, lungs, and intestinal tract. The stethoscope is also used along with the sphygmomanometer to measure blood pressure. Not all stethoscopes have a bell, but most stethoscopes have a bell and a diaphragm—the bell is used to listen to low-pitched sounds and the diaphragm for high-pitched sounds.

Heart

Listen to the heart sounds by placing the earpieces in your ears, and the diaphragm or bell of the stethoscope on the chest in the general area of the heart. The heart is located on the left side around the 4th to the 6th rib almost directly under the breast. The normal heart sounds are the regular *lubb-dubb* that represents one beat of the heart. The sounds are produced by the closing of the valves. The *lubb* sound is caused when the atrioventricular valves shut. The *dubb* sound is caused by the closing of the semilunar valves.

Certain conditions will produce other heart sounds as well. A quiet *whoosh* after the *lubb-dubb* sound is known as a murmur. This may be caused by incomplete opening or closing of the valves.

Respiratory System

Place the stethoscope on your chest and breathe in and out deeply and slowly. Different sounds can be heard in different locations. The stethoscope may also be placed on the back to listen to the lungs. For normal lungs, you should hear only the rush of air into and out of the lungs. Abnormal lung sounds include crackles and wheezes. If the lung rubs on the chest wall, there may be friction rubs. Crackles sound like a sheet of paper being crushed. They indicate that there is fluid in the lungs. Wheezes are high-pitched whistling noises. Friction rubs are squeaky sounds that you might expect when two objects are rubbed together.

Abdomen

The stethoscope can be used to listen to sounds produced by the digestive system. Place the stethoscope over the upper abdomen to hear the normal gurgling sounds of the stomach and over the lower abdomen to listen to the intestines. Gurgling sounds are normal. A doctor would determine if the digestive system is overactive or underactive.

Using the Sphygmomanometer

The sphygmomanometer is an instrument that gives an indirect measurement of blood pressure. It consists of a gauge (manometer) to register pressure, an inflatable compression bag with a strong cloth cover (cuff), an inflating device (inflation bulb or pump), and a means of deflating (pressure release valve).

Use the sphygmomanometer, the stethoscope, and the procedure outlined below to measure blood pressure:

1. The subject should be relaxed and comfortably seated with the arm extended straight at heart level.

2. Place the centre of the pressure cuff over the brachial artery in the upper arm just above the elbow (**Figure 3**). The cuff should be wrapped snugly around the arm but should not be too tight.

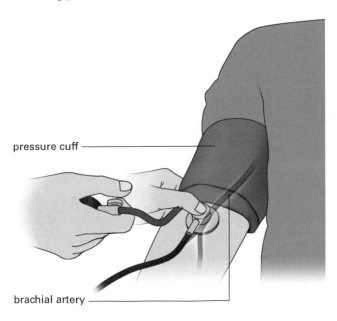

pressure cuff ————

brachial artery ————

Figure 3 Proper placement of the stethoscope and sphygmomanometer

3. Place the head of the stethoscope over the brachial artery just below the elbow (**Figure 4**). Ensure that it does not touch the pressure cuff, as this will produce noise that might interfere with your listening.

4. Close the pressure release valve and use the pump to inflate the pressure cuff to 180 mm Hg.

 Do not inflate the pressure cuff beyond 180 mm Hg, and do not leave the pressure on for longer than one minute.

5. Carefully open the pressure release valve so that the pressure drops at 2 to 3 mm Hg per second.

6. As the pressure drops, listen for clear tapping sounds. The pressure at which you can hear clear sounds for two consecutive beats is the systolic pressure.

7. Continue slowly releasing the pressure. At some point the repetitive sounds will disappear. The pressure at this point is the diastolic pressure.

8. Once both pressures have been noted, quickly release the pressure by opening the pressure release valve completely.

9. Record both measurements to the nearest 2 mm Hg.

10. It is often recommended to verify the reading by taking a second reading a few minutes after the first.

 Do not try to interpret what you consider to be abnormal observations. Only qualified medical personnel should interpret observations to make diagnoses.

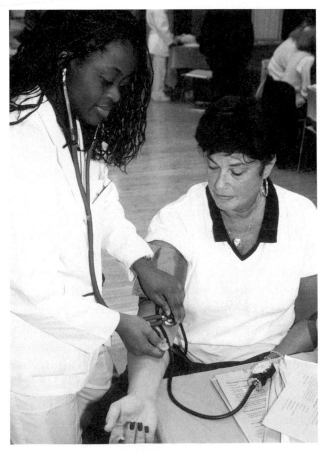

Figure 4 Using the stethoscope and sphygmomanometer to measure blood pressure

A5 Research Skills

General Research

There is an incredible amount of information available to us, from many different sources. We now have the ability to access more information than at any other time in history. Information is simply information, however. Before you can make effective use of it, you must know how to gather information efficiently and how to assess its credibility.

Collecting Information

- Before you begin your research, list the most important words associated with your research, so you can search for appropriate topics.
- Brainstorm a list of possible resources. Consider all the sources of information available to you. Rank the list, starting with the most useful resource.
- Search out and collect information from a variety of resources.
- Ask yourself, "Do I understand what this resource is telling me?"
- Check when the resource was published. Is it up to date?
- Consider the source of the information. From what perspective is it written? Is it likely to be biased?
- Keep organized notes or files while doing your research.
- Keep a complete list of the resources you used, so you can quickly find the source again if you need to, and so you can make a bibliography when writing your lab report.
- Review your notes. After your research, you may want to alter your original position or hypothesis, or research in a slightly different direction.

Assessing the Credibility of Information Sources

Understanding and evaluating the work of others is an important part of research. Think about how many messages, opinions, and pieces of information you hear and see every day. When you do research, you may access information from the Internet, textbooks, magazines, chat lines, television, radio, and through many other forms of communication. Is all of this information correct? Are all of these information sources reliable? How do we know what to believe and what not to believe? Often science, or the appearance of science, is used to convince us that claims are true. Sometimes this method of reporting is used to encourage us to buy something or just to catch our interest. Even serious stories on scientific work are sometimes difficult to interpret.

To analyze information, you have to use your mind effectively and critically. When you encounter a "scientific" report in the media, analyze the report carefully, and see if you can identify the following:

- the type of investigation that is being reported
- the dependent and independent variables in any reported investigation
- the strengths and weaknesses in the design of the investigation

PERCS

A useful framework for evaluating the credibility of information gathered from various sources is PERCS (**Table 1**). This framework, developed at Central Park East Secondary School in New York City, NY, uses a series of questions to critically assess information and arguments concerning an issue. These questions can help you evaluate the information you collect.

Table 1 The PERCS Checklist

Perspective	From whose viewpoint are we seeing or reading or hearing? From what angle or perspective?
Evidence	How do we know what we know? What's the evidence and how reliable is it?
Relevance	So what? What does it matter? What does it all mean? Who cares?
Connections	How are things, events, or people connected to one another? What is the cause and what is the effect? How do they "fit" together?
Supposition	What if…? Could things be otherwise? What are or were the alternatives? Suppose things were different.

Internet Research

The World Wide Web's accessibility and ease of use has led to an amazing increase in the amount of information available to us. However, as a research tool the Web lacks the quality assurance that editors provide with print publications. In other words, anybody can post just about anything on the Web without any proof of authenticity.

There is a huge variety of information on the Internet (facts, opinions, stories, interpretations, and statistics) created for many purposes (to inform, to persuade, to sell, to present a viewpoint, and to create or change an attitude or belief). For each of these various kinds and purposes, information exists on many levels of quality or reliability: from very good to very bad with every shade in between. Given this variability, it is crucial that you critically evaluate the material you find.

Search Strategy

Before you begin searching the Internet, you should think about the information you are searching for. What is your topic? What are the key concepts in your Question? What words would best describe your subject? Try to be as precise as possible. Are there other ways that you can express these key concepts? When you have answered these questions, you will have a list of search terms to start with. Be willing to add to and subtract from your list as you evaluate what you have found to see if it is relevant and useful. (Later we will explore how to evaluate sources.)

Table 2 shows three primary ways of searching the Internet for documents and Web pages.

Search Engines

Search engines are automated programs that create an index of Web pages in the Internet. When you use a search engine, you are not actually searching the Internet; you are searching through this index. The larger search engines currently index more than 100 million Web pages each, but no search engine indexes every single Web page. Most search engines look through, and index, all the words in the Web pages they find. When you type some words in a search engine, it searches through its index to find Web pages that contain as many of those words as it can. Search engines try to rank the pages so that the

Table 2 Ways of Searching the Internet

Search engine	Meta search engine	Subject gateway (or directory)	E-mail, discussion lists, databases
Searches using keywords that describe the subject you are looking for.	Enables you to search across many search engines at once.	Provides an organized list of Web pages, divided into subject areas. Some gateways are general and cover material on many subjects.	Puts you in touch with individuals who are interested in your research topic.
AltaVista Canada ca.altavista.com	MetaCrawler www.metacrawler.com	About www.about.com	
Lycos Canada www.lycos.ca	Search.com www.search.com	Looksmart www.looksmart.com	
Google www.google.ca	Ask Jeeves www.ask.com	Yahoo www.ca.yahoo.com	
Go.com infoseek.go.com	Dogpile www.dogpile.com	Librarians' Index to the Internet lii.org	
HotBot www.hotbot.com	Highway 61 www.highway61.com	Infomine infomine.ucr.edu	
Webcrawler www.webcrawler.com		WWW Virtual Library vlib.org/overview.html	

most relevant results are shown first. Most search engines provide online help or search tips. Always look at these to find tips for better searching.

Use a search engine to look for a specific Web site or Web page, information about a specific company or organization, or a specific subject. A very general subject search will probably produce too many results to be useful.

There are several reasons why you might not find what you are looking for. Although search engines update their indexes frequently, it can take several months for the engine to crawl the Web to find new Web pages. If the page you are looking for is new, it might not be indexed yet.

You will probably have a favourite search engine, but if you do not find what you are looking for, try using another. Many Web pages are indexed in only a couple of search engines. If you are not having much success, you could try using a meta search engine.

Meta Search Engines

Meta search engines allow you to search across several search engines at the same time. They take your search and run it in several search-engine indexes. They will only return the top few results (usually between six and ten) from each search engine.

Use a meta search engine to look for a specific Web site or Web page, information about a specific company or organization, or a specific subject. If you do not find what you are looking for, try searching individual search engines. For general subject searching, it might be better to use a subject gateway.

Subject Gateways

Subject gateways are directories of Web resources on particular subjects. Usually the gateways are compiled by subject experts and may be published by professional societies, universities, or libraries. They contain particularly useful and important resources, possibly including databases and electronic journals.

Use a subject gateway when you want resources in a particular subject area. Although subject gateways contain far fewer resources than search engines, the resources have usually been selected and evaluated by subject experts, so they are often useful places to start.

E-mail, Discussion Lists, and Databases

Although there are directories (or lists) of e-mail addresses on the Internet, which can be searched free of charge, none of them is comprehensive. Just because you do not find a person's e-mail address in the directories does not necessarily mean that the address doesn't exist. If you know the organization for which someone works, try its home page to see if an internal directory is available.

E-mail discussion lists are an extremely useful resource for researchers. They enable you to communicate with, and ask questions of, other people who are interested in similar topics. When you send an e-mail message to an e-mail discussion list, it is forwarded to all the people who are members of that particular list. Many lists maintain archives of past discussions.

There are different types of discussion lists. An open list is open to anyone, and the messages are forwarded automatically without human intervention. A closed list is available to only certain people, such as the employees of a company. A moderated list is monitored by a person, often known as the list owner, who decides whether or not to forward the messages to other members.

There are many free databases of reference material on the Internet. A useful directory to them is www.isleuth.com, which allows you to search multiple databases simultaneously for maximum results.

Search Results

Once you have done a search, you will be confronted with a list of Web pages, and a number (often very high) of "matches" for your search. This can seem daunting at first, but do not be put off. The most relevant pages should appear at the top of the list. There is often some information to help you decide which pages to look at in detail. You can always refine your search to reduce the number of "matches" you receive. There are several ways of refining or improving your search:

- Use more search terms to get fewer, more relevant records.
- Use fewer search terms to get more records.
- Search for phrases (words next to each other in the order you specified) by enclosing search terms in quotation marks (e.g., "robert menzies").

- Choose search engines that allow you to refine your search results (e.g., AltaVista).
- Limit your searches to Canadian sites by using local search engines, or limit your searches to sites with .ca at the end of their domain name.
- Use Boolean operators: + (an essential term) and – (a term that should be excluded).

Every page on the Web has a unique address or Universal Resource Locator (URL). Looking at the URL can help you decide whether or not a page will be useful. The URL sometimes tells you the name of the organization hosting the site or can give a clue that you are viewing a personal page (often indicated by a ~ symbol in the URL). Some organizations are likely to provide more reliable information than others. The address includes a domain name, which also contains clues to the organization hosting the Web page (**Table 3**). For example, the URL

weatheroffice. ec.gc.ca/canada_e.html

is a page showing a weather map of Canada. The domain name "ec.gc.ca" is for Environment Canada—probably a fairly reliable source.

Table 3 Some Organization Codes

com or co	commercial
edu or ac	educational
org	nonprofit organizations
net	networking providers
mil	military
gov	government
int	international organizations

Evaluating Your Sources

Anyone with access to a server can put material on the Web; there are almost no controls on what people choose to write and publish. It is your job as a researcher to evaluate what you find in order to determine if it suits your needs. As a result, Web pages should be viewed with even more caution than most print material.

Use the following questions to determine the quality of a Web resource. The greater number of questions answered "yes," the more likely that the source is of high quality.

Authority: Is it clear who is sponsoring the creation and maintenance of the page? Does the site seem to be permanent, or part of a permanent organization? Is there information available describing the purpose of the sponsoring organization? Is there a way of verifying the legitimacy of the page's sponsor? For instance, is a phone number or address available to contact the organization for more information? Is it clear who developed and wrote the material? Are that person's qualifications for writing on this topic stated?

Accuracy: Are the sources for factual information given so they can be verified? Is it clear who has the responsibility for the accuracy of the information presented? If statistical data are presented in graphs or charts, are they labelled clearly?

Objectivity: Is the page, and the information included, provided as a public service? Does it present a balance of views? If there is advertising on the page, is it clearly separated from the informational content?

Currency: Are there dates on the page to indicate when the page was written, first placed online, and last revised or edited? Are there any other indications that the material is updated frequently? If the information is published in print in different editions, is it clear what edition the page is from? If the material is from a work that is out of print, has an effort been made to update the material?

Coverage: Is there an indication that the page has been completed and is not still under construction? If there is a print equivalent to the Web page, is there a clear indication of whether the entire work or only a portion of it is available on the Web?

Analyzing and Evaluating Claims

Every day you are faced with scientific information and persuasive arguments that are presented as "factual" or "true." For example, there are some individuals, groups, and organizations who believe that the Apollo Moon landings were faked. These nonbelievers present information and arguments aimed at convincing the general public that they were fooled by the government of the United States, and, ultimately, at encouraging a distrust of all governments. Another example is information about the latest fad diets, such as the Atkins diet and South Beach diet, that floods bookstores and the Internet. The writers try to convince you, the consumer, that for the cost of a book or electronic information you will learn how to follow the "best" diet for weight loss and optimum health.

Such information and arguments may be relevant to decisions that you are faced with as an individual or as a member of society. Often, the information is a "sales pitch" intended to persuade you to make a particular choice or decision that may or may not be in your best interests. It is crucial for you to ensure that the information is reliable and the arguments are logical. You need reliable information in order to make informed, rational decisions, whether these decisions are personal (such as what kind of medicine to take, what type of diet to follow, or what model of car to buy) or social (such as whether to support funding of health care, basic scientific research, or environmental protection). The ability to analyze and evaluate information and arguments is an important skill in becoming scientifically literate.

Evaluating Information and Sources

Determining whether claims are scientific is difficult. The following guidelines will help you distinguish between claims that are scientific and claims that are not:

- Based on your prior knowledge, does the claim make sense or does it strike you as rather odd? This is a difficult question to answer because you may not have the prior knowledge you need to make a judgment.

- Who is making the claim? Does the individual or group stand to gain or profit from it? In other words, does the individual or group have any vested interest? For example, a drug company is unlikely to say anything negative about its new product, and an environmentalist is likely to oppose a new hydroelectric project.

- Is there confirmation of the results by an independent body? If individuals or groups with no vested interest in the claim have investigated and obtained the same results, you should have some assurance that the results are valid and reliable.

- Does the individual or group making the claim have the necessary expertise or personal credibility to make such a claim? For example, the promotion of the technical features of a car by a professional athlete should not be sufficient reason for you to go out and buy that car. Similarly, a politician who claims that scientists are wrong about global warming may not hold much credibility. It is unlikely that the politician has the scientific expertise to support the claim.

- Is there another explanation for the claim being made? Think of as many explanations as possible, and then think of ways that you might eliminate each of the alternative explanations. The explanation that survives the elimination process has a better chance of being right than the first explanation that came to mind.

- Are the hypotheses straightforward and understandable? If there are two hypotheses that explain a claim equally well, you should generally choose the simpler one.

- Are the quantitative data clear and the qualitative data unambiguous? Data that are vague or ambiguous are open to many interpretations.

- Can the claim be tested? If a claim is testable, it can be either verified or falsified. Claims that are not testable are not usually valid or reliable. If a claim is true, then you should be able to replicate any experiments and get the same results.

- Is the claim backed up by scientific research? Look for carefully designed and controlled experiments. If there are variables that can be tested, each variable must be tested separately and objectively so that the variable causing the result can be identified. For example, when two different medications are tested, it makes no sense for the test subjects to take both medications at the same time. If the condition improved, the reseacher would not be able to tell which medication was effective. Furthermore, it may be important for the sponsors of the study or the manufacturer of the medication not to know which group has been given which drug. It may be necessary to set up a double-blind study so that only the researcher knows which group is taking which medication. It may also be necessary to compare the study groups to a control group: a group that is not given any medication or is given a fake medication (a placebo).

- Do the arguments of the individual or group making the claim contain any fallacies or flaws in reasoning? (See "Evaluating Arguments: Identifying Common Fallacies.")

Evaluating Arguments: Identifying Common Fallacies

Determining whether an argument is reasonable and logical is really a question of being able to recognize any fallacy in the argument. A fallacy is simply a flaw in the reasoning. It can be either a faulty premise (the assumption on which the argument is based) or a faulty conclusion. To determine if an argument is fallacious, you must determine whether the premise(s) is acceptable, and if it is, whether the conclusion drawn from the premise(s) is logical. For example, advertisers often appeal to celebrities to sell their products. The implied argument is that if a celebrity endorses a product, then it must be good. The fallacy in this argument is that it appeals to an "authority"—a celebrity—who probably has no more expertise for deciding whether the product is good than you do. Thus, the premise is acceptable, but the conclusion does not necessarily follow.

Just as you need to analyze and evaluate other people's arguments, you also need to evaluate your own arguments before using them to persuade others. **Table 4** summarizes some of the more common logical fallacies that lead to invalid arguments.

Table 4 Summary of Common Logical Fallacies

ad hominem	This Latin expression means "to the man." Thus, an *ad hominem* fallacy is characterized by an attack on the person rather than an attack on the argument itself. The character or circumstance of the person has no bearing on the truth or falsity of the proposition being argued. An example is arguing against the prime minister's proposed plan for a tax increase because the prime minister is a millionaire.
appeal to authority	An argument that relies on the opinion of an authority is fallacious if the "authority" is not qualified to have an expert opinion on the subject or if there is disagreement on the issue among authorities. Advertisers often use this fallacy to sell their products. For example, because a well-known golf professional endorses a vehicle, the vehicle must be good quality.
appeal to ignorance	Arguments with this fallacy are based on one of the following assumptions: since something has not been proven false, it must be true; or, since something has not been proven true, it must be false. For example, since a scientist cannot prove that global warming will occur, it probably will not occur.
observational selection	This type of argument is often referred to as "counting the hits and ignoring the misses." It presents evidence supporting a conclusion and downplays any evidence against it. Important evidence, which would undermine the argument, is intentionally left out. For example, a food production company argues that its product is safe for consumption and that the public should not worry. However, it fails to reveal that research studies suggest that pregnant women should avoid the product.
bandwagon fallacy	An argument is claimed to be true because a large or special segment of society holds it to be true. This type of fallacy is often used in politics: "The polls show that the XYZ party will win the election, so you may as well vote for the XYZ party."
begging the question	This type of argument is often called "assuming the answer" because the truth of the argument is assumed in the premise. For example, imposing the death penalty would discourage violent crime. Does the rate of violent crime, however, actually decrease when the death penalty is imposed?
faulty generalization	This fallacy can take several forms, but the usual form involves an unjustified generalization. The generalization is unjustified because the sample is too small, because it is biased, or because it relies on anecdotal evidence and not on empirical evidence. For example, claiming that rap music is the most popular music genre because six of your friends like rap music is not justified because the sample is biased and represents a very small proportion of the total population. A common type of generalization relies on anecdotal evidence to make an argument. For example, there are numerous stories of individuals being cured of cancer because of a special diet or alternative drug. While it is possible that an individual was indeed cured, it cannot be concluded that the cure was due to the diet or drug or, if it was, that the diet or drug would work for other individuals.
misunderstanding of statistics	Misunderstanding or misinterpreting statistics can lead to a faulty conclusion. For example, making an argument that the science program should be revised because half of the students achieve below the average is a misunderstanding of what an average is. An average score is calculated by adding all the scores and dividing by the total number of scores. Thus, you would expect that approximately half of the students would achieve below the average.

Table 4 Summary of Common Logical Fallacies (continued)

non sequitur	This Latin expression means "it does not follow." An argument that has this type of fallacy reaches a conclusion that does not logically follow from the premises. For example, you might say "If I am in Toronto, then I am in Ontario. I am not in Toronto, therefore, I am not in Ontario." Although the premise is true, the conclusion does not follow because you could be in some other city in Ontario. Here is another example: "If a paper mill is polluting a lake, then there will be more dead fish. More dead fish appear, so the mill must be polluting the lake." The premise is acceptable, but the conclusion is not logical because there could be other possible explanations for the dead fish.
post hoc, ergo propter hoc	This Latin phrase, often shortened to *post hoc*, means "after this, therefore because of this." In other words, because B followed A, B was caused by A. For example, a person who sleeps through the night after drinking a cup of coffee could argue that it must have been the coffee that helped him sleep so well. In fact, there was probably another reason for his good sleep.
correlation implies causation	This fallacy is related to the *post hoc* fallacy. Just because two events are correlated does not mean that one causes the other. For example, a research study showed that the achievement of children, aged 5 to 12, on an aptitude test had a positive correlation with shoe size. The researcher could have concluded that children with bigger feet are more intelligent. The fallacy lies in the fact that there is no real connection between intelligence and shoe size, other than the fact that children's feet get bigger as they grow older and older children might achieve better on the aptitude test.
guilt/honour by association	This fallacy involves claiming that something must be false (or true) because of the people or organizations supporting it. For example, the research of Pons and Fleischmann in the area of cold fusion, which turned out to be flawed, was conducted at the University of Utah. Therefore, the research of Dr. Smith at the University of Utah must also be flawed.
middle ground	An argument that includes this type of fallacy considers only the two extremes in a range of possibilities. Accusing someone of being part of the problem if they are not part of the solution is a middle ground fallacy. For example, a person who does not oppose a particular development project is accused of being anti-environment. Similarly, a scientist who does not accept the current prediction of global warming is accused of not believing that global warming is a problem.
short-term vs. long-term	This is related to the middle ground fallacy. The argument always emphasizes the immediate, short-term consequences. For example, the government should not spend public money on long-term initiatives, such as space exploration, when there are more immediate short-term needs, such as homeless people who need housing.
burden of proof	The burden of proof is on the people who suggest a new theory or make a claim. They must provide evidence to support it. It is not acceptable for them to say "you cannot prove it wrong so therefore it must be right." For example, people who claim that the Moon landings were a hoax have the responsibility to provide the evidence to support their claim. They cannot argue that NASA must prove that the Moon landings were real.
slippery slope	This fallacy gets its name from the belief that once you start to slide down a slippery slope, you will slide all the way to the bottom. In other words, if a proposition is unacceptable, then a sequence of increasingly unacceptable events will follow from the proposition. For example, if marijuana is decriminalized, it will be perceived as acceptable. This will lead marijuana smokers to believe that other drugs are acceptable, which will lead to an increase in the number of hard-drug users.
straw man	A straw man is literally a dummy that is used as a target, such as in combat training. A straw man fallacy sets up a weak argument that is easy to attack with the intention of defeating the other person's main argument. For example, arguing that a person must support criminals because he or she is against the gun-control legislation is setting up a straw man (accusing the person of supporting criminals) to avoid the real issue (opposition to gun-control legislation).
weasel words	This fallacy is an attempt to be ambiguous by using alternative vocabulary to present an argument that would likely not be accepted. For example, a city counsellor argues that a new fertilizer called "biosolids" is perfectly safe for agricultural use. Her argument suffers from the weasel words fallacy. She uses the term "biosolids" instead of saying "the untreated sludge from sewage treatment plants."

A6 Work Skills

Working Together

Scientific discoveries and technological inventions are almost always made by teams of people working together. Scientists and technologists share ideas, help each other design experiments and studies, analyze each other's observations, and evaluate each other's results. Group work is necessary and usually more productive than working alone.

On many occasions throughout this course, you will be expected to work with one or more of your classmates. You may be brainstorming or sharing ideas, working on an activity, doing research, designing an experiment, solving a technological problem, or resolving an issue.

There are essentially only three roles in most group efforts: a leader (may also be referred to as a chairperson, facilitator, or moderator), a recorder (or notetaker), and members. Other roles, such as timekeeper or equipment manager, may be defined and assigned as required.

General Guidelines for Effective Group Work

Here are a few guidelines that will help you and your classmates become productive members of an efficient and effective group:

- Get your group together as quickly as possible. There will always be a time limit so you need to start working right away.
- If group members have not already been assigned to the required roles, elect members fill these roles.
- As a group, work out a strategy that you will use to complete the task. For example, the group may decide to brainstorm ideas to solve a problem (see "Group Strategies: Brainstorming" on p. 386) or to divide a large task into smaller tasks and assign these smaller tasks to individual members.
- Read all the instructions and available information. This will ensure that everyone understands the task and the expectations of the group.
- Unless otherwise stated, the group is expected to reach a decision by consensus. It may be helpful, however, to decide on a decision-making procedure (such as a majority vote) in case you cannot reach a consensus.

- The leader's role is to facilitate the work of the group. The leader is not a referee, responsible for resolving conflicts or disagreements among members. The task is not a competition but a joint effort.
- Show common courtesy. Listen carefully, do not interrupt, and acknowledge the comments or questions of others.
- Everyone should make a concerted effort to understand, respect, and accept the perspectives of other members. This does not mean that you have to agree with other members' opinions or ideas. However, you should be prepared to compromise.
- Request clarification if you do not understand a word, phrase, or idea. Asking questions is a very important component of effective communication.
- Explain your reasoning or "think out loud." You cannot assume that others will understand why you proposed a solution or a course of action.
- Check the progress of the group, keeping in mind the time constraints.
- If the group gets bogged down and cannot make any progress, review what you have done so far. This will provide an opportunity for members to ask questions and may reveal something that you have overlooked.
- If the group is expected to submit a product (such as a written report, oral presentation, or audiovisual presentation), ensure that every member is involved in creating the product. This is not the role of the recorder.

Evaluating Your Group

If you are asked to evaluate the effectiveness of your group, consider the following questions:

- What were the *strengths* of your group?
- What were the *weaknesses* of your group?
- What *opportunities* were provided by working with your group?
- What possible *challenges* did working with your group present?
- How would you ensure that your group functions better next time?

Group Strategy: Brainstorming

Brainstorming is a strategy that is often used as one component of the group problem-solving process. The purpose of brainstorming is not to solve the problem but to generate many ideas that may lead to a solution. The following guidelines will help to ensure that you have an enjoyable and productive brainstorming session:

- Define the problem or task and make sure that everyone in your group understands and agrees with the definition.
- Note the time limit that your teacher has given.
- Ensure that one group member records the ideas, preferably on a chalkboard or flipchart.
- The contribution of ideas can be random or structured. In random brainstorming, members state ideas as they come to mind. In structured brainstorming, members take turns contributing ideas. They can pass their turn for a round if they cannot come up with an idea quickly.
- Follow these rules:
  - Go for quantity rather than quality. The more ideas your group generates the more likely it is that you will come up with some good-quality ideas.
  - Do not criticize! During brainstorming, the only objective is to generate lots of ideas. There will be an opportunity later to evaluate each idea.
  - Anything goes! Share your idea no matter how crazy or "off the wall" it seems. This encourages the kind of imagination and creativity that is helpful in solving problems.
  - Do not explain your idea. If your reasoning is not obvious you will have an opportunity to explain later.
  - Piggyback or hitchhike on other members' ideas. Modify, build on, or combine ideas to create a new idea.
- After the brainstorming session is over, go through the ideas and evaluate them. Eliminate duplicate ideas and ideas that are definitely not relevant to the problem. Group together similar ideas. Now that you have narrowed the list, discuss each idea that remains. You may wish to devise a method for rating the ideas. For example, establish three or four criteria that are important to the problem and give each idea a rating of 1 to 5 on each criterion. This will help you further narrow the list of possible ideas.

Other Group Strategies

There are many other group strategies that can be effective for conducting research, solving problems, or resolving issues. All of these strategies can benefit by following the general guidelines for effective group work. Here are four of the more successful strategies:

- In a **think-pair-share activity** you and a partner are given a problem. Each of you develops a solution, usually within a time limit. You then share your solutions with each other. You may also be asked to share your solutions with a larger group or the class.
- In a **jigsaw strategy** you are an active member in two teams: a home team and an expert team. As a home team member you choose or are assigned a particular area of research. You then meet with an expert team in which everyone is working on the same area of research. In your expert team, you may work together to come up with answers to questions related to that area of research. When you have completed your research in your expert team, you return to your home team. It is now your responsibility to teach what you have learned to the other members of your home team. Each member of your home team will do the same thing. The general guidelines for effective group work are very important in the jigsaw, so try to keep them in mind as you work with your expert and home teams.
- The **round table strategy** can be used to give your group an opportunity to review what you know about a problem or issue. You pass around a pen and paper and take turns writing one line of the solution. Members can pass on a turn if they wish. Check to ensure that everyone understands the solution. Finally, review the steps of the solution as a group.
- In the **fishbowl strategy**, a limited number of students engage in a discussion or debate while the rest of the class—the observers—sit around these students in a "fishbowl" arrangement. The observers think about and make notes on the progress of the discussion or debate, and can participate in the evaluation of the process and outcome.

Graphic Organizers

Graphic organizers such as those outlined in this section can help you understand a topic, and assist you in forming a clear, concise answer.

PMI Chart

A PMI chart is used to examine both sides of an issue. Positive aspects of a topic or issue are recorded in the P (plus) column. Negative aspects are recorded in the M (minus) column. Interesting or controversial questions are recorded in the I (interesting) column (**Table 1**).

Table 1 A PMI Chart

P	M	I

KWL Chart

A KWL chart can help you identify prior knowledge and experience, decide what new information you want to learn about, and reflect on your learning. Before you begin a new concept, lesson, or unit, list what you know about a topic in the K column and what you want to know in the W column. After studying the new topic, list what you learned in the L column (**Table 2**).

Table 2 A KWL Chart

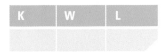

K	W	L

Venn Diagram

A Venn diagram is used to show similarities and differences in two or more concepts. Write all similarities between the concepts in the overlapping section of the circles and all unique traits of each concept in the non-overlapping parts of the appropriate circles (**Figure 1**).

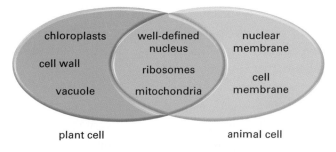

Figure 1 Venn diagram: plant and animal cells

Fishbone Diagram

A fishbone diagram is used to identify separate causes and effects. In the head of the fish, identify the effect, topic, or result. At the end of each major bone, identify the major subtopics or categories. On the minor bones that attach to each major bone, add details about the subtopics or possible causes of each effect or result (**Figure 2**).

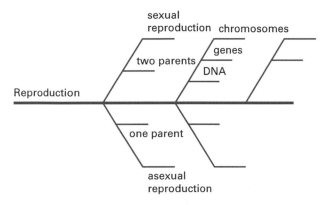

Figure 2 Fishbone diagram: reproduction

The Concept Map

Concept maps are used to show connections between ideas and concepts, using words or visuals. Put the central idea in the middle of a sheet of paper. Organize the ideas most closely related to each other around the centre. Draw arrows between the ideas that are related. On each arrow, write a short description of how the terms are related to each other (**Figure 3**).

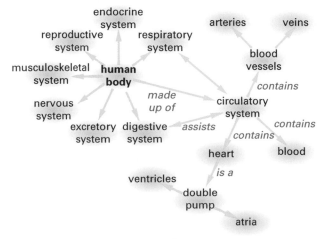

Figure 3 Concept map: human body

A7 Communicating

Written Communication

In the working world, individuals and companies often require detailed scientific information to help them make informed decisions. There are many kinds of scientific writing, for many different purposes and many different audiences. Before beginning, consider the purpose of your writing. Are you presenting facts or choices to your readers, or are you trying to convert your readers to your way of thinking? Know who your audience is. Think about how much time they will be willing to spend reading your report, and how much they already know about the subject. Your report should be helpful and easy to read. If your report is widely read and accepted, more people are likely to trust what you say. This may lead to better jobs and career opportunities!

Before you submit any kind of report, read through it and ask yourself "Is this appropriate to publish?" If you have doubts about the authenticity of your sources or the truth of your statements, or if a named person could be damaged by something in your report, consider a rewrite. Once your report is published, it cannot be taken back.

Lab Reports

When carrying out investigations, it is important that scientists keep records of their plans and results, and share their findings. In order to have their investigations repeated (replicated) and accepted by the scientific community, scientists generally share their work by publishing papers in which they provide details of their design, materials, procedure, evidence, analysis, and evaluation.

Lab reports are prepared after an investigation is completed. To ensure that you can accurately describe the investigation, it is important to keep thorough and accurate records of your activities as you carry out the investigation.

Investigators use a similar format in their final reports or lab books, although the headings and order may vary. Your lab book or report should reflect the type of scientific inquiry that you used in the investigation and should be based on the following headings, as appropriate. (See **Figure 1**, on pp. 390–392, for a sample lab report.)

Title

At the beginning of your report, write the section number and title of your investigation. In this course, the title is usually given, but if you are designing your own investigation, create a title that suggests what the investigation is about. Include the date the investigation was conducted and the names of all lab partners (if you worked as a team).

Purpose

State the purpose of the investigation. Why are you doing this investigation?

Question

This is the Question that you attempted to answer in the investigation. If it is appropriate to do so, state the Question in terms of independent and dependent variables.

Hypothesis/Prediction

Based on your reasoning or on a concept that you have studied, formulate an explanation of what should happen (a hypothesis). From your hypothesis you may make a prediction, a statement of what you expect to observe, before carrying out the investigation. Depending on the nature of your investigation, you may or may not have a hypothesis or a prediction.

Experimental Design

This is a brief general overview (one to three sentences) of what was done. If your investigation involved independent, dependent, and controlled variables, list them. Identify any control or control group that was used in the investigation.

Materials

This is a detailed list of all the materials that were used, including sizes and quantities where appropriate. Be sure to include safety equipment such as goggles, laboratory apron, gloves, and tongs, where needed. Draw a diagram to show any complicated set-up of apparatus.

Procedure

Describe, in detailed, numbered steps, the procedure you followed to carry out your investigation. Include steps to clean up and dispose of waste.

Observations

This includes all qualitative and quantitative observations you made. Be as precise as possible when describing quantitative observations, include any unexpected observations, and present your information in a form that is easily understood. If you have only a few observations, this could be a list; for controlled experiments and for many observations, a table would be more appropriate.

Analysis

Interpret your observations and present the evidence in the form of tables, graphs, or illustrations, each with a title. Include any calculations, the results of which can be shown in a table. Make statements about any patterns or trends you observed. Conclude the analysis with a statement based only on the evidence you have gathered, answering the question that initiated the investigation.

Evaluation

The evaluation is your judgment about the quality of evidence obtained and about the validity of the prediction and hypothesis (if present). This section can be divided into two parts—evaluation of the investigation and evaluation of the prediction (and hypothesis). The following questions and suggestions should help you in each part of the process.

Evaluation of the Investigation
- Did the design enable you to answer the question?
- As far as you know, is the design the best available or are there flaws that could be corrected?
- Were the steps in the investigation in the correct order and adequate to gather sufficient evidence?
- What steps, if done incorrectly, could have significantly affected the results?
- What improvements could be made to the procedure?

Sum up your conclusions about the procedure in a statement that begins like this: "The procedure is judged to be adequate/inadequate because…"

- What specialized skills (such as measuring) might have an effect on the results?

- Was the evidence from repeated trials reasonably similar?
- Can the measurements be made more precise?

Sum up your conclusions about the required skills in a statement that begins like this: "The skills are judged to be adequate/inadequate because…"

- What are the sources of uncertainty and error in my investigation?
- Based on any uncertainties and errors you have identified, do you have enough confidence in your results to proceed with the evaluation of the prediction and hypothesis?

State your confidence level in a statement like this: "Based on my evaluation of the investigation, I am certain/I am moderately certain/I am very certain of my results."

Evaluation of the Prediction (and Hypothesis)
- Does the predicted answer clearly agree with the answer in your analysis?
- Can any difference be accounted for by the sources of uncertainty or error listed earlier in the evaluation?

Sum up your evaluation of the prediction in a statement that begins like this: "The prediction is judged to be verified/inconclusive/falsified because…"

- Is the hypothesis supported by the evidence?
- Is there a need to revise the hypothesis or to replace it with a new hypothesis?

If the prediction was verified, the hypothesis behind it is supported. If the results were inconclusive or the prediction is falsified, then the hypothesis is questionable. Sum up your evaluation of the hypothesis in a statement that begins like this: "The hypothesis being tested is judged to be acceptable/unacceptable because…"

X2.5 Investigation: Movement of Water Into and Out of Cells

April 15, 2015

By Eileen Jong

Purpose

The purpose of this investigation is to examine the conditions under which water moves into and out of cells, using dialysis tubing as a model of a cell membrane.

Question

Under what conditions does water move into and out of cells?

Hypothesis/Prediction

If a model cell is placed in a hypotonic solution (having lower concentrations of solute than the cell), water will move into the cell. If a model cell is placed in a hypertonic solution (having higher concentrations of solute than the cell), water will move out of the cell.

Experimental Design

Three model cells are constructed from dialysis tubing. Two are filled with distilled water and one is filled with starch suspension. One of the cells with distilled water is placed in a beaker of starch suspension. The other two cells are placed in beakers of distilled water. Iodine is added to the distilled water in the beakers. (Iodine is used as an indicator to detect the presence of starch.) The mass of each cell is recorded and other observations are made at the beginning and after 10 min and 20 min.

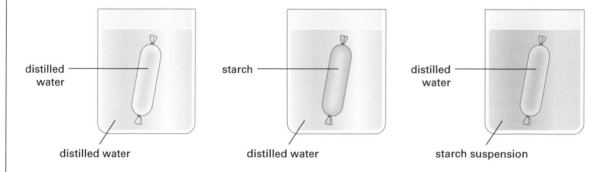

Materials

laboratory apron
medicine dropper
funnel
scissors
100-mL graduated cylinder
three 250-mL beakers
triple-beam balance

gloves
dialysis tubing
paper towels
distilled water
4% starch suspension
iodine

Figure 1   Sample lab report

Proocdure

1. A laboratory apron and gloves were put on.

2. Three strips of dialysis tubing (each about 25 cm long) were cut. The strips were then soaked in a beaker of tap water for approximately 2 min.

3. To find the opening, one end of the dialysis tube was rubbed between our fingers. A knot was tied near the other end of the tube. These steps were repeated for the other tubes.

4. Using a graduated cylinder, 15 mL of 4% starch suspension was measured. The suspension was poured through a funnel into the open end of one of the dialysis tubes.

5. The second and third dialysis tubes were filled with 15 mL of distilled water. In one tube, 20 drops of iodine were added.

6. A knot was tied in the open end of each tube to close it.

7. The outside of all the tubes was rinsed with distilled water to remove any fluids that may have leaked out during the tying process.

8. Excess water was gently blotted from the dialysis tubes and the mass of each tube was measured.

9. An observation table similar to **Table 1** was constructed and the measurements were recorded.

10. The dialysis tube with only distilled water was placed in a beaker containing 100 mL of distilled water. The dialysis tube with the starch suspension was placed in a second beaker containing 100 mL of distilled water. The dialysis tube with distilled water and iodine was placed in a third beaker containing 100 mL of starch suspension.

11. Twenty drops of iodine were added to each of the beakers containing distilled water. All three tubes were observed closely for any colour change at the beginning.

12. After 10 min, the dialysis tubes were removed from the beakers. Any excess liquid from the tubes was gently blotted off and the mass of each tube was measured and recorded.

13. The dialysis tubes were then returned to the appropriate beakers.

14. After another 10 min, the tubes were removed again and blotted dry, and the mass of each tube was measured and recorded.

15. The contents of the tubes were poured down the sink and the sink was rinsed. The tubes were placed in the regular garbage disposal.

Observations

Table 1 Observation Table

Model cell	Initial mass (g)	Mass after 10 min (g)	Mass after 20 min (g)	Other observations
dialysis tube with distilled water in beaker of distilled water	17.5	17.5	17.5	no observable change in the solution inside the tube
dialysis tube with starch suspension in beaker of distilled water	24.7	25.3	28.4	suspension inside the dialysis tube turned dark
dialysis tube with distilled water in beaker of starch suspension	18.5	17.8	15.7	starch suspension in the beaker turned dark

Analysis

- The tube with the distilled water in the beaker containing distilled water showed no change in mass.
- The tube with the starch suspension increased in mass during each 10-min period. The solution in this tube turned dark.
- The tube with the distilled water in the beaker with the starch suspension decreased in mass during each 10-min period. The starch suspension in the beaker turned dark.

The mass of the cell with the starch suspension inside increased because water moved into the cell. The suspension in this tube turned dark, which suggests that iodine also must have moved into the tube along with the water molecules.

The mass of the cell with the starch suspension outside decreased because water moved out of the cell. The suspension outside the cell turned dark, which suggests that iodine also must have moved outside the tube along with the water molecules.

The tube with the distilled water acted as a control. It had the same solution inside as outside. There was no observable change in it.

From our observations, we can conclude that water will move out of a cell in a hypertonic solution and into a cell in a hypotonic solution.

Evaluation

The design is adequate because the observations allowed us to reach a conclusion about the conditions under which water moves into and out of cells. The procedure is easy to follow and does not require any special skills.

Water or starch suspension remaining on the tubes after they were taken out of the beakers may have affected the measurement of the mass of the tubes. However, this should not make a difference since this error would have affected the mass of all tubes. Errors in measurement would probably not have accounted for the increase in the mass of the tube with the starch or the decrease in the mass of the tube with distilled water. So, while there may have been errors in measurement, they should not have affected the quality of the evidence.

The evidence supports the prediction. To verify our conclusion, we could repeat the investigation or do a similar investigation with different solutions.

Since we were working with model cells, we cannot be sure that this would happen with real cells.

Research Reports

Research reports are less rigidly structured than lab reports, but they still need a formal structure. Your aim is to present factual information in an unbiased way.

A research report should consist of three parts: an introduction, a body, and a conclusion. In the introduction, you state the purpose of your research and your main proposition or thesis. The introduction should tell your reader why you are writing the report, the main points you will address, and why your reader may be interested in your report. The body of your report, obviously the most substantial part, will contain your arguments and the evidence you have used to support them. In the conclusion, you restate your main proposition and briefly summarize your arguments. It should be obvious at this point why you have reached your conclusion.

Your school or your teacher may have a standard format for research papers and guidelines for form and style that you are expected to follow for all subjects. However, regardless of the specific format and guidelines, the following general guidelines will help you ensure that your report is well-organized and well-written.

- Start by writing an outline. The purpose of the outline is to help you think through your report and organize it before you start writing. The outline represents the overall structure of your report, but it should not be considered final. It may change as your report develops. You may use capital Roman numerals, capital letters, numbers, and lower-case letters to identify the different levels of organization in the outline. A sample outline for a report about waste is given below.

I. Introduction
II. Categories of waste
   A. Household waste
      1. Paper and paper products
         a. Bleached paper
         b. Unbleached paper
      2. Plastics
         a. SPI resin codes
         b. Sources of waste
      3. Organics
   B. Industrial waste
      1. ...
         a. ...
      2. ...

III. Waste management
   A. Methods
      1. Diversion
         a. Recycling
         b. Reusing
         c. Reducing
         d. Composting
      2. Disposal
         a. Landfill
         b. Incineration

- Include a section for each main point. Give each section a number and a title, so that your readers will be able to find information easily.
- Use a variety of sources to research information related to your topic. Record the bibliographic details for each source. Refer to **Appendix A5** for tips on conducting research.
- Organize the information you have gathered according to your outline. Select the most reliable and credible sources to ensure that the information is accurate and up to date.
- Write your first draft. Think about what you will write, and write concisely. People do not have the time to read pages of unnecessary information.
- Know your audience. You may be communicating quite advanced scientific or technical knowledge. Prepare a report that your readers can understand, but do not "talk down" to them. If possible, find out how much background knowledge your readers are likely to have. If your readers are likely to have only a small amount, you will have to teach them. Use examples that are easy to remember and that convey the required information.
- The introduction (first section) of your report is the most important. It is your chance to make the interesting aspects of your research immediately known to your readers. In one page or less, summarize what you have discovered: the most important issues and your conclusions about them.
- Unless you have been asked for your opinion on an issue, try to keep to the facts. If you make any extrapolations or assumptions, give reasons why you feel these are valid.
- In the conclusion (final section) of your report, summarize your findings and what they mean, and briefly suggest issues that could be researched further.
- Check the content of your report. Ask yourself the following questions:

- Is my proposition or thesis statement clear and concise?
- Did I follow my outline? Did I miss anything?
- Are my arguments presented in a logical sequence?
- Have I provided my proposition with strong, valid arguments?
- Have I supported my arguments with documented proof or examples?
- Have I made my intentions and points clear?

• Reread your report to check for spelling, grammar, punctuation, and style. If possible, have someone else read it as well. Ask yourself the following questions:

- Did I begin each paragraph with a proper topic sentence?
- Are there any run-on or unfinished sentences?
- Are there any unnecessary or repetitious words?
- Are the sentences of varying lengths?
- Does one paragraph or idea flow smoothly into the next?
- Are there any spelling or grammatical errors?
- Are the quotations I used accurate in spelling and punctuation?
- Are all my citations accurate and in the correct format?
- Did I avoid using contractions, such as "can't" instead of "cannot," and "don't" instead of "do not"?
- Did I use the third person as much as possible? Did I avoid indefinite phrases such as "I think," "I guess," and "I suppose"?
- Did I make my points clear and interesting while remaining objective?
- Did I leave my readers with a sense that the topic was addressed fully and completely?

• Rearrange or rewrite your first draft as necessary but do not forget your original purpose.

• Prepare a title page, table of contents (if necessary), list of references, and bibliography. The bibliography includes all the resources that you consulted while preparing your report. The references include only the sources that you referred to directly in your report. Check with your teacher for an acceptable reference and bibliography format.

• Read through your entire report one more time, and make any final changes. Be ready to submit your report a few days before the deadline!

Other Written Communication

Issue Reports

Issues are controversial because there are various points of view. When you are preparing an issue report, look at the issue from as many perspectives as possible. (See **Appendix A1**, **Table 2**, p. 366 for a description of different perspectives.) Try to anticipate who will be affected by this issue. Remember that public and government decisions are rarely based on scientific facts alone. They are usually based on a combination of different interpretations of these facts.

Keep in mind that major societal changes are unlikely to take place overnight, so make your recommendations reasonable. For example, if your issue is increased cigarette smoking among young people, one possible recommendation is a government ban on the sale of cigarettes. But how appealing would this recommendation be to a government? Your recommendation must be supported by a description of a process that would make it appealing and viable.

Position Papers

When planning a position paper, you have two choices. You may start with a position on an issue and then conduct research to support your position, or you may start by researching a topic and then decide on a position in light of your research.

State your position at the beginning of your paper, and then support it with the results of your research. You do not have to balance your paper with opposing views, but you should be aware of other positions on the issue and try to refute them. However, it is very discourteous to insult those holding opposing views. Support your arguments with evidence, reasoning, and logic.

Letters to the Editor

A letter to the editor of a newspaper or magazine is typically a shorter version of a position paper. Space is expensive and, since you are not paying for it, the publisher will likely not print a long article. Write concisely, keeping to a couple of paragraphs. It is not necessary to back up every point you make with scientific facts, but do indicate that there is some evidence to support your position. Be aware of the tone of the publication to which you are writing; each one is slightly different. Do your research by reading the editorial page of your target publication. Note the style of the letters that are printed and write accordingly.

Magazine Articles

Magazine articles are usually written in response to a request from the editor. Rarely do magazines publish unsolicited articles, and they only publish articles of interest to their readers. However, this should not stop you from submitting an article if you feel that the magazine's readers would be interested in your topic.

When writing for a magazine, you need to know the readers well. Are they experts in the field, or have they little or no background knowledge? Should the article be an in-depth, thoughtful discourse, well-supported by scientific evidence, or should it be a lighter, more general piece? The editor will generally tell you how long the article should be. There is no point in writing more than you are asked for—it will be cut! The editor will also tell you how the illustrations, if any, will be prepared.

Whatever the tone of your article, try not to stray from the truth. Be prepared to support your statements if you are challenged.

Environmental Impact Reports

Environmental impact assessments (EIAs) are a relatively new type of report. Until about 20 years ago, the environment was not a consideration when planning a new development. Today, developers must consider, study, and explain the implications of any intended actions, such as constructing an oil pipeline in northern Alberta or building subdivisions on the Oak Ridges Moraine in southern Ontario. Sometimes governments conduct EIAs to investigate environmental issues, more completely. What laws should they enact? What should be the penalties for breaking these laws? It is never easy to predict the effect of a change on the environment; every ecosystem is unique and may react in an unexpected way to a change. Putting out forest fires may seem like a good idea, but many tree species require periodic fires to open their fire-resistant cones or clear a space for them to grow. There is an environmental impact associated with almost everything we do.

Carrying out an EIA is a rather daunting task. It begins with exhaustive research into the existing environment, including both biotic and abiotic factors. The research may extend to other, similar areas, where a comparable development has already taken place. What were the effects? To what extent could the same findings be applied to the area being studied? Studies may be commissioned from various sources: geologists may be called upon to predict how the change would affect the stability of the area; hydrologists may be questioned about the water table; botanists may contribute information about how plant life would change; toxicologists might warn of potentially dangerous substances. All this information must then be drawn together and presented in a coherent report.

An EIA should generally address the following topics:

- the potential direct and indirect outcomes of the proposed development
- how these outcomes may affect the environment
- the scope and nature of these environmental effects
- how the adverse environmental effects could be alleviated
- the overall potential environmental impact of the proposed development after opportunities for alleviation have been incorporated

There is no one format to follow when writing an EIA, but the report should reflect the issues addressed in the assessment. There are a few sections that you must always include:

- a definition of the scope of the questions being researched (that is, the boundaries of the questions you are trying to answer)
- a description of how the data were collected
- a presentation of the evidence including an explanation of how the data were analyzed
- conclusions, with specific reference to questions that could not be answered
- long-term implications (which may be highly speculative)
- suggestions for further research

Oral Communication

You may be asked to make oral presentations for a variety of purposes. You could present results or take part in a debate or a role-play situation. These have different formats, but they all have something in common—you are communicating information to others using mainly your voice. Of course, your body language is also important, and you may support your oral presentation with visual material, but the primary means of communication is the spoken word.

Many people find oral presentations very stressful. They may feel exposed and alone, may be worried about forgetting what to say, and may get flustered and confused. These are very natural reactions that even experienced speakers have to overcome. Here are some general guidelines that will help you lower your stress level, improve your presentation, and help convey your message to your audience.

- Know your audience and match your presentation to your audience. Know your material well. Know yourself—your strengths and weaknesses—and focus on your strengths.
- Prepare your presentation in advance. You will usually have adequate time to prepare, but occasionally the time will be fairly short.
- Do not read from a prepared speech. Occasional glances at your script or at key points on cue cards are appropriate.
- Practise your presentation if possible to ensure that it fits into the allotted time.
- Perform like an actor. Connect with your audience using your voice and your eyes.
- Use body language (such as standing, walking about, hand gestures, facial expressions) but do not overdo it.
- Speak as if you believe what you are saying. Sound confident.
- Maintain eye contact with the audience. Look into the eyes of one person for two or three seconds before shifting your gaze to someone else.
- Remember that you are communicating. Look for clues (such as head nods and smiles) to make sure that your audience is receiving and responding to what you are saying.
- Do not rush. Include a brief pause at appropriate times to let your message sink in.
- Use humour whenever appropriate, but keep in mind that your primary purpose is not to entertain.
- Prepare any audio-visual aids (such as pictures, or slides) and check the equipment (such as a projector, computer, or screen) in advance.
- If you have a handout for your presentation, let the audience know at the beginning of your presentation.
- Know when to stop. End your presentation with a quick summary of your main points, an interesting remark, or an appropriate punch line.
- Thank your audience.

Debating

A debate is an organized argument, with some people presenting for the statement and other people presenting against it. Debates can be formal (as in Parliament or another legislative body) or fairly informal (as in a public meeting). However, for any debate there are rules that keep the debate structured and organized. The affirmative side supports the statement; the negative side opposes the statement. There should be at least two debaters on each side. A chairperson, or moderator, controls the debate. In parliamentary debating, the Speaker of the House acts as the moderator.

All debates have three phases: a constructive phase, a discussion period, and a rebuttal. During the constructive phase the arguments are presented. During the discussion period, debaters have the opportunity to ask questions of their opponents. A debater who wishes to ask an opponent a question raises his or her hand and waits to be acknowledged by the moderator. The response to a question should be limited to one minute. The moderator ensures that questions alternate from side to side and that all the debaters have an equal opportunity to contribute to the discussion. The rebuttal occurs after the discussion period. The rebuttal is an attempt to defeat the arguments that were presented by the opponents during the constructive phase and to show that the position of the opponents is not the correct one. Some debates end with a vote.

Table 2 outlines the order and recommended times for the segments in each phase of a debate.

Table 2 Recommended Times for Debate Segments

Debate segments	Suggested time (min)
first affirmative constructive phase	5
second affirmative constructive phase	5
first negative constructive phase	5
second negative constructive phase	5
discussion period	10
break	5
negative rebuttal	3
affirmative rebuttal	3
vote (if necessary)	5

Your aim is to win over the audience to your way of thinking. You may be asked to debate either from your own personal point of view or from the point of view of another person or group. The following guidelines may help you as you prepare for and participate in a debate:

- Research your topic thoroughly, keeping notes as you go.
- Pick four or five major arguments to support your position, with examples. Write them out in point form.
- Present your arguments clearly and logically, within the allowed time period.
- Listen closely to the arguments presented by your opponents. Make notes to remind you which arguments you want to address in your rebuttal. Your research may have uncovered some of your opponents' arguments so you may have already prepared questions.
- Make your presentation as persuasive as possible, while at all times showing respect for your opponents. While you can question their evidence, never resort to name-calling or rudeness.

Evaluating the Debate

If you are expected to vote on the issue at the end of a debate or help decide which team won the debate, you need to evaluate the debate. The following questions may help you:

- Which team seemed more knowledgeable about the issue?
- Which team presented the best evidence to support its position?
- In your opinion, which team had the strongest arguments?
- Which team was better organized in presenting its evidence and arguments?
- Which team provided the strongest rebuttal?
- Which team had the best presentation style? (Consider such factors as posture, eye contact, reliance on notes, voice clarity, and confidence.)
- Are there other arguments not supplied by either team that you think are relevant to the issue being debated?
- Is there any one argument that you think may be crucial to deciding the issue?
- Were the arguments of one team persuasive enough to change your opinion on the issue?

Role Playing

Role-playing is simply a variation of a debate, where you take on the role of a character. You present an opinion or decision from the point of view of this character in the form of a speech, and try to convince the audience that your position is the most appropriate.

Role-playing provides an opportunity to act out, rather than merely talk about, different points of view on an issue. It should be an enjoyable experience that provides valuable practice in dealing with real-life situations in which issues are addressed.

Most of the role-playing you will encounter in this course will involve you as a participant in a public meeting or as a member of a committee made up of people with different points of view. Your teacher may give you a role description or you may be asked to create the role yourself. If the point of view that you are representing coincides with your personal point of view, you may find the role easier to play. However, you will also have to project yourself into different points of view. Whatever the case, it is important that you thoroughly understand the perspective of the person, group, or organization that you are representing. (See **Appendix A1**, **Table 2**, on p. 366 for a list of the possible perspectives and sample viewpoints on an issue.)

Follow these guidelines as you prepare for and present your point of view:

- Research your topic and your character thoroughly, so you can give compelling reasons for your character's position.
- Organize the results of your research in a way that supports your character's position.
- Include personal examples from your character's life, to support the position you are taking and to make the experience realistic.
- If it would make you feel more comfortable, prepare a script of your presentation. However, do not just read your script. You should know your script well enough that a quick glance at it or a list of key words will prompt you.
- As you make your presentation, it is more convincing and more fun for the audience if you stay "in character." Use "I" and "my" to convince your audience that you are indeed the character you are portraying.

- Relax and have some fun with your presentation. Convince the audience that you are really committed to and passionate about your position.

It is always valuable to switch roles and have a second round of role-playing. This will help you develop an appreciation for other points of view.

Follow-Up

After the role-playing, spend a short time thinking about and discussing it. Were you really "into" the role? How were you feeling during the role-play? Why do you think you were feeling this way? What did you do that was convincing for the audience? What could you have done to improve your role-playing? With your classmates, discuss the positive and negative aspects of the whole experience.

Presenting Results of Investigations

This is a factual type of oral presentation, which must be clear and to the point. Make sure that you answer the following questions as you prepare and present your speech:

- What was the purpose of your investigation?
- Why was the topic relevant and interesting?
- What question were you trying to answer?
- What was your prediction and/or hypothesis (if applicable)?
- How did you carry out your investigation?
- What were your major results?
- Were there any problems, or sources of error or bias, that might cause you to question your results?
- What conclusion did you reach?
- How might your results help others?
- On the basis of your results, is there another investigation that could be done?

Electronic Communication

Electronic communication is becoming part of everyday life. From overhead presentations to Web pages, technology can help you communicate quickly to a wide audience. Technology can also make your communications look slick and professional. Using the various technologies take practice. Do not expect instant results from your first attempt.

When using technology for communication be careful not to get carried away with it. Remember that the technology is simply a tool for delivering the same information you might have presented in traditional written format. Just as if you were writing a report by hand, your thoughts must be clearly stated, well-organized, and clearly presented, with supporting arguments and evidence. You may want to have someone who is not involved in your presentation check it out before "going public" with it.

Creating a Presentation Using Overheads

There are several software programs (such as Microsoft PowerPoint and Corel Presentations) that allow you to create, write, edit, and illustrate a series of slides to be projected onto a screen. You can even add a sound track—including music, sound effects, and your recorded voice—to your presentation. Write your slides as point-form notes, limit yourself to no more than 10 lines of text on each slide, and make the words large enough to be easily read by the audience.

Creating a Web Page

A Web page is a way of communicating with anyone in the world who has access to the World Wide Web. Every page has its own unique address (called a universal resource locator, or URL) and may include graphics, sounds, animations, videos, and links to other Web pages, in addition to regular text. Computer technology and software are changing so quickly that any detailed instructions would soon be out of date, but the following general points may help:

- To create and "publish" a Web page, you need
  - a well-written article, input into an electronic format
  - a computer that is capable of running an HTML authoring tool that has design templates (such as Microsoft FrontPage, Macromedia Dreamweaver, or Adobe GoLine), software that can edit images and graphics, and a modem
  - an Internet Service Provider (ISP)
- All information on the Web is a series of documents formatted using a special "language," such as Hypertext Markup Language (HTML). You have to convert your article to this language using the authoring tool.
- If you want to make your Web site effective, you must be willing to invest the time and energy to create interesting page layouts and exciting graphics. When people leave your site, they remember the

graphics and the page layout as well as the entire organization of the site. They will also remember how easy or difficult it was to get the information they wanted. This is determined by the speed, clarity, simplicity, and consistency of your presentation.

- There are many programs available (such as Flash and Shockwave) that allow you to create amazing animation and special effects, and others that allow you to modify your own digitized photos. Keep in mind that graphical elements on a Web page use a lot of memory and can make your page slow to download.

- Be aware of copyright restrictions when using images downloaded from other sources. Simply using type effectively in a graphic format can help make your Web page stand out from others, and may be much more readable than a Web page that is cluttered with fancy graphics.

- You can add hypertext links to your Web page to lead the reader to more information on other Web pages. Your authoring tool will show you how to make links to other URLs. Always check that the links work.

- You will be able to receive feedback from your readers if you place your e-mail address at the bottom of your Web page.

- Do not give out any personal information about yourself (such as your home address or telephone number). The Web can be an exciting place to explore, but giving out personal information to complete strangers is dangerous.

A final word of caution: Now that you know how easy it is for you to prepare you own Web page, you know how easy it is for other people. Material that you read on the Internet comes from a variety of sources, from the totally ill-informed to the expert. Bear this in mind as you explore the Internet! (For more information, see **Appendix A5, Internet Research,** on p. 379.)

Appendix B: Safety

B1 Safety Conventions and Symbols

Although every effort is taken to make the science experience a safe one, there are some risks associated with certain scientific investigations. These risks are generally associated with the materials and equipment used, and the disregard of safety instructions that accompany investigations. However, there may also be risks associated with the location of the investigation, whether in the science laboratory, at home, or outdoors. Most of these risks pose no more danger than one would normally experience in everyday life. With an awareness of the possible hazards, knowledge of the rules, appropriate behaviour, and a little common sense, these risks can be practically eliminated.

Remember, you share the responsibility for your own safety and for the safety of those around you. Always alert the teacher in case of an accident.

In this text, chemicals, equipment, and procedures that are hazardous are highlighted in red and are preceded by .

WHMIS Symbols and HHPS

The Workplace Hazardous Materials Information System (WHMIS) provides workers and students with complete and accurate information regarding hazardous products. All chemical products supplied to schools, businesses, and industries must contain standardized labels and be accompanied by Material Safety Data Sheets (MSDS) providing detailed information about the product. Clear and standardized labelling is an important component of WHMIS (**Table 1**). These labels must be present on the product's original container or be added to other containers if the product is transferred.

The Canadian Hazardous Products Act requires manufacturers of consumer products containing chemicals to include a symbol specifying both the nature of the primary hazard and the degree of this hazard. In addition, any secondary hazards, first aid treatment, storage, and disposal requirements must be noted. Household Hazardous Product Symbols (HHPS) are used to show the hazard and the degree of the hazard by the type of border surrounding the illustration (**Figure 1**).

 Poison
If you swallow or lick this product, you could become very sick or die. Some products with this symbol on the label can hurt you even if you breathe (or inhale) them.

 Flammable
This product or the gas (or vapour) from it can catch fire quickly. Keep this product away from heat, flames, and sparks.

Explosive
Container will explode if it is heated or if a hole is punched in it. Metal or plastic can fly out and hurt your eyes and other parts of your body.

Corrosive
This material can burn your skin and eyes. If you swallow it, it will damage your throat and stomach.

Danger

Warning

Caution

Figure 1 Hazardous household product symbols

Table 1 The Workplace Hazardous Materials Information System (WHMIS)

Class and type of compounds	WHMIS symbol	Risks	Precautions
Class A: *Compressed Gas* Materials that are normally gaseous and kept in a pressurized container		• could explode due to pressure • could explode if heated or dropped • possible hazard from both the force of explosion and the release of contents	• Ensure container is always secured. • Store in designated areas. • Do not drop or allow to fall.
Class B: *Flammable and Combustible Material* Materials that will continue to burn after being exposed to a flame or other ignition source		• may ignite spontaneously • may release flammable products if allowed to degrade or when exposed to water	• Store in properly designated areas. • Work in well-ventilated areas. • Avoid heating. • Avoid sparks and flames. • Ensure that electrical sources are safe.
Class C: *Oxidizing Material* Materials that can cause other materials to burn or support combustion		• can cause skin or eye burns • increase fire and explosion hazards • may cause combustibles to explode or react violently	• Store away from combustibles. • Wear body, hand, face, and eye protection. • Store in proper container that will not rust or oxidize.
Class D, Division 1: *Toxic Material—Immediate and Serious* Poisons and potentially fatal materials that cause immediate and serious harm		• may be fatal if ingested or inhaled • may be absorbed through the skin • have a toxic effect even in small volumes	• Avoid breathing dust or vapours. • Avoid contact with skin or eyes. • Wear protective clothing, and face and eye protection. • Work in well-ventilated areas and wear breathing protection.
Class D, Division 2: *Toxic Material—Long-Term Concealed* Materials that have a harmful effect after repeated exposures or over a long period		• may cause death or permanent injury • may cause birth defects or sterility • may cause cancer • may cause allergies	• Wear appropriate personal protection. • Work in a well-ventilated area. • Store in appropriate designated areas. • Avoid direct contact. • Use hand, body, face, and eye protection. • Ensure respiratory and body protection is appropriate for the specific hazard.
Class D, Division 3: *Biohazardous Infectious Material* Infectious agents or a biological toxin causing a serious disease or death		• may cause anaphylactic shock • includes viruses, yeasts, moulds, bacteria, and parasites that affect humans • includes fluids containing toxic products • includes cellular components	• Special training is required to handle these materials. • Work in designated biological areas with appropriate engineering controls. • Avoid forming aerosols. • Avoid breathing vapours. • Avoid contamination of people and/or area. • Store in special designated areas.
Class E: *Corrosive Material* Materials that react with metals and living tissue		• eye and skin irritation on exposure • severe burns/tissue damage on longer exposure • lung damage if inhaled • may cause blindness if contacts eyes • environmental damage from fumes	• Wear body, hand, face, and eye protection. • Use breathing apparatus. • Ensure protective equipment is appropriate. • Work in a well-ventilated area. • Avoid all direct body contact. • Use appropriate storage containers and ensure proper non-venting closures.
Class F: *Dangerously Reactive Material* Materials that may have unexpected reactions		• may react with water • may be chemically unstable • may explode if exposed to shock or heat • may release toxic or flammable vapours • may vigorously polymerize • may burn unexpectedly	• Handle with care, avoiding vibration, shocks, and sudden temperature changes. • Store in appropriate containers. • Ensure storage containers are sealed. • Store and work in designated areas.

B2 Safety in the Laboratory

General Safety Rules

Safety in the laboratory is an attitude and a habit more than it is a set of rules. It is easier to prevent accidents than to deal with the consequences of an accident. Most of the following rules are common sense:

- Do not enter a laboratory unless a teacher or other supervisor is present, or you have permission to do so.
- Familiarize yourself with your school's safety regulations.
- Make your teacher aware of any allergies and other health problems you may have.
- Wear eye protection, a laboratory apron or coat, and gloves when appropriate.
- Wear closed shoes (not sandals) when working in the laboratory.
- Place your books and bags away from the work area. Keep your work area clear of all materials except those that you will use in the investigation.
- Do not chew gum, eat, or drink in the laboratory. Food should not be stored in refrigerators in the laboratory.
- Know the location of MSDS information, exits, and all safety equipment, such as the fire blanket, fire extinguisher, and eyewash station.
- Avoid sudden or rapid motion in the laboratory that may interfere with someone carrying or working with chemicals or using sharp instruments.
- Never engage in horseplay or practical jokes in the laboratory.
- Ask for assistance when you are not sure how to do a procedural step.
- Never attempt any unauthorized experiments.
- Never work in a crowded area or alone in the laboratory.
- Always wash your hands with soap and water before and after you leave the laboratory. Definitely wash your hands before you touch any food.
- Use stands, clamps, and holders to secure any potentially dangerous or fragile equipment that could be tipped over.
- Do not taste any substance in a laboratory.
- Never smell chemicals unless specifically instructed to do so by the teacher. Do not inhale the vapours, or gas, directly from the container.

Take a deep breath to fill your lungs with air, then waft or fan the vapours toward your nose.
- Clean up all spills, even water spills, immediately.
- If you are using a microscope with a mirror, never direct the mirror to sunlight. The concentrated reflected light could hurt your eyes badly.
- Do not forget safety procedures when you leave the laboratory. Accidents can also occur outdoors, at home, and at work.

Eye and Face Safety

- Always wear approved eye protection in a laboratory, no matter how simple or safe the task appears to be. Keep the safety goggles over your eyes, not on top of your head. For certain experiments, full face protection may be necessary.
- If you must wear contact lenses in the laboratory, be extra careful; whether or not you wear contact lenses, do not touch your eyes without first washing your hands. If you do wear contact lenses, make sure that your teacher is aware of it. Carry your lens case and a pair of glasses with you.
- Do not stare directly at any bright source of light (such as a burning magnesium ribbon, lasers, the Sun). You will not feel any pain if your retina is being damaged by intense radiation. You cannot rely on the sensation of pain to protect you.
- Never look directly into the opening of flasks or test tubes.

Handling Glassware Safely

- Never use glassware that is cracked or chipped. Give such glassware to your teacher or dispose of it as directed. Do not put the damaged item back into circulation.
- Never pick up broken glassware with your fingers. Use a broom and dustpan.
- Do not put broken glassware into garbage containers. Dispose of glass fragments in special containers marked "Broken Glass."
- Heat glassware only if it is approved for heating. Check with your teacher before heating any glassware.

- Be very careful when cleaning glassware. There is an increased risk of breakage from dropping when glassware is wet and slippery.
- If you need to insert glass tubing or a thermometer into a rubber stopper, get a cork borer of a suitable size. Insert the borer into the hole of the rubber stopper, starting from the small end of the stopper. Once the borer is pushed all the way through the hole, insert the tubing or thermometer through the borer. Ease the borer out of the hole, leaving the tubing or thermometer inside. To remove the tubing or thermometer from the stopper, push the borer from the small end through the stopper until it shows at the other end. Ease the tubing or thermometer out of the borer.
- Protect your hands with heavy gloves or several layers of cloth before inserting glass into rubber stoppers.

Using Sharp Instruments Safely

- Make sure your instruments are sharp. Surprisingly, one of the main causes of accidents with cutting instruments is using a dull instrument. Dull cutting instruments require more pressure than sharp instruments and are, therefore, much more likely to slip.
- Always transport a scalpel in a dissection case or box. Never carry the scalpel from one area of the laboratory to another with an exposed blade.
- Select the appropriate instrument for the task. Never use a knife when scissors would work best.
- Always cut away from yourself and others.

Fire Safety

- Immediately inform your teacher of any fires. Very small fires in a container may be extinguished by covering the container with a wet paper towel or a ceramic square to cut off the supply of air. Alternatively, sand may be used to smother small fires. A bucket of sand with a scoop should be available in the laboratory.
- If anyone's clothes or hair catch fire, tell the person to drop to the floor and roll. Then use a fire blanket to help smother the flames. Never wrap the blanket around a person on fire; the chimney effect will burn the lungs. For larger fires, immediately evacuate the area. Call the office or sound the fire alarm if close by. Do not try to extinguish larger fires. Your prime concern is to save lives. As

you leave the classroom, make sure that the windows and doors are closed.
- If you use a fire extinguisher, direct the extinguisher at the base of the fire and use a sweeping motion, moving the extinguisher nozzle back and forth across the front of the fire's base. Different extinguishers are effective for different classes of fires. The fire classes are outlined below. Fire extinguishers in the laboratory are 2A10BC. They extinguish classes A, B, and C fires.
- Class A fires involve ordinary combustible materials that leave coals or ashes, such as wood, paper, or cloth. Use water or dry chemical extinguishers on class A fires.
- Class B fires involve flammable liquids such as gasoline or solvents. Carbon dioxide or dry chemical extinguishers are effective on class B fires.
- Class C fires involve live electrical equipment, such as appliances, photocopiers, computers, or laboratory electrical apparatus. Carbon dioxide or dry chemical extinguishers are recommended for class C fires. Do not use water on live electrical devices as this can result in severe electrical shock.
- Class D fires involve burning metals, such as sodium, potassium, magnesium, or aluminum. Sand, salt, or graphite can be used to put out class D fires. Do not use water on a metal fire as this can cause a violent reaction.
- Class E fires involve a radioactive substance. These require special consideration at each site.

Heat Safety

- Keep a clear workplace when performing experiments with heat.
- Make sure that heating equipment, such as the burner, hot plate, or electric heater, is secure on the bench and clamped in place when necessary.
- Do not use a laboratory burner near wooden shelves, flammable liquids, or any other item that is combustible.
- Take care that the heat developed by the heat source does not cause any material close by to get hot enough to burst into flame. Do not allow overheating if you are performing an experiment in a closed area. For example, if you are using a light source in a large cardboard box, be sure you have enough holes at the top of the box and on the sides to dissipate heat.

- Before using a laboratory burner, make sure that long hair is always tied back. Do not wear loose clothing (wide, long sleeves should be tied back or rolled up).
- Always assume that hot plates and electric heaters are hot and use protective gloves when handling.
- Do not touch a light source that has been on for some time. It may be hot and cause burns.
- In a laboratory where burners or hot plates are being used, never pick up a glass object without first checking the temperature by lightly and quickly touching the item, or by placing your hand near but not touching it. Glass items that have been heated stay hot for a long time, even if they do not appear to be hot. Metal items such as ring stands and hot plates can also cause burns; take care when touching them.
- Never look down the barrel of a laboratory burner.
- Always pick up a burner by the base, never by the barrel.
- Never leave a lighted burner unattended.
- Any metal powder can be explosive. Do not put these in a flame.
- When heating a test tube over a laboratory burner, use a test-tube holder and a spurt cap. Holding the test tube at an angle, with the open end pointed away from you and others, gently move the test tube back and forth through the flame.
- To heat a beaker, put it on the hot plate and secure it with a ring support attached to a utility stand. (A wire gauze under the beaker is optional.)
- Remember to include a cooling time in your experiment plan; do not put away hot equipment.

To use a burner:

- Tie back long hair and tie back or roll up wide, long sleeves.
- Secure the burner to a stand using a metal clamp.
- Check that the rubber hose is properly connected to the gas valve.
- Close the air vents on the burner. Use a sparker to light the burner.
- Open the air vents just enough to get a blue flame.
- Control the size of the flame using the gas valve.

Electrical Safety

- Water or wet hands should never be used near electrical equipment such as a hotplate, a light source, or a microscope.
- Do not use the equipment if the cord is frayed or if the third pin on the plug is missing. If the teacher allows this, then make sure the equipment has a double-insulated cord.
- Do not operate electrical equipment near running water or a large container of water.
- Check the condition of electrical equipment. Do not use if wires or plugs are damaged.
- If using a light source, check that the wires of the light fixture are not frayed, and that the bulb socket is in good shape and well-secured to a stand.
- Make sure that electrical cords are not placed where someone could trip over them.
- When unplugging equipment, remove the plug gently from the socket. Do not pull on the cord.

Handling Chemicals Safely

Many chemicals are hazardous to some degree. When using chemicals, operate under the following principles:

- Never underestimate the risks associated with chemicals. Assume that any unknown chemicals are hazardous.
- Use a less hazardous chemical wherever possible.
- Reduce exposure to chemicals as much as possible. Avoid direct skin contact, if possible.
- Ensure that there is adequate ventilation when using chemicals.

The following guidelines do not address every possible situation but, used with common sense, are appropriate for situations in the high school laboratory.

- Obtain an MSDS for each chemical and consult the MSDS before you use the chemical.
- Know the emergency procedures for the building, the department, and the chemicals being used.
- Wear a laboratory coat and/or other protective clothing (such as an apron or gloves), as well as appropriate eye protection at all times in areas where chemicals are used or stored.
- Never use the contents from a bottle that has no label or has an illegible label. Give any containers with illegible labels to your teacher. When leaving chemicals in containers, ensure that the containers are labelled. Always double-check the label—once when you pick it up and a second time when you are about to use it.
- Carry chemicals carefully using two hands, one around the container and one underneath.

- Always pour from the side opposite the label on a reagent bottle; your hands and the label are protected as previous drips are always on the side of the bottle opposite the label.
- Do not let the chemicals touch your skin. Use a laboratory scoop or spatula for handling solids.
- Pour chemicals carefully (down the side of the receiving container or down a stirring rod) to ensure that they do not splash.
- Always pour volatile chemicals in a fume hood or in a well-ventilated area.
- Never pipet or start a siphon by mouth. Always use a pipet suction device (such as a bulb or a pump).
- If you spill a chemical, use a chemical-spill kit to clean up.
- Return chemicals to their proper storage place according to your teacher's instructions.
- Do not return surplus chemicals to stock bottles. Dispose of excess chemicals in an appropriate manner as instructed by your teacher.
- Clean up your work area, the fume hood, and any other area where chemicals were used.
- Wash your hands immediately after handling chemicals and before and after leaving the laboratory, even if you wore gloves. Definitely wash your hands before you touch any food.

Handling Microorganisms Safely

- If you have a cut or abrasion, take appropriate protective measures to avoid contamination with microorganisms.
- Never put anything in your mouth.
- Use sterilized equipment and aseptic procedures.
- For the aseptic transfer of cultures, wipe the laboratory work surfaces with a disinfectant solution before and after an activity (10% bleach solution or 3% Lysol or Dettol solution).
- When culturing, grow bacteria and fungi on solids (agar) rather than liquids (broth) to avoid spills and aerosol formation. Choose substances such as nutrient agar that do not favour the growth of pathogens. Disposable petri dishes should be used.
- Do not grow cultures of spores collected from telephones, door knobs, washrooms, and so on, as they could be contaminated with pathogens.
- Do not grow soil bacteria because of the possibility of culturing tetanus-causing organisms.
- Never culture microorganisms using material from waste containers of polluted water.

- Cultures should be grown at room temperature or in the range of 25°C to 32°C.
- When storing cultures, do not stack petri dishes more than three high on incubator shelves. Tall stacks are a potential hazard if they fall over when the incubator is opened.
- Clean up any spills of microorganism cultures immediately.
- Do not leave cultures for long periods before exposure.
- Dispose of anything that begins to produce an odour.
- Wash hands thoroughly with soap and water after working with any cultures.

Handling Animals and Plants Safely

- Do not perform any investigation on any animal that might cause suffering or pain, or that might pose a health hazard to you or anyone else in the school.
- Animals that live in the classroom should be treated with care and respect, and be kept in a clean, healthy environment.
- Ensure that your teacher is aware of any plant or animal allergies that you may have.
- Never bring a plant, animal, or other organism to school without receiving prior permission from the teacher.
- Keep cages and tanks clean—both for your health and the health of the organism. Most jurisdictions recommend no live mammals or birds in the laboratory. Reptiles often carry *Salmonella*.
- Wear gloves and wash your hands before and after feeding or handling an animal, touching materials from the animal's cage or tank, or handling bacterial cultures.
- Wild or sick animals should never be brought into the laboratory. Dead animals, wild or tame, that have died from unknown causes should also not be brought into the laboratory.
- Preserved specimens should be removed from the preservative with gloves or tongs, and rinsed thoroughly in running water.
- Before going on field trips, become familiar with any dangerous plants and animals that may be common in the area (e.g., stinging nettles and poisonous plants).

Waste Disposal

Waste disposal at school, at home, and at work is a societal issue. To protect the environment, federal and provincial governments have regulations to control wastes, especially chemical wastes. For example, the WHMIS program applies to controlled products that are being handled. Most laboratory waste can be washed down the drain or, if it is in solid form, placed in ordinary garbage containers. However, some waste must be treated more carefully. It is your responsibility to follow procedures and to dispose of waste in the safest possible manner according to your teacher's instructions.

Flammable Substances

Flammable liquids should not be washed down the drain. Special fire-resistant containers are used to store flammable liquid waste. Waste solids that pose a fire hazard should be stored in fireproof containers. Care must be taken not to allow flammable waste to come into contact with any sparks, flames, other ignition sources, or oxidizing materials. The method of disposal depends on the nature of the substance.

Corrosive Solutions

Solutions that are corrosive but not toxic, such as acids, bases, and oxidizing agents, should be disposed of in a container provided by the teacher, preferably kept on the teacher's desk. Do not pour corrosive solutions down the drain.

Heavy-Metal Solutions

Heavy-metal compounds (such as lead, mercury, and cadmium compounds) should not be poured down the drain. These substances are cumulative poisons and should be kept out of the environment. A special container should be kept in the laboratory for heavy-metal solutions. Pour any heavy-metal waste into this container. Remember that paper towels used to wipe up solutions of heavy metals, as well as filter papers with heavy-metal compounds embedded in them, should be treated as solid toxic waste.

Toxic Substances

Solutions of toxic substances, such as oxalic acid, should not be poured down the drain; they should be disposed of in the same manner as heavy-metal solutions, but in a separate container.

Microorganisms

For disposal, place petri dishes in a proper disposal bag labelled with a WHMIS biohazard symbol, and autoclave at 140 kPa for 20 min before discarding in the regular garbage. If an autoclave is not available, call the district Health and Safety Office for a pickup of biohazardous materials. An alternative procedure is to tape the petri dish closed completely and put it in a secondary container before disposal with regular waste or incineration.

Organic Material

Remains of plants and animals can generally be disposed of in school garbage containers. Before disposal, organic material should be rinsed thoroughly to rid it of any excess preservative.

First Aid

The following guidelines apply in case of an injury, such as a burn, cut, chemical spill, ingestion, inhalation, or splash in the eyes.

- Always inform your teacher immediately of any injury.
- Know the location of the first-aid kit, fire blanket, eyewash station, and shower, and be familiar with the contents and operation of them.
- If the injury is a minor cut or abrasion, wash the area thoroughly. Using a compress, apply pressure to the cut to stop the bleeding. When bleeding has stopped, replace the compress with a sterile bandage. If the cut is serious, apply pressure and seek medical attention immediately.
- If the injury is the result of chemicals, drench the affected area with a continuous flow of water for 15 min. Clothing should be removed as necessary. Retrieve the Material Safety Data Sheet (MSDS) for the chemical; this sheet provides information about the first-aid requirements for the chemical.

- If you get a solution in your eye, quickly use the eyewash or nearest running water. Continue to rinse the eye with water for at least 15 min. This is a very long time—have someone time you. Unless you have a plumbed eyewash system, you will also need assistance in refilling the eyewash container. Have another student inform your teacher of the accident. The injured eye should be examined by a doctor.
- If you have ingested or inhaled a hazardous substance, inform your teacher immediately. The MSDS provides information about the first-aid requirements for the substance. Contact the Poison Control Centre in your area.

- If the injury is from a burn, immediately immerse the affected area in cold water or run cold water gently over the burned area. This will reduce the temperature and prevent further tissue damage.
- In case of electric shock, unplug the appliance and do not touch it or the victim. Inform your teacher immediately.
- If a classmate's injury has rendered him or her unconscious, notify the teacher immediately. The teacher will perform CPR, if necessary. Do not administer CPR unless under specific instructions from the teacher. You can assist by keeping the person warm and by reassuring him or her once conscious.

Glossary

A

acid a substance that neutralizes bases, conducts electricity in solution, and has a pH that is less than 7 (neutral) in solution

acid precipitation any form of natural precipitation that has an unusually high acidity (pH less than 5.6)

activated sludge treatment a treatment of sludge that involves the processes of anaerobic and aerobic bacterial digestion

addition polymer a polymer that is formed when monomer units are linked through addition reactions; all atoms in the monomer are retained in the polymer

adipokine a hormone that is produced by adipose (fat) tissue; increases the body's sensitivity to insulin, which controls fat retention when fat is present in normal amounts; triggers diseases such as atherosclerosis when too much fat is present

advanced thermal treatment (ATT) a technology that is based on incineration; subjects organic matter to extremely high temperatures, either in the absence of oxygen or air, or in the presence of small amounts of oxygen; produces a mixture of combustible gases and carbon monoxide

aerobic digestion a process in which organic matter is oxidized through exposure to air, then through the cellular respiration of bacteria and other microorganisms that require oxygen; used in composting and wastewater treatment facilities

aerodynamic drag the friction that is produced when a body moves through air

aerodynamics the science that deals with the interaction of air and moving bodies

amino acid a small molecule that contains a central carbon atom attached to an amino group, a carboxyl group, and a side chain; the basic component of a protein

anaerobic digestion a process that uses microorganisms to break down organic matter or waste biomass in the absence of oxygen; designed to produce and capture biogas, an energy source

anemia a condition in which the red blood cell count is deficient or the blood volume is reduced

antioxidant a chemical that lessens the damage caused by free radicals; found in fresh fruits and vegetables

applied research research that is primarily focused on developing new and better solutions to practical problems

ARPAnet a system that was developed by a branch of the U.S. military to allow distant computers to communicate with each other over dedicated transmission lines

artificial gravity a simulated sensation of weight as might be achieved on a spacecraft in a number of ways (e.g., by rotating a section of the spacecraft)

asynchronous orbit an orbit of an object in which the object passes overhead at different times of the day

atherosclerosis a blockage of blood flow through the heart arteries, caused by the buildup of plaque

atomic number (Z) the number of protons in the nucleus of an atom of a particular element

atrium the thin-walled chamber of the heart that receives blood from the veins

atrophy muscle wasting, such as occurs when a muscle is not used

B

basal metabolic rate (BMR) the energy that is required to maintain the body at rest (awake but engaging in no physical activity)

base a substance that neutralizes acids, conducts electricity in solution, and has a pH that is greater than 7 (neutral) in solution

basic research research that helps people learn more about how the natural world works

biodegradable plastic a plastic that can be broken down through microbial action

biodegradation the breakdown of organic matter by living things, such as bacteria, fungi, insects, and worms; nature's method of recycling

biosolids solid residue or sludge from municipal sewage treatment that has been digested or treated with lime to reduce the pathogens and odour

biotechnology the knowledge, processes, tools, and skills that people use to affect the activities of living organisms

body mass index (BMI) a number that is obtained by dividing an individual's mass in kilograms by his or her height in metres squared

bone demineralization the result when bone-building processes stop but bone-destroying processes continue, such as during extended periods of microgravity

bran the part of the wheat kernel that contains B vitamins, phytochemicals, trace minerals, and fibre; separated from the germ and endosperm during flour milling

buoyancy-driven convection a process in which a warm fluid rises and cooler fluid moves in to replace it

C

Canadarm the robotic arm that is used on space shuttles to launch, manoeuvre, and recover satellites; was used in the construction of the International Space Station; also called the Shuttle Remote Manipulator System

CANDU Canada Deuterium Uranium; a type of reactor that is used in nuclear generating stations; designed in Canada using deuterium as a moderator and uranium as a fuel

carbohydrate a molecule that contains carbon, hydrogen, and oxygen in fixed ratios, primarily used by living organisms as a source of energy

carbon dioxide equivalent (CO_2 eq) the warming potential of greenhouse gases standardized against the warming potential of carbon dioxide; measured in tonnes or kilotonnes

catalyst a substance that aids in the conversion of waste products (such as carbon monoxide and nitrogen oxides) into less polluting substances (such as carbon dioxide, oxygen, and nitrogen)

catalytic converter a device that is attached to a vehicle's exhaust system to reduce pollution

centripetal force the inward force that keeps an object moving in a curved path (e.g., on a string with an object attached to one end, while twirling the string and object, the string exerts a centripetal force on the object)

chain reaction a continuous sequence of splitting atoms and releasing more neutrons, which then spilt more atoms

chemical pollution pollution that results from the release of chemicals into the environment, some of these chemicals are toxic to living things, while others are dangerous because of their impact on the environment (e.g., phosphates create algal blooms in aquatic environments)

cholesterol a dietary lipid that is found in all animal products and also occurs naturally in animals; low-density lipoprotein (LDL or "bad") cholesterol contributes to arterial plaque; high-density lipoprotein (HDL or "good") cholesterol can reverse plaque buildup in the arteries

combustible able to catch fire and burn at high temperatures

combustion reaction a chemical reaction that occurs when a substance reacts rapidly with oxygen, releasing energy

complete combustion the reaction of a fuel with excess oxygen, producing only carbon dioxide and water

composting the breakdown of organic matter by bacteria and other organisms into a nutrient-rich material that can be used to fertilize soil

computer hardware the physical components of a computer, such as the central processing unit, memory chips, keyboard, and display monitor

computer program a list of instructions that tells a computer what to do

computer software a computer program that is stored on floppy disks or CD-ROMs

condensation polymer a polymer that is formed when monomer units are linked through condensation reactions, which also produce water molecules

corrosion the deterioration of a metal as a result of a slow reaction with oxygen

corrosive able to eat away materials and living tissue by chemical action

cost–benefit analysis measuring the costs (costs or disadvantages) and benefits (advantages) associated with the development, distribution, and use of a technology, and relating these costs and benefits to one another

covalent bond a bond that occurs when two atoms share one or more pairs of electrons between them; shared electron pairs are attracted to the nuclei of both atoms

crosslinks covalent bonds that join polymer molecules to produce a rigid plastic

crystal lattice the uniform structure of molecules in a crystal

crystallization the formation of crystals

D

decomposition reaction a chemical reaction in which a molecule or ionic compound is broken down into simpler entities

diastole relaxation (dilation) of the heart, during which the atria (upper chambers) of the heart fill with blood

dietary energy supply (DES) a measure of the average daily food energy that is available per person per day at national, regional, and global levels; used by the Food and Agriculture Organization of the United Nations

dietary reference intake (DRI) the daily nutrient recommendation developed by scientists in Canada and the United States

dietary supplement any product that is taken by mouth and contains vitamins, minerals, herbs or botanicals, enzymes, amino acids, and/or other substances used to supplement the diet

disaccharide a sugar molecule composed of two monosaccharides bonded together

discovery an observation of nature that no one has made before, or that no one has made in the same way before

disinfection the stage in most sewage systems in which the effluent is exposed to chlorine to reduce or eliminate any disease-causing microorganisms

disposal a component of municipal solid waste management; involves storing wastes in landfill sites or incinerating it

diversion a component of municipal solid waste management in which wastes do not go to landfills or incinerators; includes composting, recycling, and reusing

double displacement reaction a chemical reaction in which two compounds in aqueous solution react to form two new compounds

drop tower a facility that is designed to achieve microgravity conditions on Earth, similar to an elevator, in which experiments are performed while being dropped from a great height

E

effluent a fairly clear liquid between influent and sludge that drains from the septic tank as new wastewater enters

electrolysis the process of using electrical energy to split water molecules into hydrogen molecules and oxygen molecules ($2 H_2O_{(l)}$ + electrical energy $\rightarrow 2 H_{2(g)} + O_{2(g)}$)

electrolyte a compound that, when dissolved in water, produces a solution that conducts electricity

electromagnetic radiation (EMR) an invisible form of energy that is emitted by devices with strong electric currents

electron a negatively charged particle surrounding the nucleus of an atom

elemental chlorine free (ECF) bleached without the use of elemental chlorine, although chlorine-containing compounds may be used

empirical knowledge knowledge gained by the five senses (touch, smell, taste, vision, and hearing)

endosperm the part of the wheat kernel that contains protein, carbohydrate, fat, and water; the main ingredient of white flour

enhanced greenhouse effect increased greenhouse gases above natural levels, resulting in increased global temperatures

equivalent dose (H) the most common way to describe the absorption of radiation on the human body; an estimate of the biological effects that radiation has on tissue

essential amino acid an amino acid that the body cannot produce from simpler compounds and must therefore be obtained from food; complete proteins, found in animal foods, contain all eight essential amino acids

exothermic reaction a reaction that releases heat to the surroundings

F

feedback information about the quality of a system's processes and outcomes

fibre a polysaccharide that makes up plant tissues; the part of fruits, vegetables, grains, nuts, and legumes that cannot be completely digested by humans; also known as cellulose or roughage

flammable able to catch fire and burn at normal (room) temperatures

fortified food processed food that has had some of its lost nutrients replaced in order to prevent nutritional deficiencies; also known as enriched food

friction a force that acts in the direction opposite to the motion of a vehicle and its moving parts

fuel cell a device that produces electrical energy by a reaction between hydrogen gas and oxygen gas, with water as the only waste product

functional food a food that contains components found in conventional food that appear to provide health benefits beyond their nutritional value

G

gene pool the total of all the genes that are possessed by the organisms of a species at a given time

gene the portion of a DNA molecule that controls the production of a particular protein

genetically engineered food (GEF) a food that is obtained from genetically engineered organisms

genetically engineered organism (GEO) a life form that is normally used as a food (plant, animal, fungus, bacterium), whose genetic make-up has been altered by recombinant DNA technologies

genetic engineering a set of technologies that are used to change the genetic information in a cell's DNA, and thus its inheritable characteristics

genetic pollution the uncontrolled spread of transgenes and marker genes from genetically engineered organisms to unmodified organisms in the environment

geosynchronous orbit an orbit of an object in which the object orbits Earth at the same rate as the planet spins on its axis

germ the part of the wheat kernel that contains vitamins B and E, folic acid, trace minerals, protein, fibre, and essential fatty acids; separated from the bran and endosperm during flour milling

g-force the gravitational force that is experienced during acceleration

gravitational field strength the numerical value of a body's gravitational force; the average value of Earth's gravitational field strength is 9.8 m/s^2

gravitational force field the field that surrounds every object, the strength of which is determined by the mass of the object and the distance from the field

gravity one of the four fundamental forces of nature; an attractive force, it never repels

greenhouse effect the trapping of heat energy by certain gases in Earth's atmosphere

greenhouse gas (GHG) a naturally occurring gas (such as water vapour, carbon dioxide, methane, nitrous oxide, and any of the halocarbons) that absorbs radiation from Earth and helps to retain heat in the atmosphere; also produced by human activities

H

half-life a property of radioisotopes; the time that is required for half of the original number of radioactive atoms to decay; depending on the element, half lives may vary from a fraction of a second to hundreds of thousands of years

Hazardous Household Products (HHP) symbol a symbol established under the authority of the Hazardous Products Act to indicate the dangers posed by a chemical product or its container

homeostasis the maintenance of a healthy balance of all chemical reactions in an organism

human waste the products of both egestion and excretion

hybrid vehicle a vehicle that combines two or more sources of power

hydrogen bonding a type of intermolecular force that occurs between slightly positively charged hydrogen atoms in one molecule and slightly negatively charged atoms (e.g., oxygen, nitrogen) in another molecule

hypertension high blood pressure, a condition that can weaken the arteries; associated with heart disease, stroke, and kidney failure

hypertext a system in which certain words or phrases in a document are electronically linked to related information (such as other words, phrases, images, or sounds) elsewhere in the same document or other documents

Hypertext Markup Language (HTML) a computer language that uses hypertext to link documents together

hypothesis an untested explanation that is made by a scientist to help develop a theory

I

incineration the burning of garbage to reduce volume; sometimes used as a source of energy

incomplete combustion the reaction of a fuel with insufficient oxygen, producing carbon monoxide and/or carbon in addition to carbon dioxide and water

indoor air pollution the mixture of potentially toxic gases and particles in a home or workplace

inertia the resistance to a change in motion that is caused by mass

influent wastewater that enters a septic tank or a sewage treatment system

information and communication technology the knowledge, processes, tools, and skills that people use to communication information

innovation the modification of an existing technology to serve a new purpose

input everything that is put into a system (also referred to as system resources)

integrated circuit (IC) chip a thin wafer of silicon that contains thousands of tiny interconnected electric circuits, also called a microchip

intended output the result that is planned for and desired

intermolecular force a force of attraction between two molecules

internal combustion engine (ICE) a powerful engine that converts the chemical energy of non-renewable fossil fuels into mechanical forces that make a vehicle move

internal device a basic component that makes a computer work, such as the central processing unit (CPU) and memory chips

Internet an enormous computer network that allows over 170 million computers all over the world to exchange information

invention the creative development of a novel device or process that helps people meet their needs or satisfy their desires

ionic bond a bond that results from the electrostatic force of attraction and holds positive and negative ions together

isotope a form of an element in which the atoms have the same number of protons but different number of neutrons in their nuclei, and therefore, a different atomic mass

K

Kraft pulping a process in which wood is treated with chemicals to separate the fibres for papermaking; the fibres that are produced are long, strong, and relatively dark in colour

Kyoto Protocol a document that describes the process by which the Kyoto Accord (a treaty signed in Kyoto, Japan in 1997), will be implemented; commits countries to reducing greenhouse gas emissions to levels that are 5.2% below 1990 levels, by 2008 to 2012

L

landfill a large tract of land where garbage is stored

leachate the water and other liquids that percolate down through garbage, often at a landfill

lipid a large molecule that is composed of carbon, oxygen, and hydrogen, with a higher proportion of hydrogen atoms than carbohydrates; used by animals to store energy

liquid crystal display a display (e.g., on a calculator), in which crystals partially block light entering the screen from above and produce the dark patches that form numbers and letters on the screen

M

maglev train a magnetically levitated train that is suspended in air as it moves along modified rails called guideways

marker gene a gene that is linked to a transgene and produces characteristics that scientists can recognize in the recipient cells

mass number (A) the sum of the number of nuclear particles (protons and neutrons) in an atom of a particular element

material safety data sheet (MSDS) detailed hazard and precautionary information accompanying hazardous materials

meal replacement a customized food product that must contain a minimum food energy value, a maximum amount of fat, and a specified amount and quality of protein and various vitamins and minerals

mechanical pulping a process in which wood is ground with grindstones to separate the fibres for papermaking; the fibres that are produced are relatively short and weak, and light in colour

microchip a thin wafer of silicon that contains thousands of tiny interconnected electric circuits; also called an integrated circuit (IC) chip

microgravity a condition in which the effects of gravity have been minimized, such as is achieved in free fall

microprocessor a device that contains all the electronic components needed to perform calculations on a single integrated circuit (IC) chip; also called a central processing unit (CPU) or computer chip

mineral an inorganic substance (such as copper, iron, calcium, or phosphorus) that is needed in all body structures in trace amounts for various functions, such as the transmission of nerve impulses and muscle contraction; cannot be made by the body, therefore must be supplied by foods or supplements

monomer a molecule that is linked with similar molecules to form a polymer

monosaccharide the simplest type of sugar molecule

monounsaturated fat a dietary lipid that contains fewer hydrogen atoms than saturated fat but more hydrogen atoms than polyunsaturated fat; lowers LDL ("bad") cholesterol and increases HDL ("good") cholesterol levels in the blood

myocardial infarction (MI) the death of heart muscle tissue due to a lack of oxygen and other nutrients; commonly called a heart attack (*myo*, referring to muscle, *cardial*, referring to the heart, and *infarct*, meaning "death")

N

natural health product (NHP) a product that consists of molecules and elements found in nature; sold in dosage form to maintain and improve health and to treat or prevent diseases or conditions

negative impact a negative effect of unintended system outputs on society and the environment

neutralization reaction or acid–base reaction a reaction between an acid and a base that produces a salt and water; results in a solution with a pH closer to 7

neutron a neutral or non-charged particle, found in the nucleus of an atom

Newton's first law of motion the law stating that stationary objects remain at rest and moving objects keep moving at a constant speed in a straight line until a force is applied; also called the law of inertia

Newton's law of universal gravitation the law that is used to determine the strength of the gravitational force between two objects; based on the objects' masses and the distance between the objects

Newton's second law of motion the law stating that the acceleration of an object varies directly with the force and inversely with the mass of an object; commonly written as $F = m\vec{a}$

Newton's third law of motion the law stating that the two forces in any pair are equal in strength and opposite in direction; for every action there is an equal and opposite reaction

NIMBY an acronym for "not in my backyard"; refers to the resistance of residents to new landfills, incinerators, recycling centres, composting facilities, and other "undesirable projects" in their neighbourhood

non-nutritive food additive a chemical that is added to food but does not contribute to the nutritive value of the food and is not a food itself; added to enhance product consistency, taste, and appearance, and to prolong food preservation

non-polar molecule a molecule that has no charged ends

novel food a product that has never been used as a food; a food that results from a process that has not previously been used for food; or a food that has been modified by genetic manipulation

nuclear fission the splitting of an atom into two or more different elements (e.g., when a neutron collides with the nucleus of a U-235 atom it splits into two smaller fission fragments)

nuclear reaction a reaction that changes the structure of atomic nuclei to release a considerable amount of energy

nucleation site the original seed crystal upon which a crystal grows

nutraceutical a product developed by the food and beverage industry that has a physiological benefit or provides protection against a chronic disease; isolated or purified from food and sold in a medicinal form that is not usually associated with food

nutrient an edible chemical that is broken down for the body's growth, maintenance, and energy

O

orbit the circular path that is followed by an object about another (e.g., Earth orbits the Sun)

organic food a food that is produced according to specific rules, maintaining an ecological balance among the plants, animals, and people that make up the farm environment; soil health is maintained by using composted organic matter and crop rotations

organic solvent a carbon-containing liquid compound (or mixture) that can be used to dissolve other carbon-containing substances

otolith organs two structures, called the utricle and the saccule, in the inner ear

output the end result of the input and process components of a system

overnutrition the long-term consumption of excess nutrients

P

paleoclimatology the study of prehistoric or ancient climates; relies on indirect evidence such as the chemical analysis of glacial ice or ocean sedimentation

peripheral device a component that allows a computer to perform operational functions, such as print documents, communicate with other computers, take photos, and reproduce music and sounds

personal computer (PC) the first computer that was small enough and cheap enough for everyday use

pH scale a numerical scale that is used to measure how acidic or basic a solution is; negative of the exponent to the base 10 of the hydrogen ion concentration

physical pollution pollution that results from the release of suspended solids from factories into local bodies of water; these particles can block the gills of fish and other aquatic organisms, and can also block out sunlight causing a decrease in photosynthesis in aquatic plants

phytoremediation a type of bioremediation; uses green plants to improve contaminated soil or ground water by absorbing the contaminants or by changing them into non-toxic forms

plastic a complex organic compound, that is produced by polymerization, and can be moulded into various shapes, stretched into films, or drawn into filaments

polar covalent bond a bond in which an electron pair is shared unequally between a pair of atoms that have different electronegativities

polar molecule a molecule that has a slightly positive charge on one end and a slightly negative charge on the other end

polar orbit an orbit of an object in which the object crosses near Earth's poles in each pass

polymer a compound in which the molecules are made up of many repeating subunits, called monomers

polysaccharide a complex carbohydrate that is composed of long chains of monosaccharides bonded together

polyunsaturated fat a dietary lipid that contains the fewest hydrogen atoms; found in oils that are liquid at room temperature; lowers total cholesterol levels in the blood

positive impact a beneficial impact, normally produced by the intended outputs of a system

precautionary principle the assumption that a product is unsafe until controlled scientific investigations prove otherwise

pretreatment the first stage of sewage treatment, involves screening out large debris, such as sticks, plastics, or rags

primary treatment after pretreatment, wastewater is pumped into large tanks; heavier organic solids and other solids, such as sand and gravel, settle to the bottom of the tanks, and scum and grease form on the surface; if this is the only treatment of sewage, the sludge is removed and incinerated or sent to a landfill; the primary effluent is discharged into the receiving environment, which may be a river, lake or ocean; if this is not the only treatment of sewage, the wastewater goes on to secondary treatment

principle of substantive equivalence the requirement for a genetically engineered food to have the same appearance and general chemical properties as its natural counterpart

process all the activities of a system that produce an expected result

process chlorine free (PCF) recycled and bleached without any chlorine at any time in the paper's history

protein a chemical building block for the growth and repair of body tissues and for the synthesis of hormones and enzymes; consists of a chain of amino acids

proton a positively charged particle, found in the nucleus of an atom

pulse a change in the diameter of the arteries that can be felt on the body's surface following heart contractions

R

radioactive a characteristic of an isotope that gives off one or more of three types of radiation: alpha particles, beta particles, and gamma rays

radioisotope an isotope that decays, changing the structure of the atom and resulting in an atom with a different mass number or atomic number

recombinant DNA DNA that is composed of pieces from different organisms

recycling the remanufacture of a material after it has been used, or using previously used material to manufacture new products

reducing changing consumption patterns to produce less garbage

restriction enzyme a DNA-cutting enzyme, such as EcoR1

reusing a long-term strategy that involves getting the maximum use out of a product; involves using a product for different purposes before it is discarded or recycled

reverse electrolysis a reaction that is used to generate electrical energy from the reaction of oxygen and hydrogen ($2 H_{2(g)} + O_{2(g)} \rightarrow 2 H_2O_{(l)} +$ electrical energy)

S

sanitary sewage wastewater from homes, businesses, and institutions that goes to a municipal collection system

satellites objects in orbit around other larger objects; can be natural, such as a moon, or artificial, such as the Hubble Space Telescope

saturated the point at which maximum solubility in a solution is achieved

saturated fat a dietary lipid that contains the most hydrogen atoms; usually solid at room temperature; increases LDL ("bad") cholesterol and decreases HDL ("good") cholesterol levels in the blood; closely associated with increased health risks

science the study of the natural world

scientific theory a scientific explanation that is the product of creativity and inventiveness

search engine a program that allows users to search for information on the Internet

secondary treatment after primary treatment; anaerobic bacteria digest the sludge and aerobic bacteria digest the organic matter in the primary effluent; the effluent then goes to a secondary settling tank, where the remaining solids settle to the bottom; the secondary effluent is released into the environment or sent for further treatment

sedimentation the process of materials drifting and settling as sediment, such as at the bottom of a vessel or a body of water

selective breeding the process of producing organisms with specific traits by natural means (sexual reproduction)

semicircular canals the part of the inner ear that is responsible for maintaining body balance

semiconductor an intermediate conductor of electricity (such as silicon and germanium), used to control the flow of electricity in a circuit

serendipity the act of discovering or inventing something useful by accident

sievert (Sv) a unit of measurement of the equivalent dose; 1 Sv represents the biological damage done by the quantity of radiation that is equivalent to the effects of 1 J of energy in 1 kg of body tissue

single displacement reaction the reaction of an element and a compound to produce a new element and a new compound

sink any process that removes carbon dioxide, or another greenhouse gas, from the atmosphere and stores it

sludge the solid material in a septic tank or sewage treatment system

solute a pure substance in a solution that is dissolved by a solvent; usually the substance in lesser quantity

solvent a pure substance in a solution that dissolves other components; usually the substance in greater quantity

space sickness the feelings of nausea, dizziness, and disorientation that are experienced by some people in space; also called space adaptation syndrome

SPAM unwelcome e-mails that are used to spread commercial and nonsense messages to thousands of unsuspecting recipients

sphygmomanometer a device that is used to measure blood pressure

stormwater rain and melting snow that run off the surface of the land

stroke the motion of a piston in an engine; in an Otto-cycle engine, the four strokes are the intake stroke, the compression stroke, the combustion stroke, and the exhaust stroke

supersaturated the point at which a solution has more solute dissolved in it than it normally would have at a certain temperature

surface tension the attractive force that is exerted on the surface molecules of a liquid by the molecules underneath; allows insects to stay on the surface of water

surfactant a material (such as a detergent) that will decrease the surface tension in water, often used for removing dirt; from *surface active agent*

synthesis reaction a chemical reaction in which two or more simple substances combine to form a more complex substance

system a group of components that work together to achieve a common goal

systole the contraction of the ventricles (lower chambers) of the heart, during which blood is pushed out of the heart into the arteries

T

technology the application of science that helps people satisfy some of their needs and desires

tertiary treatment or advanced treatment the third stage of sewage wastewater treatment; physical, chemical, and/or biological processes remove suspended or dissolved pollutants, such as heavy metals, organic chemicals, and nutrients from the secondary effluent; sludge that remains is transferred to a landfill, incinerated, composted, or used as fertilizer

thermal pollution pollution that occurs when water used in industrial processes is returned to the original source (lake, river, or stream), at a higher temperature; the warmer water results in a decrease in the dissolved oxygen content

totally chlorine free (TCF) bleached without using any chlorine; usually bleached with ozone or hydrogen peroxide

transgene the transplanted gene from one organism that is spliced into the DNA of another organism

transgenic organism the organism that receives the transplanted gene

transportation technology the knowledge, processes, tools, and skills that are used to move people and goods from place to place

U

unintended output the result that is not planned for or desired, and would rather be avoided

V

vegetarian a person who eats primarily plants

ventricle the muscular, thick-walled chamber of the heart that delivers blood to the arteries

vestibular system the part of the inner ear that affects the perception of movement and body position

vitamin an organic molecule that acts as a catalyst for essential chemical reactions in the body, such as converting fats and carbohydrates into energy; can be fat soluble or water soluble; cannot be made by the body, therefore must be supplied by foods or supplements

W

waste management the disposal, processing, controlling, recycling, and reusing of solid, liquid and gaseous wastes in such a way as to maintain a habitable environment

Web browser allows a computer to find, retrieve, and display Hypertext Markup Language documents that are stored in other computers connected to the Internet's World Wide Web

Web site a collection of Hypertext Markup Language documents stored at a particular location, or address, in the World Wide Web

weight the force of gravity experienced at a planet's surface; often confused with *mass*, which is a quantity of matter

weightlessness the sensation of feeling no weight; experienced during free fall

Workplace Hazardous Materials Information System (WHMIS) a Canadian system that was designed to give employers and workers information about hazardous materials; the information must be provided on container labels, on material safety data sheets, and through worker education programs

World Wide Web (WWW) a collection of electronic documents that can be viewed on a computer

X

X-ray crystallography the process in which X-rays are fired at and scattered by crystals to reveal the crystals' internal structure

Index

Credits

Photo Credits

Course Introduction:

vi (Fig 1) NASA; (Fig 2) © Paul A. Souders/CORBIS/MAGMA; vii (Fig 3) © Gregg Stott/Masterfile; (Fig 4) NASA; x www.mun.ca/biology/desmid/brian/BIOL3530_W2003/DB_Ch01/fig1_5.jpg; xi © Cliff Owen/Bettmann/CORBIS/MAGMA; xiv © Najiah Feanny/CORBIS/MAGMA; xvi Nelson Photo; xvii NOAA/DMSP.

Unit Opening Photos:

Unit A: Tobin Grimshaw/Toronto Star; Unit B: © Dick Hemingway; Unit C: © Dick Hemingway; Unit D: (top left) CORBIS/MAGMA; (top right) Photodisc; (centre) Photodisc; (right) Photodisc; (bottom left) Photodisc; (centre left) © Dick Hemingway; Unit E: NASA.

Unit A:

4 Royalty Free/CORBIS/MAGMA; 5 (Fig 2) © Alex Pytlowany/Masterfile; (Fig 3) © Owen Franken/ CORBIS/MAGMA; 6 (Fig 4) Maurice Di Giuseppe; (Fig 5) © Rick Friedman/CORBIS/MAGMA; 7 © Robert Maass/CORBIS/MAGMA; 9 © Dick Hemingway; 11 (Fig 2) © H. Mitchell; (Fig 3) Musée J. Armand Bombardier; (Fig 4) CP Photo/ Clifford Skarstedt; 12 (Fig 5) © Bettmann/CORBIS/MAGMA; Table 1 (top to bottom) Robyn Craig, © Richard Glover; Ecoscene/CORBIS/MAGMA, NASA, © Norris Blake/ Visuals Unlimited; 13 (Fig 6) © DuCane Medical Imaging Ltd./SPL/Publiphoto; (Fig 8) © Roger Ressmeyer/CORBIS/MAGMA; 14 (Fig 9a) © Andrew Syred/Photo Researchers; (Fig 9b) Eye of Science/Photo Researchers; 15 © Pitchal Frederic/CORBIS SYGMA/MAGMA; 16 (Fig 12) Royalty Free/CORBIS/MAGMA; (Fig 13) © Dick Hemingway; 18 © Richard Olivier/CORBIS/MAGMA; 21 © Dick Hemingway; 22 © Karl Mondon/Costa Times/CORBIS SYGMA/MAGMA; 23 (Fig 2) © Loren Winters/Visuals Unlimited; (Fig 3) Digital Vision; 24 (Fig 4a, b) © Dick Hemingway; (Fig 5) © Bettmann/CORBIS/MAGMA; (Fig 6) © Fairchild Semiconductor; 26 Intel Museum; 27 (Fig 10) © Chris Farina/CORBIS/MAGMA; (Fig 11) © Steve Shepard; (Fig 12) © Wulf Pfeiffer/EPA/Landov; 28 (Fig 13 a, b) PhotoDisc; (c) www.comstock.ca; 34 © Victor Last/Geographical Visual Aids; 35 Royalty Free/CORBIS/MAGMA; 38 (Fig 20) Courtesy Google; 39 (Fig 1) CP Archive/Tony Bock; (Fig 2) © Hamish Robertson; 40 Zefa/Masterfile; 42 (Fig 7) © Document General Motors/Reuters R/CORBIS/MAGMA; (Fig 8) Courtesy Daimler-Chrysler AG; 43 (Fig 9a) Courtesy Chrysler Daimler AG; (Fig 10) © Michael Syamashita/ CORBIS/MAGMA; 47 Ballard Power Systems, Inc; 48 © Charles D. Winters/Photo Researchers, Inc; 49 © Bettmann/ CORBIS/MAGMA; 50 (Fig 25) courtesy Ballard Power Systems Inc./VTA/Air Products; (Fig 26) © Orban Thierry/ CORBIS SYGMA/MAGMA; 56 © Touhig Sion/CORBIS/ MAGMA; 57 (Fig 2a) © Barrington Brown/Photo Researchers, Inc; (Fig 2b) Digital Art/firstlight.ca; 59 (Fig 5a) © Science VU/Visuals Unlimited; (Fig 5b) Eyewire/ Gettyimages (Fig 6) © Geoff Tompkinson/SPL/Publiphoto; 60 (Fig 8) © Jackson/Visuals Unlimited; (Fig 9) © Brad Mogen/Visuals Unlimited; 61 © Oliver Meckes/E.O.S./ MPI-Tubingen/Photo Researchers, Inc; 62 (Fig 12) © John O'Brien; (Fig 13) © Science VU/ Visuals Unlimited; 63 (Fig 14a) PhotoDisc; (Fig 14b) © Janice Palmer; 66 Digital Art/firstlight.ca; 71 courtesy Industrial Control Systems, NL.

Unit B:

73 © Dick Hemingway; 77 © Bob Semple; 79 © Jeff Greenberg/ Visuals Unlimited; 80 (Fig 3) © Dick Hemingway; (Fig 4) © Dick Hemingway; 82 Digital Vision; 84 © Dick Hemingway; 86 courtesy Notre Developments; 89 CP Photo/Stan Behal; 92 (Fig 1) © Gary W. Carter/CORBIS/MAGMA; (Fig 2) © Dick Hemingway; 95 (Fig 5) © City of Toronto; (Fig 6) Chris Howes/Taxi; 96 © Mach 2 Stock Exchange/Index Stock Imagery; 97 © Gunter Marx Photography/CORBIS/MAGMA; 101 © Ron Watts/CORBIS/MAGMA; 105 © George Simhoni/ Masterfile; 106 courtesy Earth on Empty; 112 Digital image © 1996 Corbis, Original image courtesy of NASA/CORBIS/ MAGMA; 113 © Jose Fuste Raga/CORBIS/MAGMA; 117 (Fig 11) © Reproduced with permission of the Minister of Natural Resources Canada, 2002; (Fig 12) The ENERGY STAR mark is administered and promoted in Canada by Natural Resources Canada and is registered in Canada by the United States Environmental Protection Agency. For information on ENERGY STAR in Canada, visit the Web site of the office of Energy Efficiency (OEE), Natural Resources Canada, located at energystar.gc.ca or call the OEE at 1-800-387-2000; (Fig 13) © Paul Taylor/Stone; 118 CP Photo/Tom Hanson; 121 CP Photo/Ian MacAlpine-Kingston Whig Standard; 123 courtesy Defence Nuclear Nonproliferation; 127 (Fig 7a) courtesy Zircatec Precision Industries; (Fig 7b) courtesy Ontario Power Generation; 129 courtesy Ontario Power Generation; 134 U.S. Department of Energy/SPL/Publiphoto; 138 (Fig 1, top) © Gabe Palmer/ CORBIS/MAGMA; (centre) © Lowell Georgia/CORBIS/ MAGMA; (bottom) © Rick Poley/Visuals Unlimited; (top right) © Jon Feingersh/Masterfile; (bottom) © Chinch Gryniewicz, Ecoscene/CORBIS/MAGMA.

Unit C:

144 (Fig 2) © Photoalto/firsthlight.ca; 145 © Christine Case/Visuals Unlimited; 154 © Science Photo Library; 157 © Dick Hemingway; 160 © Steve Strickland/Visuals Unlimited; 164 Kitchener-Waterloo Record Collection of Photographic Negatives, University of Waterloo Library; 169 CP Photo/ Richard Lam; 171 CP Photo/Jerry Gerling; 177 © Al Harvey/

The Slide Farm; 178 © Dick Hemingway; 179 AP Photo/ John Gaps III; 182 (Fig 10) © Phillippe Psaila/SPL/ Publiphoto; 185 (Fig 15) Kimberley Walther; (Fig 16) courtesy Trex Company; 187 © Dick Hemingway; 190 © Dick Hemingway; 192 STONE; 193 (Fig 22) © Al Harvey/The Slide Farm; (Fig 23) © Victor Last/Geographical Visual Aids; 197 © Dick Hemingway; 199 (Fig 3, left) © Martin B. Withers, Frank Lane Picture Agency/CORBIS/MAGMA; (right) © Daryl Benson/Masterfile; 200 © Victor Last/ Geographical Visual Aids; 202 © Victor Last/Geographical Visual Aids; 203 Royalty Free/CORBIS/MAGMA; 205 © Dick Hemingway; 207 (Fig 14a) © Dick Hemingway; (Fig 14b) © Victor Last/Geographical Visual Aids; 209 (Fig 15) © Dick Hemingway; (Fig 16) Spectrum Stock.

Unit D:

218 (Fig 2) © Allstar Media LLC/Index Stock Imagery; (Fig 3) Zefa/Masterfile; 219 © Dick Hemingway; 223 © Dick Hemingway; 224 Jeremy Jones; 229 (Fig 8) © Dick Hemingway; (Fig 9, top) © Dick Hemingway; (bottom) Brandx/firstlight.ca; 236 © Alison Barnes Martin/Masterfile; 237 (Fig 2) NASA/SPL/Publiphoto; (Fig 3) NASA/SPL/ Publiphoto; 238 Julie Greener; 239 © Dick Hemingway; 240 (Fig 7) © Dick Hemingway; (Fig 8) Jill Roberts; 242 (Fig 9a, b) Jill Roberts; (Fig 9c) © Dick Hemingway; 243 (Fig 11a, d, f) courtesy Canadian Wheat Board; (Fig 11b, c, e) courtesy The Canadian Grains Institute (www.cigi.ca); 245 (Fig 13, left) Royalty Free/CORBIS/MAGMA; (right) © Index Stock Imagery; 247 (Fig 14) Julie Greener; (Fig 15) © Dick Hemingway; 248 (Fig 1a) © Photo Researchers, Inc; (Fig 1b) © Mediscan/Visuals Unlimited; (Fig 2) Imagestate/firstlight.ca; 249 © Matthew Staver/Bloomberg News/Landov; 250 © Custom Medical Stock Photo; 251 (Fig 5, left) CORBIS/ MAGMA; (centre) CORBIS/MAGMA; (right) Photodisc; (Fig 6) Photodisc; 252 © Dick Hemingway; 254 (Fig 10) Z&B Barran/Stone; 255 (Fig 11) M. Huberland/Science Source/ Photo Researchers; 256 Sheila Terry/Science Photo Library; 257 © Lester Lefkowitz/CORBIS/MAGMA; 259 (Fig 16a) © Cabisco/Visuals Unlimited; (Fig 16b) © Alfred Pasieka/Peter Arnold; 260 © Benelux Press/firstlight.ca; 264 (Fig 1) Jill Roberts; (Fig 3) © Dick Hemingway; 265 Jill Roberts; 266 © Emma Lee/Lifefile/Photodisc; 268 © Custom Medical Stock Photo; 275 © Michael Newman/PhotoEdit; 277 © G.W. Willis MD/Visuals Unlimited; 281 Jill Roberts; 284 © Mark Richards/PhotoEdit; 288 CP Photo/Ryan Remiorz.

Unit E:

294 (Fig 1) © Bettmann/CORBIS/MAGMA; (Fig 2) NASA; (Fig 3) © Bettmann/CORBIS/MAGMA; 295 (Fig 4) NASA; (Fig 5) GRIN/NASA; 296 NASA/James McDivitt; 298 © NASA/Roger Ressmeyer/CORBIS/MAGMA; 299 © Leonard de Silva/CORBIS/MAGMA; 301 © The Purcell Teak/ CORBIS/MAGMA; 302 © 1998 Calvin J. Hamilton; 303 Paramount Canada's Wonderland; 306 (Fig 10) Zarm Centre of Applied Space Technology & Microgravity; (Fig 11)

NASA; (Fig 12) NASA; (Fig 13) NASA; 310 NASA/SPL/ Publiphoto; 311 MSFC/NASA; 312 (Fig 3) © CORBIS/ MAGMA; (Fig 4) © UPI/NASA/LANDOV; 313 (Fig 5) courtesy www.zvezda-npp.ru; (Fig 6) © Bettmann/CORBIS/ MAGMA; 314 NASA/JSC/Aircraft Operations; 315 courtesy JAXA; 316 courtesy MEDES-IMPS (LTBR.2001-2002, CNES, ESA, JAXA); 322 © NASA/Roger Ressmeyer/CORBIS/ MAGMA; 323 NASA/JSC Image Gallery; 325 Defence R&D Canada; 326 © Larry Stepanowicz/Visuals Unlimited; 327 (Fig 3a) courtesy Mineral Information Institute; (Fig 3b) © Mark Schneider/Visuals Unlimited; 328 (Fig 4) © Gregg Otto/Visuals Unlimited; (Fig 5) © Frank May/EPA/Landov; 329 © Kenneth G. Libbrecht; 330 courtesy Dr. Chris Young; 331 Nelson Photo; 332 © Zhong Ren, Renz Research, Inc. 333 (Fig 12) © Volker Steger/SPL/Publiphoto; (Fig 13) MSFC/NASA; 334 MSFC/NASA; 335 © Dennis Drenner/ Visuals Unlimited; 337 MSFC/NASA; 338 Digital Vision; 339 (Fig 19a) © Al Harvey/The Slide Farm; (Fig 19b) © Alan Towse/CORBIS; 341 (Fig 20) © Fritz Polking/Visuals Unlimited; (Fig 21) © Craig Tuttle/CORBIS/MAGMA; (Fig 22) Used with permission from the University of Missouri-Rolla; 342 (Fig 1a) © Dennis Scott/CORBIS/MAGMA; (Fig 1b) © NASA/UPI/LANDOV; (Fig 1c) courtesy Telesat Canada; 343 © SIU/Visuals Unlimited; 344 (Fig 3) MSFC/NASA; (Fig 4) © Al Harvey/The Slide Farm; 345 (Fig 5) MSFC/NASA; (Fig 6) NASA Orbital Debris Program Office; 347 (Fig 8) courtesy Telesat; (Fig 9) courtesy Environment Canada; 348 RADARSAT-1 data © the Canadian Space Agency/Agence spatiale canadienne 2003. Processed and distributed by Kongsberg Satellite Services. ENVISAT data © ESA/KSAT 2003. Courtesy of the EC Joint Research Centre—Ocenides Program; 349 (Fig 13a) courtesy RADARSAT; (Fig 13b) Canadian Space Agency; (Fig 13c) Canadian Space Agency; 350 (Fig 14) NASA,ESA,S.Beckwith (STSc1)and the HUDF Team; (Fig 15) Canadian Space Agency; (Fig 16) NASA/ WMAP Science Team; (Fig 17) NASA/CXC/SSC/J. Keohane et al; (Fig 18) SOHO/ESA & NASA; 351 (Fig 19) GRIN/ NASA; (Fig 20) GRIN/NASA; 352 (Fig 21a) NASA; (Fig 21b) Canadian Space Agency; 356 courtesy Lakeland Industries, Inc. 357 ESA, 2001; 358 (Fig 1, top) Steve Lee (University of Colorado), Jim Bell (Cornell University), Mike Wolff (Space Science Institute) and NASA; (Fig 1, bottom) NASA; 360 MSFC/NASA; 361 (Fig 2a, b, c, d) RADARSAT data © Canadian Space Agency/Agence spatiale canadienne 1996, 1997. Received by the Canada Centre for Remote Sensing. Processed and distributed by RADARSAT International; (Fig 3) MSFC/NASA.

Appendices:

362 © Spencer Grant/PhotoEdit.

Text Credits

Unit A:
4 (Table 1) With permission from www.cbc.ca; 48 (Fig 22) Redrawn from Proceedings of the Royal Society (1843).

Unit B:
74 (Table 1) Source: The Fraser Institute, Environmental Indicators, Sixth Edition, p.71; 68 (Table 2) © David R. Boyd, University of Victoria; 97 (Fig 9) from Environmental Indicator Bulletin, Urban Water Indicators: Municipal Water Use and Wastewater Treatment, Environment Canada; 98 (Table 2) 2001 Todd Zynda-MSU Tab Program; 99 (Table 3) Wastewater Working Group Final Report, June 1, 2000, Environment Canada; 104 (Fig 12) Environment Canada www.ec.gc.ca/soer_ree/English/SOER/MWWWE3.cfm; 109 (Fig 4) Environment Canada, Carbon Cycle Group, National Oceanic and Atmospheric Administration, USA. Adapted by National Indicators and Reporting Office. (Fig 5) Statistics Canada, www.estat.statcan.ca/HAE/Englsih/home.htm; 115 (Fig 9) Greenhouse Gas Division, Environment Canada, adapted by National Indicators and Reporting Office, Environment Canada; 116 (Table 3) Government of Canada, The Climate Change Plan for Canada, 2002; 117 (Table 4) The Government of Canada, the Climate Change Plan for Canada, 2002, p.46; 120 (Fig 15) Canada's Greenhouse Gas Inventory, 1990–2001, Environment Canada, August 2003, p.7, www.ec.gc.ca/pdb/ghg/1990-01-report/foreword-e.cfm; 130 (Table 3) Nuclear Waste Management Organization; 132 (Fig 12) Health Canada www.hc-sc.gc.ca/hecs-sesc/neprd/related-topics/health-effects.htm.

Unit C:
150 (Table 2) Health Canada www.hc.sc.gc.ca/hecs=sesc/cps/staysafe/preschool; 160 Adapted with permission from CBC *Marketplace*, aired March 11, 2003; 173 (Table 3) Adapted from Office Indoor Air Quality, a Web page produced by MFL Occupational Health Centre, Inc. http://www.mflohc.mb.ca; 188 (Fig 19) Adapted with permission from Weyerhaeuser.

Unit D:
218 (Table 1) courtesy the Peel Region Public Health Department, www.peelregion.ca; 229 (Fig 7) Nutrition Facts Table, Jan 2003, Health Canada. Reproduced with the permission of the Minister of Public Works and Government Services Canada, 2004; 232 (Fig 10a) Health Canada. Reproduced with the Permission of the Minister of Public Works and Government Services Canada, 2004; (Fig 10b) USDA and DHHS; (Fig 10c, d) © 2000 Oldways Preservation & Exchange Trust; 233 (Fig 11) © 2000 Oldways Preservation & Exchange Trust; 274 (Fig 1) courtesy www.sixweeks.com; 278 (Fig 7) © Donna Ciliska; 282 (Fig 10) Food and Agriculture Organization of the United Nations www.fao.org/NEWS/1998/img/NMpdfs/world-e.pdf; 283 (Fig 11a) Food and Agriculture Organization of the United Nations www.fao.org/NEWS/1998/img/NMpdfs/SSafr-e.pdf; (Fig 11b) Food and Agriculture Organization of the United Nations www.fao.org/NEWS/1998/img/NMpdfs/Seasia-e.pdf; (Fig 11c) Food and Agriculture Organization of the United Nations www.fao.org/NEWS/1998/img/NMpdfs/indust-e.pdf; 284 (Fig 13) www.cma/cmaj/vol-163/issue-11/1429.htm; 291 (Fig 1) Southern Illinois University and the University of Illinois in Urbana-Champaign through an Illinois CFAR grant.